Advances in Inorganic and Bioinorganic Mechanisms

Volume 2

Advances in Inorganic and Bioinorganic Mechanisms
Volume 2

edited by
A. G. Sykes

Department of Inorganic Chemistry
The University, Newcastle upon Tyne, England

1983

Academic Press

A subsidiary of Harcourt Brace Jovanovich, Publishers

London   New York
Paris   San Diego   San Francisco
São Paulo   Sydney   Tokyo   Toronto

ACADEMIC PRESS INC. (LONDON) LTD.
24/28 Oval Road,
London NW1

United States Edition published by
ACADEMIC PRESS INC.
111 Fifth Avenue,
New York, New York 10003

ISBN 0–12–023802–0

Filmset by Mid-County Press, London
Printed in Great Britain by Page Brothers, Norwich

Contributors

STEPHEN P. CRAMER
Corporate Research Science Laboratories
Exxon Research and Engineering Co.
Linden
NJ 07036
USA

DAVID E. FENTON
Department of Chemistry
The University
Sheffield S3 7HF
UK

HEINZ GAMSJÄGER
Institut für Physikalische Chemie
Montanuniversität Leoben
A-8700, Leoben
AUSTRIA

R. KENT MURMANN
Department of Chemistry
University of Missouri
Columbia
Missouri 65211
USA

THOMAS W. SWADDLE
Department of Chemistry
University of Calgary
2500 University Drive
Calgary
Alberta T2N 1N4
CANADA

MARTIN L. TOBE
Chemistry Department
University College
London WC1H 0AJ
UK

RALPH G. WILKINS
Department of Chemistry
New Mexico State University
Las Cruces
NM 88003
USA

Preface

The aim in this series is to continue to provide authoritative reviews in the area of inorganic mechanisms, and in the new and rapidly expanding area of bioinorganic mechanisms.

This second volume features three articles on substitution reactions by Professor Tobe (base hydrolysis), Swaddle (substitution reactions of di- and tri-valent metal ions), and Gamsjäger and Murmann (oxygen-18 exchange studies on oxo and aqua ions). On the bioinorganic side there is a survey of rapid reaction techniques by Professor Wilkins, as well as articles by Dr Fenton, in which the biochemical relevance of binucleating ligands is considered, and Dr Cramer on the subject of molybdo-enzymes. In the latter the emphasis is on structural and functional properties of the enzymes, which serve to provide the initial insight and background to more detailed mechanistic studies.

As in the first volume the style and presentation of each author has been maintained so that the vigour of each article can be better conveyed to the reader. In some cases the units used do differ. Those to note here are (1 cal = 4.2 J), concentration (M = mol l^{-1}), pressure (1 atm = 101325 Pa), and length (1 Å = 0.1 nm = 100 pm).

Judged by the response to the first volume the combination of inorganic and bioinorganic mechanisms is an appropriate choice and one which is relevant to both teaching and research needs.

Future volumes will be at approximately yearly intervals, and are already planned through to Volume 5.

On a more personal note I would like to take the opportunity of thanking all the authors for their enthusiastic co-operation in the preparation of this volume. Also Mrs Rhoda Stafford and Richard and Andrew Sykes who helped with the indexing.

A. G. Sykes

Newcastle
June, 1983

Contents

Base Hydrolysis of Transition-Metal Complexes

Martin L. Tobe

Chemistry Department,
University College, London

1

I. INTRODUCTION

A. The scope of the reaction

The base catalysed hydrolysis reactions of certain octahedral acido-amine transition metal complexes, and their mechanistically parallel base catalysed substitution reactions, have been the subject of investigation and controversy for many years. The rate law was established in 1927[1] and the currently accepted mechanism was first proposed in 1937.[2] The subject has been reviewed extensively, either in its own right or as part of a general mechanistic text,[3–5] and it probably now ranks as one of the most intensively studied inorganic reactions, second only to those of photochemical interest.

In its simplest form, the reaction can be represented stoicheiometrically as,

$$L_5MX^{n+} + S^- \rightarrow L_5MS^{n+} + X^- \tag{1}$$

where M is the metal and S^- is the lyate ion of the solvent HS. It is possible to observe the displacement of neutral ligands and, because of the acid-base relationship between solvent and lyate ion, whether free or coordinated, the reagents and products may vary according to the pH of the study, i.e. we may observe pH dependent solvolysis. The bulk of the published work relates to aqueous solutions, where $S^- = OH^-$, but it has been shown that MeO^- in methanol[6] and NH_2^- in liquid ammonia,[7–10] can act in a similar fashion. Not all lyate ions generate this catalysis and it has been shown that in acetic acid, the rates of solvolysis of complexes that are very susceptible to base catalysis in aqueous solution are unaffected by the addition of acetate ions.[11,12]

The salient feature of this reaction is the high reactivity of the complex in the presence of base which, at first sight, appears to contravene the fairly general pattern that, apart from the very characteristic behaviour of the four-coordinate planar complexes of d^8 metal ions, the rates of substitution reactions of transition metal complexes are not very sensitive to the nature of the entering group. The reaction requires the presence of at least one ammonia or primary or secondary amine ligand in the complex and is most marked when the central metal ion is Co(III) or Ru(III). The dependence of the effect upon the nature of the central ion will be discussed in this review.

B. The rate law

The normally encountered rate law for solvolysis takes the form

$$-\text{d}[\text{complex}]/\text{d}t = k_{\text{aq}}[\text{complex}] + k_{\text{OH}}[\text{complex}][\text{OH}^-] \qquad (2)$$

in aqueous solution and a similar form operates in methanol. The first-order term arises from the spontaneous aquation and, depending upon the relative magnitudes of k_{aq} and k_{OH} and the pH range over which the study is carried out, it can dominate the kinetics or make no significant contribution. Indeed, when the complex is solvolytically labile, considerable problems arise in trying to determine k_{OH}.[13] An alternative form of writing the expression is

$$-\text{d}[\text{complex}]/\text{d}t = k_{\text{aq}}[\text{complex}] + k_{\text{H}}[\text{complex}][\text{H}^+]^{-1} \qquad (3)$$

where $k_{\text{H}} = k_{\text{OH}} K_{\text{w}}$, K_{w} being the ionic product of water (with equivalent expressions in other amphiprotic solvents) and this is used when the value of k_{OH} is so much greater than k_{aq} that the catalysed reaction makes a significant contribution to the overall change even in acid solution.[14-16] This is the normal form of the rate law in liquid ammonia where added ammonium salts retard the reaction rate so that[7-10]

$$-\text{d}[\text{complex}]/\text{d}t = k_{\text{solv}}[\text{complex}] + k_{\text{H}}[\text{complex}][\text{NH}_4^+]^{-1} \qquad (4)$$

Departures from these types of rate law are rare and generally associated with the distribution of the substrate between acid and base forms of different reactivity. Sometimes the system is susceptible to general base catalysis. These deviations will be considered in detail elsewhere in this review.

II. MECHANISM

Although there is now general agreement as to the major features of the mechanism of these reactions, this was not always so, and in the period 1955–65 there was a lively controversy which served not only to promote a very large amount of work (much of it first class), but also to amuse the spectators. A humorous account of part of this controversy has been written by Professor Pearson.[17]

A. The dissociative conjugate-base mechanism

This is the mechanism that is currently accepted and was first proposed in 1937 by Garrick[2] on the basis of the similarity of the kinetics of these reactions to those of proton exchange of amine complexes. It was revived by Basolo and Pearson in 1956.[18] In this mechanism the hydroxide functions as a base rather than as a nucleophile and removes a proton from a suitably located amine ligand NHR_2, thereby generating a substitutionally labile amido species, e.g.

$$[L_4M(NHR_2)X]^{n+} + OH^- \underset{k_{-1}}{\overset{k_1}{\rightleftharpoons}} [L_4M(NR_2)X]^{(n-1)+} + H_2O \qquad (5)$$

$$[L_4M(NR_2)X]^{(n-1)+} \xrightarrow{k_2} [L_4M(NR_2)]^{n+} + X^- \qquad (6)$$

$$[L_4M(NR_2)]^{n+} + H_2O \xrightarrow{\text{fast}} [L_4M(NHR_2)OH]^{n+} \qquad (7)$$

Although the substitution of the amido conjugate base is represented above as a D mechanism (i.e. there is a definite intermediate of lower coordination number) there is evidence to suggest that the subsequent behaviour of this intermediate is not independent of its mode of formation so that, while the process is dissociatively activated, it may be better represented by the I_d label. The evidence supporting this mechanism and its consequences will be discussed in detail below. In his review in this volume, Swaddle briefly considers the effect of conjugate base formation in aqua complexes.

B. Associative substitution

In an attempt to test out the hypothesis of "edge displacement",[19] which related the steric course of substitution in an octahedral complex to the molecularity of the process (to provide a parallel to the relationship that had been developed for nucleophilic substitution at tetrahedral carbon), Ingold *et al.*[20-22] assumed on the basis of the clear-cut second-order rate law, that the reactions between cobalt(III) acido-amine complexes and hydroxide were bi-molecular. At that time it was thought that a duality of mechanism existed and that stronger nucleophiles such as N_3^-, NO_2^- and NH_3 provided kinetic criteria for bi-molecular substitution in *cis*-$[Co(en)_2Cl_2]^+$ in methanol.[19,23] Later work showed clearly that the concentration dependence and substrate specificity arose from the generation of MeO^- and OH^- by these basic nucleophiles. The base catalysed substitution could be suppressed by buffering the reagents with a small amount of acid.[24,25] There was no other evidence to support the bi-molecular mechanism for base hydrolysis and, in the absence of any other evidence for bi-molecular substitution involving strong nucleophiles other than the lyate ion in these types of complexes, the mechanism rapidly dropped out of favour.

C. The Grotthus-interchange mechanism

Before he was converted to the D_{cb} mechanism, the present author[26] suggested that the special role of the lyate ion could be explained in terms of its ability to "move" rapidly through the solvation shell of the complex by a Grotthus proton transfer mechanism. Whereas other entering groups had to be present in the innermost solvation shell to take advantage of the very-short lifetime of the reactive intermediate, a hydroxide ion could be transmitted through a number of shells of solvating water by proton jumping. This might have been a feasible mechanism if hydroxide and other outer sphere bound nucleophiles could intercept the incipient five-coordinate intermediate at an earlier stage of its development than could the solvent itself, but the evidence seems to disfavour this. Such a hypothesis could not readily explain the high rate constants that could sometimes be obtained.

The interchange mechanism (unspecified mode of activation) put forward by Chan[27] suffers from the same drawback, namely that it does not account for the unusually rapid rate of interchange required for the ion-paired hydroxide ion. A later suggestion[28] that the hydroxide ion specifically interacts with the amine proton (such hydrogen bonding assistance to ion association in complexes of this sort is well known) and that the strength of the interaction relates to the labilising power merges this mechanism with that of D_{cb}. The main evidence in support of the proposed mechanism was that for a number of chloro(penta-amine)cobalt(III) complexes there was curvature in the plot of k_{obs} against $[OH^-]$ and that this was consistent with an expression of the type, $k_{obs} = kK[OH^-]/(1 + K[OH^-])$. The values of K obtained from curve analysis were of a magnitude expected for ion association between a 2^+ cation and a 1^- anion and far too large for K_a/K_w. (The D_{cb} mechanism leads to a relationship of the same form provided the fraction of unreacted substrate in the form of the conjugate base is not negligible. In this case, K in the above expression would be the equilibrium constant for Step 5 above, K_a being the acid dissociation constant of the amine complex.) Unfortunately, these deviations from a simple first-order dependence on $[OH^-]$ could not be repeated, even when higher concentrations of hydroxide were used.[29] However, such deviations have since been found in other systems.

D. Redox pathways

One worrying feature of the D_{cb} mechanism is that it does not provide a satisfactory explanation of the fact that labilisation through deprotonation of an amine ligand is only strong in Co(III) and Ru(III) acido-amine complexes. It was pointed out many years ago[30] that these two centres had readily accessible (+II) oxidation states whereas Cr(III) and Rh(III) did not. Gillard[31] proposed that the role of hydroxide was neither that of a base nor that of a nucleophile but that of a one-electron reducing agent. The Co(II) species and ȮH radical remained as a trapped radical pair long enough for the substitutionally labile Co(II) to undergo substitution

$$[Co^{III}(NH_3)_5X]^{2+} + OH^- \rightleftharpoons \underset{\text{encounter complex or ion pair}}{[Co^{III}(NH_3)_5X]^{2+} \ldots OH^-} \tag{8}$$

$$[Co^{III}(NH_3)_5X]^{2+} \ldots OH^- \rightarrow \underset{\text{trapped radical pair}}{[Co^{II}(NH_3)_5X]^+ \ldots \dot{O}H} \tag{9}$$

$$[Co^{II}(NH_3)_5X]^+ \ldots \dot{O}H \rightarrow [Co^{II}(NH_3)_5H_2O]^{2+} \ldots \dot{O}H + X^- \tag{10}$$

$$\left. \begin{array}{l} [Co^{II}(NH_3)_5H_2O]^{2+} \ldots \dot{O}H \rightarrow [Co^{III}(NH_3)_5H_2O]^{3+} \ldots OH^- \\ [Co^{III}(NH_3)_5H_2O]^{3+} \ldots OH^- \rightarrow [Co^{III}(NH_3)_5OH]^{2+} + H_2O \end{array} \right\} \tag{11}$$

This mechanism does not account for the need for an amine group to be present in the coordination shell of the metal ion and it is surprising that nucleophiles with much greater reputations as reducing agents do not exert a similar effect.[32] It has been totally discredited on energetic grounds by Endicott,[33] but, nevertheless, it has many features in common with the $S_{RN}1$ mechanism for substitution at aromatic carbon[34] in which the potential nucleophile acts as a one-electron reducing agent in the initiation stage to generate a reactive radical which undergoes rapid substitution. It differs in that the inorganic radical [i.e. Co(II)] after undergoing dissociative substitution, does not participate in a chain reaction by reducing a molecule of substrate as does the organic radical in the $S_{RN}1$ reaction. The involvement of a single electron transfer is not totally discredited and, as we shall see below, it remains a plausible alternative explanation for some of the very high labilising effects of the amido nitrogen.

E. The E_2 mechanism

An interesting and novel mechanism, which is characterised by general base catalysis (a requirement of rate-limiting deprotonation), and a sensitivity of rate upon the nature of the leaving group (suggesting that the breaking of the bond with the leaving group is important in the rate-determining transition state) has been suggested by Hay[35,36] to account for the observation of these phenomena in the base hydrolysis of *cis*-$[Co(cyclen)X_2]^+$ (cyclen = 1,4,7,10-tetraazacyclododecane; X = Cl, Br). Called the E_2 mechanism because of the similarity of the first part to bi-molecular base catalysed elimination reactions in which a saturated organic material $RR'CHCH_2X$ loses HX to give $RR'C{=}CH_2$, it requires that loss of X^- is synchronous with the act of deprotonation

$$HO^- + H-\overset{|}{\underset{|}{N}}-\overset{|}{\underset{|}{Co}}-X \longrightarrow HOH + \overset{|}{N}=\overset{|}{\underset{|}{Co}} + X^-$$

$$\downarrow {+ H_2O}$$

$$H-\overset{|}{\underset{|}{N}}-\overset{|}{\underset{|}{Co}}-OH$$

However, the dependence of rate upon the nature of X may simply reflect the fact that these complexes contain two *cis* equivalent halides which can affect the magnitude of k_1 for the amine proton *trans* to themselves. The rate constants k_1, k_{-1} and k_2 appearing here and elsewhere in the text are defined by equations (5) and (6). Since, as we shall see elsewhere, the labilising amido group is best situated *cis* to the leaving group while the proton labilising phenomenon is a *trans* effect, a pair of equivalent *cis* ligands might produce the observed results without the need to invoke the E_2 mechanism. A direct study of proton exchange in these complexes is required before the mechanism is properly established. In the base hydrolysis of the highly sensitive $\alpha\beta$-[Co(picdien)X]$^{2+}$ species (see Fig. 15) (picdien = 1,9-bis(2-pyridyl)-2,5,8-triazanonane) there is also a 10-fold increase in reactivity on going from the chloro to the bromo complex. At one time it was thought that the high rate constants, e.g. 2×10^7 M^{-1} s^{-1} and 14.8×10^7 M^{-1} s^{-1} for the *syn*-$\alpha\beta$ chloro and bromo isomers respectively, coupled with very-low activation energies (8.4 and 9.5 kcal mol^{-1} respectively), were strong indications that deprotonation was rate limiting and so this system was a good candidate for an E_2 mechanism withouth the ambiguity of a pair of *cis* equivalent leaving groups.[16] However, direct examination of the proton exchange kinetics of these substrates indicates that the most labile proton (that *trans* to the leaving group) exchanges considerably faster than the complex solvolyses and the proton on the nitrogen *cis* to the leaving group (whose removal leads to the formation of the labile conjugate base) also exchanges more rapidly than solvolysis. In the case of the chloro complex the ratio $k_{-1}/k_2 = $ ca 5.[37] The change of leaving group Cl to Br has little effect upon the lability of the amine protons (even those *trans* to the acido groups) but does increase k_2 which not only leads to the observed increase in k_{OH} but also brings the bromo complex to a point where $k_{-1} \sim k_2$. The lesson to be learned from this study is that the enthalpy of activation is not a good criterion for distinguishing rate determining deprotonation from rapid reversible proton transfer. The presence or absence of general base catalysis is much more reliable but has not yet been applied in this system for technical reasons.

III. A DETAILED DISCUSSION OF THE D_{cb} MECHANISM

A. Further consideration of the rate law

If one assumes that the amido species is sufficiently reactive with respect to reprotonation and/or ligand substitution for the steady-state approximation to be valid, a simple treatment of the processes indicated by equations (5)–(7) leads to the relationship

$$-d[L_4M(NHR_2)X]/dt = d[L_4M(NHR_2)OH]/dt$$

$$= \frac{k_1 k_2}{k_{-1} + k_2} [L_4M(NHR_2)X][OH^-] \qquad (12)$$

i.e. the simple second-order rate law is predicted and the experimental second-order rate constant, k_{OH}, is related to the individual rate constants by the relationship

$$k_{OH} = \frac{k_1 k_2}{k_{-1} + k_2} \qquad (13)$$

In reality, however, there has never been a study of the base hydrolysis of a complex in which there is a single removable amine proton. Such compounds would be of considerable use in resolving many of the questions that remain unanswered but, as yet, have not been used in this context, if indeed they have ever been made. All the published work relates to many proton systems. For example, the simple $[Co(NH_3)_5Cl]^{2+}$ contains 12 protons on the nitrogens *cis* to the chlorine and three on the nitrogen *trans* to it, free rotation about the N—Co bond preventing any further differentiation. *Trans*-$[Co(en)_2Cl_2]^+$ has eight amine protons that are equivalent on a time scale that is long compared with that of the inversion of the *gauche* chelate rings (there are two sets of four in the frozen conformations). In β-*cis*-$[Co(RR,SS-2,3,2-tet)Cl_2]^+$ (2,3,2-tet = 1,9-diamino-3,7-diazanonane, R and S designate the configurations of the asymmetric coordinated secondary nitrogens) none of the six amine protons are equivalent.[38] The presence of more than one proton does not complicate the observed rate law but the relationship between the observed rate constant and those for the individual steps must take this into account. If there are n equivalent protons, as for example in *trans*-$[Co(NH_3)_4Cl_2]^+$, a statistical factor is all that is required, so that $k_{OH} = (nk_1k_2/k_{-1} + k_2)$, where k_1 would be the rate constant from proton exchange, i.e. the slope of the plot of $\ln(1 - F_{ex})$ against time divided by $[OH^-]$, assuming that there is no isotopic dilution. If there are sets of non-equivalent protons, each of which is associated with its own k_1 and amido conjugate base (and hence k_{-1} and k_2) the relationship becomes

$$k_{OH} = \sum \frac{n^i k_1^i k_2^i}{k_{-1}^i + k_2^i} \tag{14}$$

where n^i, k_1^i, k_{-1}^i and k_2^i are the statistical terms and the rate constants defined in (5)–(7) for the ith set of n^i equivalent protons. Although of considerable interest to any detailed study of this reaction, no complete analysis has ever been carried out on any system. There is reason to believe that, in most cases, one set of equivalent protons may dominate the reaction.

The two fates of the conjugate base are not related and there is no reason why the two rate constants should be of similar magnitude and so it is convenient to discuss the two limiting cases, at this stage in general terms but later in a much more specific way.

1. The case where $k_{-1} \gg k_2$

Here, the relationship for a single set of equivalent protons reduces to

$$k_{OH} = n k_1 k_2 / k_{-1} \tag{15}$$

and k_1 must therefore be much greater than k_{OH}. Under these circumstances the processes involving proton transfer can be treated as a pre-equilibrium generation of the reactive amido species with $n k_1/k_{-1} = K_{hy} = K_a/K_w$, where K_a is the relevant acid dissociation constant of the amine complex and K_w the ionic product of water. (In the more general context we would use the ionic product of the amphiprotic solvent.) In those systems where proton transfer is rapid and reversible the simple first-order dependence upon the concentration of unreacted substrate would be maintained even when the concentration of the amido conjugate base was too large for the steady-state approximation to be used. The dependence upon $[OH^-]$ becomes more complex and the pseudo first-order rate constant determined in buffered conditions, k_{obs}, takes the relationship

$$k_{obs} = K_{hy} k_2 [OH^-]/(1 + K_{hy}[OH^-]) \tag{16}$$

which reduces to the simple second-order rate law when $1 \gg K_{hy}[OH^-]$ and becomes independent of $[OH^-]$ (i.e. $k_{obs} = k_2$) when $K_{hy}[OH^-] \gg 1$. In systems where different sets of amine protons have widely differing acidities even more complicated dependences of k_{obs} on $[OH^-]$ are observed. These will be discussed in detail below. Reactions where proton transfer is fast compared with subsequent reaction will be subject to specific base catalysis, i.e. the rate depends upon $[OH^-]$ and is unaffected by the concentration of other Brønsted bases that might be present in the system.[39]

2. The case where $k_2 \gg k_{-1}$

Until 1968 it was generally thought that the proton transfer processes would always be much faster than base hydrolysis, partly because only specific base catalysis had been observed and partly because it had been assumed, quite erroneously, that k_{-1} would always be diffusion controlled and therefore much greater than k_2. But in the early 1960s, on making a comparison of the general trends of k_{OH} as a function of the structure and composition of the Co(III) substrate with those of k_1 for similar but substitutionally inert species we suspected that, in compounds of the type $trans$-$[Co(L_4)X_2]^+$ (L_4 is a suitable combination of amine donors from mono-, bi- or multidentate ligands; X = Cl, Br), the rate constants for base hydrolysis and proton exchange might be of similar magnitude. Indeed the subsequent study was motivated by the hope that the D_{cb} mechanism might be disproved by showing that the act of base hydrolysis was not necessarily accompanied by proton transfer. In the event it was proved that the act of base hydrolysis was accompanied by the exchange of one proton, thereby providing the first direct evidence in favour of the D_{cb} mechanism.[40-42] When $k_{-1} \ll k_2$ the relationship simplifies to $k_{OH} = nk_1$, i.e. the act of protonation becomes rate determining. Such systems are susceptible to general base catalysis, i.e. the rate law takes the form

$$-d[\text{complex}]/dt = [\text{complex}](k_{OH}[OH^-] + \sum k_B[B]) \qquad (17)$$

The detection of general base catalysis is diagnostic of a process in which there is not a rapid, reversible, pre-equilibrium proton transfer, but the converse is less reliable because it is not always easy to distinguish experimentally between true specific base catalysis and a general base catalysis where the Bronsted coefficient, α, in the relationship $\log k_B = \alpha(pK_a BH^+) + c$, is so large that all other contributions are swamped by that of the most basic species, OH^-.[43]

Systems where k_2 is large compared with k_{-1} (and even the borderline situation where both constants have a similar magnitude) are of considerable interest in their application to the study of a wide variety of problems associated with reactivity and mechanism in the base hydrolysis reaction.[5] In a rapidly exchanging substrate, an isotopic label (D or T) will be lost before any significant amount of substitution had occurred. When deprotonation becomes rate limiting, however, not only can isotopic labelling be used to demonstrate the D_{cb} mechanism, it can also be used to identify the site of deprotonation that gives rise to the reactive amido species which is a necessary prerequisite in any study of the stereochemistry, at nitrogen, of the reaction. The direct connection between proton exchange and base hydrolysis allows one to use the more accurately monitorable ligand substitution reaction to study the kinetic features of the proton transfer reaction.

B. Departures from a simple first-order dependence on [OH⁻]

Departures that reflect a saturation effect, i.e. $k_{obs} = a[OH^-]/(1 + b[OH^-])$ are not uncommon and may arise from a number of causes, for example, when the concentration of conjugate base ceases to be negligible, i.e. $K_{hy}[OH^-] \nless 1$, or when the hydroxide ion pair of the substrate is well developed, and these will be discussed in their own context. The base hydrolysis of $[Co(NH_3)_5(OC(NH_2)_2)]^{3+}$ shows such a deviation at high $[OH^-]$[44]; it is thought that this is due to deprotonation of the coordinated urea which converts the substrate into one far less reactive. Ion association is ruled out because $[Co(NH_3)_5(OS(CH_3)_2)]^{3+}$ and $[Co(NH_3)_5(OP(OMe)_3)]^{3+}$ do not show this effect under comparable conditions.[44] However, using a more elaborate acido-penta-amine system, t-$[Co(tren)(NH_3)(OS(CH_3)_2)]^{3+}$ (tren = tris-(2-aminoethyl)amine; the t isomer has the Me_2SO *trans* to the tertiary nitrogen), Buckingham[45] has observed a departure from a simple first-order dependence at $[OH^-] > 0.025$ M.

A more complicated departure is found in the base hydrolysis of $[Co(NH_3)_5(CO_2CF_3)]^{2+}$, where the hydroxide dependence takes the form, $k_{obs} = k_{OH}[OH^-] + k'_{OH}[OH^-]^2$.[46] Isotopic labelling studies indicate two parallel pathways, the normal k_{OH} pathway, in which there is Co—O fission, and the k'_{OH} pathway which involves C—O fission and hydroxide attack on the carbon in the hydroxide adduct.

$$[(NH_3)_5Co-\overset{*}{O}-\underset{\underset{O}{\|}}{C}-CF_3]^{2+} + OH^- \;=\; [(NH_3)_5Co-\overset{*}{O}-\underset{\underset{O}{|}}{\overset{\overset{OH}{|}}{C}}-CF_3]^+$$

$$[(NH_3)_5Co-\overset{*}{O}-\underset{\underset{O}{|}}{\overset{\overset{OH}{|}}{C}}-CF_3]^+ + OH^- \;\rightarrow\; [(NH_3)_5Co-\overset{*}{O}-\underset{\underset{O}{|}}{\overset{\overset{O}{|}}{C}}-CF_3] + H_2O$$

$$\downarrow$$

$$[(NH_3)_5Co-\overset{*}{O}]^+ + CF_3COO^-$$

$$\downarrow {\scriptstyle +H_2O}$$

$$[(NH_3)_5Co-\overset{*}{O}H]^{2+} + OH^-$$

Departure from a simple first-order dependence on [complex] while [OH⁻] was held constant over the range 0.03 to 0.2 M has been reported in the base hydrolysis of $[Ru(NH_3)_5X]^{2+}$ (X = Cl, Br, I).[47] It has been suggested that these departures, which occur at the early stages of the reaction, indicate the build up of significant quantities of the amido species and that hydroxide substitution involved parallel bi-molecular attack on the amine species and its conjugate base. A computer based analysis of the data gives the second-order rate constants for these two processes as 0.113 and 0.678 $M^{-1} s^{-1}$ at 15 °C for X = Cl, and the rate constant for deprotonation of $[Ru(NH_3)_5Cl]^{2+}$ = 0.0920 $M^{-1} s^{-1}$. Although this proton exchange has not been measured directly, it is likely that the true value is many orders of magnitude larger. Studies at lower $[OH^-]$ did not indicate any abnormalities[30] and the second-order rate constant at 25 °C (4.9 $M^{-1} s^{-1}$) would suggest that the reaction being studied at the higher $[OH^-]$ is something subsequent to the displacement of chloride. The departure from a simple first-order rate plot is possibly just the overlapping of this step with the tail end of the faster displacement of the chloride. This system is well worth re-examining.

There is a great deal yet to be learnt about changes to the base hydrolysis at very high hydroxide concentrations. The so-called "Walden Inversion" of octahedral complexes, first discovered by Bailar,[48] and subsequently shown to be due to a change in steric course of the reaction Δ-*cis*-$[Co(en)_2Cl_2]^+$ + $2OH^-$ = *trans* + Δ-*cis* + Λ-*cis*-$[Co(en)_2(OH)_2]^+$ in which there was more Λ than Δ *cis* product, has been the subject of much study. There does not appear to be any anomaly in the displacement of the second chlorine, while the first stage is too fast to be examined independently under the high concentrations of base required. Indeed, there has been a suggestion that this is not a two-stage process but rather a synchronous loss of both chlorides.[49,50]

C. The evidence for the D_{cb} mechanism

Although the individual experiments will be considered in detail in the context of later sections, it will be useful and convenient at this point to summarise the experimental evidence that has led people to favour the D_{cb} mechanism.

In the early stages of the work this evidence generally took the form of the elimination of the possible alternatives (a common way of ascertaining mechanism), so that most of the evidence presented in favour of the D_{cb} mechanism was really evidence against direct bi-molecular attack by hydroxide, the only serious alternative at that time. The fundamental objection to the S_N2 mechanism was the unique role of hydroxide, other nucleophiles, such as CN^{-} [51] or HO_2^- [52] making no contribution to the rate of reaction once the change in pH due to their basic properties or the possible redox catalysed pathways due to Co(II) impurities,[51] was corrected for or eliminated. Green and Taube[53,54] showed that the isotope fractionation factor of oxygen in the $[Co(NH_3)_5OH]^{2+}$ product from the base hydrolysis of $[Co(NH_3)_5X]^{2+}$ (X = Cl, Br, NO₃), 1.0057, was consistent with H_2O being the entering species and not OH$^-$, where a factor of 1.040 would have been expected. The similarity of the factor for all three leaving groups was taken as evidence for a common intermediate. The more direct evidence favouring the D_{cb} mechanism generally relates to the demonstration of the involvement of a reactive amido conjugate base or to demonstrating the dissociative nature of the reaction.

1. Proton transfer/acid base processes

The close parallel between the kinetics of proton exchange and those of base hydrolysis was the basis of Garrick's original suggestion of the involvement of the amido conjugate base. However, in the cases where $k_{-1} \gg k_2$, it is not possible to devise a definitive experiment to show that a deprotonation is a necessary step in the reaction with hydroxide. However, in substrates where $k_{-1} \ll k_2$, it is possible, as has already been indicated, to make this connection.

2. The dissociative nature of the process

When Basolo and Pearson reintroduced the "$S_N 1cb$" mechanism, the subtleties of the distinction between the D and the I_d modes of dissociative activation were not as well appreciated by inorganic chemists as they are today. This criticism cannot be directed at the above authors who showed clearly in the first edition of their classic textbook the conceptual distinction between the $S_N 1(lim)$ and $S_N 1$ mechanisms of substitution.[55] The criterion for assigning a dissociative mechanism was the demonstration of the existence of a trappable intermediate of lower coordination number, best done by showing the occurrence of base catalysed substitution. This was first attempted in a non-aqueous environment in order to reduce competition from water and it was shown that the reactions, *trans*-[Co(en)$_2$NO$_2$Cl]$^+$ + NO$_2^-$ = *trans*-[Co(en)$_2$(NO$_2$)$_2$]$^+$ + Cl$^-$[56] and the displacement of the chloride from *cis*-[Rh(en)$_2$NO$_2$Cl]$^+$ or *trans*-[Rh(en)$_2$(CH$_3$NH$_2$)Cl]$^+$ by N$_3^-$ or NO$_2^-$[57] in dimethylsulfoxide, were catalysed strongly by traces of hydroxide. The inability of non-basic nucleophiles, Y, to increase the rate of consumption of the substrate indicated a dissociative mode of activation, although occasional higher-order contributions to the rate law by hydroxide in strong base solution have sometimes been observed. This is discussed in Section III.B.

The molecularity of the reaction between water and the conjugate base cannot be determined from the kinetics and a bi-molecular process has occasionally been invoked to account for some departures from the expected pattern, such as the change in the isotopic discrimination factor for the base hydrolysis of [Co(NH$_3$)$_5$X]$^{n+}$ when X = F, and SO$_4^{2-}$.[53,54] It is unwise to invoke molecularity changes in this way because the system is not so finely balanced between mechanistic pathways that minor changes will lead to molecularity changes of this sort. The dissociative activation would require that the distribution of the product between the lyato complex, e.g. L_5MOH and the substitution produce, L_5MY should depend upon the concentration and the nature of Y, since the trapping of the five-coordinate intermediate is an associatively activated process. An extreme D process involving an intermediate long enough lived to equilibrate its own environment would lead to a product distribution and product stereochemistry that was independent of the nature of the leaving group. A great deal of detailed work has now been done and shows that this simplicity is not always found. This will be considered in detail in Section VII. It is clear that, with charged substrates, leaving groups and nucleophiles in polar solvents, the lifetime of the intermediate is rarely long enough, compared with the time required for the complete equilibration of its environment, for it to lose all memory of its origin.

It appears that this type of work (however demanding and difficult it may be to carry out) serves to show better than anything else in the field of inorganic substitution reactions that the borderline between D and I_d is not sharp and a whole spectrum of possibilities lies between the equally rare long-lived intermediate at the one extreme and the truly synchronous interchange (bond making and breaking within a single vibration) at the other. A purist might therefore wish to label the mechanism D(ish)cb or even I_d(ish)cb.

IV. THE DEPENDENCE OF THE SENSITIVITY OF THE SUBSTRATE TOWARDS BASE HYDROLYSIS UPON THE CENTRAL ION AND THE LIGANDS

A. General comments

The second-order rate constants, k_{OH}, which will be used as a measure of the sensitivity towards base hydrolysis, relate to reactions involving anionic hydroxide and, with very few exceptions, cationic substrates. They will therefore be subject to primary salt effects which can be quite considerable for $2+$ and $3+$ cations and the absence of a commonly agreed ionic strength at which to work (occasionally, but becoming rare nowadays, no attempt is made to control the ionic strength or to report it) makes direct comparison of rate constants difficult if one is searching for relatively small effects (less than one order of magnitude). Guided extrapolations to $\mu = 0$, which ought to resolve this difficulty, are not very reliable for $\mu > 0.2$ and much of the literature data, especially for systems that have to be studied in buffer solution, are related to $\mu = 1.0$. Consequently, unless there happens to be a particular need to compare rate constants of similar magnitude, I have left the rate constants unchanged, and as found in the original paper. In order to reduce the complexity of some of the Tables, I have made no attempt to record the ionic strengths at which the measurements were carried out. Anyone wishing to use these data for comparisons of their own is strongly recommended to go to the original paper and to pay full attention to the ionic strength and reaction conditions recorded therein.

It is not my intention to provide a comprehensive and up to date list of all the published data up to the time of writing but rather to provide a commentary and guide to the work published in this area.

1. The general case of cobalt(III)

The published work on the base catalysed hydrolysis of octahedral complexes is so dominated by studies of Co(III) systems that there is a tendency to take mechanistic deductions based on these systems as applying to other reaction centres as well. Although a great deal remains to be done with these other systems, it is already clear that, certainly as far as the details are concerned, cobalt(III) is unique; indeed, each of the reaction centres to be considered in this chapter has its own mechanistic characteristics.

B. The dependence of the sensitivity of the cobalt(III) complex to base catalysis on the nature of the ligands

1. The leaving group

Although the rates of dissociatively activated substitution processes will be very dependent upon the nature of the leaving group, this aspect is probably the least important of the factors to be discussed in this section and is best dealt with first. The number of systematic studies covering a sufficiently wide range of leaving groups are few, the bulk of the published work being restricted to a comparison of chloride to bromide (with nitrate occasionally thrown in as well). Iodo complexes of Co(III) are fairly uncommon because of the redox processes that interfere with their preparation, and fluoro complexes are not very popular. The most fully documented system for leaving group effects is $[Co(NH_3)_5X]^{n+}$ and it is here that the well-known linear relationship between $\log k_{aq}$ and $\log K$ for the process

$$[Co(NH_3)_5X]^{(3-x)+} + H_2O \xrightarrow{k_{aq}} [Co(NH_3)_5H_2O]^{3+} + X^{x-}; K \qquad (18)$$

was established, points for leaving groups X of similar charge lying on lines that are parallel to each other with slopes of 1.0.[58-60] This has been interpreted as evidence for a fully dissociative mechanism for the aquation of the cobaltammine complexes and a similar linear relationship between log k_{OH} and K' for the reaction

$$[Co(NH_3)_5X]^{(3-x)+} + OH^- \xrightleftharpoons{k_{OH}} [Co(NH_3)_5OH]^{2+} + X^{n-}; \quad K' \qquad (19)$$

has been taken as strong evidence that the base hydrolysis is also dissociatively activated.[32] Since the ratio K/K' is simply the equilibrium constant for the acid-base reaction of the aquo complex, $[Co(NH_3)_5H_2O]^{3+} + OH^- = [Co(NH_3)_5OH]^{2+} + H_2O$ ($= K_a/K_w$, where K_a is the acid dissociation constant of the aquo complex and K_w the ionic product of water) and clearly independent of the nature of X, the slope of 1.00 in the above treatment of the aquation and the base hydrolysis data would suggest that the ratio k_{OH}/k_{aq} should be independent of the nature of X. House has discussed this point in his review[61] and plotted log k_{OH} against log k_{aq} for some 20 different acido-pentammine complexes. The points are widely scattered but appear to be randomly distributed about a line of slope 1.0. It is instructive to look at the actual ratios and these are collected in Table 1. The bulk of the entries have a ratio that lies between 3×10^4 and 3×10^5 and some of the departures can be logically explained. For example, in the case of $X = ReO_4^-$,[62] the reaction is known to proceed by Re—O fission and is therefore irrelevant to any discussion of substitution at cobalt, but the displacement of carboxylates has been shown to take place with Co—O bond fission provided the hydroxide concentration is not too high.[62] In the case of the nitropentammine complex it has now been established that the rate constant for the displacement of NO_2^- must be lower than that for the loss of ammonia *trans* to it (the process that is actually being followed).[64] The ratio in Table 1 therefore is just a lower limit. The most strongly bound ligands cannot be completely displaced in the aquation reaction unless reagents are added to completely remove them as such from the system. In the reactions with the leaving groups of reasonable basicity the reactions have been forced to completion by adding acid and, in a number of cases, e.g. $X = NO_2^-, N_3^-, F^-$, etc., the aquations are subject to acid catalysis. The extrapolation to $[H^+] = 0$ and to 25 °C are themselves liable to introduce considerable error.

There is no need to get too agitated about the lack of a close quantitative relationship between k_{OH} and k_{aq} even after the effects of bad experimentation or misidentification of reaction have been eliminated. The nature of the leaving group may affect the other parameters that determine the value of k_{OH}, namely k_1 and k_{-1} in equation (5). As will be seen later, k_1 can be very sensitive to the nature of the other ligands in the complex, and, unless there is a parallel and cancelling effect on k_{-1} (i.e. the nature of the other ligands affects ammine proton lability but not the acidity), this may affect the value of k_{OH} in a way that does not parallel k_{aq}. However, it appears that the major proton labilising effect occurs at the nitrogen *trans* to the variable ligand, which in this case is

TABLE 1

Leaving group effects. A comparison of the rate constants for the base hydrolysis (k_{OH}) and the uncatalysed aquation (k_{aq}) of $[Co(NH_3)_5X]^{n+}$ at 25 °C[a]

X	$10^4 k_{OH}/$ $M^{-1}s^{-1}$	Reference	$10^7 k_{aq}/s^{-1}$	Reference	$(10^{-4}k_{OH}/k_{aq})/$ M^{-1}
PO_4^{3-}	0.0050	[65]	0.033	[65]	0.015
NH_3	0.0071	[66]	0.000058	[67]	12.2
NO_2^-	0.016	[64]	0.67	[68]	0.0024
malonate^{2-}	0.10	[69]	0.098	[70]	0.102
$S_2O_3^{2-}$	0.60	[71]	1.6	[71]	0.038
$C_2O_4^{2-}$	2.5	[69]	0.042	[72]	5.9
N_3^-	3.0	[73]	0.021	[73]	14.3
NCS^-	5.0	[74]	0.0037	[74]	135
HCO_2^-	5.8	[32]	0.026	[32]	22
$CH_3CO_2^-$	9.6	[75]	0.27	[76]	3.5
$CHCl_2CO_2^-$	58	[77]	1.5	[78]	3.9
F^-	130	[79]	0.86	[80]	15.1
$CF_3CO_2^-$	220	[46]	1.7	[76]	13
CCl_3CO_2	220	[77]	5.8	[78]	3.8
SO_4^{2-}	490	[81]	8.9	[82]	5.5
Cl^-	2300	[83]	18	[61]	13
Br^-	14 000	[83]	39	[84]	36
I^-	32 000	[83]	83	[85]	39
$(CH_3)_2SO$	54 000	[44]	180	[44]	30
NO_3^-	55 000	[83]	241	[61]	23
$(NH_2)_2CO$	150 000	[44]	510	[44]	29
$CH_3SO_3^-$	550 000	[86]	2000	[86]	28
$(CH_3O)_3PO$	790 000	[44]	2500	[87]	32
$p-NO_2(C_6H_4)SO_3^-$	2 700 000	[86]	6300	[86]	43
ReO_4^-	290 000 000	[62]	3120	[62]	9300
$CF_3SO_3^-$	10 000 000 000	[86]	270 000	[86]	3700

[a] Where the primary data need to be extrapolated values from reference [61] are used.

also the leaving group (see Section V) whereas the activating amido group should be *cis* to the leaving group (Section VI) so this contribution does not, in general, account for wide fluctuations in the ratio k_{OH}/k_{aq}. On the other hand, it does seem that the total charge on the complex affects the proton acidity so that one might expect to find that the ratio k_{OH}/k_{aq} will decrease as the charge on the complex decreases. A much more important cause of departure from the rule that k_{OH}/k_{aq} is not very sensitive to the nature of the leaving group will be found where $k_2 \gtrsim k_{-1}$ and we approach the limit where $k_{OH} \rightarrow nk_1$, i.e. deprotonation becomes rate limiting. Here one expects to find that the rate constant becomes insensitive to the nature of the leaving group (or changes with it in a way consistent with the relationship between proton exchange and the nature of the other ligands in the complex). In principle, one should move towards this limit in any system as the leaving group becomes more labile, or conversely, move away from it as the leaving group becomes more inert. In the $Co(NH_3)_5^{n+}$ system discussed above, the ratio k_{-1}/k_2 is so large (at least 10^5 for $Co(NH_3)_5Cl^{2+}$) that a weakly-bound leaving group giving $k_{OH} > 10^5$ M^{-1} s^{-1} would be required.

2. The other non-amine ligands in the complex

It is well known that the solvolytic reactions of octahedral cobalt(III) complexes are very sensitive to the nature (and position relative to that of the leaving group) of the other ligands in the complex and, therefore, it is of considerable interest to see how these effects are modified in the presence of the strongly labilising amido group. The complexes of the type, *cis* and *trans*-$[Co(en)_2ACl]^{n+}$ provide an abundant source of substrates for the study of the way in which variation of the nature and position of ligand A affects the sensitivity towards base hydrolysis. A selection of these data are collected in Table 2 together with the activation parameters and the ratios k_{OH}/k_{aq}. This Table is not comprehensive, an enormous number of complexes where A = a primary amine (or even a cyclic secondary amine) have been studied and, apart from some significant exceptions which have been included in the Table, all of the rate constants are much the same. The data can be found in the excellent comprehensive compilation by House.[61] At one time an attempt was made to invoke a duality of mechanism because of the way in which k_{OH} varied with the inductive effect of R in a series of complexes of the type *cis*-$[Co(en)_2(RNH_2)Cl]^{2+}$,[100] but it was later shown that the irreproducibility between laboratories was as large as the differences that were being discussed.[101] Another series of complexes in which a systematic variation of a substituent can be examined is *trans*-$[Co(en)_2(RCO_2)Cl]^+$ and k_{OH} has been determined for a number of different R substituents, see Table 3. There is a rough dependence of k_{OH} upon the basicity of RCO_2^- (as measured by the pK_a of RCO_2H), the least basic anion, $CNCH_2CO_2^-$ giving the most labile complex and the variation of the rate constant from the least basic to the most basic carboxylato complex spans a factor of 30. It would be of interest to see whether the substituent effect was reflected in the proton exchange rate constants because it works in the opposite direction to what might be expected for an inductive assistance of the bond breaking in the k_2 step.

On examining the data in Table 2 a number of features deserve comment. First, the ratio k_{OH}/k_{aq} (using k_{OH} measured at 0 °C and k_{H_2O} at 25 °C does not affect the argument) changes markedly with the nature of A and, in some cases (particularly A = Cl, Br and NCS) with its position relative to the leaving group. The dependence of k_{OH} upon the nature and position of ligand A clearly

TABLE 2

Rate constants and activation parameters for the base hydrolysis of some *cis*- and *trans*-[Co(en)$_2$(A)Cl]$^{n+}$ complexes[a][b]

A	Cis					Trans				
	$k_{OH}/$ M^{-1} s^{-1}	Reference	$10^{-4}k^0_{OH}/$ k^{25}_{aq}	$\Delta H^{\ddagger}/$ kcal mol^{-1}	$\Delta S^{\ddagger}/$ cal K^{-1} mol^{-1}	$k_{OH}/$ M^{-1} s^{-1}	Reference	$10^{-4}k^0_{OH}/$ k^{25}_{aq}	$\Delta H^{\ddagger}/$ kcal mol^{-1}	$\Delta S^{\ddagger}/$ cal K^{-1} mol^{-1}
Cl$^-$	15	[26]	6.3	24	+37	85	[26]	240	23	+35
Br$^-$	23	[26]	16	22	+31	110	[26]	240	24	+42
OH$^-$	0.37	[26]	0.0031	22	+21	0.017	[26]	0.0011	22	+17
O$_2$CCH$_3^-$						0.32[c]	[88]	10.3	22	+21
O$_2$CC$_6$H$_5^-$						0.22[c]	[88]	18	25	+25
OCO$_2^{2-}$						0.011[c]	[89]	109	25	+25
NCS$^-$	1.4	[20]	12.7			0.35	[20]	700	23	+27
N$_3^-$	0.17	[90]	0.065			0.41	[90]	0.21		
NO$_2^-$	0.032	[22]	0.029			0.080	[22]	0.0082	24	+24
imid$^-$ —(d)	31[e]	[91]	0.061	23	+17					
benzimid$^-$ —(f)	18[g]	[92]	1.6							
CN$^-$	0.0089	[93]	0.144	23	+18	0.13	[94]	0.16	23	+22
NH$_3$	0.50	[21]	100	23	+24	1.25	[21]	370		
NH$_2$CH$_3$	0.17	[95, 96]	106	23	+29					
NH$_2$C$_2$H$_5$	0.16	[95, 96]	76	21	+20					
pyridine	34	[97, 61]	2400							
4-CH$_3$py	30	[97]	1250							
3-CH$_3$py	29	[97]	1800							
NH$_2$C$_6$H$_5$	2400	[28, 98]	660 000	24	+40					
imidH	207[e]	[91, 264]	36 000							
benzimidH	290	[92, 264]	30 000							
H$_2$O	43 000[g]	[99]	10 000 000							

[a] k_{OH} at 0 °C except where otherwise indicated.
[b] Ionic strength variable.
[c] Extrapolated.

[d] imid$^-$ =

[e] At 31 °C.

[f] benzimid$^-$ =

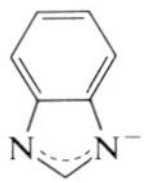

[g] At 25 °C.

TABLE 3

Rate constants for the base hydrolysis of *trans*-$[Co(en)_2(RCO_2)Cl]^+$ at 25°C

R	pK_a of RCO_2H	$k_{OH}/M^{-1} s^{-1}$		Reference
		$\mu = 0.1$	$\mu = 1.0$	
NH_2CH_2	9.87[a]		6.3	[102]
$(CH_3)_3C$	5.03	3.8		[103]
CH_3CH_2	4.87	9.5		[103]
CH_3	4.75	11.2	37.4	[102, 88]
C_6H_5	4.19	7.6		[88]
H	3.75	43		[103]
$ClCH_2$	2.85		50.9	[102]
$BrCH_2$	2.69		42.4	[102]
$NCCH_2$	2.45		113	[102]

[a] This is the pK_a of the Zwitterion. The pK_a of the formal amino acid would be considerably smaller than this.

does not parallel the dependence of k_{aq}. In particular, whereas the *cis*-$[Co(en)_2OHCl]^+$ is the most solvolytically labile complex listed in the Table, it figures among the less reactive with respect to base hydrolysis. A similar effect is to be noted for *trans*-$[Co(en)_2NO_2Cl]^+$.

Since the uncatalysed and base catalysed substitution reactions are both thought to be dissociatively activated one might have expected that the labilising effect of A would be maintained in the base hydrolysis reaction, albeit at a lower level because of the dominating role of the amino group. This is clearly not so and it was long ago suggested[104] that the reason for the low sensitivity of the nitro-chloro complex was due to the nitro group, acting as a π-acceptor and sidetracking the π-donation effect of the amido group. However, caution should be urged, for, while accepting that the nitro group and the amido group might have different mechanisms for labilisation and therefore interfere with one another's contribution, the same answer cannot be applied to the hydroxo-chloro complex since both are formulated as π-donors. In any case k_{OH} is a composite term and it is likely that k_1 (and probably also k_{-1}) is sensitive to the nature and position of the other ligands in the complex and until such time as a full analysis of the variation of all the rate constants (k_1, k_{-1} and k_2) with the nature and position of these ligands it is speculative to do anything other than note that the dependence of the rate constants for the base catalysed and for the uncatalysed reactions do not follow one another. Another point to note (but not explain) is the similarity of all the enthalpies of activation listed in Table 2 (they have been rounded off to the nearest kcal, which is well within the reliability of many of the numbers). The major variation that parallels the rate constant is the entropy of activation. This was pointed out many years ago[26] but the explanation has not stood the test of time.

3. The amine ligands in the complex

In keeping with the idea that the deprotonation of one amine ligand in the complex and the subsequent involvement of the amido group in the substitution reaction is an essential feature of this base catalysis, it is not surprising that k_{OH} is very sensitive to the nature and the disposition of the amine ligands within the complex. Since a discussion of the way in which the reactivity depends upon the nature and the position of the amido group forms a major part of the later sections, it is convenient, at this stage, simply to indicate the magnitude of the effect and to make a preliminary attempt at subdivision.

There is now a great deal of information about acidopentamine complexes of the type $[M(N_5)X]^{n+}$, where (N_5) represents any combination of five nitrogen donors in mono-, bi- or multidentate ligands. Much of the data relates to $M = Co(III)$ and this situation is likely to remain for a long time in spite of the increasing interest in $M = Cr(III)$ and Ru(III). The data for $M = Co(III)$ and Cr(III) up to August 1976 are comprehensively reviewed by House.[61] Another, but far less extensive, series is found among the diacido-tetramine complexes of the type, $[M(N_4)X_2]^{n+}$ (X = Cl, Br), where, in addition to the various ways of compiling and distributing (N_4) there is also the *cis* and *trans* arrangement of X_2 to consider. There are also a few examples of $[M(N_4)AX]^{n+}$ (where X is the leaving group) but apart from the case where $(N_4) = en_2$, which has already been considered, such series are not extensive. See Table 7.

The acidity of the amine group. We have already seen elsewhere that, provided $k_{-1} \gg k_2$, k_{OH} will depend, at least in part, on the acidity of the amine (k_1/k_{-1}) provided, of course, that the donor in question is able to function effectively as a labilising amido group. The thought that the most acidic amine need not provide the labilising amido group has come late to many workers in the field. Furthermore, it is not necessarily true that the acidity is related to the exchange lability and it is wrong to assume that the reprotonation (k_{-1}) is necessarily diffusion controlled. It can be seen (Table 2) that k_{OH} for *cis*-$[Co(en)_2(PhNH_2)Cl]^{2+}$ is very large and it is assumed that the "acidic" aniline nitrogen provides the labilising amido group. On the other hand, *cis*-$[Co(en)_2(imidH)Cl]^{2+}$ has a much lower value for k_{OH} despite the greater acidity of the imidazole. While there is not necessarily an inverse dependence of k_2 on the acidity of the amine (which would serve to cancel out the effect) a loose relationship of this sort would not be surprising since one of the factors that would increase the acidity of the amine, the extent to which the amido lone pair could be delocalised over the conjugate base, would also decrease the ability of the nitrogen to function as a π-donor to the metal.

Steric hindrance. In order to establish the dissociative character of the base catalysed substitution, a number of studies have been made of the effect of varying the bulkiness of the ligands around the complex. When one is dealing with a multidentate ligand system it is not easy to separate the effects from non-specific bulkiness which would arise from the non-bonding interactions between parts of the ligand, and the more subtle constraints placed upon the orientations of the individual donor atoms by their linkages within the multidentate ligand. Consequently, it is best to confine steric hindrance discussion to acido penta(monodentate amine) complexes, where the effect of the substituent upon the acidity can be estimated from a knowledge of the properties of the corresponding quaternary ammonium species, or less reliably from a knowledge of k_1, see Table 4. The consequence of increasing the

TABLE 4

The effect of steric acceleration on k_{OH} in the base hydrolysis of $[Co(RNH_2)_5Cl]^{2+}$ at 25 °C ($\mu = 1.1$). Data from reference [105]

R	$k_{OH}/$ $M^{-1} s^{-1}$	$10^6 k_{aq}/$ s^{-1}	$10^{-6} k_{OH}/$ k_{aq}	$10^{-4} k_1/$ $M^{-1} s^{-1}$	k_{-1}/k_2
H	0.23	1.77	0.15	5	2 600 000
CH$_3$	3100	36.7	84	30	770
CH$_3$CH$_2$CH$_2$	11 000				(220)[a]
(CH$_3$)$_2$CHCH$_2$	150 000	180	830		(16)

[a] Values in parentheses assume $k_1 = 3 \times 10^5 M^{-1} s^{-1}$.

bulkiness of the amine is considerable, the change from five ammonias to five isobutylamines increasing k_{OH} by some six orders of magnitude. The non-catalysed aquation rate constants also increase, but less markedly and it has been suggested[105] that this indicates that the transition state for the base hydrolysis is more open (i.e. dissociated) than that for aquation. The effect is shown best in the ratio k_{OH}/k_{aq}. The increase in k_{OH} on going from $[Co(MeNH_2)_5Cl]^{2+}$ to $[Co(i\text{-}BuNH_2)_5Cl]^{2+}$ cannot owe much to any change in the acidity of the coordinated amine and must be due mainly to an increase in k_2 as a result of steric acceleration, as expected in a substitution that is dissociatively activated. The change in k_1 on going from $[Co(NH_3)_5Cl]^{2+}$ to $[Co(MeNH_2)_2Cl]^{2+}$ accounts for less than one of the four orders of magnitude increase in k_{OH}. Values for the ratio k_{-1}/k_2 (obtained from the relationship $k_{OH} = nk_1k_2/k_{-1}$) are also listed in Table 4. It has been assumed that the active amido group must be *cis* to the leaving group (see Section VI), that all of the protons on the *cis* amines are equivalent, and isotope effects and changes in ionic strength have been ignored. (k_1 for exchange on the amine *trans* to Cl is generally some two orders of magnitude greater but n is only one quarter of that for *cis* labilisation.) The ratio drops dramatically on going from the ammonia to the methylamine complex, presumably due to changes in k_2. The absence of exchange data for the other complexes prevents a proper computation but it would seem unlikely that the value for k_1 would increase greatly with further alkyl substitution at a site remote from the nitrogen (it is conceivable that it could decrease as a result of the generation of a lyophobic environment about the amine protons). Assuming no further change in k_1 the value of k_{-1}/k_2 decreases almost to the point where the assumption $k_{-1} \gg k_2$ no longer holds. In other systems the lack of a response to increased steric hindrance might simply mean that the act of substitution is no longer rate determining.

Another very significant steric effect originating from the amine is the enhanced labilising power of six-membered diamine rings compared with five-membered ones. This is well documented for spontaneous aquation but does not necessarily manifest itself in k_{OH}. It has been suggested that the 10^3-fold increase in k_{aq} for *trans*-$[\text{Co(NH}_2(\text{CH}_2)_n\text{NH}_2)_2\text{Cl}_2]^+$ when n increases from two to three is due to the extra, inter- or intraligand strain caused by increasing the ring size being relieved when the leaving group departs.[106] A similar difference in reactivity is found between the RSSR and RRRR isomers of *trans*-$[\text{Co(cyclam)Cl}_2]^+$ where, although the ring sizes are obviously the same, the more labile species is able to change to a trigonal bipyramid while the unreactive isomer is constrained to a square-based pyramid by the configuration of the four nitrogens of the macrocycle.[107] This would seem to suggest that the achievement of a trigonal bipyramidal form is a major requirement of this sort of labilisation. However, in both examples, the big lability differences are not found in the values of k_{OH}, see Table 5. The reason is quite clear. These are all systems where deprotonation is rate limiting (or

TABLE 5

Steric acceleration of uncatalysed aquation that is not paralleled by base hydrolysis[a]

Complex	$10^{-4}k_{OH}/$ $M^{-1}\,s^{-1}$	Reference	$10^5 k_{aq}/$ s^{-1}	Reference
trans-$[\text{Co(en)}_2\text{Cl}_2]^+$	0.31	[26]	3.5	[108]
trans-$[\text{Co(tn)}_2\text{Cl}_2]^+$	0.60	[109]	5330	[110]
trans-$[\text{Co(RSSR-cyclam)Cl}_2]^+$	6.5	[13]	0.11	[111]
trans-$[\text{Co(RRRR-cyclam)Cl}_2]^+$	15.7	[13]	175	[107]

[a] At 25 °C.

M. L. Tobe

nearly so) and therefore arguments which relate to contributions from k_2 will be irrelevant. No comparison has yet been made of a *trans*-[Co(en)$_2$ACl]$^+$ with its tn$_2$ analogue while deprotonation is not rate limiting.

Skeletal features of the amine group. Table 6 contains data for a selection of complexes of the type [Co(N$_5$)Cl]$^{2+}$ in which N$_5$ is derived from totally aliphatic ligands containing NH$_3$, $-$NH$_2$, $>$NH or $\gg$N only. The variation in k_{OH} in the data presented covers a wide range of at least seven orders of

TABLE 6

Rate constants for the base hydrolysis of chloro-penta-amine cobalt(III) complexes, [Co(L$_5$)Cl]$^{2+}$, where L$_5$ is any combination of five amine nitrogen donors

				"Flat" secondary nitrogens *cis* to leaving group		
				$10^{-4}k_{OH}^{25°}/$ $\mathrm{M^{-1}\,s^{-1}}$	10^{-7} $\dfrac{k_{OH}}{k_{aq}}\Big/\mathrm{M^{-1}}$	Refer-ence
Pentadentate						
1.[a] $\alpha\beta$-*syn*-[Co(tetren)Cl]$^{2+}$[b]				3.5	97 000	[112]
2. $\alpha\beta$-*anti*-[Co(tetren)Cl]$^{2+}$				1.0[c]	11 000	[112]
Quadridentate-monodentate						
3. *syn*-β_2-[Co(trien)(NH$_3$)Cl]$^{2+}$				23		[113]
4. *anti*-β_2-[Co(trien)(NH$_3$)Cl]$^{2+}$				4.8		[113]
5. *trans*-RR(SS)-[Co(3,2,3-tet)(NH$_3$)Cl]$^{2+}$				3.6		[114]
6. *trans*-RR(SS)-[Co(3,2,3-tet)(NH$_2$Me)Cl]$^{2+}$				76		[114]
7. *trans*-[Co(cyclam)(NH$_3$)Cl]$^{2+}$				1.4	19 000	[115]

Terdentate-bidentate
Complexes of the type *mer*-[Co(triamine)(diamine)Cl]$^{2+}$, see 8.

	x	y	z			
anti-	2	2	2	3.0	17 000	[116, 117]
anti-	2	2	3	50	8900	[118]
anti-	3	3	2	0.22	10	[116, 117]
syn-	3	3	2	0.86	74	[118]
syn-	3	3	3	0.28	16	[118]
syn-	2	3	2	1.1		[119]
anti-	2	3	2	0.12		[119]
syn-	2	3	3	59		[119]
anti-	2	3	3	9.4		[119]

				"Flat" secondary nitrogen *trans* to leaving group		
Pentadentate						
9. *sym*-[Co(trenen)Cl]$^{2+}$				0.052		[120]

TABLE 6—*continued*

	$10^{-4}k_{OH}^{25°}/$ $M^{-1}\,s^{-1}$	$10^{-7}\dfrac{k_{OH}}{k_{aq}}\Big/M^{-1}$	Reference

"Bent" secondary nitrogen cis to leaving group

Tetradentate-monodentate
10. α-[Co(trien)(NH$_3$)Cl]$^{2+}$	0.0010		[113]
11. α-[Co(trien)(NH$_2$CH$_2$CO$_2$Et)Cl]$^{2+}$	0.0074		[113]

Terdentate-bidentate
unsym-fac-[Co(dien)(en)Cl]$^{2+}$ (x=y=z=2)	0.0027	10	[121, 117]
unsym-fac-[Co(dien)(tn)Cl]$^{2+}$ (x=y=2; z=3)	0.0138	3.2	[118]

"Bent" secondary nitrogen trans to leaving group

Terdentate-bismonodentate
sym-fac-cis-[Co(dien)(NH$_3$)$_2$Cl]$^{2+}$ (x=y=2)	0.000070	0.22	[122]

Terdentate-bidentate
sym-fac-[Co(dien)(en)Cl]$^{2+}$ (x=y=z=2)	0.00047	5	[122]
sym-fac-[Co(dien)(tn)Cl]$^{2+}$ (x=y=2; z=3)	0.00106	5	[118]

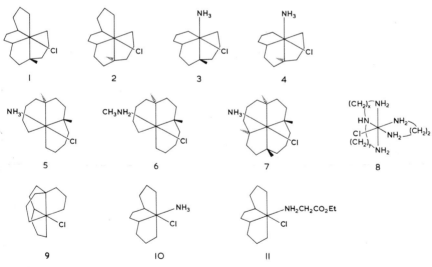

(a) Number corresponds to that of structure given below.

(b) "*syn*" indicates that N—H bond is in same direction as Co—Cl; "*anti*" indicates that it is in the reverse direction.

(c) Extrapolated from data at 70° assuming the same activation energy as the *syn* isomer.

magnitude and four to five orders of magnitude can commonly be found between different stereoisomers of the same combination of ligands. At this stage it is convenient to introduce the terms "flat" and "bent" to describe tetrahedral secondary nitrogen atoms that lie in the middle of a sequence of three donor atoms which are meridional and facial respectively. It will be seen that a major requirement for high lability is the presence of a "flat" secondary nitrogen cis to the leaving group. Part of this enhanced reactivity comes from the increase in k_1 (Section V) and part comes from an enhancement of k_2 (Section VI). The importance of a "flat" secondary amine group cis to the leaving group is not restricted to chloro pentamine type complexes (see Section VI and Table 18). An exception to this rule can be found in a recent paper[123] and is discussed in Section VI.

Macrocyclic amines. General interest in macrocylic ligands has led to information about the ways in which the lability depends upon factors such as ring size, unsaturation and ring substituents. The most comprehensive series involves 14 membered quadridentate amine rings based on the –5–6–5–6– sequence of cyclam and data for *trans* complexes of such ligands are collected in Table 7, together with ratios of k_{OH}/k_{aq} and activation parameters where known. The complexes of the unhindered cyclam itself resemble the *trans-*

TABLE 7

Rate constants for the base hydrolysis of some *trans-*$[Co(L_4)AX]^{n+}$ complexes, where L_4 is a macrocyclic tetra-amine ligand[a]

L_4	A	X	$10^{-3}k_{OH}/$ $M^{-1}s^{-1}$	$(10^{-7}k_{OH}/k_{aq})/$ M^{-1}	$\Delta H^{\ddagger}/kcal$ mol^{-1}	$\Delta S^{\ddagger}/cal$ $K^{-1}mol^{-1}$	Reference
cyclam	Cl	Cl	65[b]	5900	10.7	0	[13, 111]
cyclam	N_3	Cl	2.8	33	23.5	+36	[124]
cyclam	NCS	Cl	0.90	82 000	21.0	+25	[125]
cyclam	NO_2	Cl	0.60	1.4	19.4	+19	[126]
cyclam	NH_3	Cl	0.40	550			[115]
cyclam	CN	Cl	0.028	5.8	22.6	+24	[127]
cyclam	OH	Cl	0.0048	0.00004	23.0	+22	[128, 129]
cyclam	N_3	Br	28		17.9	+22	[130]
cyclam	NCS	Br	11		18.8	+23	[130, 131]
cyclam	NO_2	Br	14	2.5	18.9	+24	[126]
cyclam	CN	Br	0.50	17	20.1	+21	[124]
cyclam	OH	N_3	2.8		28.2	+25	[130]
tet-a	Cl	Cl	570	310			[132]
tet-a	NCS	Cl	19[b]	2700	15.9	+15	[130, 131]

TABLE 7–*continued*

L_4	A	X	$10^{-3}k_{OH}/$ $M^{-1}s^{-1}$	$(10^{-7}k_{OH}/k_{aq})/$ M^{-1}	$\Delta H^{\ddagger}/\text{kcal}$ mol^{-1}	$\Delta S^{\ddagger}/\text{cal}$ $K^{-1}\text{mol}^{-1}$	Reference
tet-a	NCS	Br	75[b]	1200	12.9	+ 7	[130, 131]
diene-I	Cl	Cl	160[b]	1.4	11.7	+ 5	[130]
diene-I	N_3	Cl	180	0.86	11.7	+ 5	[130, 133]
diene-I	NCS	Cl	130[b]	9300	12.4	+ 6	[130, 131, 133]
diene-I	NO_2	Cl	0.22[c]	0.040			[134]
diene-I	CN	Cl	160	0.64	13.6	+11	[135]
diene-I	N_3	Br	190	0.35	13.1	+10	[130, 133]
diene-I	NCS	Br	290[b]	10 000	12.7	+ 9	[130, 131]
diene-I	CN	Br	1100	11	12.4	+11	[135]
diene-I	CN	NCS	0.13		25.1	+36	[130]
diene-I	CN	N_3	0.087		23.6	+30	[130]
diene-I	CN	NO_2	0.0092		22.4	+21	[130]
diene-II	NO_2	Cl	0.25	0.067	16.5	+ 6	[134]
diene-III	Cl	Cl	800	350			[33]

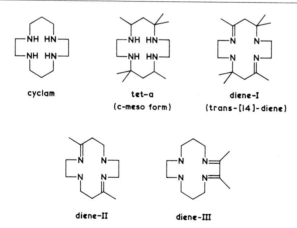

cyclam

tet-a
(c-meso form)

diene-I
(trans-[14]-diene)

diene-II   diene-III

[a] Some of the original k_{OH} values have been corrected in reference [130].
[b] These systems have been shown to follow general base catalysis.
[c] This is clearly a different ligand isomer. Poon reports a much more solvolytically labile species.[136] The question is discussed further in reference [137].

$[Co(en)_2AX]^{n+}$ species quite well. Apart from the dichloro complex[13] only one N-configurational isomer has been identified and studied and is probably the RSSR form, which is the least strained and the least solvolytically labile of the set. The most obvious difference is the extremely low enthalpy of activation of the base hydrolysis of the *trans*-dichloro species and it is known that, in this case, deprotonation is rate limiting above 25 °C.[138] The ratio k_{OH}/k_{aq} is scattered over some nine orders of magnitude but this reflects the variation of k_{aq} with the nature of ligand A rather than the variation of k_{OH} and shows that they respond to different properties in A. Retaining the saturation but introducing six methyl substituents, as in the tet-a complexes (the C-meso-hexamethyl substituted derivative of cyclam), causes a general increase in lability for steric reasons. The observation of general base catalysis[130] for the base hydrolysis of *trans*-$[Co(tet-a)(NCS)X]^+$ (X = Cl, Br) is taken as indicating that protonation is rate limiting, but the values of k_{OH} for the two complexes are as disparate as those for the *trans*-$[Co(cyclam)(NCS)X]^+$ species where the activation parameters suggest that this is not so. In the *trans*-$[Co(trans-14-diene)AX]^+$ complexes, the point has been reached where the increase in dissociative lability due to a combination of the unsaturation in the macrocycle and the steric effect of the methyl substituents has increased k_2 sufficiently for the rate to be determined by k_1. Consequently, k_{OH} is almost independent of the nature of A. For X = Cl or Br, the condition that $k_2 \gg k_{-1}$ clearly holds and the low enthalpies of activation are consistent with the idea that $k_{OH} = nk_1$. The values of k_{OH}/k_{aq} are generally much less than those observed for cases where $k_{-1} \gg k_2$ suggesting that these systems are well past the $k_1 = k_2$ borderline. With more strongly bound leaving groups, e.g. NCS^-, NO_2^- and N_3^-, the value of k_2 is reduced to the point where k_{-1} again becomes large compared with k_2.

C. Base catalysed substitution reactions at centres other than cobalt(III)

Most of the foregoing discussion has been devoted to cobalt(III) complexes where the sensitivity towards base catalysed substitution is most marked. Of the other potential reaction centres in substitutionally inert systems, only Ru(III) shows any similar marked sensitivity. Complexes of Cr(III) and Rh(III) undergo base catalysed hydrolysis, but generally this is negligible compared with the background solvolysis except in strongly basic solution. In recent years, interest in such systems, especially those of Cr(III), has increased considerably. The reactions of Ir(III) acido-amine complexes are extremely slow, base catalysis only occurs at high pH, and the temperatures required to study the reactions at a convenient rate are high.[139,140] Very few data are available. The reactions of Pt(IV) acido-amine complexes with hydroxide are very slow in spite of the extensive deprotonation. The kinetics are complicated because of some reduction to Pt(II) and the consequent redox processes which constitute the major substitution pathways.[141]

A direct observation of base catalysed substitution in labile systems, i.e. those whose study requires the measurement of the relaxation following the disturbance of equilibrium, is complicated by the irreversibility of these processes in basic solution and by the proton anomaly (i.e. from what part of the complex is the proton being removed?). The hydroxide-dependent racemisation and decomposition of low spin d^6 Fe(II) complexes of the type $[Fe(AA)_3]^{2+}$, where AA = 2,2'-bipyridine, 1,10-phenanthroline or related heterocyclic bases, is mechanistically quite distinct from the D_{cb} processes discussed in this review and is thought by some to involve addition of water across a formal N=C double bond and the removal of the proton from N (see Section VIII.A).[142] The base catalysed displacement of macrocyclic tetra-amines from their Cu(II) complexes probably involves amine deprotonation but the purpose is to change the configuration of the nitrogen involved in order to generate a less firmly bound isomer.[143]

1. Chromium(III) complexes

The early observation that the base hydrolysis of *cis*- and *trans*-$[Cr(en)_2Cl_2]^+$ was very much slower than that of the corresponding Co(III) isomer, even though the rates of the uncatalysed aquations were similar,[144] was not followed up by any extensive studies of the Cr(III) analogues of the Co(III) systems for a long time. Even now studies of the base hydrolysis of Cr(III) substrates lag behind. A major factor was the relative difficulty of preparing and, in particular, isolating the Cr(III) complexes and, once that problem had been solved there remained the question of identifying products and assigning structures. Nuclear magnetic resonance (^{1}H and ^{13}C) which has become the mainstay of structure assignment for Co(III) complexes, is not easy to apply to the complexes of the paramagnetic d^3 Cr(III) although there might be some hope in the use of ^{2}H nmr which suffers less from line-broadening effects.[145] There are now sufficient published works on the base catalysed hydrolysis of Cr(III) complexes to allow some generalised comment on the similarities and differences between Cr(III) and Co(III) (Table 8). The initial observation that Cr(III) complexes are considerably less sensitive to base hydrolysis than those of Co(III) is reasonably correct. There are no examples, so far, of cases where the Cr(III) complex is more labile towards base hydrolysis than its Co(III) analogue but there are cases where the rate constants differ by a factor of less than 10. The impression given in the literature is that the ratio k_{OH}^{Co}/k_{OH}^{Cr} does not change much outside the range 10^3 to 10^{4}[152] but, once errors are corrected and account is taken of the different ionic strengths at which the data were collected, a different pattern starts to emerge. Apart from a much greater

TABLE 8

A comparison of k_{OH} values for Cr(III) and Co(III) complexes[a]

Compound	$k_{OH}^{25°}/M^{-1} s^{-1}$		k_{OH}^{Co}/k_{OH}^{Cr}	Reference
	$M = Cr$	$M = Co$		
$[M(NH_3)_5Cl]^{2+}$	0.0079	1.6	200	[146, 61]
$[M(MeNH_2)_5Cl]^{2+}$	1.8	18 000	32 000	[146, 105]
$[M(NH_2Et)_5Cl]^{2+}$	6.4	$(71 000)^{(b)}$	(11 000)	[146, 147]
$[M(NH_2^nPr)_5Cl]^{2+}$	14.0	83 000	5900	[146, 105]
$[M(NH_3)_5Br]^{2+}$	0.22	7.7	35	[148, 61]
$[M(NH_3)_5I]^{2+}$	11.4	18.2	1.6	[148, 61]
$[M(NH_3)_5(NO_3)]^{2+}$	0.079	40	500	[149, 61]
$sym\text{-}fac\text{-}[M(dien)(en)Cl]^{2+}$	0.076	9.5	125	[150, 118]
$sym\text{-}fac\text{-}[M(dien)(tn)Cl]^{2+}$	0.080	111	1400	[150, 118]
$cis\text{-}[M(en)_2Cl_2]^+$	0.036	710	20 000	[144, 26]
$trans\text{-}[M(en)_2Cl_2]^+$	0.049	3100	63 000	[144, 26]
$trans\text{-}[M(RR(SS)\text{-}$ $2,3,2\text{-}tet)Cl_2]^+$	0.77	130 000	172 000	[153, 14]
$cis\text{-}[M(cyclam)Cl_2]^+$	12	2 800 000	230 000	[151, 13]
$trans\text{-}[M(cyclam)Cl_2]^+$	1.7	81 000	47 000	[151, 13]
$trans\text{-}[M(tet\text{-}a)Cl_2]^+$	192	2 200 000	11 000	[153, 141]
$cis\text{-}[M(en)_2(OH)Cl]^+$	2.9	11.9	4.1	[154, 26]
$trans\text{-}[M(en)_2(OH)Cl]^+$	<0.4	0.56	1.4	[154, 26]
$trans\text{-}[M(cyclam)(OH)Cl]^+$	0.012	5.4	450	[151, 129]

[a] Extrapolated to $\mu = 0$ using the expression $\log k = \log k_0 + 2 \times 0.509 z_a z_b \mu^{1/2}/(1 + \mu^{1/2})$, where z_a and z_b are the charges on the substrate (including sign) and hydroxide. This expression tends to over-correct for ionic strengths much in excess of 0.1, especially for 2+ and 3+ substrates.

[b] The data in this reference do not indicate the first-order dependence on $[OH^-]$ and no attempt appears to have been made to control μ. The value in parenthesis is "normalised" with respect to overlapping data in reference [105] and is considerably greater than the one quoted in reference [61].

sensitivity to the nature of the leaving group than that found for Co(III) which is even more marked than in the uncatalysed aquation reaction, the Cr(III) complexes seem to respond much more sluggishly to changes in their composition. There has never been any satisfactory explanation of the leaving group effect which shows up well in the change in the k_{OH}^{Co}/k_{OH}^{Cr} ratio along the series for $[M(NH_3)_5X]^{2+}$. X = NO_3 (500) > Cl (200) > Br (35) > I (1.6) and reaches a point where, in the iodo complex, the reactivities of the two complexes are almost the same. The enhanced leaving group sensitivity for the base hydrolysis reaction is also demonstrated by comparing the ratios k_{OH}/k_{aq} for the complexes of the series $[Cr(NH_3)_5X]^{2+}$, X = NO_3 (15) < Cl (196) < Br (690) < I (3700). An effect of this sort is consistent with the thought that the base catalysed process has a greater degree of dissociative character. There is a reasonable amount of steric acceleration in the series $[Cr(NH_2R)_5Cl]^{2+}$, the value of k_{OH} increasing with the size of R[146] but it is of interest to note that the response of Co on changing from the penta-amine complex to the pentakis(methylamine) species is very much greater than that found for Cr(III), possibly because the steric crowding is greater about the smaller cobalt. In the other examples collected in Table 8 it would seem that the big variation in the k_{OH}^{Co}/k_{OH}^{Cr} ratio owes much more to the response of Co(III) to changes in the nature of the substrate. The anomalous reactivity of the dichloro-tetra-amine cobalt(III) complexes, commented on elsewhere, is not found in the Cr(III) analogues and far from being four orders of magnitude less reactive than the dichloro species, the chlorohydrobis(ethylenediamine)chromium(III) cations undergo base hydrolysis faster than their precursors.[154] As a consequence, the $[Cr(en)_2Cl_2]^+$ species undergo base hydrolysis in a single step, releasing two chlorides. There is no indication that the amido group must be generated *trans* to the leaving group, the difference between the reactivities of a pair of *cis* and *trans* isomers of a diacido-tetra-amine chromium(III) complex is never large. In this sense Cr(III) resembles Co(III). At the moment any indication is lacking as to the ways in which the labilities of Cr(III) complexes depend upon the nature of the amine ligands (other than the general bulkiness), and it would be of great importance to know whether the 10^4-fold difference between the reactivity of a complex with a "flat" secondary *cis* to the leaving group and that of one with only "best" secondary amines present in a *cis* position found in Co(III) chemistry is also found for Cr(III). This would provide guidance about the importance of any trigonal-bipyramidal intermediate. Another feature that has yet to be investigated in depth is the steric course of the base hydrolysis reaction. While there is some suggestion that the base hydrolysis of $[Cr(en)_2XY]^+$ (X = Cl, Br, OH) might, in some circumstances, be accompanied by steric change,[155] it appears that retention of configuration is more common with Cr(III), as is true in the case of the non-catalysed solvolysis. Studies of the kinetics of proton exchange have barely started and the first results indicate that the values of k_1 for Cr(III) complexes can be up to 10^4 times smaller than those for the analogous Co(III) species but the ratio varies from substrate to substrate (Section V). The lower reactivity is therefore due in part to a lower acidity and only in part to a lower lability of the amido species. The two contributions still need to be unravelled.

2. Rhodium(III) complexes

In general, but with some notable exceptions, Rh(III) acido-amine complexes are less reactive than their Co(III) analogues towards uncatalysed solvolysis. It has been suggested that, as in the case of Cr(III), there is a greater tendency towards associative activation and that substitution proceeds by an I_a mechanism. The sensitivity towards base hydrolysis is very much less than that found for analogous Cr(III) species and superficially resembles that of Cr(III) until one takes a closer look. A selection of the available kinetic data for the base hydrolysis of Rh(III) acido-amine complexes is collected in Table 9 and the major point that emerges is that the absence of a deprotonatable amine group *trans* to the leaving group leads to a very unreactive substance indeed. A comparison of the reactivities of *cis*- and *trans*-[Rh(L$_4$)Cl$_2$]$^+$ species shows this convincingly. Instead of the rate constants differing by less than one order of magnitude, as they do in Co(III) and Cr(III) systems, the *cis* isomers can be up to 10^6 times more reactive than their *trans* counterparts. This is fully in keeping with the greatly increased importance of the bond weakening *trans* effect in Rh(III) chemistry and implies that labilisation by π-donation is not important.

Insofar as any comparison of leaving group effect can be made it appears that the lability decreases along the sequence Cl > Br > I. The effect is smaller than, and in the opposite direction to, that observed for Cr(III) and completely mirrors the sequence found in the uncatalysed aquation. The only attempt at variation in the nature of the amines can be found in the dichloro-tetraamine complexes where *cis*-[Rh(en)$_2$Cl$_2$]$^+$, *cis*-[Rh(cyclen)Cl$_2$]$^+$ and *cis*-[Rh(cyclam)Cl$_2$]$^+$ can be compared and the 800-fold increase in reactivity on going from the cyclam to the cyclen complex is not matched in the Co(III) system ($k_{OH} = 2.1 \times 10^7$ M^{-1} s^{-1}[35] and 2.3×10^6 M^{-1} s^{-1}[13] for *cis*-[Co(cyclen)Cl$_2$]$^+$ and *cis*-[Co(cyclam)Cl$_2$]$^+$ respectively at 25 °C. It has been suggested that the *cis*-[Co(cyclen)Cl$_2$]$^+$ complex undergoes substitution by a synchronous deprotonation and chloride expulsion and so cannot reflect the big difference in the lability of the two amido-conjugate bases.

Direct evidence for assigning a D_{cb} mechanism to these reactions of Rh(III) is sparse. There is one report of base catalysed substitution[57] which is consistent with the formation of an intermediate of lower coordination number, but this aspect has received no further attention.

Although the importance of *trans* labilisation is well established for Rh(III) complexes, a report that the product of base hydrolysis of *trans*-[Rh(en)$_2$X$_2$]$^+$ is 100% *cis*-[Rh(en)$_2$(OH)$_2$]$^+$ for X = Cl, Br and 50% *cis* + 50% *trans* when X = I deserves some further thought.[161] The steric course of the first step cannot be determined directly because the two stages of chloride release are of similar rate but independent studies of the *cis*- and *trans*-[Rh(en)$_2$OHCl]$^+$ isomers show that they undergo base catalysed hydrolysis with complete retention of configuration. This has been independently confirmed[160] and suggests that the intermediate is either trigonal, bipyramidal or else capable of rapid rearrangement. A more extensive study of the stereochemistry of the base hydrolysis of Rh(III) complexes and the effects of stereorestriction on the

TABLE 9

Rate constants for the base hydrolysis of some acido-amine complexes of rhodium(III) at 25°C (μ variable)

Complex	$10^4 k_{OH}/$ $M^{-1} s^{-1}$	$\Delta H^\ddagger$ kcal mol^{-1}	$\Delta S^\ddagger$ cal K^{-1} mol^{-1}	$(k_{OH}/k_{aq})/M^{-1}$	k_{OH}^{Co}/k_{OH}^{Rh}	Reference
[Rh(NH$_3$)$_5$Cl]$^{2+}$	4.1×10^{-4}	27.9	+20	2370	3.9×10^3	[156, 157]
[Rh(NH$_3$)$_5$Br]$^{2+}$	3.5×10^{-4}	30.0	+27	5400	2.2×10^4	[156, 157]
[Rh(NH$_3$)$_5$I]$^{2+}$	7.3×10^{-5}	32.2	+31	3700	2.5×10^5	[156, 157]
cis-[Rh(en)$_2$Cl$_2$]$^+$	2×10^{-3}	—	—	2000	3.6×10^5	[158]
cis-[Rh(cyclen)Cl$_2$]$^+$	3.7×10^1	17.6	+8	—	6.0×10^5	[159]
cis-[Rh(cyclam)Cl$_2$]$^+$	4.6×10^{-2}	19.7	+1	—	5.0×10^7	[159]
trans-[Rh(en)$_2$Cl$_2$]$^+$	9.0×10^{-9}	33.5	+17	1.5[a]	3.4×10^{11}	[160]
				0.72[a]		[161]
trans-[Rh(cyclam)Cl$_2$]$^+$	3.8×10^{-8}	35.3	+29	—	1.7×10^{12}	[162]
trans-[Rh(u-Me$_2$en)$_2$Cl$_2$]$^{+}$[b]	8.4×10^{-7}	29.5	+13	88[a]	—	[160]
cis-[Rh(cyclen)(OH)Cl]$^+$	2.8×10^{-1}	—	—	4700	—	[159]
cis-[Rh(cyclam)(OH)Cl]$^+$	7.1×10^{-3}	25.5	+17	—	—	[159]
trans-[Rh(en)$_2$(OH)Cl]$^+$	6.0×10^{-9}	35.1	+21	0.72[a]	2.8×10^6	[160]
trans-[Rh(cyclam)(OH)Cl]$^+$	6×10^{-12}	38	+28	—	7.5×10^{11}	[163]

[a] Ratio taken at a higher temperature. Two values indicate different investigators at different temperatures.

[b] u-Me$_2$en = NN-dimethyl-diaminoethane.

rates of these reactions is called for. It is of interest to note that, in the case of Co(III) the behaviour is almost completely reversed with trans-[Co(en)$_2$Cl$_2$]$^+$ giving nearly 100% trans-[Co(en)$_2$OHCl]$^+$ while trans-[Co(en)$_2$(OH)Cl]$^+$ gives more than 95% cis-[Co(en)$_2$(OH)$_2$]$^+$.[26]

3. Ruthenium(III) complexes

Although it was clear that Ru(III) complexes were sensitive to base catalysed hydrolysis as long ago as 1964[30] the difficulties associated with the preparation of suitable substrates and the other attractions of Ru(II) and Ru(III) amine chemistry (photochemistry, redox reactions, dinitrogen complexes, amine oxidation, etc.) diverted attention away from any systematic follow up. In recent years, Poon has synthesised a wide range of suitable Ru(III) complexes but the base hydrolysis studies have to compete with other exciting studies (outer sphere reductions,[164,165] electrochemical studies[166] and photochemistry[167]). The two most important features that emerge from the data collected in Table 10, and other information in the literature, is that the substitution invariably takes place with complete retention of configuration and the presence of an amine group trans to the leaving group generates a complex that is much more sensitive to base hydrolysis than the isomer where all the amine groups are cis to the leaving group. A quantitative evaluation of the differences must await publication of data for cis-diacido-

TABLE 10

Rate constants for the base hydrolysis of some ruthenium(III) acido-amine complexes at 25 °C

Complex	$k_{OH}/$ $M^{-1} s^{-1}$	$(k_{OH}/k_{aq})/$ M^{-1}	$\Delta H^{\ddagger}/$ kcal mol^{-1}	$\Delta S^{\ddagger}/$ cal K^{-1} mol^{-1}	Reference
Ru(NH$_3$)$_5$Cl^{2+}	4.9	0.7 × 10^7			[30]
Ru(NH$_3$)$_5$Br^{2+}	11.3	1.2 × 10^7			[168, 169]
Ru(NH$_3$)$_5$I^{2+}	5.1	2.0 × 10^7			[168, 169]
trans-[Ru(NH$_3$)$_4$Cl$_2$]$^+$	0.0061	3.6 × 10^3	23.3	+10	[170, 171]
trans-[Ru(en)$_2$Cl$_2$]$^+$	0.60	1.5 × 10^5	28.0	+35	[170, 171]
trans-[Ru (2,3,2-tet)Cl$_2$]$^+$	72	1.5 × 10^8	25.3	+35	[170, 171]
trans-[Ru(cyclam)Cl$_2$]$^+$	110	—	25.1	+35	[170, 171]
cis-[Ru(en)$_2$Cl$_2$]$^+$	>3000	>8.1 × 10^6			[168]
cis-[Ru(en)$_2$Br$_2$]$^+$	>3000	—			[168]
cis-[Ru(en)$_2$OHCl]$^+$	0.5	—			[168]
cis-[Ru(en)$_2$OHBr]$^+$	1.42	—			[168]

tetraamine-ruthenium(III) complexes to compare with those for the *trans* isomers. It was reported that the reaction between cis-$[Ru(en)_2Cl_2]^+$ and 10^{-4} M NaOH is too fast to measure at 0 °C,[169] which, taking account of the technique used would indicate that $k_{OH} > 3 \times 10^3$ M^{-1} s at 25 °C. This indicates at least four orders of magnitude difference in the reactivity of the *cis* and *trans* isomers. The normal way of surmounting this difficulty, namely working at lower pH in buffer solution, gave irreproducible results. The values of k_{OH} for the *trans* isomers are very sensitive to the nature of the amine, for example, in the series trans-$[Ru(L_4)Cl_2]^+$ the increase in k_{OH} from L_4 = $(NH_3)_4$, through $(en)_2$ and 2,3,2-tet to cyclam covers four orders of magnitude.[171] The range is even more extensive when the more labilising macrocycles, tet-a and tet-b (tet-b is the C-rac isomer of tet-a) are brought into the series.[172] This is almost certainly an effect that owes much to the variation of k_2 and is therefore consistent with a D_{cb} mechanism. We do not see this effect in the Co(III) analogues because the point is reached with 2,3,2-tet and nearly with cyclam and $(en)_2$ where k_2 has become large enough compared with k_{-1} for it no longer to affect k_{OH}.

The sensitivity of these Ru(III) complexes to base hydrolysis must be due, in part, to their faster proton exchange rates compared with their Co(III), Cr(III) and Rh(III) analogues. A direct measurement of the pK_a of $[Ru(NH_3)_6]^{3+}$ has been made ($= 13.1$ at 25 °C)[173] and it is possible to study the solvolysis of the conjugate base, $[Ru(NH_3)_5NH_2]^{2+}$, under conditions where it is a major equilibrium component of the substrate. The first-order rate constant for the reaction $[Ru(NH_3)_5NH_2]^{2+} + H_2O \rightarrow [Ru(NH_3)_5OH]^{2+} + NH_3$, 3.5 $\times 10^{-3}$ s^{-1} at 25 °C, ought to be compared with that for acid hydrolysis of the hexammine complex, but the reaction is too slow to study. Taking the rate constant for the displacement of Cl$^-$ from $[Ru(NH_3)_5Cl]^{2+}$ (7×10^{-7} s^{-1}) and assuming, without any justification, that the ratio of the rate constants for the aquation of the hexammine and chloropentammine complexes of Co(III) and Ru(III) are the same (data from Table 1), one might estimate that k_{H_2O} for $[Ru(NH_3)_6]^{3+}$ is between 10^{-11} and 10^{-12} s^{-1} at 25 °C. The 10^8 to 10^9-fold increase in lability on removing a proton is comparable with the magnitudes encountered in Co(III) chemistry and so the lability power of the amido group must be strong in Ru(III) chemistry. At this stage, it is not possible to say whether, as in the case of Co(III), we are dealing with a D_{cb} mechanism, but, if we are, the finer details of the mechanism whereby the complex is labilised are clearly different. Since all reactions take place with complete retention of configuration, there does not seem to be any need for a trigonal-bipyramidal intermediate. The amido group is more efficient when it is *trans* to the leaving group and is therefore unlikely to be operating as a π-donor. A σ-trans labilising effect of the type already considered for Rh(III) species has been suggested for the Ru(III) complexes as well.[171]

V. PROTON EXCHANGE AND BASE HYDROLYSIS

Irrespective of the relative magnitudes of k_{-1} and k_2, the rate constants for proton exchange, k_1, always appear in the expression determining k_{OH}. Consequently, an understanding of the factors that control the value of k_1 is an important part of an understanding of the ways in which the lability of a complex towards base hydrolysis depends upon the nature of the central atom and the other ligands and, of course, the nature of the amine itself.

The first studies of the kinetics of the exchange of the amine protons of metal-ammine complexes were made in the late 1930s using horrendous techniques such as accurate measurements of the densities of the $H_2O/HOD/D_2O$ derived from the exchanging system to assess the extent of exchange. It was one early report,[174,175] not published in detail until some years later,[176] that led Garrick[2] to suggest that the proton exchange and hydroxide substitution reactions had a common (deprotonation) mode of activation. The availability of infra-red spectrometry allowed a more convenient approach to the kinetics[177] and the early work of Basolo, Palmer and Pearson mapped out the general features of the ways in which k_1 depended upon the nature of the substrate.[178-180] They measured the absorbance of the HOD stretching overtone in the solvent but, while this technique at its best was capable of providing good data for systems with equivalent protons and even a partial analysis of systems with non-equivalent protons, it could not identify the protons concerned unless their sites could be located by the relative numbers of equivalent protons. Only with ^1H nmr and even then not until quite recently could the sites of the magnetically non-equivalent protons be assigned and their rate constants determined. This method, of course, is not readily available to paramagnetic complexes, such as those of Cr(III) and Ru(III) and the old-fashioned infra-red methods have to be applied in one form or another. Although Basolo, Palmer and Pearson did use ^1H nmr to some extent, it was confined to the measurement of the HOD peak in the solvent D_2O. Clifton and Pratt were the first to follow the changes in the areas under the N–H peaks[181] but this was incidental to their main interest and, apart from showing that protons on amine groups *trans* to Cl or RCO_2 exchange more rapidly than those *cis*, they took the matter no further. A similar observation was made by Parris, still using the infra-red technique.[182] In spite of the limitations of the ir technique, Basolo *et al.* were able to identify some of the relevant features of proton exchange, in particular the rate law (invariably first order with respect to $[OH^-]$) and the way in which it depended upon the nature of the substrate, see Table 11.

In spite of the fact that the ^1H nmr spectra of metal-amine complexes were studied extensively after 1960, few, if any, of the papers present systematic quantitative data relating to exchange lability, although the labilising power of

TABLE 11

Second order rate constants for proton exchange in hexa-amine metal complexes[a] [b]

Variation with the nature of the metal					
$[M(NH_3)_6]^{3+}$					
M	Co	Rh	Ir	Ru	Os	Cr
$10^{-6}k_1/M^{-1}s^{-1}$	1.6	0.21	0.015	600	6	2.6
$[M(en)_3]^{3+}$					
M	Co	Rh	Ir			Cr
$10^{-6}k_1/M^{-1}s^{-1}$	2.4	0.22	0.02			3.6

Variation with the nature of the amine in $[Co(LL)_3]^{3+}$ or $[Co(LLL)_2]^{3+}$				
LL or LLL	en	pn	tn	dien
$10^{-6}k_1/M^{-1}s^{-1}$	2.4	4.5	11	14[c]

[a] At 25.0 °C.
[b] From references [178, 179, 180].
[c] No specific mention of which isomeric form was used, nor any indication whether primary and secondary amine protons exchanged at the same rate.

a *trans* acido group is commented on[183] and even made use of to provide a stereochemical label, i.e. a *trans* ND_3 group, to study the stereochemistry of the catalysed substitution reactions of $[Co(NH_3)_5X]^{2+}$ (X = Cl, Br for Hg^{2+} catalysed substitution; N_3, $OCONH_2$ for NO^+ catalysed substitution).[184] A major barrier to quantitative studies must have been the high concentrations of complex required to provide an adequate signal and the consequent difficulties in maintaining a constant and well-defined hydroxide concentration. Only the largest exchange rate constants (i.e. those that lead to measurable exchange rates in 0.01 to 0.1 M acid) were accessible and then only in complexes that were not solvolytically labile.

An excellent series of papers dealing with the relationship between proton exchange, and the racemisation of asymmetric coordinated amine groups, was designed to examine the ability of a coordinated amido nitrogen to invert its configuration and any information about the relationship between proton lability and the nature of the complex was purely incidental.[185-188] However, the charge effect can be seen in the difference in the second-order rate constant for the exchange of the unique secondary amine protons in [Co(N-Me-en)(NH$_3$)$_4$]$^{3+}$ (2.97 × 10^7 M^{-1} s^{-1}, 34.3 °C, exchange in D$_2$O)[186] and *rac-trans-trans*-[Co(N-Me-en)$_2$(NO$_2$)$_2$]$^+$ (5.6 × 10^4 M^{-1} s^{-1}, 34.6 °C, exchange in D$_2$O).[187] The importance of comparing similar systems is brought out with the observation that the exchange rate constant for the dicationic

[Co(NH$_3$)$_4$(sarc)]$^{2+}$ (sarc = N-methylglycine)[185] is very close to that of the [Co(N-Me-en)(NH$_3$)$_4$]$^{3+}$ cation.

A detailed study of the way in which the nature of X affects the proton exchange rates of the *cis* and *trans* ammine groups in [Co(NH$_3$)$_5$X]$^{2+}$ was marred by the fact that no attempt was made to determine [OH$^-$] or keep it constant and so only relative rates within the same complex could be obtained[189] but this has been rectified by others.[190] The data in Table 12 shows that the dependence on the nature of X is much more marked for protons on the nitrogen *trans* to the acido group and that, whereas the much greater *trans* labilisation is confirmed for the classical acido groups Cl, F, etc., CN leads to a retardation of *trans* exchange. The results bear out, in part, the

TABLE 12

Proton exchange rate constants (k_1) for the *cis* and *trans* protons in [Co(NH$_3$)$_5$X]$^{2+}$ at 34°C in acidified D$_2$O[90]

X	NCS	F	Cl	O$_2$CNH$_2$	O$_2$CCH$_3$	NO$_2$	CN
$10^{-4}k_1$/M^{-1} s^{-1}							
trans	200	150	ca 90	40	35	12	0.49
cis	9.2	3.2	1.9	2.6	1.3	12	8.1

conclusion that it is the *trans* bond weakening effect of X that causes the variation.[189] The weaker the N—Co bond the less the charge withdrawn from the N—H bonds and hence the lower the acidity of the amine protons.

In *cis*-[Co(en)$_2$X$_2$]$^+$, the protons on the nitrogens *trans* to X are exchanged before those *cis*, even when X = CN and NO$_2$.[191] It has been suggested that the most probable deprotonation site is determined by electrostatic effects, the hydroxide approaching as far from the acido ligands as possible. It is possible to distinguish between the two non-interchangeable protons H$_a$ and H$_b$ (Fig. 1)

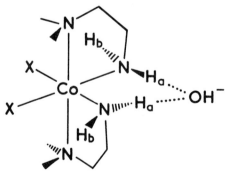

Fig. 1. Hydrogen bonding between *cis*-[Co(en)$_2$X$_2$]$^+$ and OH$^-$.

because the chemical shift of H_a is affected by ion-association and, in the case of $X = NO_2$, this is the fastest exchanging proton. This would be consistent with the idea that ion-association between OH^- and the complex involves a specific $N-H \ldots OH^-$ hydrogen bond and that this is the first stage in the act of proton transfer. However, in all the other complexes examined, $[X = CN,$ $\frac{1}{2}$(acetylacetonate), $\frac{1}{2}$(oxalate), $\frac{1}{2}$(malonate)], it is H_b that exchanges fastest. The differences in the rate constants are never great. In complexes where there is only a single proton on a nitrogen *trans* to the acido group, e.g. *cis*-$[Co(cyclam)Cl_2]$,[138] *cis*-$[Co(cyclen)Cl_2]^+$,[192] $\alpha\beta$-$[Co(picdien)X]^{2+}$[37] the proton whose chemical shift is affected by the concentration and nature of the added anion (in Me_2SO solution) is the fastest to exchange.

In *trans*-$[Co(en)_2X_2]^+$, the protons are all equivalent and *cis* to the acido groups. The rate constants for exchange are sensitive to the nature of X, increasing along the series, $X = F$ $(1 \times 10^3 \, M^{-1} \, s^{-1}$ at 25 °C)[178] $<Cl$ $(2 \times 10^3 \, M^{-1} \, s^{-1}$ at 0 °C)[41] $<NO_2$ $(68 \times 10^3 \, M^{-1} \, s^{-1}$ at 25 °C),[178] in much the same way as in the $[Co(NH_3)_5X]^{2+}$ complexes. The big difference in the rate constants for that fastest proton exchange rate constant in *cis*- and *trans*-$[Co(en)_2X_2]^+$ could be accounted for by the difference in their ion-association constants. It has been shown, in dipolar aprotic solvents at least, that the *cis*-$[Co(en)_2X_2]^+$ cations have considerably larger ion-association constants than their *trans* isomers,[193] suggesting that localised electrostatic and hydrogen bonding effects play a very important role.

The sensitivity of k_1 to the nature of the amine proton is quite considerable. The data in Table 13 shows that, not only is the rate constant sensitive to the nature of the amine bearing ligand, the rate constant for a constant amine is sensitive to the nature of the other amine ligands.[231] This work also confirms the previous ideas that the rate constants for proton exchange increase as the charge on the complexes increases. The proton exchange rate constant, k_1, covers a range of values that spans five orders of magnitude in the 2+ cationic complexes alone and, in the case of the secondary proton *trans* to Cl (or N_3) in *sym*-$[Co(trenen)X]^{2+}$, it is approaching the diffusion controlled limit. A similar rate constant $(2 \times 10^9 \, M^{-1} \, s^{-1}$, 25 °C) is observed in the proton exchange of $[Ru(NH_3)_6]^{3+}$.[195] (This is about three times larger than the older value reported in Table 11, and was determined by ^1H nmr.) The high enthalpy of activation (20 kcal mol^{-1}) is not consistent with a process that is approaching diffusion control and it has been suggested that deprotonation takes place within the ion pair and the rate-limiting step is the interchange of the water molecule carrying the label with the bulk solvent.

$$[Ru(N\overset{*}{H}_3)_6]^{3+} + OH^- \rightleftharpoons [(N\overset{*}{H}_3)_5RuN\overset{*}{H}_3^{3+} \ldots\ldots OH^-] \qquad (21)$$

$$[(N\overset{*}{H}_3)_5RuN\overset{*}{H}_3^{3+} \ldots\ldots OH^-] \rightleftharpoons [(N\overset{*}{H}_3)_5RuN\overset{*}{H}_2^{2+} \ldots\ldots \overset{*}{H}OH] \qquad (22)$$

TABLE 13

Proton exchange rate constants for some cobalt(III) amine and acido-amine complexes[(a) (b)]

Complex	Temp. °C	$10^{-6}k_1/$ M^{-1} s^{-1}	Assignment	Reference
$[Co(NH_3)_6]^{3+}$	34.5	3.3	NH_3	[231]
trans-$[Co(en)_2(NH_3)_2]^{3+}$	34.5	45	NH_3	[231]
trans-$[Co(en)_2(NH_3)_2]^{3+}$	34.5	2.2	$-NH_2$	[231]
trans-$[Co(RS-cyclam)(NH_3)_2]^{3+}$	34.5	980	NH_3	[231]
trans-$[Co(RS-cyclam)(NH_3)_2]^{3+}$	34.5	600	$>NH^{(c)}$	[231]
$[Co(NH_3)_5Cl]^{2+}$	34	0.9	$NH_3^{(d)}$	[190]
$[Co(NH_3)_5Cl]^{2+}$	34	0.019	NH_3	[190]
trans-$[Co(en)_2(NH_3)Cl]^{2+}$	34.5	2.0	$NH_3^{(d)}$	[231]
trans-$[Co(en)_2(NH_3)Cl]^{2+}$	34.5	0.085	$-NH_2$	[231]
trans-$[Co(RS-cyclam)(NH_3)Cl]^{2+}$	34.5	85	$NH_3^{(d)}$	[231]
trans-$[Co(RS-cyclam)(NH_3)Cl]^{2+}$	34.5	23	$>NH^{(c)(d)}$	[231]
trans-$[Co(en)_2Cl_2]^{+(f)}$	25	0.002	$-NH_2$	[41]
trans-$[Co(RR,SS-$ $2,3,2-tet)Cl_2]^{+(f)}$	25	0.040	$>NH^{(c)(e)}$	[232]
trans-$[Co(RS-2,3,2-tet)Cl_2]^{+(f)}$	25	0.020	$>NH^{(c)(e)}$	[41]
trans-$[Co(RSSR-cyclam)Cl_2]^{+(f)}$	25	0.013	$>NH^{(c)}$	[13]
sym-$[Co(trenen)Cl]^{2+}$	25	5000	$>NH^{(c)(d)}$	[233]
sym-$[Co(trenen)Cl]^{2+}$	25	0.3	$-NH_2$ (1 proton)	[233]
sym-$[Co(trenen)Cl]^{2+}$	25	0.1	$-NH_2$ (1 proton)	[233]
sym-$[Co(trenen)Cl]^{2+}$	25	0.1	$-NH_2$ (4 protons)	[233]
sym-$[Co(trenen)N_3]^{2+}$	25	1300	$>NH^{(c)(d)}$	[233]
sym-$[Co(trenen)N_3]^{2+}$	25	7.6	$-NH_2$ (2 protons)	[233]
sym-$[Co(trenen)N_3]^{2+}$	25	3.4	$-NH_2$ (2 protons)	[233]
sym-$[Co(trenen)N_3]^{2+}$	25	0.73	$-NH_2$ (2 protons)	[233]
β-cis-$[Co(RR(SS)-$ $2,3,2-tet)Cl_2]^{+(f)}$	25	3.6	$>NH$ (1 proton)$^{(c)(d)}$ $-NH_2$ (1 proton)$^{(d)}$	[42]
β-cis-$[Co(RR(SS)-$ $2,3,2-tet)Cl_2]^{+}$	25	2.7	not further assigned	
β-cis-$[Co(RR(SS)-$ $2,3,2-tet)Cl_2]^{+}$	25	0.95	$-NH_2$ (1 proton)$^{(d)(e)}$	[42]
cis-$[Co(RRRR(SSSS)-$ cyclam)Cl_2]^{+(f)}$	0	3.2	$>NH^{(d)(e)}$	[13]
unsym-mer-$[Co(bmp)(NH_3)_2Cl]^{2+}$	25	180	$NH_3^{(d)}$	[194]
unsym-mer-$[Co(bmp)(NH_3)_2Cl]^{2+}$	25	1.0	$-NH_2$	[194]
unsym-mer-$[Co(bmp)(NH_3)_2Cl]^{2+}$	25	0.093	NH_3	[194]
mer-$[Co(bmp)(en)Cl]^{2+}$	25	>30	$NH_2(en)^{(d)}$	[194]
mer-$[Co(bmp)(en)Cl]^{2+}$	25	2.7	$NH_2(bmp)$	[194]
mer-$[Co(bmp)(en)Cl]^{2+}$	25	0.10	$NH_2(en)$	[194]
mer-$[Co(bmp)(tn)Cl]^{2+}$	25	9.2	$NH_2(tn)^{(d)}$	[194]

(a) Variable μ.

(b) ^1H complex in ^2H_2O except where indicated.

(c) "Flat" secondary nitrogen.

(d) *trans* to an acido group.

(e) Complex undergoes base hydrolysis without exchanging other protons.

(f) ^2H complex in ^1H_2O.

$$[(N\overset{*}{H}_3)_5RuN\overset{*}{H}_2^{2+} \ldots \ldots \overset{*}{H}OH] + HOH \rightleftharpoons$$

$$[(N\overset{*}{H}_3)_5RuN\overset{*}{H}_2^{2+} \ldots \ldots HOH] + \overset{*}{H}OH \quad (23)$$

Even this does not account for the high enthalpy of activation. In order to account for the high rate constant it is suggested that, instead of one proton being transferred in this process [the final step is the reverse of (22)], there is a rapid internal transfer of proton from amine to amide by way of solvating water molecules so that one act of deprotonation may exchange up to 18 protons. This mechanism was previously invoked to account for the proton exchange in the even more acidic $[Pt(NH_3)_6]^{4+}$ cation.[196] This "multi" proton transfer cannot be operating in the *sym*-$[Co(trenen)X]^{2+}$ exchange because there is only one fast exchanging proton. Nevertheless, the idea that the proton transfer takes place within an ion pair was invoked many years ago[177] to account for the absence of general base catalysis in the proton transfer kinetics of $[Co(NH_3)_6]^{3+}$. It could also explain the low primary isotope effects ($k_1^H/k_1^D = 1.7$–2.0) that have been observed in the base hydrolysis reactions where proton transfer is rate limiting.[232] If the movement of the proton through the reaction coordinate coincided with the transition state for the whole proton transfer reaction, isotope effects of 5 to 7 would be expected.

For a long while it was believed that proton transfers involving amine complexes and hydroxide were diffusion controlled in one direction. For systems where k_1 was well below the diffusion controlled limit it was assumed that k_{-1} was diffusion controlled so that the equilibrium constant K_{hy} ($= nk_1/k_{-1}$) and in a parallel fashion the acid dissociation constant K_a (since $K_{hy} = K_a/K_w$) would reflect k_1. When k_1 approaches the diffusion controlled limit the acidity would be mirrored in the value for k_{-1}. If this were true, a change of six order of magnitude in k_1 within the complexes collected in Table 13 would indicate a pK_a change of six in the acidity of the amine protons involved. This seems rather unlikely and yet much discussion still assumes that k_1 is a measure of the acidity of the complex.

Recent studies of the proton transfer rate constants in *cis*- and *trans*-$[M(cyclam)Cl_2]^+$, Table 14, show that it is unwise to generalise about the relative proton labilities on changing the nature of M from the pioneer work on the hexammine and tris(ethylenediamine) complexes.[178-180] In the first instance, a 10^2 to 10^3-fold decrease is observed in k_1 on going from M = Co(III) to M = Cr(III) in both the *cis*- and the *trans*-dichloro species,[189] and even greater differences in other dichloro-tetraamine species are reported by House.[212] Perhaps the most surprising observation is the very large difference between the values of k_1 for the protons in *trans*-$[Rh(cyclam)Cl_2]^+$ and those *trans* to Cl in the *cis* isomer. This accounts for much of the

TABLE 14

Rate constants for the proton exchange in complexes of the type $[M(cyclam)Cl_2]^+$ together with the ratio, k_{-1}/k_2

Complex	Temp. °C	$k_1/M^{-1}s^{-1}$	k_{-1}/k_2	Reference
trans-$[Co(cyclam)Cl_2]^+$	0	2400	1.3	[138]
trans-$[Co(cyclam)Cl_2]^+$	25	13 000	0.2	[138]
cis-$[Co(cyclam)Cl_2]^+$	0	3 200 000[a)(b)]	28	[138]
trans-$[Cr(cyclam)Cl_2]^+$	0	8.9	2.3×10^3	[192]
cis-$[Cr(cyclam)Cl_2]^+$	0	8300[a)(c)]	5.3×10^4	[192]
trans-$[Rh(cyclam)Cl_2]^+$	23	8	8×10^8	[192]
cis-$[Rh(cyclam)Cl_2]^+$	20	1 400 000[a)(d)]	6×10^7	[192]
trans-$[Ru(cyclam)Cl_2]^+$	0	150 000 000	3×10^8	[192]

[a)] Protons on N *trans* to Cl.
[b)] Base hydrolysis occurs without exchange of the other protons.
[c)] Proton exchange on other protons not measured.
[d)] Studies of exchange of the other protons now in progress. k_1 is at least 10^4 times smaller.

difference in reactivity the values of the ratio k_{-1}/k_2 being not very different for the two isomers. The relatively low rate constant for proton exchange in the *trans* isomer is a great deal smaller than that reported for *trans*-$[Rh(MeNH_2)_4Cl_2]^+$ ($k_1 = 3.24 \times 10^3 M^{-1} s^{-1}$ at 22 °C)[197] but, apart from the statement that the protons on the amine *trans* to Cl in $[Rh(MeNH_2)_5Cl]^{2+}$ exchange more rapidly than those on the *cis* amines, there is no other published report to check whether the enormous *cis*:*trans* rate ratio in the cyclam complex is unique. It is likely that it is a consequence of the greater importance of σ-*trans* effect labilisation in Rh(III), the weak *trans* effect ligand, Cl, allowing a much greater drift of charge from the *trans* nitrogen towards the metal and hence a much enhanced rate constant for proton exchange.

The behaviour of the *cis*-$[Ru(cyclam)Cl_2]^+$ complex, which has not yet been studied, would be of considerable interest. If similar *trans* labilisation effects are found with Ru(III), deprotonation *trans* to Cl could be diffusion controlled and the processes invoked in the exchange reactions of $[Ru(NH_3)_6]^{3+}$ and $[Pt(NH_3)_6]^{4+}$ could well be happening here.

VI. THE AMIDO-CONJUGATE BASE

A. The labilising power of the amido group

Systems where k_2 (the rate constant for the solvolysis of the amido-conjugate base) can be measured independently are very rare, requiring as they do the presence of a relatively acidic amine and/or the means to measure very fast reactions. One such system involves cis-$[Co(en)_2(imH)X]^{2+}$ (imH = imidazole, a relatively acidic amine; X = Cl, Br) where there is a departure from the simple first-order dependence on $[OH^-]$,[91,198] which can be analysed to show that the value of k_2 for the deprotonated species, cis-$[Co(en)_2(im)Cl]^+$ is $1.3 \times 10^{-2} s^{-1}$ at 21 °C, some 10^4 times more labile towards solvolysis than its conjugate acid, cis-$[Co(en)_2(imH)Cl]^{2+}$. In this case the conjugate base itself is sensitive to base catalysis (presumably through removal of a diaminoethane proton). The analogous benzimidazole complex behaves in a similar fashion but, because of a substituent acceleration of acid hydrolysis and retardation of k_2, this enhancement is only $\sim 10^3$. This system is remarkably similar to the cis-$[Co(en)_2(H_2O)Cl]^{2+}$/cis-$[Co(en)_2OHCl]^+$ acid/conjugate base couple where the ratio $k_{(hydroxo)}/k_{(aquo)} = 7.5 \times 10^3$.[99,201] Although potentiometric and spectrophotometric titrations of cis-$[Co(en)_2(PhNH_2)OH]^{2+}$ indicate a value for K_a (presumably for the loss of the aniline proton) that is not much more than one order of magnitude greater than that of the imidazole complex[200] no-one has examined the base hydrolysis kinetics under conditions where $K_{hy}[OH^-] \gtrsim 1$. At pH = 9 the first-order dependence on $[OH^-]$ is strictly maintained. This complex is much more sensitive to base catalysis than that with imidazole, the value estimated for $k_2 = 1.3 \times 10^3 s^{-1}$ at 40 °C. Combined with $4 \times 10^{-6} s^{-1}$ for the rate constant for the uncatalysed equation at 40 °C, a deprotonation labilising factor of 3×10^8 is calculated. This system merits closer examination.

In many cases, however, it is possible to estimate the value of k_2 within an order of magnitude of two (or to set a lower limit). In systems where proton transfer is much more rapid than the overall hydrolysis ($k_1 \ll k_2$) so that $k_{OH} = nk_1k_2/k_{-1}$, use can be made of the relationship[92,199,200] $nk_1/k_{-1} = K_a/K_w$ (where K_a is the acid dissociation of the amine complex and K_w is the ionic product of water) $= K_{hy}$ in a complex where all the amine protons are equivalent. If, as is often the case, the proton whose removal generates the labilising amido group is not the most acidic one in the complex, an upper limit for K_{hy} is all that can be estimated. With one exception that leads to anomalous results,[202] direct measurement of the pK_a values of complexes that undergo base hydrolysis has not been carried out and there has been some dispute as to whether the changes observed in the visible, uv or ^{1}H nmr spectra when base is added to a non-labile amine complex is due to ion-association[203,204] or deprotonation.[205] In the case of $[Co(en)_3]^{3+}$ a value of $0.6 \pm 0.3 M^{-1}$ is reported for K_{hy} at 30 °C, $\mu = 3.0$[205] determined by ^{1}H nmr and spectrophotometry and $0.39 \pm 0.5 M^{-1}$ by ^{59}Co nmr,[206] although Goodall and Hardy[202] suggest from extrapolation of measurements made in water/dimethylsulphoxide mixtures that the acidity of $[Co(en)_3]^{3+}$ is some ten-times smaller than this. No such ambiguity exists in the case of $[Ru(NH_3)_6]^{3+}$ where the greater acidity (p$K_a = 13.1$)[173] makes K_{hy} much greater than other ion-association constants involving non-basic anions. The greater acidity of the Ru(III) amine complexes when compared with the Co(III) analogues is a typical behaviour pattern and is probably one factor involved in their sensitivity to base catalysed hydrolysis. Of course, high acidity alone is not enough, there must be a sufficiently labile leaving group and a means whereby the amido group labilises it still further. The $[Pt(NH_3)_6]^{4+}$ cation ($pK_a = 7.22$, 25 °C; $\mu = 0.07$[196]) is much more acidic than the other species discussed and yet Pt(IV) amine complexes are not sensitive to base catalysed substitution.[141]

It is possible, in principle, to estimate k_2 from the relationship $k'_{OH} = k_2 K_{hy}[OH^-]/(1 + K_{hy}[OH^-])$ (where k'_{OH} is the first-order rate constant for base hydrolysis under conditions where $[OH^-]$ is held constant in any kinetic run); a plot of $1/k'_{OH}$ against $1/[OH^-]$ should give a straight line of slope $(k_2 K_{hy})$ and intercept k_2^{-1}. With cis-$[Co(en)_2(imH)Cl]$[211] the departure from a first-order dependence is well established and the intercept is well defined. In other cases, however, the plot passes through the origin (i.e. $k'_{OH} = K_{hy}k_2[OH^-]$) and the two constants cannot be separated. Nevertheless, a knowledge of the range of hydroxide concentration over which the dependence was exactly first order makes it possible to assign an upper limit to K_{hy} and hence lower limit to k_2. For example, in the reaction of $[Co(NH_3)_5Cl]^{2+}$ the first-order dependence on $[OH^-]$ is maintained up to $[OH^-] = $ at least 1.0 M,[29] indicating that $K_{hy} < 0.1$. (It is assumed that a 10% departure from the linearity of the k_{obs} vs $[OH^-]$ plot would be easily detected.) Since $k_{OH} = 0.24$ M^{-1} s^{-1} (24.5 °C, $\mu = 1.0$) $k_2 > 2.4$ s^{-1}. The rate constant for the uncatalysed aquation of $[Co(NH_3)_5Cl]^{2+}$ is 1.77×10^{-6} s^{-1} at 25 °C[207] indicating at least a 10^6-fold increase in the lability as a result of removing one amine proton. The more labile cis-$[Co(en)_2(Bu^nNH_2)Cl]^{2+}$ cation has been shown to have a strict first-order dependence upon $[OH^-]$ at least until 0.5 M, indicating $K_{hy} < 0.2$ M.[208] Since $k_{OH} = 6.5$ M^{-1} s^{-1} (25 °C), $k_2 > 32$ s^{-1}. Compared with 4.7×10^{-7} s^{-1} (25 °C) for the parent amine complex[61] a labilisation of at least 7×10^7 on deprotonation is indicated.

Using substrates with fairly tightly bound ligands it is possible to investigate the high $[OH^-]$ region. This has not been common for a variety of reasons, including the difficulties in maintaining a constant ionic strength (indeed the whole problem of general versus specific salt effects looms large). The rate of base hydrolysis of $anti$-$unsym$-$[Co(Me-tren)(NH_3)_2]^{3+}$ (MeNH- is cis to NH$_3$; CH$_3$ is $anti$ to this NH$_3$), sym-$[Co(Me-trien)(NH_3)_2]^{3+}$ (MeNH- is $trans$ to NH$_3$) and $[Co(tren)(NH_3)_2]^{3+}$ departs from a linear dependence on $[OH^-]$ at $[OH^-] > 0.1$ and follows the above $k'_{OH} = a[OH^-]/(1 + b[OH^-])$ but there is some difficulty in identifying a and b. All three species have much the same value for b (2.3, 2.4 and 2.0 M^{-1} respectively) but differ in the limiting value of k'_{OH} when $b[OH^-] > 1$ (43, 0.65 and 0.018 s^{-1} respectively). Estimates of the value of K_{hy} from the proton exchange data suggest that, only in the case of the first complex could the kinetics be due to the saturation of the amido conjugate base. In the other two cases b is far too large and it is suggested that b represents the ion-association formation constant. It is also implied that proton transfer occurs within the ion pair.[209] This work points out the danger of taking too naive a view of these saturation kinetics. It does not point out that there is a further ambiguity in that the same kinetics would be found if ion-pair formation was an unreactive blind alley and the rate law still required a second-order interaction between the free substrate cation and hydroxide (see Section VIII.C).

The rate constant for the base hydrolysis of *syn-αβ*-[Co(picdien)Cl]$^{2+}$ as calculated from the slope of the k_{obs} vs $[H^+]^{-1}$ plot, 2×10^7 M^{-1} s^{-1} at 25 °C[16] is in reasonably close agreement with that determined in buffer solution at $[OH^-] = 1.5 \times 10^{-7}$ M, $= 6.4 \times 10^6$ M^{-1} s^{-1}.[210] This suggests that $K_{hy} < 7 \times 10^5$. The true value is probably many orders of magnitude smaller than this but the speed of the reaction does not permit measurements at much higher pHs. Preliminary studies with other [Co(picdien)X]$^{2+}$ species where X is a much less labile leaving group[211] at mugh higher pH provide no evidence for any unusual acidic properties associated with the picdien ligand. Using the upper limit for K_{hy}, k_2 must be greater than 10 s^{-1}. The uncatalysed solvolytic rate constant for this complex has not yet been measured since, even in 0.1 M acid, the reaction is dominated by the base catalysed pathway and an upper limit of 10^{-6} s^{-1} can be set. This indicated a minimum labilisation of seven orders of magnitude and, in the absence of any suggestion of unusually high acidity, the factor is more likely to be 10^{12}.

It is therefore clear that, in a typical Co(III) acido-amine complex, the great sensitivity towards base catalysed hydrolysis lies in the very-high lability of the amido-conjugate base, where factors of 10^6 to 10^9 are common and the ratio may rise as high as 10^{12} to 10^{13} in certain cases. In general, this statement applies irrespective of the nature of the leaving group since, in the absence of complications such as rate-limiting deprotonation (see below) the ratios k_{OH}/k_{aq} do not change much as the leaving group is altered. Although early work suggested that the values of k_1 for [Co(NH$_3$)$_6$]$^{3+}$ and [Cr(NH$_3$)$_6$]$^{3+}$ were similar,[180] studies now in progress suggest that k_1 values for exchange in *trans*-diacido-tetraamine cobalt(III) complexes are at least 10^2 greater than those for the corresponding Cr(III) species (Table 14),[192,212] but a major part of the difference in the overall rate constant for base hydrolysis is due to the different reactivities of the amido bases. Ruthenium(III) acido-amine complexes, which are very sensitive to base hydrolysis, exchange their protons considerably faster than those of Co(III)[180] but there must also be a considerable labilisation by the amido group.

B. Why is the amido group so labilising in Co(III) complexes?

A systematic study of the aquation of complexes of the type, *cis* and *trans*-[Co(en)$_2$AX]$^+$ (X is displaced by H$_2$O), contributed to over the years by many research groups and systematically extended to other amine ligand systems,[213] has shown that the reactivities are very sensitive to variation in the nature of ligand A and, to a lesser extent, its position with respect to the leaving group. This review is not the place for a proper discussion of these effects in general (such discussion can be found in any standard textbook dealing with inorganic substitution reactions) but, in general terms, it can be stated that such effects have been attributed to electrostatic (i.e. charge) and electronic effects (inductive, conjugative and internal electron transfer). Steric effects are not important in the types of ligand chosen for A but they can be extremely important on changing the nature of the amine ligands. Compare, for example, the 10^3-fold increase in solvolytic lability on changing from *trans*-[Co(en)$_2$Cl$_2$]$^+$ to *trans*-[Co(tn)$_2$Cl$_2$]$^+$ (tn = 1,3-diaminopropane)[106] or the similar reactivity difference between the *trans*-[Co(RSSR-cyclam)Cl$_2$]$^+$ and *trans*-[Co(RRRR-cyclam)Cl$_2$]$^+$ isomers (cyclam = 1,4,8,11-tetraazacyclo-tetradecane).[107] It is of interest to note that these large differences are not seen in the rate constant for base hydrolysis because the rate-determining step in these cases is not associated with ligand dissociation.[109,131] No studies have yet been made where A is part of a multidentate ligand in order to see how restrictions placed on its orientation can affect its labilising ability; but this can be a very important contribution to the labilising ability of an amido group when this is part of a multidentate ligand. This is discussed in detail below and could be looked upon as a steric effect. There are two types of electronic effect that have been discussed. The first, typified in the [Co(en)$_2$AX]$^{n+}$ complexes by A = NO$_2$,[22] CN[93] and SO$_3$[214] is more effective when A is *trans* to the leaving group (in the case of A = SO$_3$ the effect is very strong and confined exclusively to *trans* labilisation[218]). Such *trans* effects are associated with *trans* influences (i.e. non-kinetic effects that indicate specific bond weakening in the *trans* position) and it is believed that they are closely comparable with the *trans* influence which has been extensively studied in four-coordinate planar d^8 complexes and which can be summarised by the statement "a strong σ-donor ligand will strengthen its bond at the expense of the bond made by the ligand *trans* to it". It is of interest to note that, although the number of systematic studies is far less, this is the dominant effect observed in the substitution reactions of Rh(III) and Ru(III) complexes.

In cobalt(III), and to a smaller extent Cr(III) chemistry, there is a second effect which is observed for ligands such as OH,[201] Cl,[201] Br,[108] NCS[215] and RCO$_2$[88] which, where both isomers have been compared, is more

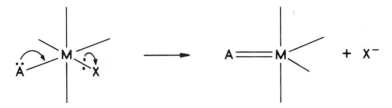

Fig. 2. Labilisation by π-donation. The five-coordinate intermediate is stabilised.

effective from the *cis* position, the extent of *cis* specificity varying from case to case. This mode of labilisation has been ascribed to the ability of all of these ligands to act as π-donors and facilitate the formation of the five-coordinate intermediate in the dissociatively activated process, see Fig. 2. Although the intermediate is represented as a trigonal bipyramid (and this could be in keeping with the general observation of stereochemical change accompanying the substitution reactions of *trans*-$[Co(en)_2AX]^{n+}$ when A is a potential π-donor[216]) this is not totally accepted and the general problem is discussed elsewhere in this review. Basolo and Pearson[203] have pointed out that the amido group can be a very effective π-donor and invoked this as the major contribution to the lability of the amido-conjugate base.

C. The relationship between the position of the labilising amido group and the leaving group

Although it is obvious that any discussion of the cause of the labilising effect of the amido group requires a knowledge of the positional requirements of labilisation, the definitive study has yet to be made. This is not through want of trying. The question to be answered is "does the activating amido group have to sit in a specific position with respect to the leaving group and, if so, is this site *cis* or *trans* to it ?" The obvious experiment to assess, quantitatively, the extent of site specificity requires the preparation and characterisation of a pair of isomers of a complex, *cis*- and *trans*-$[Co(A_4)RNH_2X]^{n+}$ where A_4 is in a combination of four donors in suitable mono- or multidentate ligands which cannot be deprotonated or which, on deprotonation, cannot generate amido groups. The substitution reactions of these complexes must be sensitive to base catalysis and this pathway must provide a major contribution to the overall reaction at rates that can be readily measured. No such system has yet been developed, although a demonstration of base catalysed hydrolysis of the ammonia in *trans*-$[Co(NH_3)_2([14]$-tetraene $N_4)]^{3+}$, which has no protons on nitrogens *cis* to the leaving group, suggests that *trans* labilisation is possible.[33] Because the *trans* position is unique, it is much easier to demonstrate a *trans* specific effect than it is to demonstrate one that is *cis* specific. It is quite clear from the fact that cobalt(III) complexes in which there is no potential amido group generator *trans* to the leaving group are often as reactive (indeed often more reactive) than the isomer where there is (see Table 2) that the amido group labilising effect is not *trans* specific for Co(III). This does not, in itself, allow us to distinguish between a *cis*-specific effect and one that is not site specific. It is of interest to note here that while this lack of *trans* specificity is true for Co(III) and Cr(III), it most certainly is not for Rh(III) and Ru(III) where the absence of an amine group *trans* to the leaving group reduces the sensitivity to base hydrolysis by many orders of magnitude (Tables 9 and 10). Conclusions reached from a study of cobalt(III) complexes cannot therefore be applied to the mechanism of similar reactions of Rh(III) and Ru(III).

Although it has not yet been possible to examine this problem with complexes containing a single amine ligand there is now a considerable accumulation of indirect evidence which, taken together, strongly suggests that the amido group exerts its labilising effect much more effectively when it is *cis* to the leaving group. For example, in a comparison of the rate constants for the base hydrolysis of complexes of the type $[Co(L)_5X]^{2+}$, where L_5 is any combination of amine nitrogen donors in any suitable combination of mono- and multidentate ligands, it was shown that certain geometric and steric constraints can exert a profound effect on the sensitivity of such complexes to base hydrolysis.[217] One requirement was that the amido group in question was *cis* to the leaving group. This is discussed in detail below.

Another indication is to be found in the elegant but difficult experiment of Buckingham[218] who used ^{15}N to signpost *trans*-$[Co(NH_3)_4(^{15}NH_3)X]^{2+}$ and thereby gain information about the steric course of substitution when there is the possibility of formation of a symmetrical intermediate. They found that base hydrolysis gave 60% *trans*- and 40% *cis*-$[Co(NH_3)_4(^{15}NH_3)OH]^{2+}$ which indicated clearly that the intermediate was not square pyramidal with the water entering at the site vacated by X (100% *trans* predicted) (although the authors did, in fact, make the rather far-fetched suggestion that the intermediate was indeed a square pyramidal species with the cobalt pulled well out of the square plane and with equal probability of the entry of water from the side adjacent to and remote from the axial NH_3 to account for their original results, 50% *cis* and 50% *trans*[219]). The results rule out a long-lived trigonal bipyramidal intermediate where the ^{15}N label is scrambled throughout the molecule by Berry twists with the amido group acting as pivot (83.3% *cis* predicted), or the amido group scrambled by proton transfer (80% *cis* predicted). (It has been suggested that internal proton transfer in the amido base of $[Pt(NH_3)_5NH_2]^{3+}$ by way of hydrogen-bonded solvation pathways is fast and that the rate-determining step is the transfer of the labelled water with

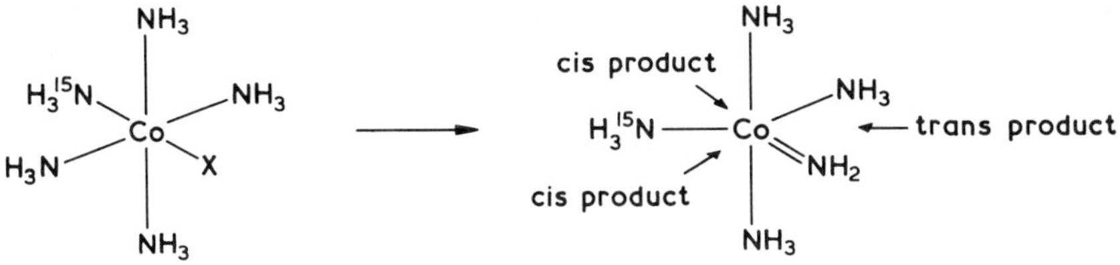

Fig. 3. If re-entry is equally likely at all three edges, product composition will be 67% *cis* + 33% *trans*. If re-entry must be *cis* to $=NH_2$ (reverse pathway to *cis* labilisation) product will be 50% *cis* + 50% *trans*.

bulk solvent.[196]) Nordmeyer[220] suggested that the 50:50 *cis*:*trans* ratio originally predicted could easily be explained if the amido group had to be *cis* to the leaving group AND *cis* to the entering water. It is the *cis* relation of re-entry that is important here, a trigonal bipyramid with the amido group in the trigonal plane, formed simply by a mutually *trans* pair of ligands following the leaving group out and then lying in the trigonal plane, Fig. 3, would lead to 66.7% *cis* and 33.3% *trans* irrespective of whether the *cis* or *trans* amine ligands were deprotonated if re-entry at all three sites in the trigonal plane was statistically equivalent. In spite of this, the Nordmeyer paper is often cited as the evidence for the *cis* labilising effect of an amido group.

D. Electrostatic effects

The removal of a proton from an amine complex will reduce the cationic charge (or increase the anionic charge) by one unit. In a purely electrostatic model for the bonding this should facilitate dissociative substitution, especially of an anionic leaving group. It is not possible to assess the magnitude of such an effect unambiguously and any attempt to estimate its magnitude through the study of model systems is hindered by one's inability to change the charge on the complex without, at the same time, altering the electron displacement properties of the ligands. Nevertheless, a comparison of the reactivity of aquo and hydroxo complexes (this conjugate acid-base pair is much more amenable to analysis than the amine-amide pair) when the leaving group is anionic (e.g. Cl^-) or neutral (e.g. H_2O).

Table 15 indicates that the electrostatic consequences of deprotonation cannot allow for a labilisation of more than about two orders of magnitude. It is of interest to note that the Co(III) system responds more to the change from H_2O to OH than does the equivalent Cr(III) system and it is possible that part of this enhanced effect is due to the response of Co(III) to the potential π-basicity of hydroxide. However, since all of these complexes contain potentially deprotonatable ligands, one should not discount the possibility of an

TABLE 15

Comparison of the rate constants for the aquation of some aquo complexes with those of their hydroxo conjugate bases

Complex	k_{aq}^{25}/s^{-1}	k_{cb}/k_{ca}	Reference
cis-[Co(en)$_2$(H$_2$O)Cl]$^{2+}$	1.6×10^{-6}	7.5×10^3	[99]
cis-[Co(en)$_2$(OH)Cl]$^+$	1.2×10^{-2}		[201]
cis-[Cr(en)$_2$(H$_2$O)Cl]$^{2+}$	$3 \times 10^{-5(a)}$	1×10^2	[221]
cis-[Cr(en)$_2$(OH)Cl]$^+$	3.3×10^{-3}		[154]
cis-[Co(en)$_2$(H$_2$O)$_2$]$^{3+}$	$3.8 \times 10^{-6(b)}$	2.5×10^2	[222]
cis-[Co(en)$_2$(OH)(H$_2$O)]$^{2+}$	9.3×10^{-4}		[222]
trans-[Co(en)$_2$(H$_2$O)$_2$]$^{3+}$	$5.5 \times 10^{-6(b)}$	2.0×10^2	[222]
trans-[Co(en)$_2$(OH)(H$_2$O)]$^{2+}$	1.2×10^{-3}		[222]

(a) Extrapolated from data at 35 °C.
(b) Divided by two for statistical correction.

internal proton transfer from nitrogen to oxygen, so that the labilising power of hydroxide is indirect and results from its ability to generate an amido-conjugate base internally.[223] Support for this view comes from the observation that, in the *trans*-[Co(RSSR-cyclam)ACl]$^{n+}$ series, the rate constants for acid hydrolysis are generally less than those for the corresponding *trans*-[Co(en)$_2$ACl]$^{n+}$ complexes, with the exception of A = OH, which is more labile.[224,225]

It is possible that the electrostatic effect makes a major contribution to the amido labilising effect in Cr(III) and the less reactive (no NHR$_2$ *trans* to the leaving group) complexes of Rh(III) and Ru(III).

E. Is it a strong σ-donor bond weakening (*trans*) effect or a π-donor transition state strengthening effect?

The key to the test of electron displacement effects lies in the knowledge of the stereochemical requirements and consequences of the base catalysed hydrolysis and substitution reactions. It is clear from even a cursory glance at the general features of base catalysed hydrolysis (Table 16) that the stereochemical properties of Co(III) [and in this context possibly also Cr(III)] complexes are quite different from those of Rh(III) and Ru(III). One should not therefore expect to find any similarity in the detailed intimate mechanism of the labilisation of the amido-conjugate base. The discussion will therefore be confined to the reactions of Co(III) complexes (since this is where the bulk of the information is available) and the conclusions from this will therefore only apply to Co(III).

TABLE 16

A comparison of the significant features of the base hydrolysis of Co(III), Cr(III), Rh(III) and Ru(III) acido-amine complexes

	Labilising effect of amido group		Position of labilising amido group with respect to leaving group		Steric course at the metal	
	Weak	Strong	*cis*	*trans*	Stereo change	Retention
Co(III)		×	×		×	
Cr(III)	×		×		×	×
Rh(III)	×			×	×	×
Ru(III)		×		×		×

The strong σ-donor, bond weakening, effect was considered by Basolo and Pearson,[203] who looked upon it as a non-site-specific inductive effect coming from a strong base and ruled it out because of the minor role played by such inductive effects in determining the lability towards aquation of species such as *cis*-[Co(en)$_2$amCl]$^{2+}$ where the proton basicity of am (a primary amine or heterocyclic nitrogen base) did not have much effect upon the lability.[226] However, irrespective of its proton basicity, the amido group should function as a strong σ-donor to cobalt and therefore generate a strong *trans* influence of the sort encountered in d^8 systems, which should be observed as a ground state bond weakening effect in non-kinetic properties, such as bond length, in addition to its labilising *trans* effect. No one has yet been able to make such *trans* influence measurements on amido complexes of Co(III). Endicott,[33] however, has pointed out that in the isoelectronic sequence HO$^-$, H$_2$N$^-$, H$_3$C$^-$, the extremely high σ-*trans* effect of methyl is well known and he invokes a similar *trans* effect in the relatively high sensitivity of *trans*-[Co(14-tetraene N$_4$)(NH$_3$)$_2$]$^{3+}$, where there can only be *trans* labilisation, if one discounts covalent hydration of the macrocycle N═C bond (see Section VIII.A).

The π-donor effect is somewhat easier to pin down (or disprove) because of its more stringent stereochemical requirements (Fig. 4). The overlap of the lone pair on nitrogen with the empty orbital on cobalt is maximised if this is in a mainly p-orbital. Consequently, the three groups bound to nitrogen should lie in a trigonal plane. The best overlap between nitrogen and cobalt will occur if the five-coordinate cobalt(III) is trigonal bipyramidal, with the nitrogen sitting in the trigonal plane with its lone pair perpendicular to the three-fold axis.[227] The trigonal plane of the nitrogen should therefore be perpendicular to the

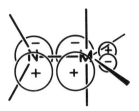

Fig. 4. Orientation of M and the amido nitrogen to provide maximum π-overlap.

TABLE 17

Stereochemical requirements for σ-donor and π-donor labilisation by the amido group

Mechanism of labilisation	σ-donor	π-donor
Preferred shape of intermediate	Square pyramid[a]	Trigonal bipyramid with $=NH_2$ in trigonal plane
Stereochemical consequence	Retention at Co	Stereochemical change at Co
Geometry of amido nitrogen in intermediate	Pyramidal	Planar
Stereochemical consequence	Retention at N	Stereochemical change at N. Racemisation of common product
Effect of orientation of N (in multidentate ligands)	None	Sensitive to the ability of the nitrogen to align its coordination plane perpendicular to trigonal plane of Co

[a] The ligand field stabilisation energy of the square pyramid in a d^6 system is always greater than that of the trigonal bipyramid.[228]

trigonal plane of the cobalt. The stereochemical consequences of these requirements are summarised in Table 17.

It has long been known that base catalysed substitution reactions in the acido-amine complexes of Co(III) are accompanied by stereochemical change. This is most easily accounted for by invoking trigonal bipyramidal five-coordinate intermediates with the possibility of the entering group (H_2O in base hydrolysis, X^- in base catalysed substitution) attacking one of the three edges of the trigonal plane. This is not universally accepted and Buckingham[229] has recently discussed the stereochemistry of base catalysed substitution in terms that are strongly reminiscent of Ingold's "edge displacement" hypothesis,[19] although in this case the mechanism is I_d rather than I_a.

It is not a trivial matter to distinguish between: (a) an octahedral to square pyramidal change in the transition state leading to bond fission, followed by a subsequent rearrangement to the more stable trigonal bipyramid; (b) a synchronous bond stretching and rearrangement so that the transition state for bond breaking of the metal-ligand bond as a mainly trigonal-bipyramidal arrangement of the other five donors; and (c) the limiting I_d process where the departure of the leaving group is synchronous with (but not affected energetically by) the attachement of the entering group. These points are discussed in more detail elsewhere (Section VII), but it is important to note that the occurrence of stereochemical change does not mean that the transition state for bond fission is necessarily incipiently trigonal bipyramidal.

The more difficult problem of ascertaining the stereochemistry at the amido nitrogen was first tackled by Buckingham[120] who examined the relationship between the proton exchange, racemisation and base hydrolysis of *sym*-[Co(trenen)X]$^{2+}$ (trenen = 1,8-diamino-3-(2-ethylamino)-3,6-diazaoctane; X = Cl, N$_3$), Fig. 5a. The symmetrical skeletal isomer was resolved into two enantiomers differing in the chirality of the secondary nitrogen, which, in this isomer, is *trans* to X, and the induced chirality of the gauche five-membered rings that contain it. The proton exchange rate constants, k_1 were very sensitive to the nitrogen atom involved, that for the secondary amine proton being extremely large, 5×10^9 M^{-1} s^{-1} (X = Cl, 34 °C), the others being some

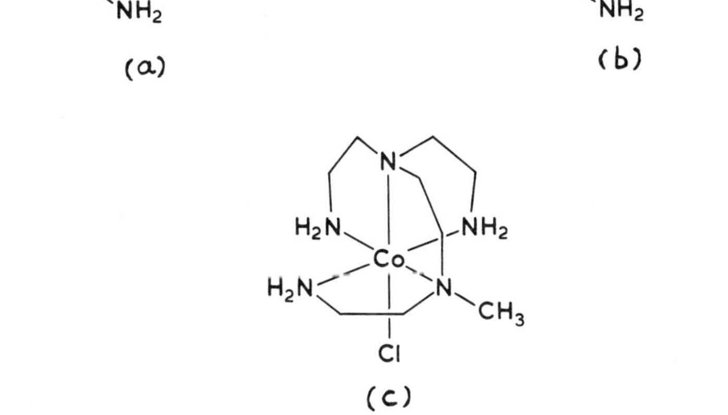

Fig. 5. Some isomers of [Co(trenen)Cl]$^{2+}$ (or its N-methyl derivative).

four orders of magnitude smaller. In the azido complex, which did not readily undergo base hydrolysis, the secondary amine proton (*trans* to azide) exchanged a little more slowly (1.3×10^9 M^{-1} s^{-1}), but the protons on nitrogens *cis* to the acido group exchanged somewhat more rapidly ($7.3 \times 10^5 - 10^6$ M^{-1} s^{-1}). The loss of optical activity followed the same $[OH^-]$ dependent rate law but the rate constant was very much smaller. This is a normal observation for this type of experiment[185,230] and it has been suggested that racemisation of an amine complex of this sort, not subject to concurrent displacement of any of its ligands, was due to the inversion of the nitrogen while it was in the amido form, the rate-limiting process being the necessary accompanying ring inversion.[186] The significant observation in this work was that, apart from the solvolysis independent racemisation, there was no further loss of optical activity as a result of the base hydrolysis of the chloro complex. It was therefore concluded, quite correctly, that the stereochemically labelled nitrogen did not go planar in the act of base hydrolysis (or if it did, there was no enough time for the memory of its original configuration, stored in the adjacent five-membered rings, to be erased by their conformational rearrangement). It was also concluded, without any justification, that, since k_1 at this nitrogen was at least 10^4 times greater than that at the others, it MUST be the site of the labilising amido group. Therefore, the labilisation did not involve π-donation with a planar nitrogen. The obvious experiment to follow this, far, far easier said than done, would have been to synthesise the unsymmetrical isomer with the "flat" secondary nitrogen *cis* to the leaving group, see Fig. 5b, separate the *syn* and *anti* forms and see whether the same conclusion could be drawn. Instead attempts were made to block the site by methylating the secondary nitrogen.[233] The change decreased the rate constant for base hydrolysis by a factor of 18 (k_{OH} = 518 and 29 M^{-1} s^{-1} at 25 °C; μ = 1.0 for *sym*-[Co(trenen)Cl]$^{2+}$ and [Co(Me-trenen)Cl]$^{2+}$ respectively)   (Me-trenen = 1,8-diamino-3-methyl-3-(2-ethyl-amino)-3,6-diazaoctane), but it was also shown that the complex formed with the N-methylated ligand was a different skeletal isomer, see Fig. 5c. This work was not followed up to bring it to a proper conclusion and, while ignoring the large body of evidence that had built up over the years that the position of the labilising nitrogen relative to the leaving group was much more important than the exchange lability of its protons, these authors have finally accepted *cis* labilisation in order to interpret some of their own results.[234]

Although not with the trenen system, the required experiment with the signposted nitrogen *cis* to the leaving group has been carried out by Marty.[235] He has resolved the appropriate skeletal isomer of [Co(dien)(dapo)Cl]$^{2+}$ (dien = 1,5-diamino-3-aza-pentane; dapo = 1,3-diaminopropan-2-ol), Fig. 6 (characterised by ^{1}H nmr rather than single crystal X-ray diffraction) and shown that the base hydrolysis of this complex is

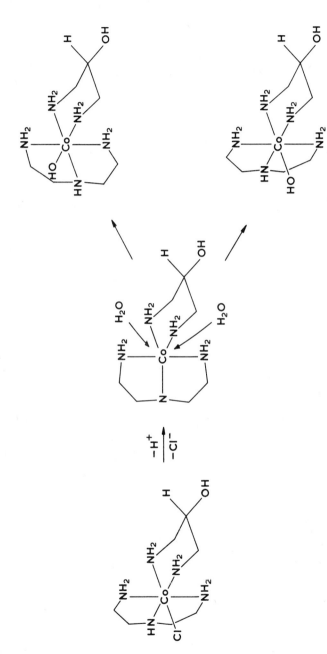

Fig. 6. Evidence for a trigonal bipyramidal intermediate in the base hydrolysis of *mer*-[Co(dien)(dapo)Cl]²⁺.

accompanied by complete racemisation while the meridional arrangement of the terdentate ligand is maintained. The independently-prepared, optically-active hydroxo reaction product racemised far too slowly for this loss of optical activity to occur subsequently to the act of base hydrolysis. A symmetrical five-coordinate intermediate with a planar nitrogen can account very well for these observations, see Fig. 6. However, in this case although it is strongly plausible that the secondary nitrogen is indeed the site of the active amido group (it is very difficult to explain the synchronous loss of optical activity and loss of chloride other than by this mechanism) there is no unambiguous evidence that this is so. It is not known whether proton exchange is much faster than base hydrolysis (i.e. $k_{-1} \gg k_2$) but the rate constant for base hydrolysis [c.f. 5×10^5 M^{-1} s^{-1} at 25 °C for the corresponding isomer of [Co(dien)(tn)Cl]$^{2+}$ (tn = 1,3-diaminopropane)[118] is approaching the magnitude expected for k_1 in a pentamine complex for a proton on a flat nitrogen cis to chloride, but probably k_{-1} is still sufficiently large compared with k_2 for a deuterium label to exchange before it can be used to identify the site of the active amido group unambiguously.

A proper identification of the site of the active amido group and its stereochemical labelling can be found in the much more tractable, but stereochemically less elegant, [Co(2,3,2-tet)Cl$_2$]$^+$ system (2,3,2-tet = 1,9-diamino-3,7-diazanonane) which has been characterised in the RS-*trans*, RR(SS)-*trans* and RR(SS)-*β-cis* forms so far,[236,237] Fig. 7. Base hydrolysis of these three isomers gave the same product, RS-*trans*-[Co(2,3,2-tet)(OH)(Cl)]$^+$, under conditions where isomerisation of the other possible species was too slow to account for the observation[238] and it was pointed out at the time that this result indicated a common intermediate that could readily be formed if the five-coordinate intermediate was trigonal bipyramidal with the remaining chloride in the trigonal plane together with a planar deprotonated secondary amido nitrogen, Fig. 7. Subsequently it was shown, in the case of the *trans* (RS)[41] and the *trans*-RR(SS)[42] isomers that there was no exchange of protons in the recovered unreacted material from base hydrolysis and that, once correction had been made for subsequent exchange in the reaction product, only one proton was exchanged with solvent in the act of base hydrolysis. This was identified as one of the two secondary amine protons, thereby locating the site of the active amido group. The *β-cis* dichloro complex exchanges three of its amine protons (those *trans* to Cl) much more rapidly than it undergoes base hydrolysis (i.e. $k_{-1} \gg k_2$) while the other three pass through the act of base hydrolysis without exchange.[38] The site of the active amido base cannot therefore be identified unambiguously.

The investigation of the extent to which the orientation of the plane of the amido group is critical in determining its ability to labilise the conjugate base has been carried out using the facultative[236] demands of multidentate

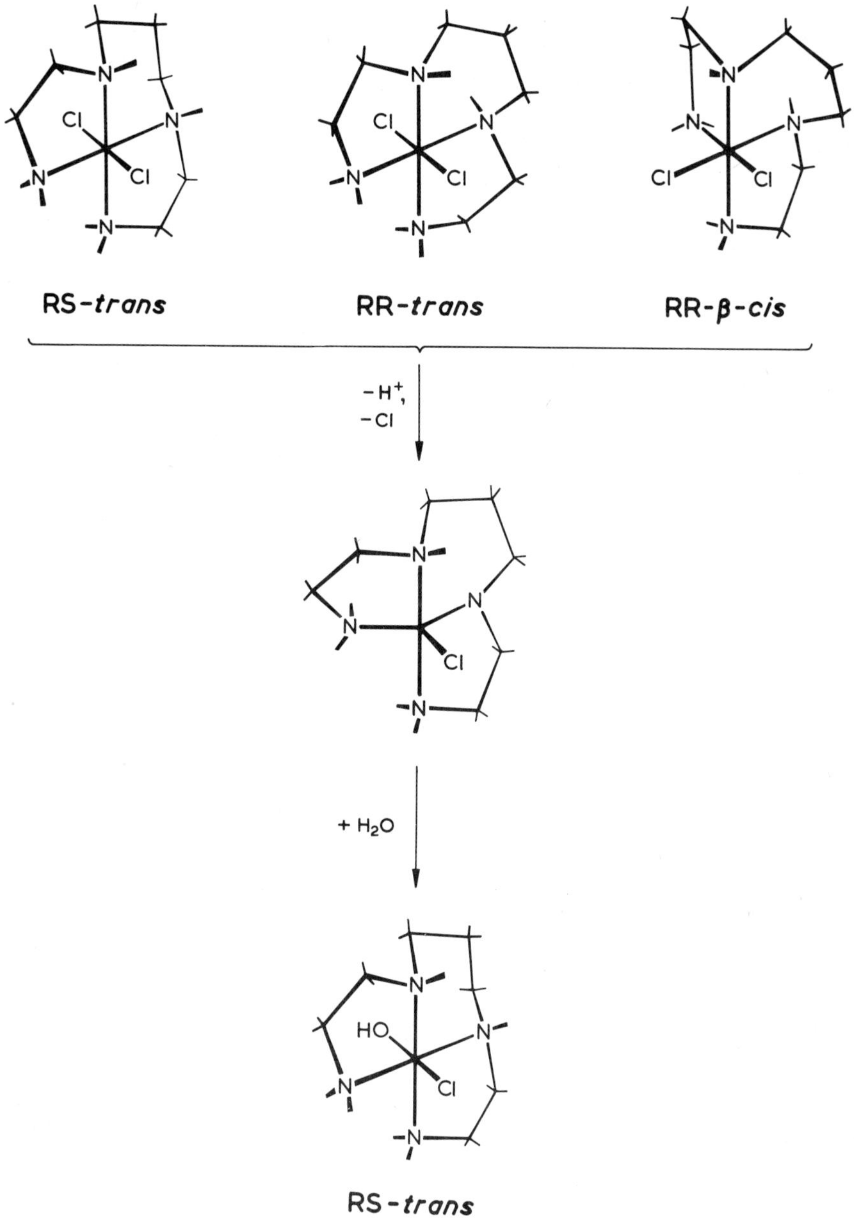

RS-*trans*   **RR-*trans***   **RR-β-*cis***

$-H^+$,
$-Cl$

$+ H_2O$

RS-*trans*

Fig. 7. Loss of a proton from the "flat" secondary amine leads to a common five-coordinate intermediate if the amido group generated is planar and the intermediate is trigonal bipyramidal.

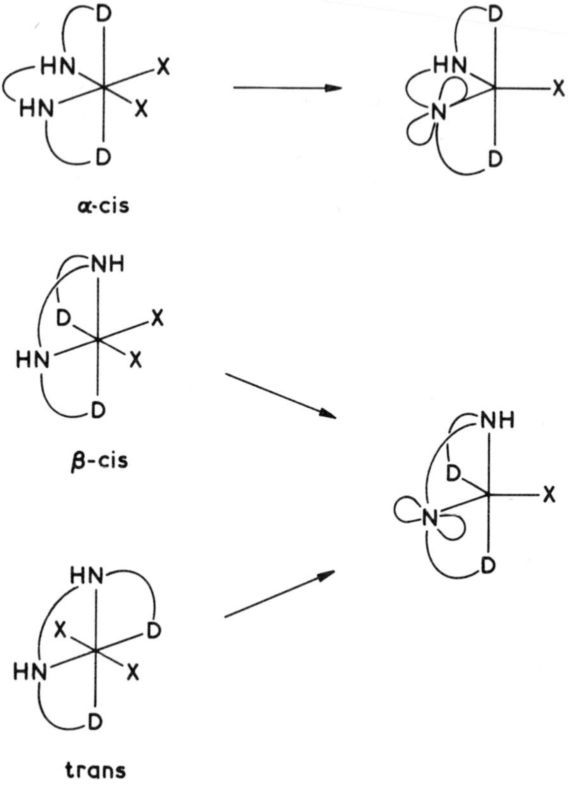

Fig. 8. The inability of a "bent" nitrogen to orient the plane of the derived amido group to maximise π-overlap with the metal in the five-coordinate intermediate.

ligands. A typical and useful system uses linear quadridentate ligands which can adopt three possible skeletal arrangements about the metal, *α-cis* (or sym-*cis*), *β-cis* (or unsym-*cis*) and *trans*. A ligand with a secondary nitrogen in one of the two inner positions will allow the deprotonated, planar amido group generated from it in the act of base hydrolysis to be oriented perpendicularly to the trigonal plane of the metal only when the original substrate had the *trans* or *β-cis* configuration. Such an orientation is prevented in the case of the *α-cis* substrate (Fig. 8). It is rarely possible, in practice, to find one ligand that gives all possible isomers, especially one with no other amino groups that might be deprotonated to provide an alternative labilising pathway, and comparison has to be made of complexes in which a small change in the nature of the ring may result in a different isomeric form being obtained. Results are collected in Table 18 where it will be seen that the *α-cis* complexes are some four orders of magnitude less sensitive to base hydrolysis than the equivalent *β-cis* or *trans*

TABLE 18

Base hydrolysis rate constants, k_{OH}, and the ratio k_{OH}/k_{aq} for some dichloro complexes of the type $[Co(L_4)Cl_2]^+$ at 25°C [a]

L_4	α-cis		β-cis		trans		Reference
L_4	$10^{-4}k_{OH}/$ $M^{-1}s^{-1}$	$10^{-7}\left\|\dfrac{k_{OH}}{k_{aq}}\right\|/$ M^{-1}	$10^{-4}k_{OH}/$ $M^{-1}s^{-1}$	$10^{-7}\left\|\dfrac{k_{OH}}{k_{aq}}\right\|/$ M^{-1}	$10^{-4}k_{OH}/$ $M^{-1}s^{-1}$	$10^{-7}\left\|\dfrac{k_{OH}}{k_{aq}}\right\|/$ M^{-1}	
edda (1)[b]	0.114	0.55	2980	1700	—	—	[217, 239]
tmdda (2)	—	—	—	—	180	8.6	[217]
picen (3)	0.111	100	—	—	—	—	[217]
picpn (4)	—	—	1980	650 000[c]	—	—	[217]
pictn (5)	—	—	210	6200[c]	—	—	[217]
RR(SS)-trien (6)	0.0068	0.040	114	81	161	46	[217, 240]
RR(SS)-2,3,2-tet (7)	—	—	2.5[a]	2.3	6.8	32	[38, 232, 238]
RS-2,3,2-tet (7)	—	34	—	—	3.4	230	[232, 238]
eee (8)	0.415	34	—	—	—	—	[217, 241]
ete (9)	0.58	3.9	—	—	1.54[c]	375	[242]
Me$_2$trien (10)	—	—	0.0030	0.000095	—	—	[217]

(a) At various ionic strengths between 0.05 and 0.15.
(b) Number corresponds to that of structure given below.
(c) Extrapolated from data at other temperatures.

isomer. This is also true when amine groups are also present in the terminal positions. The test can be extended to complexes containing linear terdentate ligands as well.

An isomer in which there is a "flat" nitrogen (i.e. one that is at the centre of a group of three meridionally disposed donors) *cis* to the leaving group is very much more labile towards base hydrolysis than those in which the nitrogen in question is "bent" (i.e. the centre of three facially disposed donors). This is part, at least, of the rationalisation of the data in Table 6, the flat nitrogen in the right position will allow good p_π–d_π overlap in the formation of the five-coordinate intermediate whereas the bent one will not. It must, of course, be realised that these arguments assume that the contribution to k_{OH} is through k_2 alone. We have already seen that k_1 (and presumably k_{-1}) is strongly dependent upon the type of nitrogen atom to which the proton is attached, R_2NH having a higher value of k_1 than an equivalent RNH_2 group and a "flat" R_2NH having a greater k_1 than a "bent" one. Furthermore, if the system is one in which $k_2 \gg k_{-1}$, arguments relating k_{OH} to k_2 are clearly invalid since deprotonation would be the rate-determining step.

Recently,[123] the partially macrocyclic pentadentate ligands, datn and dats (Fig. 9) were synthesized and their chloro(pentamine)-cobalt(III) complexes studied. Only the unsymmetrical isomers have been isolated and their sensitivity to base hydrolysis is considerably greater than might be predicted

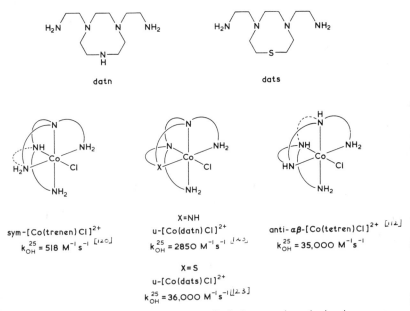

datn

dats

sym-[Co(trenen)Cl]$^{2+}$
k_{OH}^{25} = 518 M^{-1}s^{-1} [120]

X=NH
u-[Co(datn)Cl]$^{2+}$
k_{OH}^{25} = 2850 M^{-1}s^{-1} [123]

X=S
u-[Co(dats)Cl]$^{2+}$
k_{OH}^{25} = 36,000 M^{-1}s^{-1} [123]

anti-$\alpha\beta$-[Co(tetren)Cl]$^{2+}$ [112]
k_{OH}^{25} = 35,000 M^{-1}s^{-1}

Fig. 9. Labile complexes without a "flat" nitrogen *cis* to the leaving group.

from the above rules. These species can be looked upon as derived either from *sym*-[Co(trenen)Cl]$^{2+}$ or $\alpha\beta$-[Co(tetren)Cl]$^{2+}$ by linking an appropriate pair of *cis* nitrogens by —CH$_2$CH$_2$—, and it is interesting to note that the value of k_{OH} lies between that of the non-cyclic species. There is no longer a flat secondary nitrogen which, *cis* to the chloride in the $\alpha\beta$-[Co(tetren)Cl]$^{2+}$, was invoked to account for the large value of k_{OH} relative to *sym*-[Co(trenen)Cl]$^{2+}$ where it was *trans* to the leaving group. The only secondary amine group in [Co(datn)Cl]$^{2+}$ cannot be invoked as the site of the activating amido group because its replacement by S in [Co(dats)Cl]$^{2+}$ increases rather than decreases the reactivity. It must be assumed that, as in the case of the [Co(eee)Cl$_2$]$^{+}$, [Co(ete)Cl$_2$]$^{+}$ and [Co(Me$_2$trien)Cl$_2$]$^{+}$ species, the terminal amine groups provide the labilising amido nitrogen.[217] Here is a case where the simple rules controlling k_2 do not appear to hold. Non-quantitative evidence has been presented to show that all amine protons are exchanged within the half life of base hydrolysis, but whether the result can be explained in terms of an unusually high value of k_1 as a result of the increase in the hydrophobicity of the back of the ligand must await a quantitative determination of the proton exchange kinetics.

F. Single electron transfer from the amido group

Although, up to now, much of the discussion has assumed an electron displacement mechanism that retains the formal oxidation state of the central metal atom, there still remains a sneaking suspicion that this is not capable of accounting for all of the phenomena associated with the lability of amido species. Although the π-donor effect, and to a lesser extent, the σ-donor *trans* effect seem qualitatively convincing, it is difficult to see how even they can account for some of the larger labilisation increases (10^{10}–10^{13}) encountered on deprotonating some of the Co(III) complexes. The much smaller sensitivity of Cr(III) complexes to base catalysed substitution was explained in terms of its much smaller electron affinity compared with that of Co(III) and presumably its ability to accept an amido lone pair,[30] although we know now that part of this lower reactivity is associated with the deprotonation rate constants. The electron affinity argument cannot explain the differences between Ru(III) and Rh(III). It had not escaped the attention of some that the reaction centres most susceptible to base hydrolysis were those with an accessible lower oxidation state and indeed Gillard proposed his radical pair mechanism[31] to meet this point.

An alternative mechanism that has been suggested in passing,[243] but never been the subject of an outright statement, involves the amido group functioning as a single electron donor to the metal so that, transiently, there is a low spin Co(II) species formed. In view of the preference of low spin Co(II) for five-coordination, this would rapidly lose one ligand, thereby generating a five-coordinate intermediate which would fulfil the same function as that usually postulated for this reaction.

$$[L_4Co^{III}\dot{N}R_2X]^{(n-1)+} \rightarrow [L_4\dot{C}o^{II}\dot{N}R_2X]^{(n-1)+} \tag{24}$$
reagent amido base

$$[L_4\dot{C}o^{II}\dot{N}R_2X]^{(n-1)+} \rightarrow [L_4\dot{C}o^{II}\dot{N}R_2]^{n+} + X^- \tag{25}$$

$$[L_4\dot{C}o^{II}\dot{N}R_2]^{n+} + Y^- \rightarrow [L_4\dot{C}o^{II}\dot{N}R_2Y]^{(n-1)+} \tag{26}$$

$$[L_4\dot{C}o^{II}\dot{N}R_2Y]^{(n-1)+} \rightarrow [L_4Co^{III}\dot{N}R_2Y]^{(n-1)+} \tag{27}$$

$$or \quad [L_4\dot{C}o^{II}\dot{N}R_2]^{n+} \rightarrow [L_4Co^{III}\dot{N}R_2]^{n+} \tag{28}$$

$$[L_4Co^{III}\dot{N}R_2]^{n+} + Y \rightarrow [L_4Co^{III}\dot{N}R_2Y]^{(n-1)+} \tag{29}$$

Recombination with H_2O instead of Y^- would give the hydroxo product after proton redistribution.

The intervention of such nitrogen radical complexes has often been postulated to account for a wide variety of processes in transition metal chemistry and their existence has been demonstrated in the reaction between $[Ni(tet-a)(CH_3CN)_2]^{3+}$ and bases where, either synchronously with or subsequent to deprotonation, there is a single electron transfer from the amido nitrogen to nickel(III).[244] This species rapidly decomposes by a variety of possible pathways including hydrogen abstraction from another reagent to given $[Ni(tet-a)]^{2+}$, or hydrogen atom loss to another reagent to give the imine complex, see Fig. 10. The two processes working together might yield a disproportionation. Metal catalysed amine oxidations of this sort are very common indeed, not only with nickel[245] but also with iron[246] and especially with ruthenium.[247,248] Surprisingly cobalt does not catalyse such reactions, possibly because the internal electron transfer is greatly favoured over any external redox processes. Most of the interest in the amine oxidation catalysis has been concentrated upon the oxidation of the catalyst and the internal electron transfer has received much less attention.

To what extent is the evidence already put forward in support of the classical π-donor mechanism also compatible with the single electron transfer mechanism? Cobalt(II) tetramine complexes generated by pulse radiolysis of solutions containing the Co(III) species are certainly axially labile[249] and the bulk of the evidence arising from the study of cationic nitrogen radicals of the type $R_3\dot{N}^+$ (analogous to our species with the metal occupying the place of one of the R groups) suggest that they are frequently planar. The trigonal-bipyramidal geometry is far from mandatory in five-coordinate low spin Co(II) complexes and examples of square pyramidal low spin Co(II) species are at least as common, the geometry adopted depending upon secondary factors.

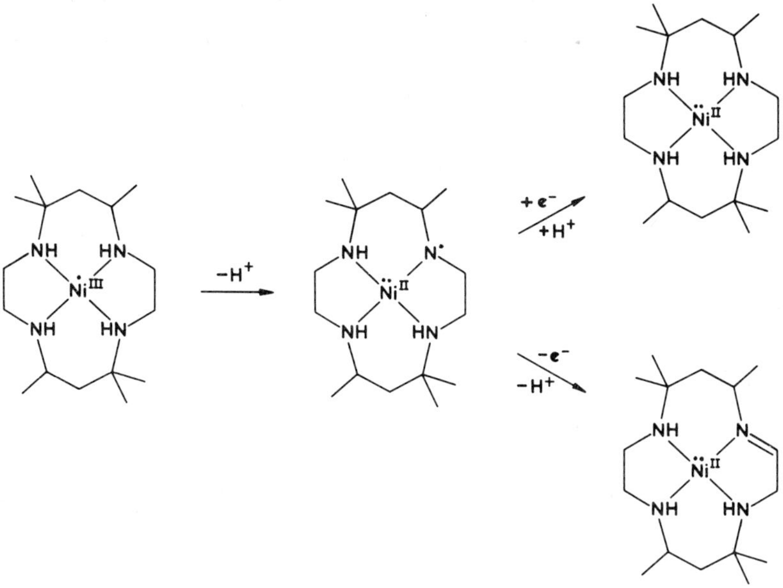

Fig. 10. Single electron transfer mechanism for ligand oxidation in [Ni[III](tet-a) $(CH_3CN)_2]^{3+}$. (The acetonitrile ligands are omitted for the sake of clarity.)

In view of the wide interest in internal electron transfers as well as the importance in settling the finer details of the mechanism of the base catalysed substitution reactions of transition metal amine complexes, this possible mechanism should be examined. It is not necessary to abandon the old established theories yet; it may well prove that, even if single electron transfer does play a part in the labilising power of the amido nitrogen, it only operates in addition to the shared electron displacement. Although the high lability of the lower oxidation state of Cr and Co arises from a desire for a lower coordination number or distortions from a regular octahedral geometry due to Jahn–Teller effects, the d[6] ruthenium(II) species will remain octahedral. Nevertheless, there is a very large increase in substitutional lability on going from Ru(III) to Ru(II).

VII. THE NATURE OF THE INTERMEDIATE IN THE ACT OF SUBSTITUTION

One of the major preoccupations in the study of the mechanism of base hydrolysis has been to learn about the nature of the intermediate, if indeed there is one. This question was thoroughly reviewed some years ago[250] but much work has been done since. The questions to be answered are the following: (i) is there an intermediate of lower coordination number?; (ii) how long does it last?; (iii) what is its geometry?; (iv) is its geometry at the time of consumption the same as at its time of formation? The answers to some of these questions are of considerable interest outside the specialist area of base catalysed hydrolysis of octahedral complexes and can be applied to any system, organic and inorganic, when the substitution is dissociatively activated.

A. Demonstration of a species of lower coordination number

One of the major pieces of evidence to support the D_{cb} mechanism has been the demonstration of the formation of a very reactive intermediate species that can be trapped by nucleophiles other than the solvent. Although, in principle, this could be demonstrated kinetically by mass law retardation of the rate (i.e. in the base hydrolysis of L_5MX the rate should be retarded by increasing the concentration of free ligand X) no one seems to have managed to do this successfully (or else has not tried), and the bulk of the evidence comes from careful studies of the reaction products. There was, at first, a conviction that it would not be easy to compete with solvent water and the first studies were made in dimethylsulphoxide where it was shown that the reaction between trans-[Co(en)$_2$NO$_2$Cl]$^+$ and NO$_2^-$ to give trans-[Co(en)$_2$(NO$_2$)$_2$]$^+$ was strongly catalysed by small quantities of OH$^-$.[56] Similar base catalysed substitutions were later observed in the reactions between cis-[Rh(en)$_2$NO$_2$Cl]$^+$ or trans-[Rh(en)$_2$(CH$_3$NH$_2$)Cl]$^{2+}$ and NO$_2^-$ or N$_3^-$ in dimethylsulphoxide.[57] It is likely that the very first demonstration of base catalysed substitution, although not recognised as such by the authors, was the observation that the rate of reaction between cis-[Co(en)$_2$Cl$_2$]$^+$ with basic nucleophiles such as N$_3^-$ and NO$_2^-$ in unbuffered methanol solution was dependent on the nature and concentration of the nucleophile.[6]

The first successful demonstration of base catalysed substitution in aqueous solution[251] showed that reaction of [Co(NH$_3$)$_5$X]$^{2+}$ (X = Cl, Br, I, NO$_3$) with hydroxide in the presence of a large excess of an anionic nucleophile, Y$^-$, gave significant quantities of [Co(NH$_3$)$_5$Y]$^{2+}$ as product. It was shown that Y$^-$ could not have entered the complex before the act of base hydrolysis, nor could it have displaced OH$^-$ from the product [Co(NH$_3$)$_5$OH]$^{2+}$. Consequently it must have been formed in competititon with the hydroxo complex after a common act of activation. This vital demonstration of the dissociative nature of the reaction in basic solution has been followed by many others where the quantitative study of the distribution and stereochemistry of the products as a function of a large number of perameters such as the charge on the complex, the nature of the leaving group, the concentration of the entering nucleophile, the nature of the entering nucleophile and so on. These will be discussed in the context of the headings listed above. Base catalysed substitution in Co(III) acido-amine complexes, and through it the dissociative nature of the reaction, is well established. There is little or no work on analogous systems with other central metal ions.

B. The lifetime of the intermediate

An assessment of the lifetime of the intermediate relative to the time it requires to equilibrate its inner solvation shell is fundamental to any distinction between a D and an I_d mechanism. Ideally, a D mechanism requires that the five-coordinate intermediate lives long enough to lose all memory of its precursor so that the distribution of the product resulting from the competition between different nucleophiles and the stereochemistry of each of these products should be independent of the nature of the leaving group. Quantitative studies have shown that the competitition ratio, $[Co(NH_3)_5Y^{2+}]/[Co(NH_3)_5OH^{2+}]$, increases almost linearly with increase in Y^- [44] and is independent of $[OH^-]$.[251] This is consistent with competition between the nucleophile Y^- and water for the reactive intermediate and indicates that hydroxide is not directly involved in the act of substitution. It is claimed that the linearity holds to $[Y^-] = 1$ M, indicating that the capture of the intermediate by the anionic reagent does not require that the two species must be held together by ion-association before the act of dissociation (ion-association occurring before or after deprotonation). Ion-association would be quite extensive at these concentrations (especially with 3 + cations) and the absence of "saturation" kinetics indicate that the intermediates from the free ion and ion pair have the same competition properties. These conclusions are contested and it is claimed that the relationship between competition, the nature of the leaving group, the concentration of the reagents and the steric course can only be explained if the anion is in ion-association with the substrate before the act of dissociation.[229,252] For lack of a better word, the term "antedissociation" will be applied to the process where the reagents must come together before dissociation and the effects it causes, and it is to be distinguished from "postdissociation" which will relate to influences exerted by the leaving group after the act of dissociation. The bulk of the evidence for antedissociation will be discussed below.

An examination of the data in Table 19 shows that the competition ratios are not completely independent of the nature of the leaving group, as would be required by a limiting D mechanism, nor is the nucleophilic discrimination of the intermediate large. Both observations suggest that there is not time enough for the five-coordinate intermediate to fully equilibrate its environment before

TABLE 19

Product ratios ($[Co(NH_3)_5Y^{2+}]/[Co(NH_3)_5OH^{2+}]$) for the reaction between $[Co(NH_3)_5X]^{n+}$ and Y^- [1.0 M] in the presence of OH^- (0.1 M)

X	n	$Y^- = N_3^-$	Reference	$Y^- = NCS^-$	Reference
Me_2SO	3	0.140	[44]	0.284	[44]
$(MeO)_3PO$	3	0.143	[44]		
$(NH_2)_2CO$	3	0.143	[44]		
I^-	2	0.111	[251]	0.190	[83]
Br^-	2	0.095	[251]		
Cl^-	2	0.093	[251]		
NO_3^-	2	0.116	[251]	0.205	[83]
$CH_3SO_3^-$	2	0.111	[86]		
$CF_3SO_3^-$	2	0.107	[86]		
ClO_4^-	2	0.115	[86]		
FSO_3^-	2	0.103	[253]		
SO_4^{2-}	1	0.062	[44]		

it is captured by a suitable nucleophile. Little has yet been done to investigate the relationship between nucleophilic discrimination (as a measure of the lifetime of the intermediate) and structure, but it has been pointed out that one-third of the intermediate generated by the sterically crowded $[Co(NH_2CH_3)_5Cl]^{2+}$ cation is trapped by 0.5 M N_3^- as against only one-twentieth of the intermediate generated by $[Co(NH_3)_5Cl]^{2+}$ under similar conditions.[105] It is suggested that the steric crowind lengthens the lifetime of the former intermediate and allows it to show a much greater discrimination.

In the pentaamine system the leaving group dependence relates to charge rather than any chemical feature and it is best seen in reactions where $Y^- = N_3^-$. Since the charge on the complex and the charge on the leaving group are inseparable variables in these experiments it is not easy to distinguish between the effects of antedissociation (where there is more ion-association with complexes of the highest charge) and those of postdissociation (an anionic leaving group is retained longer in the vicinity of the intermediate than a neutral one). Most discussion in the literature seems to have concentrated on the antedissociation aspects and the idea that the leaving group may still have an influence on the subsequent behaviour of a fully developed intermediate has not been properly considered. Some indication of the leaving group lingering in the vicinity of the five-coordinate intermediate can be seen in the linkage isomerisation of thiocyanato complexes. In the base catalysed substitution of $[Co(NH_3)_5Cl]^{2+}$ in the presence of SCN^- (0.1 M), the major part of the acido product (77%) is the unstable S-thiocyanato isomer, $[Co(NH_3)_5(SCN)]^{2+}$. This, incidentally, is consistent with the lack of discrimination of the five-coordination intermediate and reflects the orientation of the SCN^- ion at the moment of capture.[83] The S-thiocyanato complex has a lability towards base hydrolysis similar to that of the chloro species but the product of base hydrolysis includes the stable (and inert) N-thiocyanato complex, $[Co(NH_3)_5(NCS)]^{2+}$ (26%) as well as the expected $[Co(NH_3)_5OH]^{2+}$ (74%) in the *absence* of added SCN$^-$. Isotopic labelling shows that the —SCN to —NCS change, while base catalysed, takes place without significant exchange between coordinated and free thiocyanate. This suggests that the lifetime of the intermediate can be shortened by recapture of the leaving group before the latter has had time to equilibrate with the bulk solution (which differs from competition recapture that would lead to mass-law retardation). This is only detectable when some chemical change can occur while the reagents are in this position, in this case the turning round of the SCN$^-$ ion. How frequently the SCN$^-$ rejoins the cobalt through S cannot be estimated from these results but the $[Co(NH_3)_5(NCS)^{2+}]/[Co(NH_3)_5OH^{2+}]$ product ratio suggest that, in spite of the larger number of available water molecules in the vicinity of the intermediate, the N-thiocyanato trapping is quite efficient. With *trans*-$[Co(en)_2(NH_3)(SCN)]^{2+}$, the amount of base catalysed —SCN to NCS isomerisation is much less (8%), 1% of which is assigned to competition for the five-coordinate intermediate. There is a small, but real amount of *cis*-$[Co(en)_2(NH_3)(NCS)]^{2+}$ (1%) formed in this reaction, half of which is formed without exchange of leaving group and free ligand. This confirms that the leaving SCN$^-$ is able to move around the incipient five-coordinate intermediate before it is in a position to exchange with SCN$^-$ in the bulk solvent.[254]

Another way to introduce competition for the five-coordinate intermediate is to have a potential chelate, bound as a monodentate, in the coordination shell of the substrate. In the base hydrolysis of *cis*-$[Co(en)_2(NH_2CH_2CO_2)X]^+$ (X = Cl, Br; glycinate bound through N) the product consists of the chelated $[Co(en)_2(NH_2CH_2CO_2)]^{2+}$ species (40.8%) and the monodentate hydroxo species $[Co(en)_2(NH_2CH_2COO)OH]^+$ (59.2%) when 1.0 M NaOH is used.[255] At lower hydroxide concentrations the amount of ring closing is higher (46.1%). For the six-membered ring analogue, *cis*-$[Co(en)_2(NH_2CH_2CH_2CO_2)X]^+$, the amount of ring closing is very much less (9%).[256] This is consistent with the relative ease of closing five- and six-membered rings[257] but the inefficiency of the proximal carboxylate group is surprising, suggesting that it is held back by hydrogen bonding with an amine proton on one of the ligands. Addition of N_3^- introduces fresh competition, proportional to $[N_3^-]$, but more at the expense of the chelate species than the hydroxo product. Again, this is inconsistent with the carboxylate group sitting in an inner site that is favourable for competition and the results have been used to support the idea that an ion pair, external with N_3^- or internal with —CO_2^-, is needed if there is to be any competition with the solvent to form the product, i.e. an almost synchronous I_d substitution in the conjugate base.

C. The geometry of the intermediate at formation and consumption

A large number of base catalysed substitution reactions of Co(III) acido-amine complexes take place with stereochemical change and it is generally, though not universally, accepted that a trigonal-bipyramidal species is formed somewhere in the act of substitution. However, one needs to examine this question with a little more sophistication. Three possibilities should be considered.

(i)   The act of bond dissociation is accompanied by a change in overall geometry so that, in the transition state for bond dissociation, the remaining five-bonds have taken up a shape well on the way to a trigonal bipyramid.

(ii) The act of bond dissociation generates a square pyramidal intermediate which subsequently changes to a trigonal bipyramid. A subdivision of this class might be a fluxional five-coordinate species (square pyramidal or trigonal bipyramidal) that allows steric change during the lifetime of the intermediate. In order to satisfy the requirements of microscopic reversibility, the consumption of the intermediate would be expected to follow the reverse of the path for its formation.

(iii) No intermediate is formed, the act of bond making and bond breaking being synchronous but dissociatively activated. Any act of stereochemical change must be the consequences of the synchronous movement of the entering and leaving groups.

Discussions about the relative merits of (i) and (ii) have accompanied discussions of octahedral substitution reactions ever since Taube showed that the racemisation and *trans-cis* isomerisation of the $[Co(en)_2(H_2O)_2]^{3+}$ cations had a much higher enthalpy of activation than the much faster water exchange process.[222] If the stereochemical change was the direct consequence of the geometry of the rate-determining transition state for water exchange the two processes would have been expected to have the same enthalpy of activation. When they are different it is not possible (when the exchange is much faster) to distinguish between a pair of consecutive reactions, the second of which is the rearrangement of the five-coordinate intermediate, and a pair of synchronous reactions, the one leading to stereochemical change having the higher activation enthalpy. The observation that the entropies of activation of the aquation of those complexes of *trans*-$[M(en)_2ACl]^{n+}$ (M = Co, Cr, Rh; replacement of Cl by H_2O) that occur, with retention of configuration, are considerably less positive (or more negative) than those of the reactions which occur with steric change led to the suggestion that the system has decided the shape of the intermediate by the time it achieves the transition state for the substitution.[216]

Quantitative discussion of the steric course of the base catalysed substitution reactions of Co(III) has relied to a great extent on the results obtained in the reactions of the *cis*- and *trans*-$[Co(en)_2AX]^{n+}$ isomers. While it has generally been assumed that the intermediate has taken a trigonal-bipyramidal form by the time the nucleophile enters, little attention has been paid to the question as to whether the trigonal bipyramid is formed synchronously with or subsequently to the act of bond dissociation. In general, the signposting of the *cis* isomer is quite efficient if one enantiomer is used. Working on the basis that the trigonal bipyramid is formed by the displacement of a mutually *trans* pair of ligands that were *cis* to the leaving group in the original complex, it follows that two intermediates are possible and, provided they do not rearrange by some sort of pseudorotation, the consequences of their participation are different, see Fig. 11. Intermediate "Eq" with the signpost in the trigonal plane retains the chirality of the original *cis* species and can only give *cis* product of the same chirality as the substrate together with *trans*. Intermediate "Ax", with the signpost in an axial position, can only give the racemic *cis* product, there being no pathway for the formation of *trans* product. A *trans* substrate will only give intermediate "Eq". The steric courses of the base hydrolysis of the $[Co(en)_2AX]^{n+}$ have been analysed in terms of the relative importance of intermediates "Eq" and "Ax" and the part played by the signpost ligand A.[258-260]

There has been some discussion as to whether the amido group remains unprotonated until it captures a nucleophile[220] or whether it is rapidly reprotonated.[229] If we accept the argument that the amido group stabilises the five-coordinate intermediate by some sort of electronic movement we should also accept the argument that this very same act will reduce the proton basicity of the amido group in question while the metal is five-coordinate. The observation, that different protons in a complex can exchange at widely different rates, rules out the possibility of an internal proton transfer of the sort proposed for $[Pt(NH_3)_5NH_2]^{3+}$[196] where, after the initial deprotonation, proton transfer from NH_3 to NH_2 by way of a solvating water molecule, allows a large number of amine protons to be exchanged before reprotonation occurs. Such a mechanism would also allow initiation at a site with a favourable k_1 to be followed by an internal proton transfer to generate a different amido site with a favourable k_2, a phenomenon not yet observed in these systems.

If the amido group remains in the five-coordinate intermediate throughout its lifetime at the site at which it was generated, it will reduce the symmetry of the intermediate and constitute another influence on the path followed by the incoming group. Nordmeyer's proposal that the labilising amido group must be *cis* to the leaving group is coupled with the requirement that water enters *cis* to the amido group.[220] There is no reason why an acido group should follow

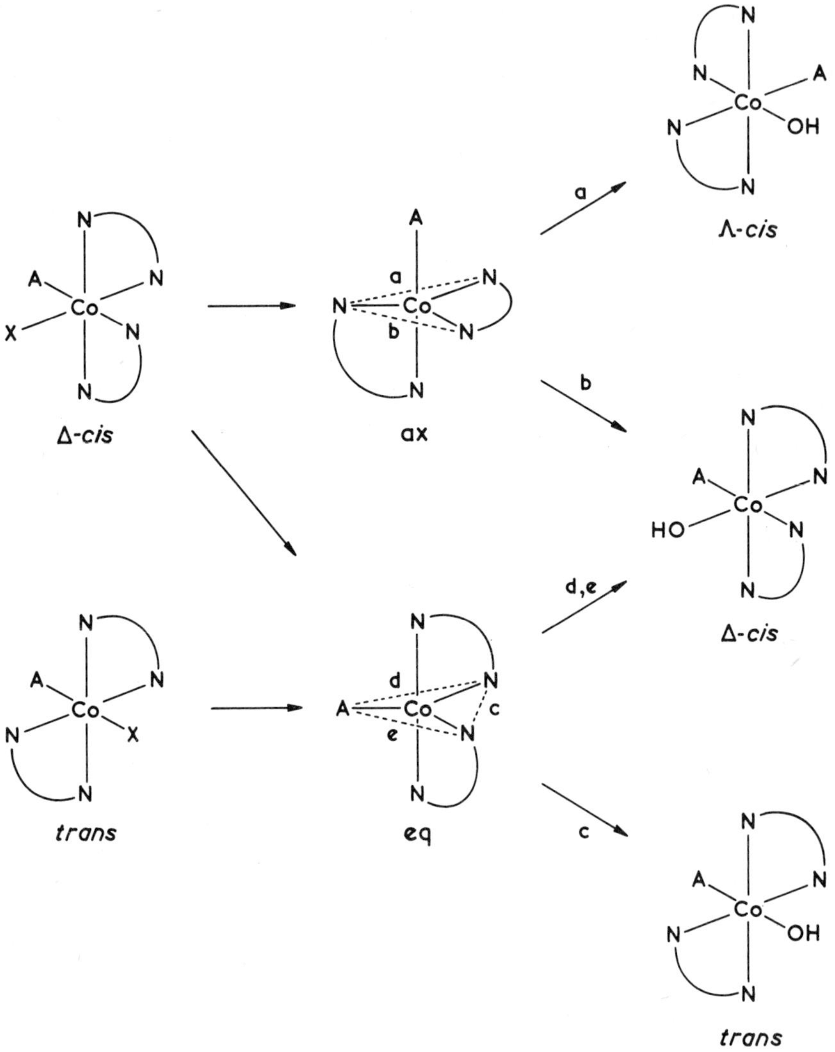

Fig. 11. Trigonal bipyramidal intermediates and pathways for re-entry in substitution reactions of $[Co(en)_2AX]^{n+}$ complexes.

the same pathway as an entering water molecule and so the steric courses of
base catalysed hydrolysis and other base catalysed substitutions need not be
the same even if there is a limiting D mechanism. A proper test for such a
mechanism is that the steric course of any one process should be independent
of the nature of the leaving group. This test was applied many years ago to the
base hydrolysis reaction and, it was concluded that any scatter was well within

TABLE 20

The steric course of base hydrolysis of *cis*- and *trans*-$[Co(en)_2AX]^{n+}$. From reference [261]

A	X	% *cis*	A	X	% *cis*
trans-OH	Cl	94	*cis*-OH	Cl	97
trans-OH	Br	90	*cis*-OH	Br	96
trans-Cl	Cl	5	*cis*-Cl	Cl	37
trans-Cl	Br	5	*cis*-Cl	Br	30
trans-NCS	Cl	76	*cis*-NCS	Cl	80
trans-NCS	Br	81			
trans-NCS	N_3	70	*cis*-NCS	N_3	70
trans-N_3	Cl	27	*cis*-N_3	Cl	59
trans-N_3	N_3	30	*cis*-N_3	N_3	55
trans-NO_2	Cl	6	*cis*-NO_2	Cl	55
trans-NO_2	NCS	10	*cis*-NO_2	NCS	67

experimental error (which was large at the time),[261] see Table 20. Subsequent refinement of the data by improved product analysis techniques has been confined mainly to the $[Co(en)_2(NH_3)X]^{2+}$ system and the ratio of *cis*:*trans* product does remain remarkably constant, see Table 21. However, if an enantiomeric form of the *cis* complex is studied and the enantiomeric forms of the *cis* product are considered separately, it is claimed that there is a very marked variation in the distribution of the *cis* product between the retained and the inverted form when the leaving group is changed and that this is greater than the experimental error.[229] The neutral leaving groups lead to more retention of configuration than the anion. This can be understood as a typical consequence of postdissociation blocking by the leaving group which

TABLE 21

Steric course of base hydrolysis of *cis*- and *trans*-$[Co(en)_2(NH_3)X]^{n+}$

	Λ-*cis* substrate product analysis/%				*trans* substrate product analysis/%		
X	Λ-*cis*	Δ-*cis*	*trans*	Reference	*trans*	ΛΔ-*cis*	Reference
Cl^-	61	16.5	22.5	[262, 229]	36	64	[262]
Br^-	61	17	22	[229]			
NO_3^-		77	23	[262]	37	63	[262]
$(CH_3)_2SO$	64	13	23	[229]			
$(CH_3O)_3PO$	65	12	23	[229]			

will decrease the amount of retention (particularly in the "Ax" intermediate which does not offer an alternative pathway for retention). Steric course studies of the base catalysed entry of N_3^- in the $[Co(en)_2(NH_3)X]^{n+}$ complexes indicate that the cis:trans product ratio of the $[Co(en)_2(NH_3)OH]^{2+}$ product consists of 66% cis and 34% trans and this ratio is independent of $[N_3^-]$ and the nature of X. Once again the amount of retention of configuration within the cis product increases on going from an anionic to a neutral leaving group.[229] It is claimed that these results indicate that, in order to compete with water for a place in the product, the azide ion must be linked with the substrate before the act of dissociation, a classical I_d mechanism.

$$[L_5CoX]^{n+} + N_3^- = [L_5CoX]^{n+} \ldots N_3^-, K_{IP}$$

$$H_2O, \Big\downarrow OH^- \qquad\qquad H_2O, OH^- \Big| N_3^-, OH^-$$

$$[L_5CoOH]^{2+} + X^{(3-n)-} \qquad [L_5CoN_3]^{2+} + X^{(3-n)-}$$

The differences in the amount of retained product, however real they might be, are too small for such a firm conclusion. If, as suggested, the ion pair leads almost exclusively to the azido product (i.e. the amount of hydroxo complex formed from the ion pair is negligible) one might expect a much greater difference in the steric courses of the reaction of the 2+ and 3+ complexes because the anionic azide would take up a position as far from the coordinated bromide as possible,[191] while the structure of the ion pairs of the 3+ cation could be quite different.

With the more elaborate Λ-cis-$[Co(en)_2(NH_2CH_2CO_2)Cl]^+$ cation (where NH_3 is replaced by a monodentate, N-bonded glycinate) the fraction of $[Co(en)_2(NH_2CH_2CO_2)OH]^+$ product in the trans form (17%) is a little less than in the case of the corresponding chloro-ammine species and the amount of the $[Co(en)_2(NH_2CH_2CO_2)N_3]^+$ product in the trans form (25–28%) is also a little less.[255] The anionic carboxylate free end of the glycine, which is said to be competing with the azide ions for the ion-association sites and subsequent entry into the intermediate appears to slightly block the sites trans to the leaving group although it cannot itself enter in that position.

The products of the base hydrolysis of β_2-RR(SS)-$[Co(trien)(NH_2CH_2CO_2)Cl]^+$ and β_2-RR(SS)-$[Co(trien)(NH_2CH_2CO_2Et)Cl]^{2+}$ are a mixture of β_2-RR(SS)- and β_2-RS-$[Co(trien)(NH_2CH_2CO_2)]^{2+}$ [ring closing in the latter substrate being accompanied by a synchronous (internal S_N2 by coordinated hydroxide) or subsequent facile hydrolysis of coordinated ester function] together with β_2-RR(SS)- and β_2-RS$[Co(trien)(NH_2CH_2CO_2R)N_3]^{2+}$ (R = H or Et, H^+ lost from former in basic solution) if azide is present when hydroxide is added.[243] (β_2-RR(SS) is structurally similar to 4 and its enantiomer in Table 6, while β_2-(RS) is to be compared with 3.[89]) It is of interest to note that the total amount of azide product in the presence of 1.0 M

NaN_3 is greater (15%, mainly RS). This is not consistent with the idea that N_3^- must be associated with the substrate before the act of dissociation if it is to compete successfully, nor is it consistent with the conclusions drawn above about competition between external ion pairs and internal ion pairs. The partial inversion of the configuration of the "flat" secondary nitrogen *cis* to the leaving group, which does not take place before or after the act of substitution, identifies this as the site of deprotonation to give the labilising amido group. It is curious that the authors do not consider the possibility that this might indicate a planar nitrogen in the five-coordinate intermediate but the stereochemical lability of an electron deficient nitrogen radical $R_2\dot{N}$-Co^{II} (see Section VI.F) is suggested as a possible explanation.

A more sophisticated approach uses the t-$[Co(tren)(NH_3)X]^{2+}$ isomer (the one with the leaving group *trans* to the tertiary nitrogen). The two chloro isomers had been shown to differ markedly in their sensitivity towards base hydrolysis, the p-isomer (X *trans* to a primary amine) being considerably more reactive ($k_{OH} = 3.6 \times 10^2$ M^{-1} s^{-1}, 25 °C, C = Cl) than the t-isomer ($k_{OH} = 2.0 \times 10^{-2}$ M^{-1} s^{-1}, 25 °C, X = Cl). This was taken as evidence for the importance of *trans* labilisation by the amido group[263] but could be better explained in terms of the importance of forming a trigonal-bipyramidal intermediate,[217] which is easier to achieve from the p-isomer. The steric course of the substitution is consistent with this, p gives 100% p-hydroxo product while t gives 23% t + 77%-p-$[Co(tren)(NH_3)(OH)]^{2+}$ when Cl is displaced. In order to decide whether the mixed product was obtained from a trigonal bipyramid formed synchronously with bond breaking or whether a square pyramid, which formed first, then rearranged to the symmetrical trigonal bipyramid, the dependence of the steric courses of base catalysed hydrolysis and azide substitution upon the nature of the leaving group was examined.[45] The amount of t-$[Co(tren)(NH_3)OH]^{2+}$ (the rest being the p-isomer) depends upon the nature of the leaving group X = $MeSO_3^-$ (25.2%) > Cl^- (22.5%) > Me_2SO (15.3%) > NO_3^- (12.1%), a sequence which relates neither to the charge on the leaving group nor the relative reactivity of the substrate. Clearly this indicates that the five-coordinate intermediate has been consumed before it has had the chance to lose all memory of its origin and the authors suggest that the results indicate that the leaving group partially blocks one of the pathways for the entry of water (alternatively it funnels it towards the other pathway), i.e. that this is a postdissociation effect.

It is of interest to note that 1.0 M $NaClO_4$ tends to push the product composition towards a leaving group independent value. This was ascribed to ClO_4^- ion-pair effects but the effect of the added electrolyte upon the "viscosity" of the solvation shell (i.e. if the solvation shell is loosened, the leaving group might be able to escape before the intermediate is consumed) should not be ignored.

The base catalysed substitution by azide is expected to trap the intermediate at an earlier state of its formation if, as claimed, the azide is in ion-association with the substrate before dissociation, and a $3:1$ distribution of the azido product between t- and p-$[Co(tren)(NH_3)N_3]^{2+}$ (independent of the nature of the leaving group) lends support to the idea that the intermediate starts out as a square pyramid and then rearranges. However, the relative proportion of t-hydroxo product also increases. It was suggested that, as in the case of cis-$[Co(en)_2NH_3X]^{2+}$,[229] the azide can only compete with water if it is associated with the substrate before dissociation but, in the tren complex, the ion pair could also lead to some hydroxo product, but with an increase in the amount of t-hydroxo isomer. One might have thought that an ante-association mechanism of this sort would lead to differences in the product distribution according to the charge on the complex (reflected in a dependence on the charge of the leaving group). For a given concentration of NaN$_3$, the amount of $3+$ substrate in the form of the ion pair should be significantly greater than the amount of $2+$ substrate.

Whether the formation of 100% p-$[Co(tren)(NH_3)OH]^+$ from the p substrate is due to a square-pyramidal intermediate or to the symmetrical nature of the trigonal-bipyramidal species has been tested by using the p-equivalent of $[Co(N-Me-tren)(NH_3)X]^{2+}$ which has three isomeric forms, Fig. 12.[252] A square-pyramidal intermediate would give complete retention of

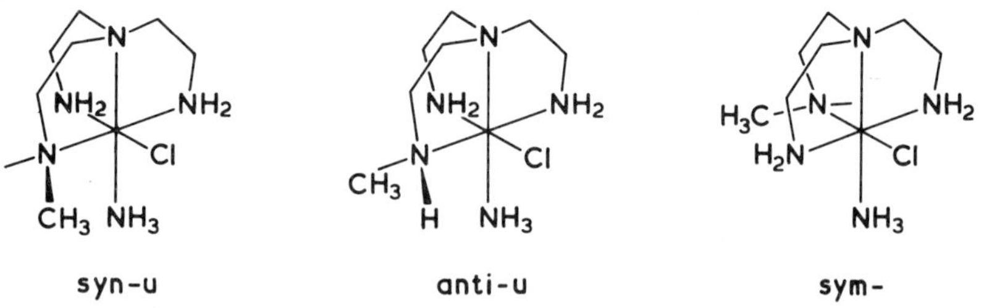

syn–u   anti–u   sym–

Fig. 12. Three of the geometric isomers of $[Co(N-Me-tren)(NH_3)Cl]^{2+}$.

configuration but all three isomers could give a common trigonal-bipyramidal intermediate on losing X provided the original site of deprotonation is lost, either by reprotonation or by solvent mediated internal proton transfer of the type proposed for $[Pt(NH_3)_5NH_2]^{2+}$.[196] The lack of a common product shows this not to be so. Both syn-p and $anti$-p substrates give 100% $anti$-p-$[Co(N-Me-tren)(NH_3)OH]^+$, but it seems that the interconversion of these species is fast compared with their formation and so nothing can be said about the composition of the original product. The s-isomer gives between 51 and 58% $anti$-p product, the rest being the s-isomer, the actual amount depends upon $[OH^-]$. If, as we have already suggested, the location of the amido group is fixed at the time of deprotonation and does not change, and the deprotonated secondary amine provides a better labilising site, application of Nordmeyer's rule[220] will predict the observed result if there is a trigonal-bipyramidal intermediate. However, evidence is presented to suggest that the secondary amine proton is not involved in the labilisation of the *anti-p* complex (or else its removal is rate limiting) and a change in the nature of the leaving group has a considerable effect on the distribution of the products of the reaction of the *s*-isomer, i.e. *s*-[Co(N-Me-tren)(NH$_3$)X]$^{n+}$ gives 39% *s*- and 61%-*anti-p*-[Co(N-Me-tren)(NH$_3$)OH]$^{2+}$ when X = Br and 71% *s*- and 29%-*anti-p* product when X = NH$_3$. The *anti-p*-[Co(N-Me-tren)(NH$_3$)$_2$]$^{3+}$ complex gives 10% *s* product. Since the *anti-p* product is more stable than the *s*-isomer the explanation must come from a kinetic and hence mechanistic argument. In view of the impressive quality and quantity of the experimental work that was required it would be churlish to suggest that the NN-dimethyltren (both methyls on the same nitrogen) complexes would have resolved this problem less ambiguously.

Clearly these fine-tuned experiments are throwing a considerable amount of light on the finer details of the act of substitution and the last word is far from having yet been spoken.

VIII. MISCELLANEOUS FEATURES

A. Unusual labilisation by heterocyclic nitrogen bases

Although the rate constants for the aquation of complexes of the type *cis*-[Co(en)$_2$(am)Cl]$^{n+}$ do not differ greatly in magnitude, in spite of wide variation in the nature of the nitrogen donor represented by am (see Table 17 in reference [61]), there is a very significant enhancement of the sensitivity towards base hydrolysis when a heterocyclic amine base, such as pyridine, is present, see Table 2. Similar large (or even much larger) values are found for k_{OH} when am is an "acidic" amine that can be deprotonated when coordinated, such as aniline and imidazole but, in these cases, the effect can be assigned to the enhanced acidity of the complexes (k_1/k_{-1}) rather than any labilisation of the amido-conjugate base (k_2) (Section VI.A). When this effect was first observed[226] the enhancement of the lability by pyridine seemed remarkably large but was not commented on for many years. The effect was missed in the magnificent compilation by Edwards *et al.*[265] who accidentally inverted the sign of the exponent of the rate constant. Subsequent studies[266,194,267] indicated that this published value was overestimated by a factor of 10 or so, but, even when corrected, the added labilisation is still quite significant and not just confined to pyridine. Table 22 contains a collection of k_{OH} values for complexes where a pyridine or pyridyl ligand is present, either as a

TABLE 22

Some examples of the labilising effect of a pyridyl group in the coordination shell of a cobaltamine complex (and some exceptions) [a]

Complex	$10^{-4}k_{OH}/M^{-1} s^{-1}$	$k_{OH}^{py}/k_{OH}^{NH_3}$	Reference
α-*cis*-$[Co(picen)Cl_2]^+$	0.11	16	[217]
α-*cis*-$[Co(trien)Cl_2]^+$	0.0068		[217]
β-*cis*-$[Co(picpn)Cl_2]^+$	2000	18	[217]
β-*cis*-$[Co(trien)Cl_2]^+$	110		[217]
β-*cis*-$[Co(pictn)Cl_2]^+$	210	78	[217]
β-*cis*-$[Co(2,3,2-tet)Cl_2]^+$	2.7		[38]
cis-$[Co(en)_2(py)Cl]^{2+}$	0.050	62	[266]
cis-$[Co(en)_2(NH_3)Cl]^{2+}$	0.00081		[101]
syn-$\alpha\beta$-$[Co(picdien)Cl]^{2+}$	1980	570	[16]
syn-$\alpha\beta$-$[Co(tetren)Cl]^{2+}$	3.5		[112]
anti-$\alpha\beta$-$[Co(picdien)Cl]^{2+}$	760	760	[16]
anti-$\alpha\beta$-$[Co(tetren)Cl]^{2+}$	1.0[b]		[112]
trans-$[Co(CR4H)Cl_2]^+$	4000	400	[266]
trans-$[Co(cyclam)Cl_2]^+$	6.4		[13]
mer-$[Co(bmp)(en)Cl]^{2+}$	0.048	0.012	[194]
anti-*mer*-$[Co(dien)(en)Cl]^{2+}$	3.0		[121]
mer-$[Co(bmp)(tn)Cl]^{2+}$	0.77	0.015	[194]
mer-$[Co(dien)(tn)Cl]^{2+}$	50		[118]

[a] At 25 °C.
[b] Extrapolated from data at 70 °C assuming the same activation energy as that of the *syn* isomer.

monodentate or as part of a multidentate ligand system, and these are compared with the values of k_{OH} for an analogous complex (i.e. the same isomeric form) where the pyridine is replaced appropriately by NH_3, —NH_2 or >NH depending upon the nature of the complex.

An apparent exception to this rule lies in the comparison of the unsymmetrical *mer*-$[Co(bamp)(AA)Cl]^{2+}$ (bamp = 2,6-bis(amino-methyl)pyridine, AA is a chelating diamine) with the corresponding $[Co(dien)(AA)Cl]^{2+}$, where the pyridino complex is less reactive.[266] This serves to demonstrate the high labilising power of the "flat" secondary amine when it is *cis* to the leaving group. In bamp this is replaced by the pyridine. In all of the other examples quoted where the presence of the pyridyl group leads to an increase in reactivity, such a group is either not present or remains present in the pyridine containing ligand. This observation already provides a strong hint that the pyridyl group is not serving as an efficient alternative π-donor.

In all of the cobalt(III) complexes so far prepared, the pyridine nitrogen is *cis* to the leaving group and, in spite of many attempts to prepare the *trans* isomer, no example with the pyridine *trans* to the leaving group has yet been isolated. (Species such as *cis*-$[Co(bipy)_2Cl_2]^+$ might be looked upon as an exception to the above statement.) One such study made use of the complexes of the linear quadridentate, 3,2,3-tet, (1,10-diamino-4,7-diazadecane), which strongly favours the *trans* disposition of the remaining two ligands. Here, the reaction of the *trans*-$[Co(3,2,3-tet)Cl_2]Cl$ with amines gave *trans*-$[Co(3,2,3-tet)am Cl]^{2+}$ when aliphatic amines were used but, apart from one unrepeatable occasion when the β-*cis*-$[Co(3,2,3-tet)(py)Cl]$ was isolated, no product could be obtained in the reactions with pyridine or its derivatives.[114] Some time ago, we speculated that the labilisation might be due to the addition of hydroxide to the 2− (or 4−) position of the pyridine, thereby converting the donor into an amido species which might serve to labilise the complex in the usual way,[4] Fig. 13. This was taken up as one more example of covalent hydration in a very broad canvas painted by Gillard,[142] the addition of water to the pyridine (covalent hydration) generating a new amine of higher acidity (rather like aniline or imidazole), Fig. 14. Assuming that the acts of covalent hydration and proton transfer are fast compared with the rate of base hydrolysis this mechanism will give the rate law $k_{obs} = k_2 K'_{hy}[OH^-]/(1 + K'_{hy}[OH^-])$ with $K'_{hy} = K_1 K_2$. Although no one has set out to look for departures from the simple first-order dependence on $[OH^-]$ when $K_{hy}[OH^-]$ becomes significant compared with 1, none appears to be present in the pH range 8.7 to 10.0 since the agreement between the two groups working at these different pHs is reasonably good once correction for the different ionic strengths used has been made.[268,194] Of course, it is possible (but not likely) that the second $[OH^-]$ dependent step (deprotonation of en in the $[Co(en)_2(pyOH)Cl]^+$ complex) might mask the first limiting behaviour, as is possible in the *cis*-$[Co(en)_2(aniline)Cl]^{2+}$ complex (Section VIII.C). It is not easy to test out the hypothesis of "covalent hydration" in this context but such evidence as is available suggests that it is not important. For example, it has been shown that *cis*-$[Co(en)_2(py)Cl]^{2+}$ and *cis*-$[Co(en)_2(^2H_5-py)Cl]^{2+}$ undergo base hydrolysis at the same rate.[268] Since an isotope effect would be expected

between and and none is found, this is re

asonably strong evidence that such a process does not contribute to the reaction.

A more elaborate study, using the *syn*- and *anti*-$\alpha\beta$-$[Co(picdien)X]^{2+}$ isomers (X = Cl, Br) provides further strong evidence against the covalent hydration mechanism. These complexes are very sensitive towards base

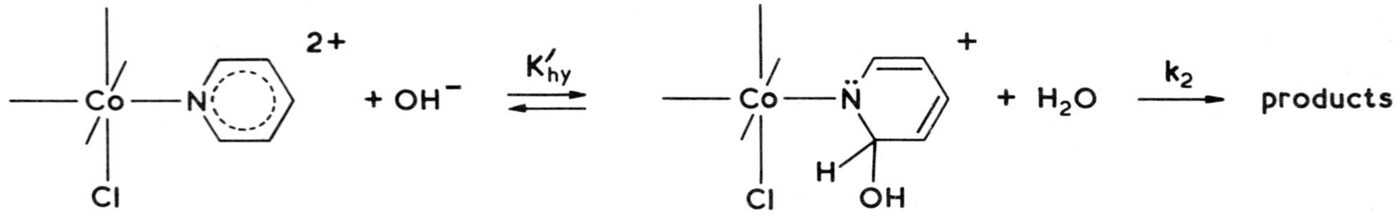

Fig. 13. An alternative pathway for the base hydrolysis of pyridine containing Co(III) complexes.

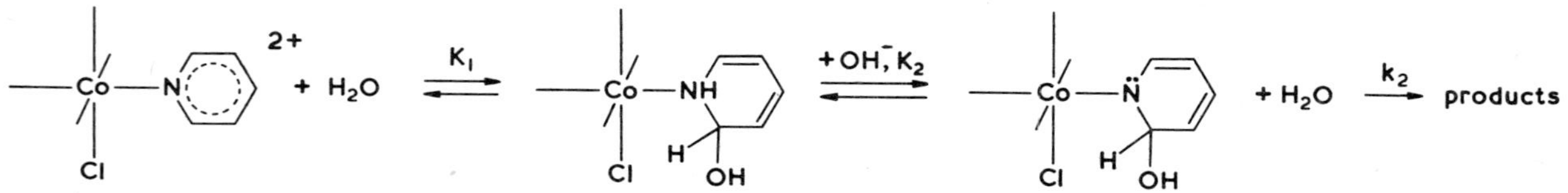

Fig. 14. "Covalent hydration" of a coordinated pyridine (or pyridyl group) and the generation of a labilising amido nitrogen.

hydrolysis, the rate law taking the simple form, Rate $= k_H[\text{complex}][H^+]^{-1}$ in acid solution, with no significant acid independent contribution detected over the range of acidity studied (10^{-1}–10^{-3} M [H^+]).[16] Assuming that the rate law is really, Rate $= k_{OH}[\text{complex}][OH^-]$, $k_{OH} = k_H/K_w$ and the very large values for k_{OH} suggested to us, at one time, that this might be a system where covalent hydration might be found. However, if as a result of covalent hydration, the pyridine nitrogen were to provide the labilising amido group, we would expect it to follow the rules discussed in Section VI.E. In particular, if a trigonal bipyramid with the amido nitrogen in the trigonal plane, its lone pair also lying in the trigonal plane, were required, only pyridyl A could do this. The lone pair of pyridyl B would lie perpendicular to the trigonal plane in which its nitrogen sits, see Fig. 15. Labilisation from B is unlikely unless there is extensive rearrangement. If A provides the labilising amido group, the "flat" nitrogen, marked with an asterisk would have to be in an axial position. Whereas the *anti* isomer could tolerate the change from octahedron to trigonal bipyramid, the *syn* isomer could not, the folding taking place in the same direction as the N—H bond. The fact that the rate constants of the two isomers do not differ greatly is strong evidence against covalent hydration is this system.

Nevertheless, an extension of this reasoning to the complexes of the macrocyclic pentadentate ligands containing pyridine, $[\text{Co}(\text{CP}_{222}4\text{H})\text{Cl}]^{2+}$ and $[\text{Co}(\text{CP}_{232}4\text{H})\text{Cl}]^{2+}$, Fig. 16, would predict that, for the same reasons quoted for the *mer*-$[\text{Co(bmp)(en)Cl}]^{2+}$ cation[194] these should not be particularly sensitive to base hydrolysis. The skeletal arrangement of the complex with a macrocyclic pentadentate is limited to one form, although there is considerable scope for stereoisomerism coming from the different ways in which the unique pyridine donor can be positioned, the arrangement of the two methyl groups and the amine protons. The requirement that the pyridine nitrogen must occupy one of the "flat" nitrogen sites severely restricts the possibilities. A published structure for one isomer of $[\text{Co}(\text{CP}_{222}4\text{H})\text{Cl}](\text{Cl})_4)_2$ indicates that, as expected, the pyridine nitrogen is "flat". The two methyl groups point towards the chlorine, as does the proton on the other flat nitrogen.[269] The same reference also gives the structure of the trigonal bipyramidal $[\text{Cu}(\text{CP}_{222}4\text{H})](\text{PF}_6)_2$ which shows the pyridine nitrogen in an equatorial position with the two adjacent nitrogens occupying the axial positions. It is not possible to put the pyridine into an axial position without considerable strain, and with the pyridine equatorial it is not possible to place the other "flat" nitrogen, deprotonated in the conjugate base, in an equatorial position beside it (Fig. 17). Indeed with the pyridine occupying a position in the trigonal plane it is not possible to orient any other planar amido group in the trigonal plane with its lone pair either parallel to or perpendicular to the trigonal plane. This is a situation already encountered in the explanation of the

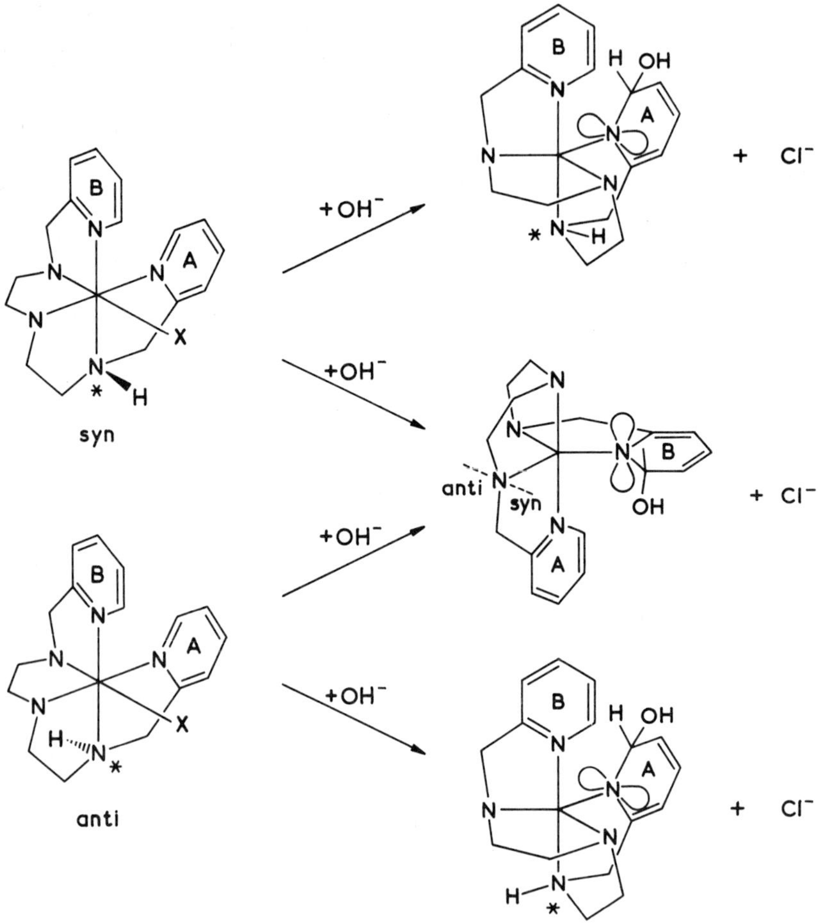

Fig. 15. If pyridine A were providing π donation, the *syn* isomer would be much more strained than the *anti* in the trigonal-bipyramidal intermediate.

relatively low values of k_{OH} found for α-*cis*-$[Co(trien)Cl_2]^+$ and other similar systems. However, $[Co(CP_{222}4H)Cl]^{2+}$ and $[Co(CP_{232}4H)Cl]^{2+}$ are very sensitive to base hydrolysis with $k_{OH} = 10^7\,M^{-1}\,s^{-1}$ at 25 °C. In the dependence of their rates of solvolysis on $[H^+]$ they closely resemble the $[Co(picdien)Cl]^{2+}$ and $[Co(picditn)Cl]^{2+}$ complexes.[16] Without assigning a much more leading labilising role to the pyridine (covalent hydration), or suspending the well obeyed rules governing the relationship between the configuration and position of secondary nitrogen atoms and the lability of the complex, it is hard to see how these observations can be explained.

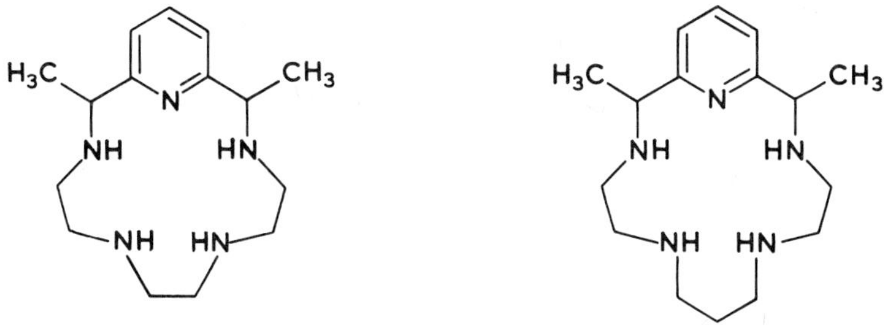

CP$_{222}$4H   CP$_{232}$4H

Fig. 16.

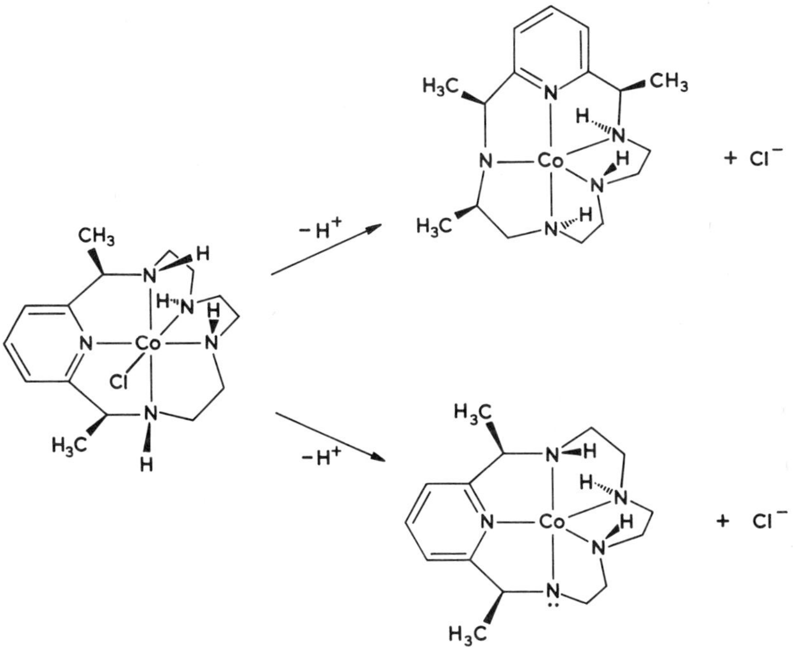

Fig. 17. The problem of orienting the "flat" nitrogen in the substitution reactions of [Co(CP$_{222}$4H)Cl]$^{2+}$.

If the covalent hydration explanation of the labilising role of a coordinated pyridine is incorrect, what other explanation can be offered? In the study of the proton exchange properties of the [Co(picdien)X]$^{n+}$ complexes it seems that a proton on a nitrogen *trans* to pyridine can be nearly as labile towards exchange as one *trans* to chloride.[37] For *syn-αβ*-[Co(picdien)Cl]$^{2+}$ in D$_2$O/DClO$_4$ at 22.5 °C, $\mu = 0.043$; NH *trans* to Cl, $k_1 = 1 \times 10^9$ M^{-1} s^{-1}.

"Flat" NH *trans* to py, $k_1 = 8 \times 10^7$ $M^{-1}s^{-1}$. "Bent" NH *trans* to py, $k_1 = 8 \times 10^6$. However, if the enhanced lability of $[Co(en)_2pyCl]^{2+}$ is to be explained by an increase in k_1 at the nitrogen *trans* to the pyridine, it would be predicted that the intermediate with the pyridine and the amido group in the trigonal plane would be preferred. This retains the original chirality of the octahedron and would lead to a mixture of *trans* and *cis* products with retained configuration. However, it has been shown that the base hydrolysis of Λ-*cis*-$[Co(en)_2(py)Cl]^{2+}$ (and the analogous substituted pyridine complexes) leads to a significantly larger amount of the racemic *cis* product than is found in the corresponding complexes with aliphatic amines.[260] This indicates that the intermediate with the pyridine axial makes a strong contribution. (See Section VII for a more detailed discussion.) One concludes that the question as to why pyridine labilises the system is not yet answered and the definitive experiment remains to be done.

B. Activation enthalpies as a means of detecting rate limiting deprotonation

Attention has already been drawn to the observation that the variation in k_{OH} for a variety of complexes of the type *cis*- and *trans*-$[Co(en)_2ACl]^{n+}$ was mirrored much more in the variation of $\Delta S^{\ddagger}$ than it was in $\Delta H^{\ddagger}$. No explanation was offered and care should be taken in interpreting the finer details of the mechanism through these quantities because k_{OH} can be a composite term. For the series of complexes, $[Co(L_4)Cl_2]^+$ (where L_4 is a combination of nitrogen donors), the enthalpy of activation is very dependent upon the nature of L (see Table 7). It is known that this group of complexes provides the best examples of cases where deprotonation becomes rate limiting and it has been suggested that the enthalpy of activation might provide a convenient indication of rate-limiting deprotonation[4,230,232] and this has been confirmed in cases where the ratio k_{-1}/k_2 could be independently determined. For the two limiting cases, (i) $k_{-1} \gg k_2$, and (ii) $k_2 \gg k_{-1}$, k_{OH} simplifies to $k_{OH} = nk_1k_2/k_{-1}$ and $k_{OH} = nk_2$ respectively, so that, in case (i) $\Delta H^{\ddagger}_{OH} = \Delta H^{\ddagger}_1 + \Delta H^{\ddagger}_2 - \Delta H^{\ddagger}_{-1}$, while in case (ii) $\Delta H^{\ddagger}_{OH} = \Delta H^{\ddagger}_1$. The intermediate region is of course of considerable interest when $\Delta H^{\ddagger}_2 \neq \Delta H^{\ddagger}_{-1}$ because the ratio k_{-1}/k_2 will vary with temperature and the Eyring plot ($\ln (k_{OH}/T)$ vs $1/T$) will be curved in this region.[232] This has now been properly demonstrated in the case of *trans*-$[Co(RSSR\text{-}cyclam)Cl_2]^+$ where the published data has now been extended to 0 °C[138] and the indication of curvature previously reported[13] has now been confirmed, see Fig. 18. Measurement of $\Delta H^{\ddagger}_1$ under conditions where no complications arise from parallel base hydrolysis have been restricted to substitutionally inert systems and there values between 13 and 14 kcal mol^{-1} have been reported[185,230] for

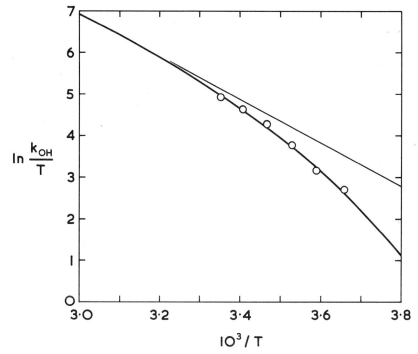

Fig. 18. Plot of ln (k_{OH}/T) against $1/T$ for the base hydrolysis of *trans*-[Co(RSSR-cyclam)Cl$_2$]$^+$.

exchange of H in D_2O (exchange of D in H_2O gives values of $\Delta H_1^\ddagger$ about 2 kcal mol^{-1} higher than this.[186,230]) The similarity of the values of $\Delta H_{OH}^\ddagger$ when deprotonation is rate limiting and these directly determined values for $\Delta H_1^\ddagger$ is satisfying but, while a value of $\Delta H_{OH}^\ddagger$ much in excess of 15 kcal mol^{-1} may be diagnostic of class (i) substitutions, a low activation energy does not necessarily signify a class (ii) substitution. A good example is to be found in the case of *cis*-[Co(RRRR(SSSS)-cyclam)Cl$_2$]$^+$ where the enthalpy of activation for base hydrolysis, 9.4 kcal mol^{-1}[13] is considerably smaller than the values associated with deprotonation so far. Direct measurement of proton exchange in this complex shows this to be considerably faster than base hydrolysis and $k_{-1}/k_2 = 28$ at 0 °C.[138] Since it is unlikely that $\Delta H_1^\ddagger$ can be very much smaller than the measured value of $\Delta H_{OH}^\ddagger$ in this system, one is forced to conclude that $\Delta H_2^\ddagger$ is of a similar magnitude to $\Delta H_{-1}^\ddagger$ if not smaller than it, in which circumstances $\Delta H_{OH}^\ddagger$ will be less than $\Delta H_1^\ddagger$. If we can measure the base hydrolysis kinetics over a temperature range that straddles the point where $k_{-1} = k_2$, the upper temperature limiting slope would correspond to the situation where proton transfer is reversible, while the lower temperature limit would correspond to $\Delta H_1^{\ddagger}$. For this type of situation, irrespective of mechanism, the Eyring plot will always go from a lower negative slope at smaller $1/T$ (higher T) to a larger negative slope at higher $1/T$ (lower T). We are unable to measure k_1 for this system with sufficient accuracy to obtain adequately reliable values for $\Delta H_1^{\ddagger}$. Similar conclusions must be drawn from the *syn*- and *anti*-$\alpha\beta$-[Co(picdien)X]$^{2+}$ (X = Cl, Br) complexes, where $\Delta H_{OH}^{\ddagger}$ lies within the range 8.4 and 13.5 kcal mol^{-1},[16] and yet at least two of the three amine protons exchange faster than base hydrolysis. If we assume that the "flat" nitrogen *cis* to the leaving group is the site of the labilising amido group then we estimate that $k_{-1}/k_2 = 5$ for the chloro isomers and significantly less for the bromo species.[37] The low activation energy associated with the base hydrolysis of *cis*-[Co(cyclen)Cl$_2$] (12.7 kcal mol^{-1})[36] is said to be consistent with the E$_2$ mechanism (synchronous removal of H$^+$ and the loss of Cl$^-$) but, in view of these other observations, it could be consistent with a situation where $k_{-1} > k_2$.

C. The proton anomaly

Although the departures from first-order dependence on [OH$^-$], summarised by the expression, $k_{obs} = a[OH^-]/(1 + b[OH^-])$, can be interpreted in terms of a distribution of the substrate between a relatively unreactive amine form and a highly reactive amido form ($a = K_{hy}k_2$, $b = k_2$), many other mechanisms will lead to the same form of rate law, e.g. ion-association with OH$^-$ and proton transfer within the ion pair. However, the species that has lost the proton (or gained the hydroxide) need not be the reactive entity and we ought to consider the "blind alley" mechanisms, e.g. deprotonation of the leaving group to form a much more tightly bound entity, as in the case of [Co(NH$_3$)$_5$(OC(NH$_2$)$_2$)]$^{3+}$.[44] The deprotonation blind alley need not necessarily be associated with the leaving group and the general concept can be demonstrated in the context of *cis*-[Co(en)$_2$(AH)X]$^{2+}$ (where AH is a potentially acidic ligand such as imidazol, benzimidazol, aniline or even water).

$$cis\text{-}[Co(en)_2(AH)X]^{2+} + OH^- \overset{K_{hy}^{AH}}{=\!=} cis\text{-}[Co(en)_2(A)X]^+ + H_2O$$

(generally [Co(en)$_2$(A)(OH)]$^+$ but depends upon pH)

Here, in addition to the pathway in which the deprotonated (at AH) substrate (K_{hy}^{AH}) undergoes first-order solvolysis (k_{aq}^{II}, corresponding to k_2 in previous schemes) we also consider solvolysis by way of deprotonation of the diaminoethane with rate constants k_{OH}^{I} and k_{OH}^{II}. The uncatalysed solvolysis (k_{aq}^{I}) is also included for completeness.

The overall rate law will be

$$-d[\text{complex}]/dt = k_{aq}^{I}[\text{I}] + k_{OH}^{I}[\text{I}][\text{OH}^-] + k_{aq}^{II}[\text{II}] + k_{OH}^{II}[\text{II}] \tag{30}$$

If the proton transfers are fast and reversible

$$[\text{I}] = [\text{complex}]/(1 + K_{hy}[\text{OH}^-])$$

and $\hspace{11cm}$ (31)

$$[\text{II}] = K_{hy}[\text{complex}][\text{OH}^-]/(1 + K_{hy}[\text{OH}^-])$$

so that

$-d[\text{complex}]/dt$

$$= \frac{k_{aq}^{I} + k_{OH}^{I}[\text{OH}^-] + k_{aq}^{II}K_{hy}[\text{OH}^-] + k_{OH}^{II}K_{hy}[\text{OH}^-]^2}{1 + K_{hy}[\text{OH}^-]}[\text{complex}]$$

i.e. $\hspace{11cm}$ (32)

$$k_{obs} = \frac{k_{aq}^{I} + (k_{OH}^{I} + k_{aq}^{II}K_{hy})[\text{OH}^-] + k_{OH}^{II}K_{hy}[\text{OH}^-]^2}{1 + K_{hy}[\text{OH}^-]} \tag{33}$$

In acid solution, when $K_{hy}[\text{OH}^-] \ll 1$ and all the $[\text{OH}^-]$ containing terms are negligible, $k_{obs} = k_{aq}^{I}$ unambiguously. When $[\text{OH}^-]$ is large enough for $K_{hy}[\text{OH}^-] \gg 1$

$$k_{obs} = k_{aq}^{I}/K_{hy}[\text{OH}^-] + (k_{OH}^{I}/K_{hy} + k_{aq}^{II}) + k_{OH}^{II}[\text{OH}^-] \tag{34}$$

The identification of k_{OH}^{II} as the slope of the plot of k_{obs} vs $[\text{OH}^-]$ in this region is unambiguous but the intercept is not necessarily identifiable as k_{aq}^{II}, it is possible that this is dominated by the k_{OH}^{I}/K_{hy} term. (The same is true if the contribution from a k_{OH}^{II} term was negligible, the limiting $[\text{OH}^-]$ independent value of k_{obs} would also correspond to the middle term in equation 34.) In order to resolve this problem it is necessary to consider the magnitudes of the derived constants to see whether any are unreasonable and to pay regard to the chemical features of the system before any decision could be made. It is of interest to give some though to the case where AH = H_2O. Over quite a range of pH, where the substrate is in the form of $[\text{Co(en)}_2(\text{OH})X]^+$ (X = Cl, Br), the rate of reaction is independent of $[\text{OH}^-]$ and it is usually assumed that one is following the uncatalysed aquation of the hydroxo complex. However, the suggestion has been made that the labilising power of the hydroxide ligand is due to its abstraction of an amine proton[223] and the unusual reactivity of *trans*-[Co(cyclam)(OH)Cl]$^+$,[224] commented upon elsewhere in this review, is also consistent with this proposal, as is the alternative that we are looking at the base hydrolysis of the aquo complex. A value of k_{OH} for *cis*-[Co(en)$_2$(H$_2$O)Cl]$^{2+}$ (pathway involving deprotonation of en) calculated on this basis is given in Table 2. The ratio of k_{OH}/k_{aq} for *cis*-[Co(en)$_2$(AH)Cl]$^{2+}$ (AH = imidazol, benzimidazol, aniline and water) (Table 2) are all much larger than those for the other complexes listed in the Table and this might be taken as evidence that formulation of the [OH$^-$] independent pathway as base hydrolysis of the conjugate acid is untenable and the original thought that the labilising ligand is indeed A$^-$ (A$^-$ = im$^-$, bzim$^-$, PhNH$^-$, OH$^-$) is correct. But this is not a very compelling argument and further work is needed.

It is of passing interest to note that, if $(k_{OH}^I + k_{aq}^{II} K_{hy}) \sim k_{OH}^{II}$, bearing in mind that either of the terms may dominate the expression on the left-hand side, there will be no discontinuity in the first-order dependence on [OH$^-$] in the region where the major component of the substrate changes from I to II, i.e. in the region where K_{hy}[OH$^-$] changes from being much less than 1 to being much greater than 1. It is possible that this is the case in the base hydrolysis of *cis*-[Co(en)$_2$(PhNH$_2$)Cl]$^{2+}$ but the relevant part of the k_{obs} vs [OH$^-$] region has not yet been properly mapped out.

IX. SUMMARY AND CONCLUSIONS

It is now reasonably well established that the base catalysed substitution reactions of the octahedral "ligando"-amine complexes (this clumsy word has been coined to include both neutral and anionic leaving groups) of Cr(III), Ru(III), Co(III) and Rh(III) all involve a deprotonation of an amine nitrogen in the substrate that generates an amido complex, which undergoes ligand substitution by a dissociatively activated mechanism. In the case of Co(III), there is strong evidence for the existence of an intermediate of lower coordination number that almost manages to lose its memory of its mode of formation, but there is not full agreement between the workers in the field as to whether this intermediate can live long enough to discriminate between potential nucleophiles or whether it can only capture a member of its immediate environment (solvent molecule or associated anion), that it inherited from its six-coordinate precursor (i.e. an I_d cb mechanism). No systematic work, of this sort, has been carried out on complexes with reaction centres other than Co(III) but there is, as yet, no evidence to suggest that their substitutions are not dissociatively activated. The way in which the amido group actually labilises the conjugate base remains a matter for discussion and further experiment. A major part of the experimental evidence is consistent with its role as a π-donor in the Co(III) system, but this cannot properly explain some of the enormous labilisations arising from the act of deprotonation. An alternative view, that the amido groups acts as a strong σ-donor, thereby labilising the ligand *trans* to itself is less consistent with experimental evidence and likewise cannot explain some of the very high labilisations. An alternative mechanism, hinted at by a number of people but never expounded definitely by any of them, is that there is a single electron transfer from the amido nitrogen to the metal to form, in the case of Co(III), a low spin Co(II) species with a nitrogen radical ligand. Such a Co(II) species might favour five coordination and hence be labile with respect to the loss of one of its ligands. The ability of this mechanism to account for features not readily explained by the classical simple substitution (the formal oxidation state of the reaction centre remaining constant throughout) makes it increasingly attractive but, as yet, there is no definitive evidence to support it. Although Ru(III) complexes are at least as sensitive to base catalysed substitution as those of Co(III) there are many major points of difference. Cobalt(III) prefers the amido group to be *cis* to the leaving group for it to exert its maximum effect, while Ru(III) requires it to be *trans*. Substitution takes place with extensive stereochemical change in Co(III) substrates, suggesting that a trigonal-bipyramidal species is involved somewhere, while Ru(III) complexes undergo substitution with complete retention of configuration. It is also noted that Cr(III) resembles Co(III) in this context while Rh(III) is similar to Ru(III). One cannot therefore explain the differences in terms of the symmetry of the orbital on the metal that would accept the transferred electron in the single electron transfer mechanism. The lower reactivity of Cr(III) and Rh(III) complexes is due, in almost equal part, to the lower proton lability and lower dissociative lability of the amido base.

In spite of the fact that base hydrolysis has been the subject of detailed study for more than 30 years a great deal remains to be done. Highly sophisticated studies of product composition and stereochemistry, nucleophilic discrimination properties of intermediate species etc., have yet to be applied to reaction centres other than Co(III). Elegant experiments in which carefully designed substrates are synthesised and studied have yet to be extended to other reaction centres. The techniques to do this are available in most well-found laboratories but a rapid perusal of the references in this review will show that the number of groups doing this sort of work is very small indeed.

Acknowledgements

To John Cresswell for all the drawings and for his patience and forbearance. To Ginnette, Jane, Nina and Veronica, for services rendered. To my students and friends who I have neglected during the later stages of the preparation of this review.

REFERENCES

[1] Bronsted, J. N.; Livingston, R. *J. Amer. Chem. Soc.* **1927**, *49*, 435.
[2] Garrick, F. J. *Nature* **1937**, *139*, 507.
[3] Basolo, F.; Pearson, R. G. "Mechanisms of Inorganic Reactions"; 2nd Edn, Wiley: New York, 1967; pp. 177–193 and 261–265.
[4] Tobe, M. L. *Acc. Chem. Res.* **1970**, *3*, 377.
[5] Tobe, M. L. "IUPAC Coordination Chemistry 20", Banerjea, D., Ed,; Pergamon Press, 1980; p. 47.
[6] Brown, D. D.; Ingold, C. K. *J. Chem. Soc.* **1953**, 2680.
[7] Balt, S.; Pothoff, G. *J. Coord. Chem.* **1975**, *4*, 167.
[8] Balt, S.; Pothoff, G. *J. Coord. Chem.* **1975**, *4*, 247.
[9] Balt, S. *Inorg. Chem.* **1979**, *18*, 333.
[10] Balt, S.; Breman, J.; de Kieviet, W. *J. Inorg. Nucl. Chem.* **1979**, *41*, 331.
[11] Chester, A. W. *Inorg. Chem.* **1969**, *8*, 1584.
[12] Chester, A. W. *Inorg. Chem.* **1970**, *9*, 1746.
[13] Lichtig, J.; Tobe, M. L. *Inorg. Chem.* **1978**, *17*, 2442.
[14] Nanda, R. K.; Nanda, R. N. *Inorg. Chem.* **1969**, *8*, 104.
[15] Rao, B. S.; Nanda, R.; Tripathy, K. K. *Trans. Metal Chem.* **1981**, *6*, 97.
[16] Tobe, M. L.; Henderson, R. A.; Humanes, M. In press. **1983**.
[17] Pearson, R. G. *J. Chem. Educ.* **1978**, *55*, 720.
[18] Pearson, R. G.; Meeker, R. E.; Basolo, F. *J. Inorg. Nucl. Chem.* **1955**, *1*, 341.
[19] Brown, D. D.; Ingold, C. K.; Nyholm, R. S. *J. Chem. Soc.* **1953**, 2674.
[20] Ingold, C. K.; Nyholm, R. S.; Tobe, M. L. *J. Chem. Soc.* **1956**, 1691.
[21] Nyholm, R. S.; Tobe, M. L. *J. Chem. Soc.* **1956**, 1707.
[22] Asperger, S.; Ingold, C. K. *J. Chem. Soc.* **1956**, 2862.
[23] Brown, D. D.; Nyholm, R. S. *J. Chem. Soc.* **1953**, 2696.
[24] Pearson, R. G.; Henry, P. M.; Basolo, F. *J. Amer. Chem. Soc.* **1957**, *79*, 5379.
[25] Pearson, R. G.; Henry, P. M.; Basolo, F. *J. Amer. Chem. Soc.* **1957**, *79*, 5382.
[26] Chan, S. C.; Tobe, M. L. *J. Chem. Soc.* **1962**, 4531.
[27] Chan, S. C. *J. Chem. Soc. A* **1966**, 1124.
[28] Chan, S. C.; Lau, O. W. *Aust. J. Chem.* **1969**, *22*, 1851.
[29] Buckingham, D. A.; Olsen, I. I.; Sargeson, A. M. *Inorg. Chem.* **1968**, *7*, 174.
[30] Broomhead, J. A.; Basolo, F.; Pearson, R. G. *Inorg. Chem.* **1964**, *3*, 826.
[31] Gillard, R. D. *J. Chem. Soc. A* **1967**, 917.
[32] Jones, W. E.; Jordan, R. B.; Swaddle, T. W. *Inorg. Chem.* **1969**, *8*, 2504.
[33] Rillema, D. P.; Endicott, J. F.; Barber, J. R. *J. Amer. Chem. Soc.* **1973**, *95*, 6987.
[34] Bunnett, J. F. *Acc. Chem. Res.* **1978**, *11*, 413.
[35] Hay, R. W.; Norman, P. R. *J. Chem. Soc. Chem. Commun.* **1980**, 734.
[36] Hay, R. W. *Inorg. Chim. Acta* **1980**, *45*, 83.
[37] Chatterjee, C.; Cooksey, C. J.; Tobe, M. L. To be submitted. **1983**.
[38] Ahmed, E.; Tobe, M. L. *Inorg. Chem.* **1976**, *15*, 2635.
[39] Frost, A. A.; Pearson, R. G. "Kinetics and Mechanism", 2nd Edn, Wiley: New York, 1961; p. 213.
[40] Poon, C. K.; Tobe, M. L. *Chem. Commun.* **1968**, 156.
[41] Marangoni, G.; Panayotou, M.; Tobe, M. L. *J. Chem. Soc. Dalton Trans.* **1973**, 1989.
[42] Ahmed, E.; Tobe, M. L. *Inorg. Chem.* **1974**, *13*, 2956.
[43] Frost, A. A.; Pearson, R. G. "Kinetics and Mechanisms"; 2nd Edn, Wiley: New York, 1961; p. 230.

[44] Dixon, N. E.; Jackson, W. G.; Marty, W.; Sargeson, A. M. *Inorg. Chem.* **1982**, *21*, 688.
[45] Buckingham, D. A.; Clark, C. R.; Webley, W. S. *Aust. J. Chem.* **1980**, *33*, 263.
[46] Jordan, R. B.; Taube, H. *J. Amer. Chem. Soc.* **1966**, *88*, 4406.
[47] Ohyoshi, A.; Sakamoto, H.; Makino, H.; Hamada, K. *Bull. Chem. Soc. Jap.* **1975**, *48*, 3179.
[48] Bailar, J. C., Jr; Auten, R. W. *J. Amer. Chem. Soc.* **1934**, *56*, 774.
[49] Dittmar, E. A.; Archer, R. D. *J. Amer. Chem. Soc.* **1968**, *90*, 1468.
[50] Kwak, W. S.; Archer, R. D. *Inorg. Chem.* **1976**, *15*, 986.
[51] Chan, S. C.; Tobe, M. L. *J. Chem. Soc.* **1963**, 966.
[52] Pearson, R. G.; Edgington, D. N. *J. Amer. Chem. Soc.* **1962**, *84*, 4607.
[53] Green, M.; Taube, H. *Inorg. Chem.* **1963**, *2*, 948.
[54] Green, M.; Taube, H. *J. Phys. Chem.* **1963**, *67*, 1565.
[55] Basolo, F.; Pearson, R. G. "Mechanisms of Inorganic Reactions"; 1st Edn, Wiley: New York, 1958; p. 97.
[56] Basolo, F.; Pearson, R. G.; Schmidtke, H. H. *J. Amer. Chem. Soc.* **1960**, *82*, 4434.
[57] Panunzi, A.; Basolo, F. *Inorg. Chim. Acta* **1967**, *1*, 223.
[58] Langford, C. H. *Inorg. Chem.* **1965**, *4*, 265.
[59] Swaddle, T. W.; Gustalla, G. *Inorg. Chem.* **1969**, *8*, 1604.
[60] Haim, A. *Inorg. Chem.* **1970**, *9*, 426.
[61] House, D. A. *Coord. Chem. Rev.* **1977**, *23*, 223.
[62] Lenz, E.; Murmann, R. K. *Inorg. Chem.* **1968**, *7*, 1880.
[63] Jordan, R. B.; Taube, H. *J. Amer. Chem. Soc.* **1964**, *86*, 3891.
[64] Balt, S.; Dekker, C. *Inorg. Chem.* **1976**, *15*, 1025.
[65] Lincoln, S. F.; Jayne, J.; Hunt, J. P. *Inorg. Chem.* **1969**, *8*, 2267.
[66] Takemoto, J. H.; Jones, M. M. *J. Inorg. Nucl. Chem.* **1970**, *32*, 175.
[67] Newton, A. M.; Swaddle, T. W. *Can. J. Chem.* **1974**, *52*, 2751.
[68] Banerjea, D. *J. Inorg. Nucl. Chem.* **1967**, *29*, 2795.
[69] Angerman, N. S.; Jordan, R. B. *Inorg. Chem.* **1967**, *6*, 1376.
[70] Dash, A. C.; Nanda, R. K. *J. Inorg. Nucl. Chem.* **1976**, *38*, 119.
[71] Banerjea, D.; Dasgupta, T. P. *J. Inorg. Nucl. Chem.* **1965**, *27*, 2617.
[72] Dash, A. C.; Nanda, R. K. *Inorg. Chem.* **1974**, *13*, 655.
[73] Lalor, G. C.; Moelwyn-Hughes, E. A. *J. Chem. Soc.* **1963**, 1560.
[74] Gay, D. L.; Lalor, G. C. *J. Chem. Soc. A* **1966**, 1179.
[75] Campbell, M. B. M.; Wendt, M. R.; Monk, C. B. *J. Chem. Soc. Dalton Trans.* **1972**, 1714.
[76] Monacelli, F.; Basolo, F.; Pearson, R. G. *J. Inorg. Nucl. Chem.* **1962**, *24*, 1241.
[77] Angerman, N. S.; Jordan, R. B. *Inorg. Chem.* **1967**, *6*, 379.
[78] Kuroda, K. *Nippon Kagaku Zasshi* **1961**, *82*, 572.
[79] Chan, S. C.; Hui, K. Y.; Miller, J.; Tang, W. S. *J. Chem. Soc.* **1965**, 3207.
[80] Swaddle, T. W.; Jones, W. E. *Can. J. Chem.* **1970**, *48*, 1054.
[81] Po, L. L.; Jordan, R. B. *Inorg. Chem.* **1968**, *7*, 526.
[82] Monacelli, F. *Inorg. Chim. Acta* **1973**, *7*, 65.
[83] Buckingham, D. A.; Creaser, I. I.; Sargeson, A. M. *Inorg. Chem.* **1970**, *9*, 655.
[84] Reynolds, W. L.; Murati, I.; Asperger, S. *J. Chem. Soc. Dalton Trans.* **1974**, 719.
[85] Yalman, R. G. *Inorg. Chem.* **1967**, *1*, 16.
[86] Buckingham, D. A.; Cresswell, P. J.; Jackson, W. G.; Sargeson, A. M. *Inorg. Chem.* **1981**, *20*, 1647.
[87] Schmidt, W.; Taube, H. *Inorg. Chem.* **1963**, *2*, 698.
[88] Dasgupta, T. P.; Fitzgerald, W.; Tobe, M. L. *Inorg. Chem.* **1972**, *11*, 2046.

[89] Inoue, T.; Harris, G. M. *Inorg. Chem.* **1980**, *19*, 1091.
[90] Staples, P. J.; Tobe, M. L. *J. Chem. Soc.* **1960**, 4803.
[91] Dash, A. C.; Mohapatra, S. K. *J. Chem. Soc. Dalton Trans.* **1977**, 246.
[92] Dash, A. C.; Mohapatra, S. K. *J. Inorg. Nucl. Chem.* **1978**, *40*, 1596.
[93] Tobe, M. L.; Williams, C. K. *Inorg. Chem.* **1976**, *15*, 918.
[94] Chan, S. C.; Tobe, M. L. *J. Chem. Soc.* **1963**, 514.
[95] Chan, S. C.; Cheng, C. Y.; Leh, F. *J. Chem. Soc. A* **1967**, 1856.
[96] Chan, S. C.; Chan, S. F. *J. Chem. Soc. A* **1969**, 202.
[97] Chan, S. C.; Lee, C. L. *J. Chem. Soc. A* **1969**, 2649.
[98] Panasyuk, V. D.; Reiter, G. L.; Maiboroda, N. G. *Ukr. Khim. Zhur.* **1967**, *33*, 9.
[99] Chan, S. C. *J. Chem. Soc.* **1963**, 5137.
[100] Chan, S. C.; Leh, F. *J. Chem. Soc. A* **1966**, 134.
[101] Hay, R. W.; Crop, P. L. *J. Chem. Soc. A* **1969**, 42.
[102] Nolan, K. B.; Soudi, A. A. *J. Chem. Res.* (*S*) **1979**, 130.
[103] Ford, P. D.; Nolan, K. J. *J. Chem. Res.* (*S*) **1979**, 220.
[104] Basolo, F.; Pearson, R. G. "Mechanisms of Inorganic Reactions"; 2nd Edn, Wiley: New York, 1967; p. 186.
[105] Buckingham, D. A.; Foxman, B. M.; Sargeson, A. M. *Inorg. Chem.* **1970**, *9*, 1790.
[106] Couldwell, M. C.; House, D. A. *Inorg. Chem.* **1972**, *11*, 2024.
[107] Cooksey, C. J.; Tobe, M. L. *Inorg. Chem.* **1978**, *17*, 1558.
[108] Chan, S. C.; Tobe, M. L. *J. Chem. Soc.* **1963**, 5700.
[109] Chettle, C.; Tobe, M. L. Unpublished results.
[110] Jonassen, I. R.; Murray, R. S.; Stranks, D. R.; Yandell, Y. K. *Proc. Int. Conf. Coord. Chem.* **1969**, *12*, 32.
[111] Poon, C. K.; Tobe, M. L. *J. Chem. Soc. A* **1967**, 2069.
[112] Ni, T. L.; Garner, C. S. *Inorg. Chem.* **1967**, *6*, 1071.
[113] Anderson, B. F.; Bell, J. D.; Buckingham, D. A.; Cresswell, P. J.; Gainsford, G. J.; Marzilli, L. G.; Robertson, G. B.; Sargeson, A. M. *Inorg. Chem.* **1977**, *16*, 3233.
[114] House, D. A.; Blunt, J. W. *Inorg. Chim. Acta* **1981**, *49*, 193.
[115] Lee, W. K.; Poon, C. K. *Inorg. Chem.* **1973**, *12*, 2016.
[116] Hay, R. W.; House, D. A. *Inorg. Chim. Acta* **1976**, *38*, 2118.
[117] Huan, T. K.; Mulvihill, J. N.; Gainsford, A. R.; House, D. A. *Inorg. Chem.* **1973**, *12*, 1517.
[118] Dong, L. S.; House, D. A. *Inorg. Chim. Acta* **1976**, *19*, 23.
[119] House, D. A.; Gainsford, A. R.; Blunt, J. W. *Inorg. Chim. Acta* **1982**, *57*, 141.
[120] Buckingham, D. A.; Marzilli, P. A.; Sargeson, A. M. *Inorg. Chem.* **1969**, *8*, 1595.
[121] Hay, R. W.; Nolan, K. B. *J. Inorg. Nucl. Chem.* **1976**, *38*, 2118.
[122] Ha, F. A.; House, D. A. *Inorg. Chim. Acta* **1980**, *38*, 167.
[123] Graham, L. R.; Lawrance, G. A.; Sargeson, A. M. *Aust. J. Chem.* **1982**, *35*, 1119.
[124] Poon, C. K.; Tong, H. W. *J. Chem. Soc. Dalton Trans.* **1974**, 1.
[125] Mok, K. S.; Poon, C. K.; Tong, H. W. *J. Chem. Soc. Dalton Trans.* **1972**, 1701.
[126] Lui, C. K.; Poon, C. K. *J. Chem. Soc. Dalton Trans.* **1972**, 216.
[127] Poon, C. K.; Tong, H. W. *J. Chem. Soc. Dalton Trans.* **1973**, 1301.
[128] Poon, C. K. PhD Thesis. University of London, **1967**, p. 158.
[129] Poon, C. K. PhD Thesis. University of London, **1967**, p. 167.
[130] Poon, C. K.; Mak, P. W. *J. Chem. Soc. Dalton Trans.* **1978**, 216.
[131] Mak, P. W.; Poon, C. K. *Inorg. Chem.* **1976**, *15*, 1949.
[132] Kernohan, J. A.; Endicott, J. F. *Inorg. Chem.* **1970**, *9*, 1504.
[133] Lee, W. K.; Poon, C. K. *J. Chem. Soc. Dalton Trans.* **1974**, 2423.

[134] Hay, R. W.; Lawrence, G. A. *J. Chem. Soc. Dalton Trans.* **1975**, 1556.
[135] Poon, C. K.; Wong, C. L.; Mak, P. W. *J. Chem. Soc. Dalton Trans.* **1977**, 1931.
[136] Poon, C. K.; Wong, C. L. *J. Chem. Soc. Dalton Trans.* **1977**, 523.
[137] Hay, R. W.; Norman, P. R.; House, D. A.; Poon, C. K. *Inorg. Chim. Acta* **1981**, *48*, 81.
[138] Lichtig, J.; Sosa, M. E.; Tobe, M. L. In press. **1983**.
[139] Lalor, G. C.; Carrington, T. *J. Chem. Soc. A* **1969**, 2509.
[140] Lalor, G. C.; Carrington, T. *J. Chem. Soc. Dalton Trans.* **1972**, 55.
[141] Johnson, R. C.; Basolo, F.; Pearson, R. G. *J. Inorg. Nucl. Chem.* **1962**, *24*, 59.
[142] Gillard, R. G. *Coord. Chem. Rev.* **1975**, *16*, 67.
[143] Hay, R. W.; Bembi, R. *Inorg. Chim. Acta* **1982**, *62*, 89.
[144] Pearson, R. G.; Munson, R. A.; Basolo, F. *J. Amer. Chem. Soc.* **1958**, *80*, 504.
[145] Wheeler, W. D.; Kaizaki, S.; Legg, J. I. *Inorg. Chem.* **1982**, *21*, 3248.
[146] Parris, M.; Wallace, W. J. *Can. J. Chem.* **1969**, *47*, 2257.
[147] Mitzner, R.; Depkat, W. *Z. Phys. Chem. (Leipzig)* **1973**, *254*, 189.
[148] Levine, M. A.; Jones, T. P.; Harris, W. E.; Wallace, W. J. *J. Amer. Chem. Soc.* **1961**, *83*, 2453.
[149] Guastalla, G.; Swaddle, T. W. *Can. J. Chem.* **1974**, *52*, 527.
[150] Dawson, B. S.; House, D. A. *Inorg. Chem.* **1977**, *16*, 1354.
[151] Campi, E.; Ferguson, J.; Tobe, M. L. *Inorg. Chem.* **1970**, *9*, 1781.
[152] House, D. A.; Hay, R. W. *Inorg. Chim. Acta* **1981**, *54*, L145.
[153] Yang, D.; House, D. A. *Inorg. Chem.* **1982**, *21*, 2999.
[154] Olsen, D. C.; Garner, C. S. *Inorg. Chem.* **1963**, *2*, 558.
[155] Garner, C. S.; House, D. A. *In* "Transition Metal Chemistry", Vol. 6; Carlin, R. J., Ed.; **1970**, p. 216.
[156] Bushnell, G. W.; Lalor, G. C.; Moelwyn-Hughes, E. A. *J. Chem. Soc. A* **1966**, 719.
[157] Chan, S. C. *Aust. J. Chem.* **1967**, *20*, 61.
[158] Johnson, S. A.; Basolo, F.; Pearson, R. G. *J. Amer. Chem. Soc.* **1963**, *85*, 1741.
[159] Hay, R. W.; Norman, P. R. *J. Chem. Soc. Dalton Trans.* **1979**, 1441.
[160] Hancock, M. P.; Heaton, B. T.; Vaughan, D. H. *J. Chem. Soc. Dalton Trans.* **1979**, 761.
[161] Pöe, A. J.; Vuik, C. P. J. *J. Chem. Soc. Dalton Trans.* **1976**, 661.
[162] Chung, H. L.; Bounsall, E. J. *Can. J. Chem.* **1978**, *56*, 709.
[163] Fitzgerald, W. R.; Tobe, M. L. Unpublished results.
[164] Poon, C. K.; Tang, T. W.; Lau, T. C. *J. Chem. Soc. Dalton Trans.* **1981**, 2556.
[165] Poon, C. K.; Tang, T. W.; Lau, T. C. *J. Chem. Soc. Dalton Trans.* **1982**, 865.
[166] Poon, C. K.; Kwong, S. S.; Che, C. M.; Kan, Y. P. *J. Chem. Soc. Dalton Trans.* **1982**, 1457.
[167] Poon, C. K.; Lau, T. C.; Che, C. M. *J. Chem. Soc. Dalton Trans.* **1982**, 531.
[168] Broomhead, J. A.; Kane-Maguire, L. *Inorg. Chem.* **1968**, *7*, 2519.
[169] Broomhead, J. A.; Kane-Maguire, L. *Inorg. Chem.* **1969**, *8*, 2124.
[170] Poon, C. K.; Isabirye, D. A. *J. Chem. Soc. Dalton Trans.* **1977**, 2115.
[171] Poon, C. K.; Isabirye, D. A. *J. Chem. Soc. Dalton Trans.* **1978**, 740.
[172] Poon, C. K. Personal communication. **1982**.
[173] Waysbort, D.; Navon, G. *Inorg. Chem.* **1979**, *18*, 9.
[174] Anderson, J. S.; James, F. W.; Briscoe, H. V. A. *Nature* **1937**, *139*, 109.
[175] Anderson, J. S.; Spoor, N. L.; Briscoe, H. V. A. *Nature* **1937**, *139*, 508.
[176] Anderson, J. S.; Briscoe, H. V. A.; Spoor, N. L. *J. Chem. Soc.* **1943**, 361.
[177] Block, H.; Gold, V. *J. Chem. Soc.* **1959**, 966.

[178] Palmer, J. W.; Basolo, F. *J. Phys. Chem.* **1960**, *64*, 778.
[179] Basolo, F.; Palmer, J. W.; Pearson, R. G. *J. Amer. Chem. Soc.* **1960**, *82*, 1073.
[180] Palmer, J. W.; Basolo, F. *J. Inorg. Nucl. Chem.* **1960**, *15*, 279.
[181] Clifton, P.; Pratt, L. *Proc. Chem. Soc.* **1963**, 339.
[182] Parris, M. *J. Chem. Soc. A* **1967**, 383.
[183] Buckingham, D. A.; Durham, L.; Sargeson, A. M. *Aust. J. Chem.* **1967**, *20*, 257.
[184] Buckingham, D. A.; Olsen, I. I.; Sargeson, A. M. *Aust. J. Chem.* **1967**, *20*, 597.
[185] Halpern, B.; Sargeson, A. M.; Turnbull, K. R. *J. Amer. Chem. Soc.* **1966**, *88*, 4630.
[186] Buckingham, D. A.; Marzilli, L. G.; Sargeson, A. M. *J. Amer. Chem. Soc.* **1967**, *89*, 3428.
[187] Buckingham, D. A.; Marzilli, L. G.; Sargeson, A. M. *Inorg. Chem.* **1968**, *7*, 915.
[188] Buckingham, D. A.; Marzilli, L. G.; Sargeson, A. M. *J. Amer. Chem. Soc.* **1968**, *90*, 6028.
[189] Sakaguchi, U.; Maeda, K.; Yoneda, H. *Bull. Chem. Soc. Jap.* **1976**, *49*, 397.
[190] Bramley, R.; Creaser, I. I.; Mackey, D. J.; Sargeson, A. M. *Inorg. Chem.* **1978**, *17*, 244.
[191] Nakazawa, H.; Sakaguchi, U.; Yoneda, H.; Morimoto, Y. *Inorg. Chem.* **1981**, *20*, 973.
[192] Sosa, M. E.; Tobe, M. L. In press.
[193] Millen, W. A.; Watts, D. W. *Aust. J. Chem.* **1966**, *19*, 43.
[194] Tinner, U.; Marty, W. *Helv. Chim. Acta* **1977**, *60*, 1629.
[195] Waysbort, D.; Navon, G. *J. Phys. Chem.* **1973**, *77*, 960.
[196] Grunwald, E.; Fong, D. W. *J. Amer. Chem. Soc.* **1972**, *94*, 7371.
[197] Dagnall, S.; Hancock, M. R.; Heaton, B. T.; Vaughan, D. H. *J. Chem. Soc. Dalton Trans.* **1977**, 1111.
[198] Hay, R. W.; Tajik, M.; Norman, P. R. *J. Chem. Soc. Dalton Trans.* **1979**, 636.
[199] Dash, A. C.; Mohapatra, S. K. *J. Chem. Soc. Dalton Trans.* **1977**, 1207.
[200] Hay, R. W.; Norman, P. R. *Transition Metal Chem.* **1981**, *6*, 4.
[201] Baldwin, M. E.; Chan, S. C.; Tobe, M. L. *J. Chem. Soc.* **1961**, 4637.
[202] Goodall, D. M.; Hardy, M. J. *J. Chem. Soc. Chem. Commun.* **1975**, 919.
[203] Pearson, R. G.; Basolo, F. *J. Amer. Chem. Soc.* **1956**, *78*, 4878.
[204] Chan, S. C. *J. Chem. Soc. A* **1967**, 2103.
[205] Navon, G.; Panigel, R.; Meyerstein, D. *Inorg. Chim. Acta* **1972**, *6*, 299.
[206] Wilinski, J.; Kurland, R. J. *Inorg. Chem.* **1973**, *12*, 2202.
[207] Adamson, A. W.; Basolo, F. *Acta Chem. Scand.* **1955**, *9*, 1261.
[208] Hay, R. W.; Barnes, D. J. *J. Chem. Soc. A* **1970**, 3337.
[209] Buckingham, D. A.; Clark, C. R.; Lewis, T. W. *Inorg. Chem.* **1979**, *18*, 2041.
[210] Henderson, R. A. PhD Thesis. University of London, **1976**, p. 139.
[211] Chatterjee, C.; Humanes, M.; Tobe, M. L. Unpublished results.
[212] House, D. A.; Nor, O. *Inorg. Chim. Acta* **1983**, *70*, 13.
[213] Poon, C. K. *Coord. Chem. Rev.* **1973**, *10*, 1.
[214] Stranks, D. R.; Yandell, J. K. *Inorg. Chem.* **1970**, *9*, 751.
[215] Baldwin, M. E.; Tobe, M. L. *J. Chem. Soc.* **1960**, 4275.
[216] Tobe, M. L. *Inorg. Chem.* **1968**, *7*, 1260.
[217] Henderson, R. A.; Tobe, M. L. *Inorg. Chem.* **1977**, *16*, 2576.
[218] Buckingham, D. A.; Olsen, I. I.; Sargeson, A. M. *J. Amer. Chem. Soc.* **1968**, *90*, 6539.
[219] Buckingham, D. A.; Olsen, I. I.; Sargeson, A. M. *J. Amer. Chem. Soc.* **1967**, *89*, 5129.
[220] Nordmeyer, F. R. *Inorg. Chem.* **1969**, *8*, 2780.

[221] MacDonald, D. J.; Garner, C. S. *Inorg. Chem.* **1962**, *1*, 20.
[222] Kruse, W.; Taube, H. *J. Amer. Chem. Soc.* **1961**, *83*, 1280.
[223] Jackson, W. G. *Inorg. Chim. Acta* **1974**, *10*, 51.
[224] Poon, C. K.; Tobe, M. L. *Inorg. Chem.* **1968**, *11*, 2398.
[225] Mok, K. S.; Poon, C. K. *Inorg. Chem.* **1971**, *10*, 225.
[226] Basolo, F.; Bergmann, J. G.; Meeker, R. E.; Pearson, R. G. *J. Amer. Chem. Soc.* **1956**, *78*, 2676.
[227] Hoffmann, R.; Rossi, A. R. *Inorg. Chem.* **1975**, *14*, 365.
[228] Basolo, F.; Pearson, R. G. "Mechanisms of Inorganic Reactions"; 2nd Edn, Wiley: New York, 1967; p. 174.
[229] Buckingham, D. A.; Clark, C. R.; Lewis, T. W. *Inorg. Chem.* **1979**, *18*, 1985.
[230] Buckingham, D. A.; Marzilli, L. G.; Sargeson, A. M. *J. Amer. Chem. Soc.* **1967**, *89*, 825.
[231] Poon, C. K.; Tong, H. W. *J. Chem. Soc. Dalton Trans.* **1974**, 930.
[232] Ahmed, E.; Tucker, M. L.; Tobe, M. L. *Inorg. Chem.* **1975**, *14*, 1.
[233] Buckingham, D. A.; Dwyer, M.; Sargeson, A. M.; Watson, K. J. *Acta Chem. Scand.* **1972**, *26*, 2813.
[234] Buckingham, D. A.; Clark, C. R.; Foxman, B. M.; Gainsford, G. J.; Sargeson, A. M.; Wein, M.; Zanella, A. *Inorg. Chem.* **1982**, *21*, 1986.
[235] Comba, P.; Marty, W. *Helv. Chim. Acta* **1980**, *63*, 693.
[236] Bosnich, B.; Gillard, R. D.; McKenzie, E. D.; Webb, G. A. *J. Chem. Soc. A* **1966**, 1331.
[237] Hamilton, H. G.; Alexander, M. D. *J. Amer. Chem. Soc.* **1967**, *89*, 5065.
[238] Niththyananthan, R.; Tobe, M. L. *Inorg. Chem.* **1969**, *8*, 1589.
[239] Garnett, P. J.; Watts, D. W. *Inorg. Chim. Acta* **1974**, *8*, 307.
[240] Sargeson, A. M.; Searle, G. H. *Inorg. Chem.* **1967**, *6*, 2172.
[241] Jackman, T. A.; Worrell, J. H. *J. Amer. Chem. Soc.* **1971**, *93*, 1044.
[242] Tobe, M. L.; Tucker, M. L. *Inorg. Chem.* **1973**, *12*, 2994.
[243] Buckingham, D. A.; Marty, W.; Sargeson, A. M. *Helv. Chim. Acta* **1978**, *61*, 2223.
[244] Barefield, E. K.; Mocella, M. T. *J. Amer. Chem. Soc.* **1975**, *97*, 4238.
[245] Barefield, E. K.; Lovecchio, F. V.; Tokel, N. E.; Ochiai, E.; Busch, D. H. *Inorg. Chem.* **1972**, *11*, 283.
[246] Goedken, V. L.; Busch, D. H. *J. Amer. Chem. Soc.* **1972**, *94*, 7355.
[247] Diamond, S. E.; Taube, H. *J. Amer. Chem. Soc.* **1975**, *97*, 2661.
[248] Poon, C. K.; Che, C. M. *J. Chem. Soc. Dalton Trans.* **1981**, 1019.
[249] Endicott, J. F.; Lilie, J.; Kuszaj, J. M.; Ramaswamy, B. S.; Schmonsees, W. G.; Simic, M. G.; Glick, M. D.; Rilemma, D. P. *J. Amer. Chem. Soc.* **1977**, *99*, 429.
[250] Sargeson, A. M. *Pure Appl. Chem.* **1973**, *33*, 527.
[251] Buckingham, D. A.; Olsen, I. I.; Sargeson, A. M. *J. Amer. Chem. Soc.* **1966**, *88*, 5443.
[252] Buckingham, D. A.; Edwards, J. D.; McLaughlin, G. M. *Inorg. Chem.* **1982**, *21*, 2770.
[253] Jackson, W. G.; Begbie, C. M. *Inorg. Chem.* **1981**, *20*, 1654.
[254] Buckingham, D. A.; Creaser, I. I.; Marty, W.; Sargeson, A. M. *Inorg. Chem.* **1972**, *11*, 2738.
[255] Boreham, C. J.; Buckingham, D. A.; Clark, C. R. *Inorg. Chem.* **1979**, *18*, 1990.
[256] Baranaik, E. PhD Thesis. Australian National University, **1973**.
[257] Tobe, M. L.; Schwab, A. P.; Romeo, R. *Inorg. Chem.* **1982**, *21*, 1185.
[258] Pearson, R. G.; Basolo, F. *Inorg. Chem.* **1965**, *4*, 1522.
[259] Green, M. *J. Chem. Soc. A* **1967**, 762.

[260] Fenemore, D.; House, D. A. *J. Inorg. Nucl. Chem.* **1976**, *38*, 1559.
[261] Jordan, R. B.; Sargeson, A. M. *Inorg. Chem.* **1965**, *4*, 433.
[262] Buckingham, D. A.; Olsen, I. I.; Sargeson, A. M. *J. Amer. Chem. Soc.* **1968**, *90*, 6654.
[263] Buckingham, D. A.; Cresswell, P. J.; Sargeson, A. M. *Inorg. Chem.* **1975**, *14*, 1485.
[264] Fenemore, D.; House, D. A. *Int. J. Chem. Kinet.* **1976**, *8*, 573.
[265] Edwards, J. O.; Monacelli, F.; Ortaggi, G. *Inorg. Chim. Acta* **1974**, *11*, 47.
[266] Henderson, R. A. PhD Thesis. University of London, **1976**, p. 190.
[267] McKenzie, J.; House, D. A. *J. Inorg. Nucl. Chem.* **1977**, *39*, 1843.
[268] House, D. A.; Norman, P. R.; Hay, R. W. *Inorg. Chim. Acta* **1980**, *45*, L117.
[269] Drew, M. G. B.; Hollis, S. *Inorg. Chim. Acta* **1978**, *29*, L231.

Substitution Reactions of Divalent and Trivalent Metal Ions

T. W. Swaddle

Department of Chemistry,
The University of Calgary

I. INTRODUCTION

"There is something fascinating about science. One gets such wholesale returns of conjecture out of such a trifling investment of fact."
Mark Twain, *Life on the Mississippi*, 1874

This review presents a personal assessment of the status quo in the study of ligand substitution dynamics in simple metal-ion complexes. It is not intended to be comprehensive or exhaustive. In particular, complexes with macrocyclic ligands[1] have generally been excluded since properties of the ligand system often modify the characteristics of the metal-ion centre beyond recognition. Ions of elements of the main periodic groups I–III and oxo-metal complexes have been dealt with in the first volume of this series.[2,3] Apart from organochromium(III) aqua-ions[4] and complexes of the type $(\eta^6\text{-}C_6H_6)M(OH_2)_3{}^{2+}$ (M = Ru or Os),[5] organometallics can be ignored in the context of ordinary ionic solution chemistry, and accordingly attention is concentrated upon Werner complexes of di- and trivalent transition metals.

Burgess, in the closing passages of his 1978 book on metal ions,[6] intimated that the mechanisms of reaction of such ions were already well understood. This remark may have been premature; recently, some substantial cracks have appeared in the edifice of our tidy notions of a decade ago. Consider, for example, the much-studied 'paradigm' system of cobalt(III) complexes. A key experimental observation underlying the classic Haim-Wilmarth argument for assigning an S_N1 limiting[7] or extreme dissociative D[8] mechanism to water substitution in aqueous $Co(CN)_5OH_2{}^{2-}$ [9] has recently been successfully[10] challenged by Burnett and Gilfillan.[11] Fresh controversy rages over the question of the existence or longevity of common intermediates of reduced coordination number in 'induced' aquation (including base hydrolysis)[12−18] of cobalt(III) ammines and related complexes — an issue once thought clearly settled by a variety of studies, notably competition methods. The long-accepted 'rule' that complexes of the type cis-$Co(en)_2AX^{z+}$ undergo aquation stereoretentively has been shown to be entirely wrong.[19] Although the striking conjugate base effect in substitution reactions of Co(III) ammine-type complexes is customarily interpreted in terms of π-bonding from amido-N to Co,[7,20] the typical conjugate base acceleration is still observed in a complex in which such π-bonding should be suppressed.[21] According to the dissociative interchange mechanism,[8] which is almost universally accepted as describing reactions of the type

$$Co(NH_3)_5(sol)^{3+} + X^{x-} \underset{k_{sol}}{\overset{k_{an}}{\rightleftharpoons}} Co(NH_3)_5X^{(3-x)+} + sol \qquad (1)$$

where sol represents the solvent, one expects the pseudo-first-order anation rate constant k_{an} to be a non-linear function of $[X^{x-}]$ (in excess), according to the equations (2) and (3)

$$Co(NH_3)_5(sol)^{3+} + X^{x-} \xrightleftharpoons{K_{IP}} \text{ion pair} \xrightarrow{k_i} Co(NH_3)_5X^{(3-x)+} + sol \quad (2)$$

$$k_{an} = k_i K_{IP}[X^{x-}]/(1 + K_{IP}[X^{x-}]) \tag{3}$$

and that k_i will be less than the solvent exchange rate constant k_{ex} (strictly, k_{ex} within the ion pair, k_{exip}). Yet k_{an} is said to be strictly a linear function of $[X^{x-}]$ in some cases where clearly-discernible curvature would be expected[22,23] (e.g. for $X^{n-} = SO_4^{2-}$ in water, for which K_{IP} is independently known[24]). Furthermore, for some anation reactions (1) when sol = N,N-dimethyl-formamide (DMF)[25] or dimethylsulfoxide (DMSO)[26,27] where ion pairing according to equation (3) is clearly evident, k_i exceeds k_{ex}. Finally, it is not clear why, if the mode of activation of reaction (1) is so typically dissociative, the volume of activation for water exchange ($X^{n-} = $ sol = H_2O) should be only $+1.2$ cm^3 mol^{-1}[28] as against $+5.8$ for *trans*-Co(en)$_2$(OH$_2$)$_2^{3+}$,[29] $+7.2$ for the Ni(H$_2$O)$_6^{2+}$-water exchange (said to be typically I$_d$),[30] and $\sim +7$ cm^3 mol^{-1} on general theoretical considerations.[31-34]

For cationic complexes of trivalent ions other than cobalt(III), the suggestion[35] that associative activation may be the norm, i.e. that cobalt(III) ammines and related complexes are actually anomalous, seems to be valid (see below). It was *not* anticipated,[35] however, that the mode of activation for substitution in M(sol)$_6^{2+}$ might change from dissociative for M = Ni towards associative (I$_a$) for M = Mn and V, as the volumes of activation for the solvent exchange reactions imply,[30,32,33,36-40] since Mn^{2+} seems to react at much the same rate with all incoming ligands in a given solvent[30]—that is, the traditional "Eigen–Wilkins" (or I$_d$)[8] mechanism would have seemed appropriate for all M^{2+} including Mn^{2+}. The reasons for this inconsistency in mechanistic assignment, and for similar problems with Cr(III)[35,41-45] and Rh(III)[35,45-48] pentaammine complexes, stem from the limitations of mechanistic classification schemes,[45] and one of the objectives of this review is to examine how and why attempts to fit experimental observations to the Procrustean bed of mechanistic models can lead to sterile debate. It remains our view[35] that the task at hand is to attempt to understand the *kinetic properties* of metal-ion complexes, since these influence their chemistries profoundly; any mechanistic modelling should be merely ancillary to this basic aim.

II. THE STRUCTURE OF METAL IONS IN SOLUTION: KINETIC CONSEQUENCES

A. Primary solvation

Burgess remarked in 1978[6] that there was "still much ignorance on the fundamental question of solvation numbers and the nature of cation-solvent interactions". Recently, however, X-ray methods (diffraction[49-58] and EXAFS[59,60]) have confirmed and extended NMR results[6,61] to give an adequate picture of the primary and, to a lesser extent, the outer coordination spheres of many cations in solution.

Furthermore, our recent work[34] has shown that for aqueous metal ions M^{z+} the absolute partial molar volumes at infinite dilution $\bar{V}^0_{abs}$ (which we define relative to $\bar{V}^0_{abs} = -5.4\,cm^3\,mol^{-1}$ for $H^+(aq)$[62] at 298.2 K) can provide useful information about ion solvation including a surprisingly accurate measure of the primary solvation number n. As suggested by Akitt,[63] a major component in $\bar{V}^0_{abs}$ is the loss of volume when n molecules of bulk solvent water are transferred to the first coordination sphere of M^{z+}. In the limiting cases, these waters (which can be regarded as spheres of radius 138 pm) could become tetrahedrally closest-packed (cp) around an ion of radius $r_M = 31$ pm, octahedrally cp around M^{z+} of $r_M = 57$ pm, or simple-cubically cp for $r_M = 101$ pm. Thus, from simple notions of solid-state structure, we can calculate the effective molar volume of a coordinated water in the first two cases (face-centred cubic array fragments) as $8.95\,cm^3\,mol^{-1}$, and $12.66\,cm^3\,mol^{-1}$ in the latter, as compared with $18.07\,cm^3\,mol^{-1}$ for free water. This generates contributions to $\bar{V}^0_{abs}$ of -36, -55 and $-43\,cm^3\,mol^{-1}$ for these limiting four-, six- and eight-coordinate cases—clearly, this is a major effect.

In fact, these hypothetical contributions are overestimates for most ions, which do not have *closest*-packed ligands, and even for the idealized limiting cases there will be a contribution from void-spaces generated by imperfect interfacing with bulk solvent structure. We allow for this, following crystallographic experience,[64] by putting the *effective* volume of the $M(H_2O)_n^{z+}$ core equal to that of a sphere of radius $(r_M + \Delta r)$, where Δr is to be determined empirically but can be expected to be essentially the same for all first coordination spheres of water. Addition of a term for the classical Drude–Nernst solvent electrostriction[62] from $(r_M + \Delta r)$ outwards completes equation (4), for r_M in pm, at 298.15 K and 0.1 MPa.

$$\bar{V}^0_{abs} = 2.523 \times 10^{-6}(r_M + \Delta r)^3 - 18.07n - 417.5z/(r_M + \Delta r) \qquad (4)$$

One can use reliable modern values of $\bar{V}^0_{abs}$[34,62] for a few M^{2+} and M^{3+} aqueous ions of well-characterized primary coordination number[6] together with Shannon's[65] ionic radii to obtain $\Delta r = 238.7 \pm 0.5$ pm. Our approach differs from Akitt's,[63] in at least two important respects: (i) Δr is *not* set equal to the diameter of an ordinary water molecule (276 pm; the difference amounts to some 30 cm³ mol⁻¹ in the calculation), and (ii) the Shannon radius[65] *for the appropriate coordination number n* is used for r_M (the difference between r_M values for successive coordination numbers is typically 4 to 7 pm). Its success can be judged from Fig. 1, in which the coordination numbers have been taken from what we consider to be reliable estimates[6,49-61] except for some alkali and alkaline earth ions and Th^{4+}, for which the rearranged equation (4) was first used to obtain an integral value of n that fitted the observed $\bar{V}^0_{abs}$ and r_M values best. The validity of deriving primary hydration numbers in this way can be judged from its effectiveness in distinguishing eight- from nine-coordinated aqueous lanthanoid(III) ions and in identifying those in whose

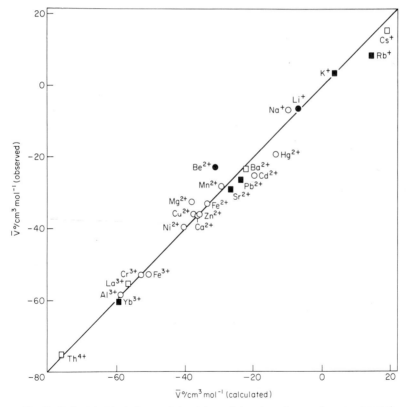

Fig. 1. Calculated and observed absolute partial molar volumes of aqueous metal ions at 298.15 K and infinite dilution, relative to $\bar{V}^0 = -5.4$ cm³ mol⁻¹ for H^+ (aq), according to equation (4). Primary coordination numbers are taken to be 4 (filled circles), 6 (open circles), 8 (filled squares) or 9 (open squares).

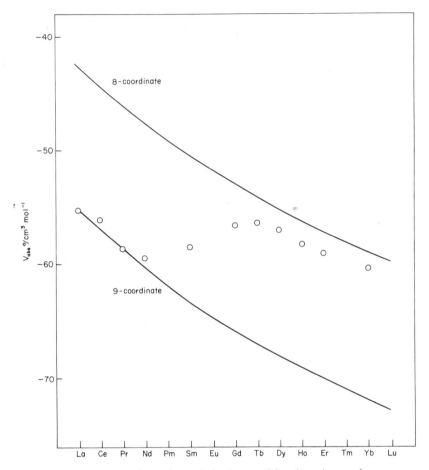

Fig. 2. Comparison of experimental absolute partial molar volumes of aqueous lanthanoid(III) ions[66] with the predictions of equation (4) for primary coordination numbers of eight and nine.

solutions *both* forms are present (Fig. 2; c.f. the suggestion of Spedding *et al.*,[66] who were, however, not in a position to predict $\bar{V}^0_{abs}$ values for the two n values); the agreement with recent X-ray results[57] is striking.

The results shown in Fig. 2 remind us that primary hydration numbers are not necessarily unique for a given M^{z+}(aq). Thus, for Ca^{2+}(aq), $\bar{V}^0_{abs}$ is -29.2 cm^3 mol^{-1}, while equation (4) predicts -15.3, -28.0 and -40.5 cm^3 mol^{-1} for $n = 6, 7$ and 8 respectively, but seven-coordination will be geometrically disfavoured for the spherically-symmetrical ion Ca^{2+} relative to a mixture of $Ca(H_2O)_6^{2+}$ and $Ca(H_2O)_8^{2+}$ (recently, this may have some relevance concerning[67] the coordination numbers of Ca^{2+} and its substitute Cd^{2+} in biological environments). The larger alkali and alkaline earth ions may similarly exist as mixtures of eight- and nine-coordinate species in water. Finally, there is spectroscopic evidence that, at high temperatures, significant concentrations of $Co(H_2O)_4^{2+}$(aq) are present along with $Co(H_2O)_6^{2+}$(aq) in aqueous cobalt(II) solutions.[68]

Equation (4) predicts that the primary hydration number of the aqueous proton ($r_M \sim 0$) is two, as expected if it occurs in a linear H-bond between two water molecules, and as is found, for example, in a solid containing the discrete ion $H_{13}O_6^+$.[69] Significantly, the trend in the enthalpies of the formation of $H(OH_2)_n^+$ from H_2O and $H(OH_2)_{(n-1)}^+$ in the gas phase, shows a sharp discontinuity when $n = 2$ and 3 (and, less dramatically, when $n = 4$ and 5).[70]

A significant feature of this analysis of partial molar volumes is that the last term in equation (4), representing the volume of electrostriction, is not very sensitive to the value of r_M. Typically, values of r_M are 80 ± 20 pm, so that $r_M + \Delta r$ can be set to 320 pm with 6% accuracy. The final term in equation (4) then can be reduced to $-1.305z^2$ cm^3 mol^{-1}, as in equation (5), where Δr has been slightly adjusted to improve the fit.

$$\bar{V}_{abs}^0 \approx 2.523 \times 10^{-6}(r_M + 238.5)^3 - 18.07n - 1.305z^2 \tag{5}$$

Equations (4) and (5) do not work for the d^6-spin-paired ion Rh^{3+}(aq);[34] evidently, crystal field effects lead to an even greater compaction than is reflected in the crystallographic ionic radius. Unfortunately, the other known spin-paired aqua ions (Co^{3+},[71] Ir^{3+},[72] Ru^{3+}[73] and Pt^{2+}[74]) present experimental difficulties, such as redox phenomena or the need to work with high excesses of acid, which hinder accurate measurement of their partial molar volumes to establish whether a separate correlation exists for low-spin aqua ions. For the aqua-complex-like ammines $M(NH_3)_5OH_2^{3+}$, however, $\bar{V}_{abs}^0$ correlates with r_M for the low-spin cases M = Co, Rh, Ir and Ru while the chromium(III) analogue is anomalous.[34]

B. Secondary solvation

The picture of M^{z+}(aq) which emerges from the success of equation (4) is one of a highly-structured first coordination sphere with as large a coordination number as possible, but with an outer region where solvent and counter ions are influenced in a basically electrostatic way, and where water has essentially its bulk dielectric properties. This is consistent with the Fuoss ion-pairing theory, as recently improved,[75] and with the Güntelberg extension[76] of the Debye–Hückel theory, which amounts to assuming a distance of closest approach to an aqueous metal ion of about 310 pm, which is much the same as the average effective radius of $M(H_2O)_n^{z+}$ from equation (4). The theoretical distance r_{MX} of closest approach of a second coordination sphere species X to the central atom in $M(H_2O)_n^{z+}$ along a three-fold interligand axis is given in pm by

$$r_{MX} = \{(r_M + 138)/\sqrt{3}\} + \sqrt{\{(r_X + 138)^2 - 2(r_M + 138)^2/3\}} \qquad (6)$$

where the water ligands and X are assumed to be hard spheres of radius 138 pm and r_X respectively. When X itself is water, r_{MX} ranges only from 338.0 to 333.2 pm over the entire theoretical range of stability of $M(H_2O)_6^{z+}$ $(57 \lesssim r_M \lesssim 101\ \text{pm})$, which indicates that (i) it is reasonable to equate the typical value of $r_M + \Delta r$ approximately with the distance of closest approach of secondary waters for purposes of qualitative discussion, and (ii) this distance of closest approach is insensitive to the identity of M^{z+}. Most of the eight possible closest-approach sites on typical $M(H_2O)_6^{z+}$ must, however, be vacant on a time-average basis, otherwise large negative z-independent terms analogous in origin to the first two on the right-hand side of equations (4) and (5) would be required to fit the experimental $\bar{V}_{abs}^0$ data, and this is not the case. The second and successive spheres of closest-packed solvation sites are evidently only partially and randomly populated and, in this sense, these regions may be regarded as relatively unstructured and amenable to treatment as a Born–Drude–Nernst continuous dielectric.   •

On the other hand, X-ray[49,53] and nmr[77] results suggest that ions such as $Cr(H_2O)_6^{3+}(aq)$ and $Al(H_2O)_6^{3+}(aq)$ interact with 12 outer-sphere water molecules through short, linear H bonds, the first-sphere waters being trigonally coordinated, and that this arrangement persists even in concentrated solutions where the relative concentration of water is low. This seems reasonable, since MO calculations have shown that 60–70% of the extra charge introduced on going from $M(H_2O)_6^{2+}(aq)$ to $M(H_2O)_6^{3+}(aq)$ must reside on the protons of the primary waters of hydration (though a roughly tetrahedral deployment of the electron pairs about the oxygens was thought likely[78]). Such H-bonded structures, however, will not be greatly different from those of the various ices or bulk liquid water, in terms of volume, and are consistent with equation (4). What the partial molar volume data do preclude are structures in which all (or even most) of the positions of closest approach to $M(H_2O)_n^{z+}$ (for $n = 6$, through the eight faces of the coordination octahedron) are occupied by water molecules in closest-packed fashion.

The average molar volume of all the waters hydrating a divalent metal ion has been variously estimated to be between 14.8 and 16.0 cm^3 mol^{-1}.[79-82] If the pressure dependence of ΔV^* for the aquation of $Co(NH_3)_5X^{(3-x)+}$ or $Cr(NH_3)_5X^{2+}$ is ascribed to solvational change alone, then the mean molar volume of the (outer coordination sphere) water of hydration in these complexes is 15.6 cm^3 mol^{-1}.[33] This last figure was derived with the assumption that the compressibility of solvating water is negligible relative to that of bulk water, and is therefore to be regarded as a lower limit, although

Stranks[83] has used Hush's potential function to calculate molar volumes of 15.0 and 15.6 cm^3 mol^{-1} for water in hypothetical second and third coordination spheres surrounding a $M(H_2O)_6^{3+}$ ion. It therefore seems fair to say that water molecules, when transferred from bulk solvent to the hydration sheath of a Werner complex ML_6^{3+}, are *on the average* subjected to an electrostatic pressure equivalent of ~ 500 MPa, and contract by ~ 2.5 cm^3 mol^{-1} in molar volume. Transfer of water from bulk solvent to the *first* coordination sphere of M, however, amounts to closest packing, in the limiting case, and would result in a contraction of up to 9.1 cm^3 mol^{-1}. These numbers provide useful guidelines in the analysis of volumes of activation for ligand substitution reactions; in particular, ΔV^* for simple dissociative aqua exchange may be set at $+9.1$ cm^3 mol^{-1}.[32–34]

C. Ion pairing

X-ray diffraction[49–55] and EXAFS[59,60] data on metal salt solutions cannot be fully analyzed without including some interactions other than those within the first coordination sphere, but the quantitive interpretation is often ambiguous. For example, a significant peak in the radial distribution functions is usually seen at 320 ± 10 pm and may well represent the closest approach of second-sphere waters of hydration to $M(H_2O)_n^{z+}$, as proposed above, but it could also represent Cl^-—OH_2 interactions if chlorides are used ($r_{Cl^-} = 181$ pm[65]). For $Fe(H_2O)_6^{3+}$ chloride solutions, the primary Fe—O distances are ~ 204 pm,[55] which confirms the validity of setting r_{H_2O} for coordinated water to 138 pm (since r_M is 64.5 pm for octahedral Fe^{3+}[65]), and a separation of ~ 410 pm is attributed to outer-sphere Fe—Cl interactions. Equation (6) gives 390 pm for the hard-sphere closest-packed $Fe(H_2O)_6^{3+}$—Cl^- interaction, while Akitt's model[63] of $Fe(H_2O)_6^{3+}$ as a sphere of radius $r_M + 2r_{H_2O}$ would suggest 522 pm. Thus, chloride ion seems to approach $Fe(H_2O)_6^{3+}$ along the three-fold interligand axes almost as closely as it possibly can, in the ion pair.

The significance of this, in the mechanistic context, is that the anion in an ordinary ion pair is probably ideally sited for attack on the central metal ion. It must, however, be borne in mind that specific hydrogen bonding or dipolar interactions could alter the anion's effectiveness as a nucleophile stereospecifically, particularly in non-aqueous[84] but also in aqueous[85] systems. Such specific effects would also invalidate the calculation of ion-pair formation constants by the Fuoss method, which is widely used to estimate K_{IP} and hence k_i values for reactions proceeding by presumed interchange mechanisms [equation (3)]. Even in apparently "simple" interchange reactions, such as in the $Fe(H_2O)_6^{3+}$—Cl^- ion pair discussed above, the Fuoss ion-pair formation constants may seem inconsistent with the kinetic data,[86] while the total lack of kinetic evidence for ion pairing in a recent study of reaction (1)[22] runs counter to spectrophotometric observations.[24]

It may be that an assemblage that counts as an ion pair conductimetrically or in the Fuoss theory may not be active kinetically or spectroscopically, for which closest approach of the anion to the ML_n^{z+} unit is probably necessary. Alternatively, ion pairing by the "inert" electrolytes (usually perchlorates), normally added to maintain constant ionic strength, may have to be taken into account. This latter possibility was considered in detail by Burnett,[87] and, although in a previous article[35] the counter-arguments of Barber and Reynolds[88] were endorsed, it now seems that Burnett's case has considerable merit.

The essential point is that, while perchlorate ion (or $CF_3SO_3^-$, or BF_4^-, etc.) may be assumed to have a negligible tendency to coordinate directly to the central metal ion in ML_n^{z+} in *dilute* solutions, it is comparable with many uninegative ions in its tendency to form ion pairs.[89-95] The similarity is closer in water than in dipolar aprotic solvents such as DMSO or DMF which solvate anions poorly, but the K_{IP} values in non-aqueous solvents are higher than in water so that the influence of perchlorate ion pairing on kinetics can be more easily seen. Thus, the solvent exchange rate of $Cr(DMF)_6^{3+}$ with DMF decreases slowly as $[ClO_4^-]$ is increased, reaching a limiting value of $\sim 77\%$ of the free-ion rate at $[ClO_4^-] \gtrsim 1$ mol l^{-1}; other anions reach completion of ion pairing at lower concentrations than this, but the retardation is not much greater than for ClO_4^-, suggesting that the effect of ion pairing is simply to deprive the solvent of one of the close-in sites from which it could exchange with bound DMF.[95] The effect of ion pairing on the rates of aquation reactions such as the reverse of (1) in water, on the other hand, is usually acceleration,[89,96,97] presumably by electrostatic assistance of the departure of X^{x-}, but clearly retardation is also possible because of exclusion of solvent.

Few workers are willing to invest the necessary effort to study reactions such as (1) over a range of ionic strengths to permit extrapolation to conditions of extreme dilution where the ion-pairing dilemma disappears. Pavelich, Maxey and Pfaff,[48] however, have done so for the reaction of $Rh(NH_3)_5OH_2^{3+}$ with chloride ion in water to produce $Rh(NH_3)_5Cl^{2+}$, and, in doing so, torpedoed the original pieces of evidence[98,99] around which the case for associative activation at Rh(III) was built. It transpired that k_i [equation (3)] is *not* greater than the solvent exchange rate constant k_{ex} if one goes to dilute conditions. This does not actually rule out associative activation, since water (which is in large excess anyway, in the Rh—Cl ion pair) may be a better nucleophile than Cl^- for Rh(III), but conversely it does not permit us to rule out dissociative activation, and other criteria must be sought.

Studies with non-aqueous solvents[95] affirm that the effect of ion pairing on solvent exchange rates is small[100] and is a retardation rather than an acceleration, which suggests that the criterion $k_i > k_{ex}$ for associative activation in an ion pair (I_a mechanism) might be valid even when k_{ex} *within* the ion pair cannot be measured. This may hold for water, but in the replacement of coordinated DMSO by X^- in $Co(NH_3)_5DMSO^{3+}$ in DMSO solvent,[26] or of DMF in $Co(NH_3)_5DMF^{3+}$ in DMF,[25] for which an I_d process is indicated by other criteria (ΔV^* for solvent exchange, etc.), we find k_{ex} is exceeded by a factor of two to three by k_i. It must be remembered that M-solvent bond breaking can be followed by one of three possibilities: pickup of a new ligand X (k_i); pickup of a new solvent molecule (k_{ex}, observable by isotopic labelling); or of the *same* solvent molecule (recombination, unobservable). Thus, k_{ex} in the absence of X is not necessarily a reliable measure of M-solvent bond-breaking rates, especially when the solvent molecule is large (as with DMF or DMSO) and few can be available locally for exchange rather than recombination. Similarly, insertion of a relatively small (halide, pseudohalide, etc.) X into the first coordination sphere may be favoured sterically over bulky solvent. A better kinetic criterion of dissociative activation in interchange processes is the equality of the enthalpies of activation ΔH_i^* (corresponding to k_i) for inner-sphere entry of all X^-; ΔH^* values are independent of the essentially statistical complications outlined above. Measurement of ΔH_i^* is difficult, but it transpires that $\Delta H_{ex}^* = \Delta H_i^*$ for substitution in $Co(NH_3)_5DMSO^{3+}$ in DMSO, confirming that the common kinetically-controlling step is Co—DMSO bond breaking (I_d mechanism).[26]

Finally, measurements of the volume changes ΔV_{IP}, associated with ion pairing involving aqueous cationic complexes, suggest that there is extensive desolvation of the anion, though less of the cation, and that ΔV_{IP} values are not sufficiently different from the volumes of formation of the corresponding inner-sphere complexes to allow differentiation of the two processes on volumetric data.[101,102] Thus, formation of the $\{La^{3+}, SO_4^{2-}\}$ aqueous ion pair apparently involves the loss of about 11 waters of hydration;[103] our guideline of ~ 15.6 cm^3 mol^{-1} for the mean molar volume of water solvating Co(III) pentaammines (Section II.B) combines with ΔV values for the formation of *inner* and *outer*-sphere complexes from $Co(NH_3)_5OH_2^{3+}$ and SO_4^{2-} to suggest the release of 9–10 and 7–8 waters respectively[101,104] and it may be that $\{La^{3+}, SO_4^{2-}\}$ should also be regarded as inner-sphere. For Mg^{2+} and SO_4^{2-} in water, the apparent value of ΔV_{IP} according to Raman spectroscopic measurements differs from those obtained by other procedures, apparently because only the "contact" ion pair is detected by the laser Raman technique;[105] this reinforces our suspicions (above) that ion pairing means different things in different contexts.

In summary, its seems that discussion of mechanisms in terms of ion pairing is a veritable quicksand. The striking fact about the rates of anation of $Co(NH_3)_5OH_2^{3+}$ by X^- in water, for example, is that the rates are virtually the same for all mononegative X^- at least; when one worries about the details of the supposed interchange process according to equations (2) and (3), this simple truth becomes obscured, as in the case of $X^- = N_3^-$.[106] Accordingly, although one is obliged to invoke ion pairing in many studies involving non-aqueous solvents of low dielectric constant, Occam's razor can often be beneficially wielded in discussions of reactions of ions in water and some other solvents.

D. Conjugate base formation ("hydrolysis")

Conjugate base formation by aqueous amine complexes of metals can be distinguished from ion pairing by OH^- in favourable cases, such as $Ru(NH_3)_6^{3+}$, if the spectrum of the ion pair can be estimated from those of pairs with other anions.[107] The dramatic substitution rate increases associated with conjugate base formation in cobalt(III) or ruthenium(III) ammines[6-8] are less striking for water exchange on $Fe(H_2O)_6^{3+}$ (750-fold at 25 °C)[108] or $Cr(H_2O)_6^{3+}$ ($\sim$ 60-fold),[35] while the absence of a significant contribution from conjugate-base pathways in substitution in $V(H_2O)_6^{3+}$ has been ascribed to the importance of associative activation in this t_{2g}^2 ion.[109] This is in accordance with the trend in ΔV^* values for the acid-independent water exchange on $Fe(H_2O)_6^{3+}$,[110] $Cr(H_2O)_6^{3+}$[111] and $V(H_2O)_6^{3+}$[36] (-5.4, -9.3 and -10.1 cm^3 mol^{-1} respectively), which could be taken to reflect the increasing importance of associative activation in that order; these associative processes may be said to outpace increasingly a dissociative alternative for water exchange on $M(H_2O)_6^{3+}$ which would be the direct analogue of the dissociative aqua exchange on $M(H_2O)_5OH^{2+}$.[110]

The volume change ΔV_a of conjugate base formation from $M(H_2O)_6^{3+}$ or $M(HN_3)_5OH_2^{3+}$ is invariably near zero.[83,110,112] This has seemed anomalous, since simple arguments have suggested $\Delta V_a \sim +25$ cm^3 mol^{-1} on the grounds of charge dispersal,[112] but equation (5) explains this readily. Since $M(H_2O)_6^{3+}$ and $M(H_2O)_5OH^{2+}$ will be virtually identical in their effective volumes [the first two terms on the right of equation (5)], the only contributions of any significance to ΔV_a will be $\bar{V}_{abs}^0(H^+) = -5.4$ cm^3 mol^{-1}, and the difference in the electrostriction terms, $-1.30\Delta(z^2)$; the calculated ΔV_a is thus $+1$ cm^3 mol^{-1}, just as is found for iron(III) hydrolysis.[110]

Chromium(III) affords a convenient model ion for the study of hydrolytic polymerization, since first-coordination-sphere substitution is slow. Connick and coworkers[113,114] have shown that the important hydrolytic polymers of Cr(III) in acidic solution are $(H_2O)_4Cr(OH)_2Cr(OH_2)_4^{4+}$, $(H_2O)_5Cr(OH)Cr(OH_2)_5^{5+}$ and a trimer $Cr_3(OH)_4^{5+}$(aq); the first two are present in comparable concentrations at equilibrium at 300 K in 2 mol l^{-1} acid. The dihydroxo dimer is also formed in the oxidation of Cr^{2+}(aq) by air,[115] but benzoquinone oxidizes $Cr^{2+}(aq)$ to $(H_2O)_5CrOCr(H_2O)_5^{4+}$[116]; the uv-visible spectra of these dimers are very different, however, so there is no doubt that the dihydroxo species is the relevant one in ordinary hydrolytic equilibria of chromium(III). For aqueous iron(III), on the other hand, $(H_2O)_5FeOFe(OH_2)_5^{4+}$ seems to be the important hydrolytic dimer, according to the Mössbauer and visible spectra,[117] and this may have relevance to Thompson and Connick's observation[113] that magnetic coupling is stronger in dimeric hydrolyzed iron(III) than in the chromium(III) hydrolytic dimers. In aluminium(III) solutions, after rapid hydrolysis with Na_2CO_3, ^{27}Al nmr shows that the polymeric species present are $Al_2(OH)_2^{4+}(aq)$ and the triskaidecamer $[Al\{OAl_3(OH)_6(OH_2)_3\}_4]^{7+}$, although further uncharacterizable polymers appear on aging or in slow hydrolysis. The rate of decomposition of the triskaidecamer on acidification is fast, being ultimately controlled by the rate of water substitution on Al(III), but the tight organization of the ion around the central tetrahedral Al with double OH bridges between the 12 octahedral aluminiums means that a large fraction of these hydroxo bridges must be protonated before cleavage of the core oxo links can be effected. Thus, the triskaidecamer is surprisingly stable in quite highly acidic solutions.[118,119]

The simple hydrolysis of trivalent metal ions is markedly endothermic $(\Delta H_a \sim +40\ kJ\ mol^{-1})$ in water, i.e. hydrolysis is favoured by rising temperatures and hence by a falling dielectric constant. It is therefore understandable in retrospect that Merbach *et al.*[120] were unable to make $Fe(CH_3OH)_6^{3+}$ in solution in anhydrous methanol; the only important iron(III) species in quite strongly acidic methanolic iron(III) perchlorate solutions is apparently $Fe(CH_3OH)_5(OCH_3)^{2+}$. It would be interesting to determine whether this is a general phenomenon in hydroxylic solvents; hexasolvates of iron(III) and other trivalent metals are known to exist in aprotic solvents such as DMF or DMSO, but Fairhurst and Yano, in my laboratory, found it impossible to make an acetonitrile solution containing $Fe(CH_3CN)_6^{3+}$, free of hydrolytic material, starting from hydrated iron(III) salts.

E. Solvent structure

Major articles concerning the structure of water continue to appear,[121-125] and Symons has suggested that chemical reactivity of organic solutes in aqueous and mixed-aqueous solutions can be correlated with the spectroscopically-determined numbers of free (non-H-bonded) —OH groups and lone pairs on the water molecules.[125] It remains to be seen whether this approach can be extended to aqueous solutions of metal ions.

There can be little double that solvent structure is an important factor in the behaviour of metal ions in solution; indeed, many substances which cannot break the structure of water are virtually insoluble in it but dissolve readily in the relatively poorly-structured solvent DMSO.[126] The Bennetto–Caldin approach,[127] in which the structural properties of the solvent, as represented by the heat of evaporation and its fluidity, are introduced into a modified Eigen–Wilkins model of ligand substitution with the aid of the Fuoss equation for ion pairing, still seems promising but may be relevant only to the formation of the *outer* sphere complex, since, in reactions of the type $ML_5X + Y \rightarrow$, the rate of solvent exchange at M is rather insensitive to bulk solvent structure, when M, L, X and Y are the same and the solvent is changed.[128] Coetzee and coworkers[129-131] have pointed out several limitations in the Bennetto–Caldin approach, notably that it is based on observations on a rather limited selection of complexes (nickel polypyridine cations) for which the Fuoss equation is inadequate, apparently because of π-interactions which give added stability to the outer-sphere complexes. It appears that the substitution process is a complicated interplay of factors such as the size and ligand field strength of the ligands, steric effects, the donor strength of the solvent, and the structure of the solvent in the outer coordination spheres relative to that in the bulk.

Solvation and reaction kinetics in mixed solvents present all the problems of interpretation of phenomena in single solvents plus a whole range of new ones, particularly in relation to the fractionation of solvent composition between bulk solvent and the outer coordination spheres of solutes. Nuclear magnetic resonance methods offer important insights into the question of preferential solvation and reaction mechanism in mixed solvents,[132] but attempts to apply mixed-solvent concepts from organic chemistry (e.g. Winstein–Grunwald Y-values) to metal ion kinetics[6] have not been very informative. What is clear, however, is that trace concentrations of water can have very marked effects on the kinetics of ionic reactions in dipolar aprotic solvents such as acetonitrile[133] or DMF (Dr Sisley, here in Calgary, found that the anation of $Cr(DMF)_6^{3+}$ by Br^- in DMF was accelerated by some 30% by moisture picked up from the atmosphere).

III. MECHANISTIC CLASSIFICATION PROBLEMS

A. Interchange processes

Because many complexes of metal ions are cations and therefore tend to preassociate with anions or dipolar nucleophiles prior to ligand substitution, the tripartite Langford–Gray categorization[8] of ligand replacement mechanisms into associative (A), dissociative (D) and interchange (I) seems preferable to the older S_N1/S_N2 dichotomy.[7] Within the I category, Langford and Gray proposed a subdivision in two groups, corresponding ostensibly to predominance of dissociative (I_d) or associative (I_a) activation, on the operational criterion that, if the reaction were "approximately as sensitive (or more sensitive) to a variation of the entering group as to variation of the leaving group", the I_a description applied, otherwise the mechanism was considered I_d. But this criterion is too restrictive; in practice, it is more useful to seek to distinguish between those interchange reactions in which there are clear indications of at least *some* associative contribution to the activation process (through incoming group influences within the encounter complex, steric effects, pressure phenomena, etc.) and those in which there are not. In my review of 1974,[35] the I_a/I_d distinction was redefined along the latter lines, and in fact most authors seem to have taken the same view independently.

I have commented at length elsewhere[45] on the inherent weaknesses of operational definitions—in essence, a classification based on one particular measurable property (and a truly operational criterion uses only one) will almost invariably lead to a somewhat different grouping of phenomena than some other classification based on another, equally valid, operational criterion. I say "invariably" because, sooner or later, borderline cases will be found. Thus, it seemed at one time that for the Cr(III) analogues of reaction (1) in water, anation rates were sufficiently insensitive to the nature of incoming X^{n-} (or, equivalently, that the free energy relationship of $\ln k_{aq}$ with $-\ln Q$, where Q is the stability constant of $Cr(NH_3)_5X^{(3-x)+}$, was linear with slope α sufficiently close to unity) to justify the I_d label,[41–43] whereas pressure effects and steric hindrance in N-methylated analogues indicated I_a.[45,46] Pressure effects do not constitute criteria for the original Langford–Gray I_a/I_d classification, in strict operationist terms, and I have played the devil's advocate[45] in suggesting, not too seriously, an alternative "PA/PD" operational classification, meaning pressure-accelerated/pressure-decelerated and referring to solvent exchange reactions (to which the Langford–Gray criterion is inapplicable in any case) or to the intrinsic or non-solvational part of the volume of activation. The PA/PD scheme has the advantage of being clear cut (almost always, a reaction is *either* accelerated *or* retarded by pressure), whereas the original I_a/I_d distinction is not. Recent studies[44] show that the $Cr(NH_3)_5OH_2^{3+}$–X^{x-} reaction rate does show some significant dependence on the nature of X^{x-}, the Brønsted slope of the free energy plot for the corresponding *aquations* being in the range 0.7–0.9, but, again, this slope would have to be 0.5 or less to meet the strict Langford–Gray criterion for I_a, which would place in the I_d category a great many reactions in which associative activation is evidently important.

The basic problem is that we are dealing with a continuous range of phenomena, and it is not really useful to force-fit the experimental facts to a bi- or tripartite mechanistic classification. The gradation of the classical S_N1 into S_N2 in organic chemistry has been recognized for some time.[134]

Jencks[135,136] has recently reviewed the questions of when the presence of an actual intermediate should be inferred in an organic substitution reaction, and why the reaction should "choose" one mechanism over another. One way of representing the degree to which the path of a reaction $ML_nX + Y \rightarrow ML_nY + X$ approaches the limiting S_N1 (D) or limiting S_N2 (A) models is with a More–O'Ferrall diagram,[135–138] which is essentially a square whose sides represent M—X and M—Y bond order changes from 0 to 1 (Figs 3 and 4). The two opposite corners between those representing

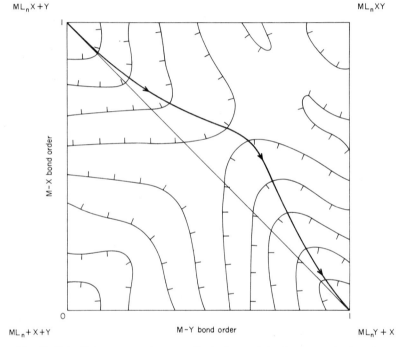

$ML_nX + Y$ ML_nXY

M–X bond order

0   1

$ML_n + X + Y$ M–Y bond order $ML_nY + X$

Fig. 3. Potential energy contour map illustrating an interchange mechanism that involves substantial associative activation but no intermediates on the reaction coordinate.

reactants and products correspond to intermediates of reduced $(ML_n + X + Y)$ and expanded (ML_nXY) coordination numbers, and the disposition of the potential energy contours (sketched arbitrarily in Figs 3 and 4) will determine how closely the reactants-to-products trajectory approaches these corners and hence the limiting mechanisms.

In substitution at aliphatic carbon, the total bond order between 3L, $M(= C)$, X and Y cannot exceed four, so that the trajectories are limited to the

$ML_nX + Y$ ML_nXY

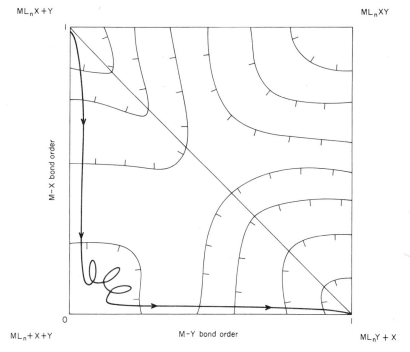

ML_n+X+Y M-Y bond order $ML_nY + X$

Fig. 4. Potential energy contour map illustrating a dissociatively activated
reaction mechanism in which an intermediate ML_n survives for a few collisions
with X, Y and molecules of the solvent cage.

half of Fig. 3 or 4 below and including the reactants-to-products diagonal, but
for ligand substitution at most metal ions an expansion of coordination
number (not necessarily just by one) as well as a reduction is entirely feasible,
since empty metal orbitals are usually accessible, and any smooth path
through More O'Ferrall space could be followed if it represented a path of
minimal potential energy (there could be more than one such path, for given
M, L, X and Y). There are potential wells corresponding to both ML_nXY and
$\{ML_n + X + Y\}$ as intermediates in Figs 3 and 4, and their presence affects the
potential-energy topography to various degrees so that the trajectories of least
resistance correspond to a substantial degree of associative activation without
formation of an intermediate (I_a) in Fig. 3, and formation of an intermediate of
reduced coordination number that survives for a few molecular vibrations and
collisions with surrounding molecules (D) in Fig. 4. The reactants-products
diagonal could be taken as dividing I_a from I_d processes, much as in the
original definition of Langford and Gray,[8] but obviously the distinction
would be arbitrary for trajectories close to this diagonal.

One might suppose that for solvent exchange on metal ions, which is a

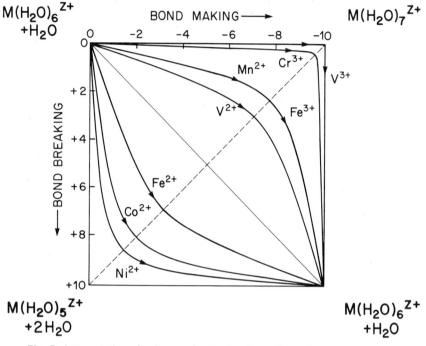

Fig. 5. Interpretation of volumes of activation for water exchange on aqueous $M(H_2O)_6^{z+}$ in terms of contributions (in cm³ mol⁻¹) from bond making and bond breaking.

symmetrical reaction, the axes of a More O'Ferrall plot could be scaled in terms of a physical parameter such as volume, as has been done in Fig. 5, in which the scales have been set to accommodate the most negative ΔV^* value recorded to-date for water exchange (-10.1 cm³ mol⁻¹ for $V(H_2O)_6^{3+}$[36] which, with an empty t_{2g} orbital, is probably capable of forming an actual intermediate of expanded coordination number). In constructing such a diagram, it is implicitly assumed that bond making and breaking are the sole contributors to ΔV^* and that they contribute on the same scale regardless of the nature of the central metal ion. Symmetry considerations then require that the maximum value of ΔV^* for water exchange be $+10.1$ cm³ mol⁻¹, which is in fair agreement ($+10\%$) with the prediction for a D mechanism according to the hard-sphere model of Section II.B. In Fig. 5, the algebraic sum of the coordinates of a given point on a trajectory represents the instantaneous volume of the system at that point, and, for an interchange mechanism (no intermediates), will be numerically largest and equal to ΔV^* on crossing the broken diagonal line. Thus, Fig. 5, taken at face value, suggests that ΔV^* for water exchange on Fe^{2+} is made up of contributions of -3.1 and

$+6.9$ cm^3 mol^{-1}, respectively, while for Fe^{3+} the corresponding values are -7.8 and $+2.4$, approximately.

It is tempting to identify Fig. 5 with the more usual More O'Ferrall diagram, complete with S$_N$1/S$_N$2 or D/I$_d$/I$_a$/A labels, in which case the mechanism of aqua exchange on Cr^{3+} would be considered I$_a$, verging on A. Strict application of the original Langford–Gray definitions,[8] however, would place the anation reactions of this same ion in the I$_d$ category, since the Brønsted slope for *anation* (0.41–0.44[35]) is less than 0.50, yet it seems to be neither constructive nor correct to suppose that there is any fundamental mechanistic difference between anation and water exchange. This serves to emphasize the problem of matching up different operational definitions of the mechanism.

Despite its obvious limitations, Fig. 5 does provide a means of visualizing, in a crudely quantitative way, the presumed interplay between bond breaking and bond making in simple interchange processes, and suggests that the latter varies widely in importance but can rarely be ignored entirely. Thus, if the concepts of dissociative and associative contributions to the activation process are to be retained, it would be better to abandon attempts at a two-way (I$_d$/I$_a$ or S$_N$1/S$_N$2) classification of reactions and to try instead to establish a continuous scale that measures the importance of the associative contribution to activation. That is, we need to measure the *selectivity* of a metal complex toward various incoming nucleophiles.

B. "Long-lived" intermediates

There can be little question that intermediates of *expanded* coordination number are important in ligand substitution in square planar complexes, since in some cases these can actually be directly detected.[6–8,139,140] For instance, in the classic example[7] of a complex which is labile despite high thermodynamic stability, Ni(CN)$_4^{2-}$, the rapid rate of exchange with aqueous CN$^-$ relates to the formation of the well-characterized Ni(CN)$_5^{3-}$. For octahedral complexes thought to react via an intermediate of *reduced* coordination number, however, particularly those of cobalt(III), the evidence for the existence of the intermediate is almost always of an indirect nature, e.g. the constancy of competition ratios of various nucleophiles for supposed common intermediates from a series of related precursors, but, as noted in the Introduction, much of the evidence is now beginning to look inconclusive.

Purely kinetic evidence for a D versus an I$_d$ process can be misleading.[11,141] It is evidently not enough simply to demonstrate curvature of a plot of pseudo-first-order substitution rate constants k_{obs} against nucleophile concentration consistent with a limiting rate, as this could alternatively be attributable to medium effects; an actual limiting rate should be *observed*. This is the case, for example, for the reaction of aqueous CN^- with *trans*-$Co(CN)_4SO_3(OH_2)^{3-}$[142] and for some *exchanges* of nitrogen heterocycle ligands L (as distinct from replacement of coordinated water) in aqueous $Fe^{II}(CN)_5L$,[143] but more usually k_{obs} for water replacement shows an essentially first-order dependence on nucleophile concentration even when there is other evidence that the mechanism is of the D type.[144,145] For cationic complexes, there is, of course, the added possibility of preassociation of substrate and nucleophile (I mechanism) to give eventually a limiting rate k_i according to equation (3).

It is still very probable that substitution of water in $Co(CN)_5OH_2^{2-}$ is appropriately described by the D mechanism, although only the competition study of Haim and Wilmarth[9] seems unequivocal. The volumes of activation for anation by NCS^-, Br^- and I^- are all close to $+9$ cm^3 mol^{-1},[146] which is precisely the limiting value estimated in Section II.B for dissociative release of a water molecule, but it must be borne in mind that the pressure dependence measured was that of the pseudo-second-order rate coefficient and *not* of the limiting first-order rate coefficient, which would have provided a direct measure of ΔV^* for $(NC)_5Co–OH_2$ bond breaking but, as noted above, is inaccessible experimentally. Solvent effects[147] provide, at best, only indirect evidence of mechanism. The need for a direct determination of the rate of water exchange of $Co(CN)_5OH_2^{2-}$(aq) is increasingly clear; Dr Sisley, in our laboratories, has attempted this by several methods other than that of Haim and Wilmarth,[9] which gave unexpectedly fast but erratic exchange rates, and it seems that water exchange may indeed be faster than is required by the analysis of the anation rate data, although reproducibility is inadequate. We are reinvestigating the aqua exchange reaction at present.

Recent controversy over the D/I_d distinction in base hydrolysis and "induced" hydrolyses of cationic cobalt(III) amine complexes[12-19,148] seems to derive from disagreement over just what is meant by a "common intermediate of reduced coordination number" in a series of hydrolyses in which only the leaving group is varied. A reasonable definition of such an intermediate would be "a species which has lost all memory of the departing group". This means, in effect, that the leaving ligand (which is frequently an anion) must have left the outer coordination sphere of the complex, i.e. the intermediate would have to be longer lived than the relaxation time of the solvation sheath of the complex including any paired anions. As Eigen[149] has pointed out, the relaxation of ion pairs may make itself felt for periods of up to as much as 100 ns, whereas an intermediate of reduced coordination number can be created in a vibration-like action on the 0.1 ps time-scale. Thus, the departing ligand and the solvation sheath structure of the precursor complex can exert *some* influence on the intermediate for periods of up to a million-fold longer than the duration of the intimate activation process on which so much attention is usually focussed.

Instead of attempting to distinguish I_d from D processes in cobalt(III) cations, it would be more constructive to aim to set up a series of relative lifetimes of intermediates, initially on a qualitative basis, but with a view to eventual quantification. Similar ideas are discernible in two recent papers by Buckingham *et al.*[18] (who suggest an upper limit of ~ 10 ps for the lifetime of the presumed five-coordinate intermediates in the base hydrolysis and Hg^{2+}- and NO^+-induced aquations of $[Co(Me(tren))(NH_3)X]^{2+,3+}$ isomers) and Sargeson and coworkers[148] (who point out that the often-invoked intermediate $Co(NH_3)_4NH_2^{2+}$ survives long enough to undergo rearrangement but not to equilibrate with its surroundings).

An example of experiments which suggest the existence of successive intermediates of different lifetimes is the effect of pressure on the water exchange[150] and the somewhat slower thermodynamically favoured isomerization[151] of *trans*-$Co(en)_2(OH_2)_2^{3+}$, for which ΔV^* is respectively $+6\ cm^3\ mol^{-1}$ (pressure independent) and $+14\ cm^3\ mol^{-1}$ (diminishing with increasing pressure). Clearly, both reactions are predominantly dissociatively activated but do *not* both go through the same ultimate transition state. Evidently, stereoretentive water exchange involves a short-lived, tetragonal-pyramidal $Co(en)_2OH_2^{3+}$ intermediate; this may relax to a trigonal-bipyramidal $Co(en)_2OH_2^{3+}$ which is necessary for rearrangement to occur but which evidently causes some breakup of the inherited solvation sheath as the ethylenediamines relocate themselves, since the pressure dependence of the unusually large ΔV^* (at atmospheric pressure) is typical of desolvation[33,35]—the loss of the equivalent of three to four solvating waters would account for this (Section II.B). An alternative explanation involves a change in the electronic multiplicity of Co(III) (see Section IV.G).

In general, the more extensive the stereochemical change, the longer lived must be the five-coordinate Co(III) intermediate, for related complexes. It is, however, likely that, in all cobalt(III) amine complexes at least, the intermediate retains some "memory" of the departing group or the structure of the environment of the precursor complex or both, and that the mechanism may therefore fall short of qualifying as a D process as commonly defined.

IV. REACTIVITY AND SELECTIVITY

A. Free energy and isokinetic relationships

The basic concepts underlying the interpretation of relationships between the free energies of activation ($\Delta G^* \propto -\ln k$) and reaction ($\Delta G^0 \propto -\ln K$, where k and K are respectively the rate and equilibrium constants for a reaction) for a series of related ligand substitution reactions were examined previously.[35] In particular, it was pointed out that any free energy relationship (FER) can be strictly linear only in the limiting case of *no* selectivity toward nucleophiles as

T. W. Swaddle

is the case for the reaction series (1); otherwise, a *curved* FER can be expected, but it may *seem* linear over the necessarily limited range of rates spanned by a given reaction series. This general conclusion has evoked some skepticism,[44] but has subsequently been noted independently in a variety of contexts.[152-157]

A perceptive review and analysis of the general problem of structure-reactivity correlations, including FERs, has recently been given by Agmon,[157] who has considered some metal-ion substitution reactions along with the usual organic examples. Progress along the reaction coordinate can be described by a parameter which I shall call θ that represents the instantaneous order of the bond being formed ($0 \leqslant \theta \leqslant 1$), with θ^* being the order in the transition state, corresponding to ΔG^*. One can write for the instantaneous free energy $G(\theta)$ corresponding to θ

$$G(\theta) = \theta\Delta G^0 + \lambda M(\theta) \tag{7}$$

where the reaction series is specified by the value of λ and M is assumed to be a function of θ only. A reasonable choice for $M(\theta)$ might be $\theta(1 - \theta)$, expressing the complementarity of bond making θ and breaking $(1 - \theta)$ (c.f. Figs 3 and 4), and this generates relationships of the type

$$\theta^* = (1 + \Delta G^0/\lambda)/2 \tag{8}$$

and

$$\Delta G^* = \lambda/4(1 + \Delta G^0/\lambda)^2 \tag{9}$$

These are encouragingly similar to results of the widely successful Marcus–Levich–Dogonadze approaches to electron and proton transfer reactions, which may be adaptable to ligand substitution reactions, as remarked previously.[35] Unfortunately, this choice of $M(\theta)$ would lead to θ^* values outside the permissible range of 0 to 1 for $|\Delta G^0| > \lambda$. Of three other selected functions $M(\theta)$ for which θ^* remains within these limits, Agmon concludes that the expression

$$M(\theta) = -\theta \ln \theta - (1 - \theta) \ln (1 - \theta) \tag{10}$$

is the best suited to the derivation of structure-reactivity relationships. We note in passing that, notwithstanding the limitations of equation (8) and (9), theories of the Marcus type seem to be applicable to the problem of rate-equilibrium relationships in organic S_N2 reactions.[158]

Agmon shows (Fig. 2 of reference [157]) that θ^* will vary only slowly with ΔG^0 when ΔG^{0*} ($= \Delta G^*$ for which $\Delta G^0 = 0$) is at least comparable with the range of $|\Delta G^0|$ values being considered. For ligand substitution in non-labile complexes of "hard" metal ions, this is certainly the case; ΔG^* values are on the order of 100 kJ mol^{-1}, while $|\Delta G^0|$ is rarely more than a quarter of this. This is the reason for the apparent linearity of FERs for substitution at (e.g.) chromium(III), since, according to the Leffler–Grunwald assumption,[159] the Brønsted slope α of the FER may be equated with θ^*. [N.B. Following an early precedent,[8] free energy relationships in coordination chemistry are usually presented in terms of *solvolysis*, i.e. a series of complexes reacting with a common nucleophile (solvent). This is the inverse of the practice of most chemists, who consider a common substrate in its reactions with a series of nucleophiles, as in the foregoing discussion. If the Brønsted slope for the latter case is α, that for the corresponding solvolysis is $(1 - \alpha)$. Thus, for reaction (1), α is 0.0 for anation, 1.0 for aquation.] The same probably holds for most organic reactions, which would account for the conviction of some physical organic chemists that FERs are genuinely linear.[160]

If we accept that FERs for slow ligand substitution are, for practical purposes, linear, the question arises as to whether the Brønsted slope will be the same for different temperatures, as seemed to be at least approximately true[161] for the reactions

$$Cr(H_2O)_5X^{2+} + H_2O \rightleftharpoons Cr(H_2O)_6^{3+} + X^- \tag{11}$$

Exner[162] points out that the validity of a linear FER at more than one temperature is dependent upon the existence of an isokinetic relationship, i.e. that ΔH^* and ΔS^* are linearly related, as is frequently the case for ligand substitution reactions. There is, however, no particular significance to the isokinetic temperature (the slope of the isokinetic plot).[162] Nor should any special significance be attached to the *existence* of isokinetic relationships; trends in enthalpy and entropy are *normally* mutually compensatory to some degree, and the isokinetic temperature is a measure of the degree in the kinetic context. A generalized explanation of this phenomenon is given in Section IV.G. A common source of variations in ΔH^* and ΔS^* which almost cancel in ΔG^* is solvational change.[35] This is strikingly illustrated by the temperature dependence of the free energies of solvation of aqueous NaCl and $CuCl_2$ over the temperature range 0–350 °C, which is very slight despite huge opposing changes in the enthalpies and entropies of hydration, especially above 250 °C.[163]

B. Limitations of the free-energy-relationship approach

The chief obstacle to development of a coherent theory of reactivity in ligand substitution of aqua-ions, or of other complexes containing ionizable protons, is the so-called "proton ambiguity", i.e. the tendency of the more basic incoming nucleophiles X^{x-} to abstract a proton from the complex, so that the reactive species could well be $HX^{(x-1)-}$ and the conjugate base of the complex (which is usually relatively labile).[35,157] If one tries to avoid these problems

T. W. Swaddle

by going to an aprotic dipolar solvent system, solubility problems and, sometimes, attack of the reagents upon the solvent limit the scope of the reactions amenable to study, and besides the simplification that ion pairing can be ignored (Section II.C) is no longer permissible for solvents of relatively low dielectric constant. Furthermore, one may be driven to study highly contrived systems which have little direct relevance to the original question. The proton ambiguity problem is often still not fully appreciated; thus, assignments of an I_a mechanism for substitution in aqueous $Cr(H_2O)_6^{3+}$, on the grounds that anation rates (usually for attack by a carboxylate species) exceed that of water exchange, or that ΔH^* for anation is different from that water exchange, are not justified.[164]

A further mechanistic problem with oxoanionic ligands is uncertainty over the site of reaction. King and coworkers[165,166] have shown that DMSO reacts rapidly with aqueous $Cr(H_2O)_5NO_3^{2+}$ to produce eventually $Cr(DMSO)_5OH_2^{3+}$ and nitrate, which strongly suggests O—N rather than Cr—O bond breaking; this would account for the deviation of $X^- = NO_3^-$ from the $Cr(H_2O)_5X^{2+}$ FER.[161] The same is probably true for the case $X^- = CCl_3CO_2^-$,[167] which might otherwise have provided a data-point free of the proton ambiguity. Attention must also be paid, in cases where the "non-reacting" ligands are not solvent, to their replacement at rates comparable with the process being studied; this is especially important when oxoanions are present, even just as the "inert" electrolyte.[168–171]

The expectation that α will have a value somewhere in mid-range between 0 and 1 if there is an appreciable degree of associative activation is valid only if no long-lived intermediates of expanded coordination number are involved, i.e. for interchange processes.[35,45] Thus, for some solvolyses of Pd(II)[172] and Pt(II)[173] complexes for which other evidence indicates an A mechanism, there exists LFERs of slope 1.0, and the arguments of Section IV.A become irrelevant.

Because the data set available to establish a FER is usually limited for the above reasons, experimental error can distort the correlation seriously. A disagreement over the ΔG^0 value for the case $X^{x-} = Br^-$ in the aquation of $Cr(NH_3)_5X^{(3-x)+}$ led to α values of 0.91[41] and 0.69[174]; the latter (more recent) value is probably the more realistic, in the light of subsequent additions to the data base,[44] but the case $X^{x-} = H_2O$ should not be included in the FER[174] because of the impossibility of expressing the water concentration appropriately.[132] Fortunately, this controversy does not obscure the most interesting feature of FER—that its slope (say, 0.8 ± 0.1) is clearly steeper than that for the corresponding aquations of the complexes $Cr(H_2O)_5X^{(3-x)+}$ (0.56),[161] which confirms Sykes' view that the associative contribution to the activation process is less fully developed in the pentaammine than in the pentaaqua series (see also below).[41–44]

C. Measures of selectivity

It would be gratifying if we could express the selectivity S_A of a substrate A relative to that (S_B) for a substrate B as the reagent is changed, giving changes $\delta \Delta G_A^*$ and $\delta \Delta G_B^*$ in the corresponding free energies of activation, in the manner set forth by Leffler and Grunwald[159] which uses the Brønsted slope α to relate S_A and S_B to thermodynamic properties.

$$\frac{S_A}{S_B} = \frac{\delta \Delta G_A^*}{\delta \Delta G_B^*} = \frac{\alpha_A \delta \Delta G_A^0}{\alpha_B \delta \Delta G_B^0} \tag{12}$$

As noted in the previous section, however, data sufficient for such a systematic approach are often lacking. An alternative is to use a fixed pair of reagents, which react in a conveniently measurable manner with a wide variety of A, B, etc. and are free of the problems noted in Section IV.B, to define $\delta \Delta G_A^*$, $\delta \Delta G_B^*$, etc. Sasaki and Sykes[175] suggested using the ratio $R = k_{an}(NCS^-)/k_{an}(Cl^-)$ for the anation of aqua-complexes, with the caveat that thiocyanate or chloride may react in atypical ways with some substrates. Indeed, this may well be the case for NCS^-, which preferentially attaches to "hard" metal centres like Cr(III) through the N atom but through the S atom to "softer" centres such as Pt(II) and, perhaps, Rh(III). Nevertheless, Sasaki and Sykes' choice is still the best available, and some R values for various metal aqua ions are listed in Table 1.

TABLE 1

Rates R of substitution of water by thiocyanate relative to chloride, and volumes of activation ΔV_{ex}^* for water exchange, in aqueous $ML_5OH_2^{z+}$

$ML_5OH_2^{z+}$	R	$\Delta V_{ex}^*/cm^3\ mol^{-1}$	Reference
$V(H_2O)_6^{3+}$	$\geqslant 36$	-10.1	[175, 36]
$Mo(H_2O)_6^{3+}$	62	—	[175]
$Cr(H_2O)_6^{3+}$	55(a)	-9.3	[176, 111]
$Co(H_2O)_6^{3+}$	$\geqslant 43$	—	[175]
$Cr(NH_3)_5OH_2^{3+}$	6	-5.8	[41, 35]
$Fe(H_2O)_6^{3+}$	14	-5.4	[175, 110]
$Mn(H_2O)_6^{2+}$	—	-5.4	[30]
$Rh(NH_3)_5OH_2^{3+}$	0.6	-4.1	[98, 35]
$Co(NH_3)_5OH_2^{3+}$	0.5	1.2	[7, 177]
$Fe(H_2O)_6^{2+}$	—	3.8	[30]
$Co(H_2O)_6^{2+}$	—	6.1	[30]
$Fe(H_2O)_5OH^{2+}$	0.6	7.0	[175, 110]
$Cr(H_2O)_5OH^{2+}$	1.0	—	[176]
$Co(H_2O)_5OH^{2+}$	2.0	—	[175]
$Ni(H_2O)_6^{2+}$	—	7.2	[30]

(a) In [176], k_{an} for $NCS^- + Cr(H_2O)_6^{3+}$ should read $1.66 \times 10^{-6}\ l\ mol^{-1}\ s^{-1}$.

Sasaki and Sykes[175] suggested that the value of R could serve as a criterion to distinguish I_a from I_d mechanisms, I_a being indicated where R equalled or exceeded an order of magnitude. This arbitrary distinction is subject to the reservations expressed in Section III.A, and I prefer to say that R is a selectivity parameter which increases with the growth in importance of associative activation at the respective metal centres. Since ΔV_{ex}^* for aqua exchange can also be taken to indicate the relative importance of associative activation (Fig. 5 and related discussion, above), it is encouraging that a fair correlation exists between the ΔV_{ex}^* and R values in Table 1. In general, negative ΔV_{ex}^* values are associated with $R \gg 1$ for all entries other than $Rh(NH_3)_5OH_2^{3+}$, for which an anomalous mode of attack by NCS^- may be operative.

Mønsted[174] points out that the slopes α of quasi-linear FERs for the aquations of X^- from $Cr(H_2O)_5X^{2+}$, $Cr(NH_3)_5X^{2+}$, $Rh(NH_3)_5X^{2+}$, $Ir(NH_3)_5X^{2+}$ and $Co(NH_3)_5X^{2+}$ correlate linearly with ΔV_{ex}^* for water exchange on the corresponding aqua-ions. The obvious conclusion, as with the data of Table 1, is that the contribution of bond formation to the activation process decreases to essentially nil as we proceed along this series from left to right, or as we descend Table 1. Conversely, selectivity can be said to increase in the opposite direction.

D. The reactivity-selectivity principle

The foregoing leads us to the problem of selectivity, or rather lack thereof, in reactions of $Mn(H_2O)_6^{2+}$. Merbach et al.[30] found a markedly negative ΔV_{ex}^* for water exchange on this ion, and argued (correctly, I believe[32]) that this is indicative of a substantial associative contribution to activation in Mn^{2+}(aq).[37] Certainly, for $Fe(H_2O)_6^{3+}$ (which, coincidentally, also has $\Delta V_{ex}^* = -5.4 \ cm^3 \ mol^{-1}$) there is clear evidence for substantial selectivity towards nucleophiles, as was pointed out in 1974[35] and has been confirmed many times since then,[108–110,178–181] although the proton ambiguity causes some complications. Yet Merbach et al.[30] could find no evidence in the literature for significant selectivity in reactions of Mn(II), partly because of the paucity of precise data, but no doubt selectivity is genuinely low (inviting characterization of the substitution mechanism as I_d).

The reason is two-fold. First, the selectivity of "hard-hard" interactions is not expected to be great[35]; the known range of anation rates of a "hard" complex such as $Cr(H_2O)_6^{3+}$ is small relative to the range for "soft" Pt(II) complexes reacting with "soft" ligands. But this does not fully explain the lack of selectivity by Mn(II) relative to other hard centres like Fe(III) or Cr(III). The second factor is the reactivity-selectivity correlation: for reasons discussed at length elsewhere,[134,157,159,160] selectivity declines among similar classes of reactions as the rates of reaction become faster. It therefore becomes readily understandable that the R value declines three-fold from $Cr(H_2O)_6^{3+}$ (substitution time scale $\sim 10^6$ s) to $Fe(H_2O)_6^{3+}$ ($\sim 10^{-2}$ s), so that an R value of perhaps four would be anticipated for $Mn(H_2O)_6^{2+}$ ($\sim 10^{-7}$ s), and such low selectivity could easily be missed in view of the experimental difficulties.

Examples from transition metal chemistry that clearly illustrate the reactivity-selectivity principle are rather limited. Romeo and Cusumano[182] compared the rates of the reactions of $Pt(dien)OH_2^{2+}$ and $Pt(dien)DMSO^{2+}$ with a variety of nucleophiles in water. For the former series at least, a single-path associative type of mechanism has been established,[183] and undoubtedly applies to the reactions of the sulphur-bonded DMSO complex too. Romeo and Cusumano found that the DMSO complex was about three orders of magnitude less reactive than the aqua complex, and was about 15% more selective, in the sense that a plot of the logarithms of the second-order rate coefficients for substitution in $Pt(dien)DMSO^{2+}$ against those for substitution in $Pt(dien)OH_2^{2+}$ was a straight line of slope 1.15.

Another pair of reaction series suitable for comparison would be water substitution by X^{x-} in aqueous $Cr(H_2O)_6^{3+}$ and $Cr(NH_3)_5OH_2^{3+}$, for which substantial degrees of associative activation are evident. Because the range and reliability of data for the reverse reactions (aquation of $Cr(H_2O)_5X^{(3-x)+}$ and $Cr(NH_3)_5X^{(3-x)+}$) are greater, as seen in Table 2, it is desirable to recast the problem in terms of relative rates of aquation. Given that a linear FER of slope α exists for the aquation reactions, we have

$$\delta \ln k_{aq} = -\alpha \delta \ln Q \tag{13}$$

and

$$\delta \ln k_{an} = (1 - \alpha)\delta \ln Q \tag{14}$$

where Q is the stability constant of the X-complex. Then, since

$$k_{an}/k_{aq} = Q, \tag{15}$$

$$\delta \ln k_{an} = (1 - \alpha^{-1})\delta \ln k_{aq} \tag{16}$$

If S is the selectivity of $Cr(H_2O)_6^{3+}$ [A in equation (12)] relative to $Cr(NH_3)_5OH_2^{3+}$ [B in equation (12)]

$$S = \delta \ln k_{an}^A / \delta \ln k_{an}^B$$
$$= \{(1 - \alpha_A^{-1})\delta \ln k_{aq}^A\}/\{(1 - \alpha_B^{-1})\delta \ln k_{aq}^B\} \tag{17}$$

Relevant data are collected in Table 2. As has recently been noted by Mønsted and Mønsted,[184] and demonstrated rigorously by Moore et al.,[185] the rates of isotopically labelled solvent exchange of "all six" ligands in $M(solvent)_6^{z+}$ and of a particular *one* of those six ligands are *the same*, and the

TABLE 2

Rate coefficients k_{aq} (25 °C), and enthalpies ΔH^{*}_{aq} and entropies ΔS^{*}_{aq} of activation, for the aquation of $CrL_5X^{(3-x)+}$ (L = $H_2O^{(a)}$ or NH_3)

X^{x-}	L	$\ln(k_{aq}/s^{-1})$	$\Delta H^{*}_{aq}/$ kJ mol^{-1}	$\Delta S^{*}_{aq}/$ J K^{-1} mol^{-1}	Reference
H_2O	H_2O	$-12.87^{(b)}$	109.6	$+16.2^{(b)}$	[111]
H_2O	NH_3	-9.86	97.1	0.0	[188]
Cl^-	H_2O	-15.11	101.7	-29.7	[35, 161]
Cl^-	NH_3	-11.48	91.2	-34.5	[189, 190]
Br^-	H_2O	-12.46	99.6	-14.6	[35, 161]
Br^-	NH_3	-9.25	90.8	-17.3	[189, 190]
I^-	H_2O	-9.39	96.2	-10.9	[35, 161]
I^-	NH_3	-6.87	90.0	-0.2	[189, 190]
NO_3^-	H_2O	-9.54	90.4	-21.3	[191, 192]
NO_3^-	NH_3	-7.13	85.4	-18.0	[168]
NH_3	H_2O	-20.08	117.6	-17.2	[193]
NH_3	NH_3	-15.54	102.9	-28.9	[168]
HCN	H_2O	-5.74	68.9	-61.8	[194]
HCN	NH_3	-4.22	71.9	-38.9	[195]
NCS^-	H_2O	-18.53	115.0	-13.1	[196]
NCS^-	NH_3	-15.56	100.4	-37.6	[197]
$CCl_3CO_2^-$	H_2O	-13.35	93.0	-44	[167]
$CCl_3CO_2^-$	NH_3	-12.52	90.0	-47.3	[198]

(a) Acid-independent rates.
(b) Note errors in references [111, 186, 187] (see text).

experimental k_{ex} should *not* be divided by a statistical factor of six (or ΔS^* reduced by $R \ln 6$) as was erroneously done in references [111] and [186] and, unfortunately, has been perpetuated in a widely-used compilation.[187] Data said to refer to the exchange of "all six" ligands in our papers to-date are the correct ones (I thank Professor Merbach and the Mønsteds for drawing my attention to this). The Mønsteds' data[193] for the aquation of $Cr(H_2O)_5NH_3^{3+}$ are based on a wider temperature range and require less extrapolation than our own,[168] and have therefore been adopted. In all cases, calculations of ΔH^* and ΔS^* have been repeated. Ammonia loss has been allowed for where appropriate[168,197]; it is possible, however, that the rate of NCS^- aquation in $Cr(NH_3)_5$–NCS^{2+} has still been underestimated, since the reported rate of NH_3 loss seems slow relative to that in $Cr(NH_3)_6^{3+}$,[168] and acid hydrolysis of the thiocyanate ion itself could cause complications.

The first 14 entries in Table 2 are represented by

$$\ln k^{H_2O}_{aq} = (1.26 \pm 0.02) \ln k^{NH_3}_{aq} - (0.58 \pm 0.17) \tag{18}$$

and

$$\Delta H^*_{H_2O} = (1.59 \pm 0.05)\Delta H^*_{NH_3} - (45.2 \pm 4.7) \tag{19}$$

with correlation coefficients $r = 0.9995$ and 0.9974 respectively. Inclusion of the data for $X^{x-} = NCS^-$ actually improves the ΔH^* fit slightly (slope $= 1.60 \pm 0.04$), but one of the rate coefficients for NCS^- seems to be in error by a factor of about five, probably for the reasons given in the preceding paragraph. The data for $X^{x-} = CCl_3CO_2^-$ are clearly anomalous, however, which seems to confirm that an aberrant mechanism (probably C—O bond breaking) is operative in that case[167]; conversely, the conformity of $X^{x-} = NO_3^-$, with clearly different data for $L = NH_3$ and H_2O, suggests that Cr—O bond breaking occurs here, despite doubts raised in Section IV.B.[165,166] The obvious implication of these results is that the ammines all react *faster* than the aqua-ions (because of trends in ΔH^* which are only partially compensated by trends in ΔS^*) and that they also show a distinctly *narrower* spread of rates.

To rephrase this in terms of relative selectivity, we have from equations (17) and (18)

$$S = 1.26(1 - \alpha_A^{-1})/(1 - \alpha_B^{-1}) \tag{20}$$

which, adopting $\alpha_A = 0.56$[161] and $\alpha_B = 0.69$,[174] give S, the selectivity of $Cr(H_2O)_6^{3+}$ relative to $Cr(NH_3)_5OH_2^{3+}$ in water replacement, $= 3.2$. Thus, the less reactive species displays markedly greater selectivity, just as the Leffler–Grunwald principle states.[159] The value of S calculated via equation (17) is, however, rather sensitive to the values of α_A and α_B used, and directly measured water replacement rates would be preferable if available.

E. Enthalpies of activation

Predictions of ligand substitution rate phenomena by quantum mechanical calculations are more easily made if the mechanism is assumed to be dissociative and if attention is confined to ΔH^* rather than ΔS^*. It is increasingly clear, however, that a variable degree of associative activation is operative in most substitution reactions involving metal ions. The theory of Hush[200] (inadvertently omitted from a previous review[351]) assumed an "octahedral wedge" (C_{2v}) geometry for the transition state in octahedral substitution, which is higly likely in view of the ability of an incoming ligand to make its closest approach to the metal centre down a three-fold axis of the octahedron (Sections II.B and II.C) and is consistent with the usual,[35,201] though not universal,[202] stereoretentivity of associatively-activated octahedral substitution in the absence of rupture of the supposedly non-reacting ligand-metal bonds.[35,201,203,204] Hush's approach, however, leaves the lengths and angles of the bonds between the metal and the incoming and outgoing ligands undetermined, and these critically affect the outcome of the calculations.

German and coworkers[205] have extended their theoretical examination of octahedral substitution[35] to cover steric effects. A pentagonal-bipyramidal (D_{5h}) geometry is assumed for the transition state, and it is found that the activation energy for *cis* replacement is always more favorable than for *trans* substitution except for the fully symmetrical (bond angles $2\pi/5$) case, which explains the predominance of stereoretention without invoking an "octahedral wedge" transition state. The bending of metal-ligand bonds is seen to require less energy than stretching; we have suggested elsewhere,[206] not altogether seriously, that metal-ligand bond fission could, in the case of a departing polyatomic ligand, be more readily achieved by a bending motion than by stretching.

Mønsted[207] has completed some angular overlap model calculations for ligand aquation in $Cr(H_2O)_5X^{(3-n)+}$ and $Cr(NH_3)_5X^{(3-n)+}$. He concludes that there is a significant associative contribution to activation, and that the "octahedral wedge" geometry is the preferred one for the transition state. The correlations that exist between ΔH^* (or $\ln k_{aq}$) and the spectroscopic d-orbital splitting parameter Dq[207-209] for Cr(III) complexes are thereby rationalized.

Burdett[210] used a molecular-orbital (MO) method in place of the traditional crystal-field approach[7] to analyze the reaction kinetics of $M(H_2O)_6^{2+}$ ions in water, with the now questionable[30] assumption of a dissociative mechanism. In the MO approach, stabilization energy losses on going to the transition state are always positive, which is conceptually more satisfying than are the occasional negative values predicted by the crystal-field theory.[7] Burdett has also published[211] a general molecular orbital treatment of substitution at square planar d^8 centres which covers the kinetic *trans* and *cis* effects; the barrier to entry of the incoming ligand is predicted to be the dominant influence on the reaction rate in a larger number of cases.

Tanaka[212] expresses the enthalpy of activation ΔH_{ex}^* for solvent exchange in terms of the enthalpies ΔH_d of solvent dissociation from the metal ion and ΔH_v of evaporation, somewhat along the lines of the Bennetto–Caldin theory.[127]

$$\Delta H_{ex}^* = a\Delta H_d + b\Delta H_v \tag{21}$$

The coefficients a and b were evaluated for the Mn^{2+}, Fe^{2+}, Co^{2+} and Ni^{2+} exchanges with several solvents, and were found to rise monotonically in that order. Since a and b can be expected to increase as the importance of dissociative activation increases, the claim of Merbach and coworkers,[30] that there is a mechanistic crossover from I_a to I_d along this series, is supported. The importance of including solvent properties as well as metal-ligand interactions had previously been emphasized by Jordan and coworkers,[213] who propose an equation

$$\Delta H^*_{ex} = a_M g_M Dq_{Ni\text{-}sol} + b_{sol} \tag{22}$$

in which a_M and b_{sol} are constants specific to a given metal ion M (or electronic configuration d^n?) and solvent *sol* respectively, while g_M converts $Dq_{Ni\text{-}sol}$ for the nickel(II) hexasolvate ion to the corresponding value for $M(sol)_6^{2+}$. The correlation is good, with a very few exceptions.

The importance of considering more than just the interactions between the metal ion and its first coordination sphere of ligands is also recognized by Rode, Reibnegger and Fujiwara,[214] who have successfully used the MESQUAC (mixed electrostatic quantum chemical) method to calculate the hydration energies of aqueous metal cations. They find that most metal ions seem not to build up more than two "significantly ordered hydration shells"; this is essentially the same conclusion as that drawn in Sections II.A–C. The experimental ΔG^*_{ex} values for aqua-exchange correlate well ($r = 0.991$) with the calculated stabilization energies $\Delta E(I)$ per water molecule in the *first* coordination sphere according to equation (23); strictly speaking, a correlation should be sought between ΔH^*_{ex} and $\Delta E(I)$, but the availability of reliable enthalpies of activation is limited and the authors show that inclusion of the $T\Delta S^*_{ex}$ term would not affect their conclusions materially.

$$\Delta G^*/kJ\,mol^{-1} = 0.118\Delta E(I) + 5.4 \tag{23}$$

Rode *et al.*[214] consider that the low coefficient of $\Delta E(I)$ in equation (23) rules out a purely dissociative mechanism for aqua exchange, and conclude that the "ascent" of a water molecule from the first coordination sphere to the outer sphere is synchronous with the "descent" of the incoming water molecule, i.e. that the mechanism is properly described as I_a or even A in all cases. Although associative contributions to activation in ligand substitution are almost certainly important in many cases and indeed "normal", as argued above, at least some of the energy reduction needed to compensate $\Delta E(I)$ in the activation process probably comes from changes in the interaction between the central metal ion and the non-reacting ligands in the first coordination sphere, as Langford has repeatedly stressed[8,31,208] and as is apparent from the general shortening of metal-ligand bonds that occurs as the primary coordination number is reduced.[64,65] The importance of recognizing the contribution of non-reacting ligands to the activation process in octahedral substitution is illustrated by the comparison made in Section IV.D between reactions of the pentaaqua- and pentaamminechromium(III) series of complexes, which receives quantitative expression in equations (18) and (19).

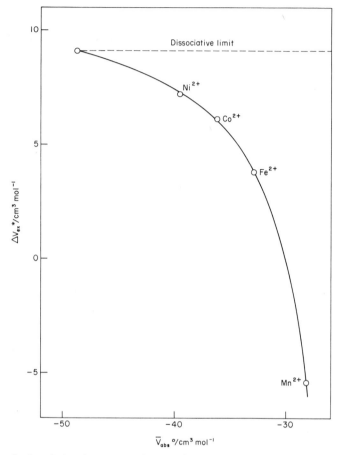

Fig. 6. Correlation between volumes of activation for water exchange on $M(H_2O)_6^{2+}$ and the corresponding absolute ionic partial molar volumes for M^{2+} (aq). The dissoviative limit refers to the hypothetical closest-packed $M(H_2O)_6^{2+}$ with $r_M = 57.2$ pm, for which V_{abs}^0 is calculated from equation (4).

F. Volume relationships

This topic has been well served by reviews in recent years[33,35,36,45,83,215-219] and comment here will be limited to one current issue.[33,34,220] For water exchange on M^{2+}(aq) (M = Mn, Fe, Co, Ni) and $M(NH_3)_5OH_2^{3+}$(aq) (M = Co, Rh, Ir, Cr) at least, ΔV_{ex}^* correlates *inversely* with the partial molar volumes $\bar{V}_{abs}^0$ of the cations, as shown in Figs 6 and 7.[34,220] The implication is that the partial molar volumes of the transition states $\bar{V}^*$ (which may be represented by $\Delta V_{ex}^* + \bar{V}_{abs}^0 + \bar{V}_{H_2O}^0$, although the last term is common

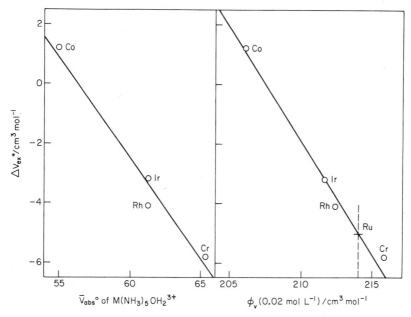

Fig. 7. Correlations of volumes of activation ΔV_{ex}^* for water exchange on $M(NH_3)_5OH_2^{3+}$ (aq) with the corresponding ionic absolute partial molar volumes at infinite dilution (left) and the apparent molar volumes ϕ_v of the aqueous perchlorate salts at a reference concentration within the experimental range (right). For $Ru(NH_3)_5OH_2^{3+}$, a measured ϕ_v value permits prediction of $\Delta V_{ex}^* = -5$ cm³ mol⁻¹.[34]

throughout the series and may be dropped) are very similar for a given water exchange reaction series, i.e. $\bar{V}^*$ is much less sensitive to the identity of M than is $\bar{V}_{abs}^0$.

A simple, generalized explanation of this may be found in equations (4) and (5), which show that variation in $\bar{V}_{abs}^0$ within a series of ions is almost entirely due to changes in the first term, which represents the metal ion plus its first coordination sphere only; the contribution to volume properties of the outer sphere is relatively insensitive to r_M and therefore to the identity of M. In an interchange mechanism, the transition state is characterized by extensive reorganization of the *outer* coordination sphere around a relatively static core complex of an "anonymous" M^{z+}. Thus, $\bar{V}_{abs}^0$ is markedly dependent on both r_M and z, but $\bar{V}^*$ should show marked sensitivity only to z (in the absence of sterically demanding ligands). In other words, the activation process corresponds to establishing a momentary predominance of outer sphere properties over inner sphere properties instead of vice-versa. The sign of ΔV_{ex}^* will be positive or negative depending upon whether expansion or contraction of the relatively well-organized ground-state assemblage of ion plus inner and outer coordination spheres is necessary to reach the less structured system, dominated by outer-sphere movements and their steric requirements, which we call the transition state.

The importance of considering the *whole* assemblage (ion + first coordination sphere + outer sphere), in discourses on kinetics and mechanisms of reactions of metal ions is nowhere more clear than in the field of volume (pressure) effects. In the aquation of $Co(NH_3)_5X^{(3-x)+}$ ions, for example, large negative changes in volume due to solvational (outer sphere) effects completely swamp a small positive "intrinsic" volume effect.[33,35]

G. Reactivity, mechanism and electronic structure

One can conclude from the foregoing discussion that associative contributions to the activation process in ligand substitution may be considered normal, and that where these are suppressed ΔH^* will be increased and the reaction will be relatively slow. The effect of heightened ΔH^* barriers will be offset somewhat by increases in ΔS^* because organizational restrictions are reduced. In terms of contour maps (c.f. Figs 3 and 4), it is easy enough to find high passes over a mountain barrier, but approaches leading to the few low ones are limited. In mechanistic parlance, bond formation by the incoming ligand serves to reduce ΔH^* (see Section IV.E), steric hindrance and ligand field effects apart, but at the cost of tying down that formerly free molecule and obstructing its free rotation, so reducing ΔS^*. Either way, the existence of isokinetic relationships is to be expected even if the degree of associative activation goes from very high to essentially zero, within a series of ligand substitution reactions. In other words, the existence of isokinetic correlations tells us nothing about the intimate mechanism of reactions.

As has long been recognized,[221-223] volume parameters often correlate loosely with the corresponding entropies, since both are similarly influenced by gain or loss of translational or rotational degrees of freedom, and consequently the more negative ΔV^* values will, as with ΔS^*, tend to be associated with the lower ΔH^*, within a series of legitimately comparable reactions such as various solvent exchanges on Mn^{2+}, Fe^{2+}, Co^{2+} and Ni^{2+} (Table 3). Where solvational change is unimportant, as in these solvent exchange reactions, low ΔV^*, ΔS^* and ΔH^* and, on balance, faster reaction rates can be expected to accompany increased associative contributions to the activation process.

Which series of reactions are "legitimately comparable" in this context? The ligands being replaced should be the same, as should the charge $z+$ on the complex and also, in an octahedral complex, the e_g electron population, i.e. the number of σ-antibonding electrons derived from metal d-orbitals, since these

TABLE 3
Rate and activation parameters for selected solvent exchange reactions

Exchange reaction	k (298.2 K) /s^{-1}	ΔH^*/kJ mol^{-1}	ΔS^*/J K^{-1} mol^{-1}	ΔV^*/cm^3 mol^{-1}	Reference
$V(H_2O)_6^{2+}/H_2O$	87	62	0	-4.1	[36]
$Mn(H_2O)_6^{2+}/H_2O$	2.1×10^7	33	6	-5.4	[30]
$Fe(H_2O)_6^{2+}/H_2O$	4.4×10^6	41	21	$+3.8$	[30]
$Co(H_2O)_6^{2+}/H_2O$	3.2×10^6	47	37	$+6.1$	[30]
$Ni(H_2O)_6^{2+}/H_2O$	3.2×10^4	57	32	$+7.2$	[30]
$Mn(CH_3OH)_6^{2+}/CH_3OH$	3.7×10^5	26	-50	-5.0	[38]
$Fe(CH_3OH)_6^{2+}/CH_3OH$	5.0×10^4	50	13	$+0.4$	[38]
$Co(CH_3OH)_6^{2+}/CH_3OH$	1.8×10^4	58	30	$+8.9$	[38]
$Ni(CH_3OH)_6^{2+}/CH_3OH$	1.0×10^3	66	34	$+11.4$	[38]
$Mn(CH_3CN)^{2+}/CH_3CN$	1.4×10^7	30	-9	-7.0	[39]
$Fe(CH_3CN)^{2+}/CH_3CN$	6.6×10^5	41	5	$+3.0$	[39]
$Co(CH_3CN)^{2+}/CH_3CN$	3.4×10^5	50	27	$+6.7^{(a)}$	[36]
$Ni(CH_3CN)^{2+}/CH_3CN$	2.8×10^3	64	37	$+7.3^{(a)}$	[36]
$V(H_2O)_6^{3+}/H_2O$	1×10^3	42	-47	-10.1	[36]
$Cr(H_2O)_6^{3+}/H_2O$	2.8×10^{-6}	110	16	-9.3	[111]
$Fe(H_2O)_6^{3+}/H_2O$	160	64	12	-5.4	[110]
$Cr(NH_3)_5OH_2^{3+}/H_2O$	5.2×10^{-5}	97	0	-5.8	[188]
$Co(NH_3)_5OH_2^{3+}/H_2O$	5.7×10^{-6}	111	28	$+1.2$	[28]
$Rh(NH_3)_5OH_2^{3+}/H_2O$	8.4×10^{-6}	103	3	-4.1	[188]
$Ir(NH_3)_5OH_2^{3+}/H_2O$	6.1×10^{-8}	118	11	-3.2	[150]

(a) Reference [206], by ^{14}N nmr (for reliable comparison with data of reference [39]).

latter two factors govern in large measure how firmly the original ligands are held. The effectiveness of associative activation, on the other hand, will be largely controlled by the ease of approach of the nucleophile along the three-fold axes; the greater the t_{2g} electron density, the less effective associative activation will be. This explains the trends in rates and activation parameters for solvent exchange as we go from $Mn^{2+}(t_{2g}^3 e_g^2)$ to $Ni^{2+}(t_{2g}^6 e_g^2)$ or from $V^{3+}(t_{2g}^2 e_g^0)$ to $Cr^{3+}(t_{2g}^3 e_g^0)$ on the basis of t_{2g} orbital occupancy (Table 3). The same applies to $Cr(NH_3)_5OH_2^{3+}$ ($t_{2g}^3 e_g^0$) in comparison with $Co(NH_3)_5OH_2^{3+}$ ($t_{2g}^6 e_g^0$). The anomalies in ΔH^* and k (but not in ΔV^* or ΔS^*, which are in each case characteristic of substantial association activation) for V^{2+} and Cr^{3+} (both $t_{2g}^3 e_g^0$) vis-à-vis Mn^{2+} and Fe^{3+}($t_{2g}^3 e_g^2$) reflect the absence of antibonding e_g electrons in the former pair, resulting in greater difficulty in dislodging the existing ligands.[32,33,36-40]

Similar trends can be expected as we descend a periodic group for a given d-electron configuration, since the metal d-orbitals become more diffuse.[32] Alternatively, one can say that the central metal atom becomes more polarizable as the atomic number increases. This explains the surprisingly high rates and low ΔH^* for substitution in $Mo(H_2O)_6^{3+}$ relative to $Cr(H_2O)_6^{3+}$.[175] For water exchange on $M(NH_3)_5OH_2^{3+}$, associative influences are minimal for $M = Co$ because of the very high t_{2g} electron densities which show up clearly as eight lobes directed along the pseudo-three-fold axes of $Co(NH_3)_6^{3+}$, $Co(CN)_6^{3-}$ and $Co(NO_2)_6^{3-}$ in X-ray diffraction difference studies.[224,225] Not surprisingly, the effectiveness of associative activation in $Rh(NH_3)_5OH_2^{3+}$ and $Ir(NH_3)_5OH_2^{3+}$ substitution reactions is apparently low too, but it seems to be necessary to admit *some* degree of entering-ligand participation to explain trends in ΔV^*, ΔH^*, steric effects and Brønsted slopes,[35,46,174,226-231] so that the resistance put up by the t_{2g}^6 configuration to nucleophilic attack would indeed seem to diminish as one goes from Co(III) to Rh(III).

The approach of a nucleophile down a three-fold axis of an octahedral complex (and, by microscopic reversibility, the departure of the expelled ligand) will not be significantly affected by pure σ-electron release from the other five ligands, since the interaction is primarily with the t_{2g} (π) orbitals of the complex, although some involvement of the a_{1g} (σ) orbitals is also possible. Consequently, the fact that the replacement of X^{x-} in aqueous $Cr(NH_3)_5X^{(3-x)+}$ is faster than in $Cr(H_2O)_5X^{(3-x)+}$ is quite consistent with a substantial degree of associative activation. The greater σ-electron releasing power of NH_3 relative to H_2O will result in labilization through weakening of the Cr—X bond whether activation is purely dissociative or significantly associative, though the importance of bond making will be less in the ammines (Section IV.D).

The situation in $Co^{III}L_5X$ complexes is more complicated because of the $3d^6$ spin-paired ($t_{2g}^6e_g^0$) configuration of the metal centres. It is now certain that aqueous $Co(H_2O)_6^{3+}$ is in the spin-paired singlet state,[711] but consideration of the Tanabe–Sugano plot for d^6 shows that the high-spin $t_{2g}^4e_g^2$ quintet state of the hexaaqua complex should be accessible at excitation energies on the order of typical activation enthalpies for ligand substitution, resulting in high lability of $Co(H_2O)_6^{3+}$ relative to $Co(NH_3)_5OH_2^{3+}$ (etc.) because of the introduction of two antibonding e_g electrons. Furthermore, the evident importance of associative activation in the hexaaqua complex[175] and lack of it in the pentaammines[6-8,35] is to be expected if the reactive form of $Co(H_2O)_6^{3+}$ has only four t_{2g} electrons rather than six.

This is not to say, however, that the singlet-quintet transition is un-important in reactions of the ammines and other strong-field complexes of cobalt(III). Vanquickenborne and Pierloot[232] have shown that stereo-chemical change in such complexes is possible only if the quintet state is involved somewhere along the reaction coordinate. This explains why stereomobility in $t_{2g}^6e_g^0$ complexes decreases as Dq increases, as this makes the quintet states less accessible. It also provides an alternative explanation for the observation (Section III.B) that ΔV^* is $\sim +14\ cm^3\ mol^{-1}$ and pressure dependent for the $trans \rightarrow cis$-isomerization of $trans$-$Co(en)_2(OH_2)_2^{3+}$, but only $+6\ cm^3\ mol^{-1}$ and pressure independent for aqua exchange on the $trans$-isomer. The increase in volume in $Co^{3+}(aq)$ on going to the quintet from the singlet state is only $4.6\ cm^3\ mol^{-1}$, according to equation (4), but the effect of the change in the ionic radius of Co^{3+} in $Co(en)_2(OH_2)_2^{3+}$ would be increased by amplification through the chelating ligands. This accounts qualitatively for the larger ΔV^* for isomerization, but it is less clear why it should be pressure dependent if there is only one (quintet) pathway to isomerization unless desolvation is also important. Presumably, both the explanations offered, here and in Section III.B, are partially correct and are complementary.

Spin change in the activation process has also been invoked on the grounds of ΔV^* data for the racemizations of tris(1,10-phenanthroline)Fe(II) ions and neutral tris(thiocarbamato)Co(III) complexes, both $3d^6$ singlet systems, in various solvents.[215] Furthermore, the possibility of spin change as a consequence of associative activation at Cr(III) and other centres was raised in 1968 by Spees, Perumareddi and Adamson,[232] and deserves reconsideration. Nevertheless, the kinetic behaviour of cobalt(III) complexes seems increasingly to be anomalous in the context of trivalent transition metal cations,[25,150] and from this standpoint Langford's choice[31] of the $Co(NH_3)_5OH_2^{3+}$ reaction as a representative one when interpreting ΔV^* values for water exchange appears to be inappropriate. We note that the ionic radius of Co^{3+} (low spin) is several pm smaller[65] than the cavities formed by six closest-packed H_2O or NH_3 ligands, and that unusually severe steric congestion is revealed on going from $Co(NH_3)_5OH_2^{3+}$ to $Co(NH_2CH_3)_5OH_2^{3+}$,[46] so that volume relationships involving the penta-amminecobalt(III) core are not likely to be representative of transition metal ions in general.

H. Anomalous reactivity

Several examples exist of complexes of Cr(III) which show anomalously high lability. These include porphinato-complexes,[233-235] Schiff base chelates,[236] and $Cr(EDTA)OH_2^-$ and related species,[237-241] and the phenomenon may be general for other usually non-labile centres such as Ru(III).[242] These serve to remind us that generalizations concerning the characteristics of simple aqua-ions, ammines, etc. may not be directly extensible to seemingly analogous complexes in which large multidentate ligands are present—indeed, it was stated in the Introduction that complexes of macrocyclic ligands and similar chelates would generally not be considered for this reason.

Nevertheless, the lability of these chelates may not be so very unusual. Porphinato complexes contain two amido-type nitrogens; thus, the appropriate reference complexes would not be ammines like *trans*-$Cr(NH_3)_4X_2^{(3-2x)+}$ but rather $Cr(NH_3)_2(NH_2)_2X_2^{(1-2x)+}$, a double conjugate base for which very high lability would most certainly be expected. A similar argument could be advanced to explain the stopped-flow-range lability of Schiff base complexes such as N,N'-ethylenebis(salicylideniminato)Cr(III), although this is an O-base rather than an N-base complex; Ramasami and coworkers[236] point out that the lability could originate in distortion of the ligand environment of Cr(III) in the ground state, but the authors of the original structural study[243] regarded the departure from octahedral geometry as "slight".

Finally, the lability of many polycarboxylate complexes may well be due to internal associative activation, possibly by a pendant carboxylate group as suggested by Ogino,[239] Sykes[238] and Shepherd[240] and their coworkers. This does not explain the moderate enhancements of lability in aminopoly-carboxylates of Cr(III) in which there is no pendant carboxylate function, however, and Goff *et al.*[241] again draw attention to deviations from exact octahedral coordination in these complexes. Another possibility is that internal associative activation *is* the labilizing factor, but that it results from ring closure of monodentate carboxylate ligands to form transient bidentate structures. We suggested this previously to account for the specific *cis*-labilizing effect of coordinated nitrate[168] in simple Cr(III) ammines, but it seems to apply to carboxylate functions equally well[169-171] and, multiplied several times over in a *poly*carboxylate complex, could well explain the anomalous lability.

The essential point is that many of the kinetic features considered special in multidentate and macrocyclic complexes, or molecules of biological interest having active metal centres, may well be manifestations of properties that are best demonstrated in simple metal-ligand systems but which are compounded in the more complicated complexes.

The continuation of studies of the simplest systems involving metal ions in solution needs no apology.

Acknowledgements

Figures 1, 2, 6 and 7 are reproduced by courtesy of the National Research Council Canada and the Editorial Board of the *Canadian Journal of Chemistry*. I thank the Natural Sciences and Engineering Research Council Canada (and formerly the National Research Council) for consistent and unrestricted financial support of my research since 1964.

REFERENCES

[1] Endicott, J. F.; Durham, B. *In* "Coordination Chemistry of Macrocyclic Complexes"; Melson, G. A., Ed.; Plenum Press: New York, 1979; p. 393.

[2] Lockhart, J. C. *In* "Advances in Inorganic and Bioinorganic Mechanisms"; Vol. 1. Sykes, A. G., Ed.; Academic Press: London, 1982, p. 217.

[3] Saito, K.; Sasaki, Y. *In* "Advances in Inorganic and Bioinorganic Mechanisms"; Vol. 1. Sykes, A. G., Ed.; Academic Press: London, 1982, p. 179.

[4] Espenson, J. H. *In* "Advances in Inorganic and Bioinorganic Mechanisms"; Vol. 1. Sykes, A. G., Ed.; Academic Press: London, 1982, p. 1.

[5] Hung, Y.; Kung, W.-J.; Taube, H. *Inorg. Chem.* **1981**, *20*, 457.

[6] Burgess, J. "Metal Ions in Solution"; Ellis Horwood Ltd.: Chichester, 1978.

[7] Basolo, F.; Pearson, R. G. "Mechanisms of Inorganic Reactions"; 2nd Edn, J. Wiley: New York, 1967.

[8] Langford, C. H.; Gray, H. B. "Ligand Substitution Processes"; Benjamin: New York, 1966.

[9] Haim, A.; Wilmarth, W. K. *Inorg. Chem.* **1962**, *1*, 573, 583.

[10] Haim, A. *Inorg. Chem.* **1982**, *21*, 2887.

[11] Burnett, M. G.; Gilfillan, W. M. *J. Chem. Soc. Dalton Trans.* **1981**, 1578.

[12] Reynolds, W. L.; Hafezi, S. *Inorg. Chem.* **1978**, *17*, 1819.

[13] Reynolds, W. L.; Alton, E. R. *Inorg. Chem.* **1978**, *17*, 3355.

[14] Jackson, W. G.; Lawrance, G. A.; Sargeson, A. M. *Inorg. Chem.* **1980**, *19*, 1001.

[15] Buckingham, D. A.; Clark, C. R.; Lewis, T. W. *Inorg. Chem.* **1979**, *18*, 1985.

[16] Boreham, C. J.; Buckingham, D. A.; Clark, C. R. *Inorg. Chem.* **1979**, *18*, 1990.

[17] Buckingham, D. A.; Clark, C. R.; Webley, W. S. *J. Chem. Soc. Dalton Trans.* **1980**, 2255.

[18] Buckingham, D. A.; Edwards, J. D.; McLaughlin, G. M. *Inorg. Chem.* **1982**, *21*, 2770.

[19] Jackson, W. G.; Sargeson, A. M. *Inorg. Chem.* **1978**, *17*, 1348.

[20] Henderson, R. A.; Tobe, M. L. *Inorg. Chem.* **1977**, *16*, 2576.

[21] Tinner, U.; Marty, W. *Inorg. Chem.* **1981**, *20*, 3750.

[22] van Eldik, R.; Palmer, D. A.; Kelm, H. *Inorg. Chem.* **1979**, *18*, 1250.

[23] Coronas, J. M.; Vicente, R.; Ferrer, M. *Inorg. Chem. Acta* **1981**, *49*, 259.

[24] Posey, F. A.; Taube, H. *J. Amer. Chem. Soc.* **1953**, *75*, 1465; **1956**, *78*, 15.

[25] Lo, S. T. D.; Sisley, M. J.; Swaddle, T. W. *Can. J. Chem.* **1978**, *56*, 2609.

[26] Lo, S. T. D.; Oudeman, E. M.; Hansen, J. C.; Swaddle, T. W. *Can. J. Chem.* **1976**, *54*, 3685.

[27] Reynolds, W. L.; El-Nasr, M. S. *Inorg. Chem.* **1979**, *18*, 2864.

[28] Hunt, H. R.; Taube, H. *J. Amer. Chem. Soc.* **1958**, *80*, 2642.

[29] Tong, S. B.; Krouse, H. R.; Swaddle, T. W. *Inorg. Chem.* **1976**, *15*, 2643.

[30] Ducommun, Y.; Newman, K. E.; Merbach, A. E. *Inorg. Chem.* **1980**, *19*, 3696.

[31] Langford, C. H. *Inorg. Chem.* **1979**, *18*, 3288.

[32] Swaddle, T. W. *Inorg. Chem.* **1980**, *19*, 3203.

[33] Swaddle, T. W. *In* "Mechanistic Aspects of Inorganic Reactions"; Rorabacher, D. B. and Endicott, J. F., Eds; American Chemical Society, Washington, DC; ACS Symp. Ser., 1982, *198*, 39.

[34] Swaddle, T. W.; Mak, M. K. S. *Can. J. Chem.* **1983**, *61*, 473.

[35] Swaddle, T. W. *Coordin. Chem. Rev.* **1974**, *14*, 217.

[36] Merbach, A. E. *Pure Appl. Chem.* **1982**, *54*, 1479.

[37] Newman, K. E.; Merbach, A. E. *Inorg. Chem.* **1980**, *19*, 2481.

[38] Meyer, F. K.; Newman, K. E.; Merbach, A. E. Inorg. Chem. 1979, 18, 2142; J. Amer. Chem. Soc. 1979, 101, 5588.
[39] Yano, Y.; Fairhurst, M. T.; Swaddle, T. W. Inorg. Chem. 1980, 19, 3267.
[40] Sisley, M. J.; Yano, Y.; Swaddle, T. W. Inorg. Chem. 1982, 21, 1141.
[41] Ramasami, T.; Sykes, A. G. Inorg. Chem. 1976, 15, 2885; J. Chem. Soc. Chem. Commun. 1976, 378.
[42] Ramasami, T.; Taylor, R. S.; Sykes, A. G. Inorg. Chem. 1976, 15, 2318.
[43] Nor, O.; Sykes, A. G. J. Chem. Soc. Dalton Trans. 1973, 1232.
[44] Ferrer, M.; Sykes, A. G. Inorg. Chem. 1979, 18, 3345.
[45] Swaddle, T. W. Rev. Phys. Chem. Jap. 1980, 50, 230.
[46] Swaddle, T. W. Can. J. Chem. 1977, 55, 3166.
[47] Buchacek, R. J.; Harris, G. M. Inorg. Chem. 1976, 15, 926.
[48] Pavelich, M. J.; Maxey, S. M.; Pfaff, R. C. Inorg. Chem. 1978, 17, 564.
[49] Caminiti, R.; Licheri, G.; Piccaluga, G.; Pinna, G. J. Chem. Phys. 1976, 65, 3134; 1978, 69, 1; Faraday Disc. Chem. Soc. 1978, 64, 64.
[50] Licheri, G.; Piccaluga, G.; Pinna, G. J. Chem. Phys. 1975, 63, 4412; 1976, 64, 2437.
[51] Albright, J. N. J. Chem. Phys. 1972, 56, 3783.
[52] Caminiti, R.; Licheri, G.; Paschina, G.; Piccaluga, G.; Pinna, G. J. Chem. Phys. 1980, 72, 4522.
[53] Caminiti, R.; Licheri, G.; Piccaluga, G.; Pinna, G.; Radnai, T. J. Chem. Phys. 1979, 71, 2473.
[54] Sandström, M.; Persson, I.; Ahrland, S. Acta Chem. Scand. 1978, A32, 607.
[55] Wertz, D. L.; Steele, M. L. Inorg. Chem. 1980, 19, 1652.
[56] Magini, M. Inorg. Chem. 1982, 21, 1535.
[57] Habenschuss, A.; Spedding, F. H. J. Chem. Phys. 1979, 70, 2797, 3758; 1980, 73, 442.
[58] Glaser, J.; Johansson, G. Acta Chem. Scand. 1982, A36, 125.
[59] Sandstrom, D. R.; Dodgen, H. W.; Lytle, F. W. J. Chem. Phys. 1977, 67, 473.
[60] Sandstrom, D. R. J. Chem. Phys. 1979, 71, 2381.
[61] Lincoln, S. F. Coordin. Chem. Rev. 1971, 6, 309.
[62] Millero, F. J. In "Water and Aqueous Solutions"; Horne, R. A., Ed.; Wiley-Interscience: New York, 1972, Chapter 13.
[63] Akitt, J. W. J. Chem. Soc. A 1971, 2347.
[64] Shannon, R. D.; Prewitt, C. T. Acta Cryst. 1969, B25, 925.
[65] Shannon, R. D. Acta Cryst. 1976, A32, 751.
[66] Spedding, F. H.; Pikal, M. J.; Ayres, B. O. J. Phys. Chem. 1966, 70, 2440.
[67] Rodesiler, P. F.; Amma, E. L. J. Chem. Soc. Chem. Commun. 1982, 182.
[68] Swaddle, T. W.; Fabes, L. Can. J. Chem. 1980, 58, 1418.
[69] Bell, R. A.; Christoph, G. G.; Fronczek, F. R.; Marsh, R. E. Science 1975, 190, 151.
[70] Lau, Y. K.; Ikuta, S.; Kebarle, P. J. Amer. Chem. Soc. 1982, 104, 1462.
[71] Navon, G. J. Phys. Chem. 1981, 85, 3547.
[72] Beutler, P.; Gamsjäger, H. J. Chem. Soc. Chem. Commun. 1976, 554; J. Chem. Soc. Dalton Trans. 1979, 1415.
[73] Harzion, Z.; Navon, G. Inorg. Chem. 1980, 19, 2236; 1982, 21, 2606.
[74] Gröning, Ö.; Drakenberg, T.; Elding, L. I. Inorg. Chem. 1982, 21, 1820.
[75] Fuoss, R. M. J. Phys. Chem. 1978, 82, 2427.
[76] Güntelberg, E. Z. Phys. Chem. 1926, 123, 199.
[77] Akitt, J. W. J. Chem. Soc. Dalton Trans. 1973, 1177.

[78] Clack, D. W.; Farrimond, M. S. *J. Chem. Soc. A* **1971**, 299.
[79] LoSurdo, A.; Millero, F. J. *J. Phys. Chem.* **1980**, *84*, 710.
[80] Shimizu, K. *Bull. Chem. Soc. Jap.* **1979**, *52*, 2429.
[81] Millero, F. J.; Ward, G. K.; Lepple, F. K.; Hoff, E. V. *J. Phys. Chem.* **1974**, *78*, 1636.
[82] Padova, J. *J. Chem. Phys.* **1964**, *40*, 691.
[83] Stranks, D. R. *Pure Appl. Chem.* **1974**, *38*, 303.
[84] Palmer, D. A.; Watts, D. W. *Inorg. Chem.* **1971**, *10*, 281.
[85] Sakaguchi, U.; Nakazawa, H.; Yoneda, H. *J. Chem. Soc. Chem. Commun.* **1979**, 356.
[86] Perlmutter-Hayman, B.; Tapuhi, E. *J. Coordin. Chem.* **1978**, *8*, 75.
[87] Burnett, M. G. *J. Chem. Soc. A* **1970**, 2480, 2486, 2490.
[88] Barber, E. C.; Reynolds, W. L. *Inorg. Chem.* **1973**, *12*, 951.
[89] Archer, D. W.; East, D. A.; Monk, C. B. *J. Chem. Soc.* **1965**, 720.
[90] Alei, M. *Inorg. Chem.* **1964**, *3*, 44.
[91] Johannson, L. *Chem. Scripta* **1976**, *9*, 30.
[92] Reimarsson, P.; Lindman, B. *Inorg. Nucl. Chem. Lett.* **1977**, *13*, 449.
[93] Heck, L. *Inorg. Nucl. Chem. Lett.* **1971**, *7*, 701.
[94] Johannson, L. *Coordin. Chem. Rev.* **1974**, *12*, 241.
[95] Lo, S. T. D.; Swaddle, T. W. *Inorg. Chem.* **1976**, *15*, 1181.
[96] Campbell, M. B. M.; Wendt, M. R.; Monk, C. B. *J. Chem. Soc. Dalton Trans.* **1972**, 1714.
[97] Naik, N. C.; Nanda, R. K. *J. Inorg. Nucl. Chem.* **1974**, *36*, 3793.
[98] Bott, A. L.; Poë, A. J.; Shaw, K. *J. Chem. Soc. A* **1970**, 1745.
[99] Monacelli, F.; Viel, E. *Inorg. Chim. Acta* **1967**, *1*, 467.
[100] Duffy, N. V.; Earley, J. E. *J. Amer. Chem. Soc.* **1967**, *89*, 272.
[101] Spiro, T. G.; Revesz, A.; Lee, J. *J. Amer. Chem. Soc.* **1968**, *90*, 4000.
[102] Hemmes, P. *J. Phys. Chem.* **1972**, *76*, 895.
[103] Chen, C.-T.; Millero, F. J. *J. Solution Chem.* **1977**, *6*, 589.
[104] Sisley, M. J.; Swaddle, T. W. *Inorg. Chem.* **1981**, *20*, 2799.
[105] Adams, W. A.; Davis, A. R.; Chatterjee, R. M. *J. Phys. Chem.* **1978**, *82*, 496.
[106] Swaddle, T. W.; Guastalla, G. *Inorg. Chem.* **1969**, *8*, 1604.
[107] Waysbort, D.; Evenor, M.; Navon, G. *Inorg. Chem.* **1975**, *14*, 514.
[108] Grant, M.; Jordan, R. B. *Inorg. Chem.* **1981**, *20*, 55.
[109] Perlmutter-Hayman, B.; Tapuhi, E. *J. Coord. Chem.* **1979**, *9*, 177; **1980**, *10*, 219.
[110] Swaddle, T. W.; Merbach, A. E. *Inorg. Chem.* **1981**, *20*, 4212.
[111] Stranks, D. R.; Swaddle, T. W. *J. Amer. Chem. Soc.* **1971**, *93*, 2783.
[112] Swaddle, T. W.; Kong, P.-C. *Can. J. Chem.* **1970**, *48*, 3223.
[113] Thompson, M.; Connick, R. E. *Inorg. Chem.* **1981**, *20*, 2279.
[114] Finholt, J. E.; Thompson, M. E.; Connick, R. E. *Inorg. Chem.* **1981**, *20*, 4151.
[115] Kolaczkowski, R. W.; Plane, R. A. *Inorg. Chem.* **1964**, *3*, 322.
[116] Holwerda, R. A.; Peterson, J. S. *Inorg. Chem.* **1980**, *19*, 1775.
[117] Knudsen, J. M.; Larsen, E.; Nielsen, J. E.; Nielsen, O. F. *Acta Chem. Scand.* **1975**, *A29*, 833.
[118] Akitt, J. W.; Farthing, A. *J. Chem. Soc. Dalton Trans.* **1981**, 1609, 1617, 1624.
[119] Akitt, J. W.; Mann, B. E. *J. Magn. Reson.* **1981**, *44*, 584.
[120] Meyer, F. K.; Monnerat, A. R.; Newmann, K. E.; Merbach, A. E. *Inorg. Chem.* **1982**, *21*, 774.
[121] Stillinger, F. H. *Science* **1980**, *209*, 451.
[122] Rice, S. A.; Sceats, M. G. *J. Phys. Chem.* **1981**, *85*, 1108.

[123] Benson, S. W. *J. Amer. Chem. Soc.* **1978**, *100*, 5640.
[124] Ohtomo, N.; Tokiwano, K.; Arakawa, K. *Bull. Chem. Soc. Jap.* **1981**, *54*, 1802.
[125] Symons, M. C. R. *Acc. Chem. Res.* **1981**, *14*, 179.
[126] Ahrland, S. *Pure Appl. Chem.* **1979**, *51*, 2019.
[127] Bennetto, H. P.; Caldin, E. F. *J. Chem. Soc. A* **1971**, 2191, 2198; *J. Solution Chem.* **1973**, *2*, 217.
[128] Langford, C. H.; Tong, J. P. K.; Merbach, A. E. *Can. J. Chem.* **1975**, *53*, 702.
[129] Coetzee, J. F.; Gilles, D. M. *Inorg. Chem.* **1976**, *15*, 400, 405.
[130] Chattopadhyay, P. K.; Coetzee, J. F. *Inorg. Chem.* **1973**, *12*, 113.
[131] Coetzee, J. F. *Pure Appl. Chem.* **1977**, *49*, 27.
[132] Langford, C. H.; Tong, J. P. K. *Acc. Chem. Res.* **1977**, *10*, 258.
[133] Bennetto, H. P.; Imani, Z. S. *J. Chem. Soc. Chem. Commun.* **1975**, 333.
[134] Dewar, M. J. S. "The Molecular Orbital Theory of Organic Chemistry"; McGraw-Hill Book Co.: New York, 1969, p. 306.
[135] Jencks, W. P. *Acc. Chem. Res.* **1980**, *13*, 161.
[136] Jencks, W. P. *Chem. Soc. Rev.* **1981**, *10*, 345.
[137] More O'Ferrall, R. A. *J. Chem. Soc. B* **1970**, 274.
[138] Harris, J. M.; Shafer, S. G.; Moffatt, J. R.; Becker, A. R. *J. Amer. Chem. Soc.* **1979**, *101*, 3295.
[139] Wernberg, O.; Hazell, A. *J. Chem. Soc. Dalton Trans.* **1980**, 973.
[140] Hall, A. J.; Satchell, D. P. N. *J. Chem. Soc. Chem. Commun.* **1976**, 163.
[141] Ewen, J. A.; Darensbourg, D. J. *J. Amer. Chem. Soc.* **1976**, *98*, 4317.
[142] Tewari, P. H.; Gaver, R. W.; Wilcox, H. K.; Wilmarth, W. K. *Inorg. Chem.* **1967**, *6*, 611.
[143] Toma, H. E.; Malin, J. M. *Inorg. Chem.* **1973**, *12*, 1039.
[144] Macartney, D.; McAuley, A. *Inorg. Chem.* **1981**, *20*, 748; *J. Chem. Soc. Dalton Trans.* **1981**, 1780.
[145] Toma, H. E.; Malin, J. M. *Inorg. Chem.* **1973**, *12*, 2080.
[146] Palmer, D. A.; Kelm, H. *Z. Anorg. Allgem. Chem.* **1979**, *450*, 50.
[147] Blandamer, M. J.; Burgess, J.; Dupree, M.; Hamshere, S. J. *J. Chem. Res. (S)* **1978**, 58.
[148] Dixon, N. E.; Jackson, W. G.; Marty, W.; Sargeson, A. M. *Inorg. Chem.* **1982**, *21*, 688.
[149] Eigen, M. *Pure Appl. Chem.* **1963**, *6*, 97.
[150] Tong, S. B.; Swaddle, T. W. *Inorg. Chem.* **1974**, *13*, 1538.
[151] Stranks, D. R.; Vanderhoek, N. *Inorg. Chem.* **1976**, *15*, 2639.
[152] Erni, I.; Geier, G. *Helv. Chim. Acta* **1979**, *62*, 1007.
[153] Raycheba, J. M. T.; Geier, G. *Inorg. Chem.* **1979**, *18*, 2486.
[154] Levine, R. D. *J. Phys. Chem.* **1979**, *83*, 159.
[155] Scandola, F.; Balzani, V. *J. Amer. Chem. Soc.* **1979**, *101*, 6140.
[156] Ekstrom, A.; McLaren, A. B.; Smyth, L. E. *Inorg. Chem.* **1975**, *14*, 2899.
[157] Agmon, N. *Int. J. Chem. Kinetics* **1981**, *13*, 333.
[158] Wolfe, S.; Mitchell, D. J.; Schlegel, H. B. *J. Amer. Chem. Soc.* **1981**, *103*, 7692, 7694; Brauman, J. I. *In* "Mechanistic Aspects of Inorganic Reactions"; Rorabacher, D. B. and Endicott, J. F., Eds; American Chemical Society, Washington, DC; ACS Symp. Ser., 1982, *198*, 81, and ensuing discussion.
[159] Leffler, J. E.; Grunwald, E. "Rates and Equilibria of Organic Reactions"; J. Wiley: New York, 1963.
[160] Johnson, C. D. *Chem. Rev.* **1975**, *75*, 755.
[161] Swaddle, T. W.; Guastalla, G. *Inorg. Chem.* **1968**, *7*, 1915.

[162] Exner, O. *Coll. Czech. Chem. Commun.* **1974**, *39*, 515.
[163] Cobble, J. W.; Murray, R. C. *Faraday Disc. Chem. Soc.* **1978**, *64*, 144.
[164] Tyagi, S. C.; Khan, A. A. *Inorg. Chem.* **1979**, *18*, 1515; *J. Inorg. Nucl. Chem.* **1978**, *40*, 1899; *J. Chem. Soc. Dalton Trans.* **1979**, 420.
[165] Mitchell, M. L.; Montag, T.; Espenson, J. H.; King, E. L. *Inorg. Chem.* **1975**, *14*, 2862.
[166] Wang, S.-J.; King, E. L. *Inorg. Chem.* **1980**, *19*, 1506.
[167] Hansen, P. J.; Birk, J. P. *Int. J. Chem. Kinetics* **1981**, *13*, 1203.
[168] Guastalla, G.; Swaddle, T. W. *Inorg. Chem.* **1974**, *13*, 61; *Can. J. Chem.* **1974**, *52*, 527.
[169] Choi, S. N.; Carlyle, D. W. *Inorg. Chem.* **1974**, *13*, 1818.
[170] Kallen, T. W.; Hamm, R. E. *Inorg. Chem.* **1979**, *18*, 2151.
[171] Ramasami, T.; Wharton, R. K.; Sykes, A. G. *Inorg. Chem.* **1975**, *14*, 359.
[172] Kane-Maguire, L. A. P.; Thomas, G. *J. Chem. Soc. Dalton Trans.* **1975**, 1890.
[173] Romeo, R.; Tobe, M. L. *Inorg. Chem.* **1974**, *13*, 1991.
[174] Mønsted, L. *Acta Chem. Scand.* **1978**, *A32*, 377.
[175] Sasaki, Y.; Sykes, A. G. *J. Chem. Soc. Dalton Trans.* **1975**, 1048.
[176] Espenson, J. H. *Inorg. Chem.* **1969**, *8*, 1554.
[177] Hunt, H. R.; Taube, H. *J. Amer. Chem. Soc.* **1958**, *80*, 2642.
[178] Mentasti, E.; Secco, F.; Venturi, M. *Inorg. Chem.* **1982**, *21*, 602, 2314.
[179] Mentasti, E. *Inorg. Chem.* **1979**, *18*, 1512.
[180] Mentasti, E., Baiocchi, C. *J. Coord. Chem.* **1980**, *10*, 229.
[181] Perlmutter-Hayman, B.; Tapuhi, E. *J. Coord. Chem.* **1976**, *6*, 31.
[182] Romeo, R.; Cusumano, M. *Inorg. Chim. Acta* **1981**, *49*, 167.
[183] Kotowski, M.; Palmer, D. A.; Kelm, H. *Inorg. Chim. Acta* **1980**, *44*, L113.
[184] Mønsted, L.; Mønsted, O. *Acta Chem. Scand.* **1980**, *A34*, 259.
[185] Merbach, A. E.; Moore, P.; Howarth, O. W.; McAteer, C. H. *Inorg. Chim. Acta* **1980**, *39*, 129.
[186] Lo, S. T. D.; Swaddle, T. W. *Inorg. Chem.* **1975**, *14*, 1878.
[187] Margerum, D. W.; Cayley, G. R.; Weatherburn, D. C.; Pagenkopf, G. W. "Coordination Chemistry"; Martell, A. E., Ed.; American Chemical Society: Washington, DC, 1978; Chapter 1, Vol. 2.
[188] Swaddle, T. W.; Stranks, D. R. *J. Amer. Chem. Soc.* **1972**, *94*, 8357.
[189] Guastalla, G.; Swaddle, T. W. *Can. J. Chem.* **1973**, *51*, 821.
[190] Jones, T. P.; Phillips, J. K. *J. Chem. Soc. A* **1968**, 674.
[191] Ardon, M.; Sutin, N. *Inorg. Chem.* **1967**, *6*, 2268.
[192] Swaddle, T. W. *J. Amer. Chem. Soc.* **1967**, *89*, 4338.
[193] Mønsted, O.; Mønsted, L. *Acta Chem. Scand.* **1973**, *27*, 2121.
[194] Wakefield, D. K.; Schaap, W. B. *Inorg. Chem.* **1969**, *8*, 512.
[195] Riccieri, P.; Zinato, E. *Inorg. Chem.* **1980**, *19*, 853.
[196] Postmus, C.; King, E. L. *J. Amer. Chem. Soc.* **1955**, *59*, 1216.
[197] Lindholm, R. D.; Zinato, E.; Adamson, A. W. *J. Phys. Chem.* **1967**, *71*, 3713.
[198] Zinato, E.; Furland, C.; Lanna, G.; Riccieri, P. *Inorg. Chem.* **1972**, *11*, 1746.
[199] Jones, W. E.; Carey, L. R.; Swaddle, T. W. *Can. J. Chem.* **1972**, *50*, 2739.
[200] Hush, N. S. *Aust. J. Chem.* **1962**, *15*, 378.
[201] Jackson, W. G.; Fee, W. W. *Inorg. Chem.* **1975**, *14*, 1161, 1170, 1174.
[202] Mønsted, L.; Mønsted, O. *Acta Chem. Scand.* **1973**, *27*, 2121; **1974**, *A28*, 23, 569; **1975**, *A29*, 29; **1978**, *A32*, 19; **1982**, *A36*, 365.
[203] Vaughn, J. W. *Coordin. Chem. Rev.* **1981**, *39*, 265.
[204] Linck, R. G. *Inorg. Chem.* **1977**, *16*, 3143.

[205] Moiseev, I. I.; Vargaftig, M. N.; Dogonadze, R. R.; German, E. D.; Kuznetsov, A. M. *J. Coord. Chem.* **1977**, *6*, 141.
[206] Fairhurst, M. T.; Yano, Y.; Swaddle, T. W. *Inorg. Chem.* **1980**, *19*, 3267.
[207] Mønsted, O. *Acta Chem. Scand.* **1978**, *A32*, 297.
[208] Langford, C. H. *Can. J. Chem.* **1971**, *49*, 1497.
[209] Glerup, J.; Mønsted, O.; Schaeffer, C. E. *Inorg. Chem.* **1976**, *15*, 1399.
[210] Burdett, J. K. *J. Chem. Soc. Dalton Trans.* **1976**, 1725.
[211] Burdett, J. K. *Inorg. Chem.* **1977**, *16*, 3013.
[212] Tanaka, M. *Inorg. Chim. Acta* **1981**, *54*, L129.
[213] Rusnak, L. L.; Yang, E. S.; Jordan, R. B. *Inorg. Chem.* **1978**, *17*, 1810.
[214] Rode, B. M.; Reibnegger, G. J.; Fujiwara, S. *J. Chem. Soc. Faraday II* **1980**, *76*, 1268.
[215] Lawrance, G. S.; Stranks, D. R. *Acc. Chem. Res.* **1979**, *12*, 403.
[216] Palmer, D. A.; Kelm, H. *In* "High Pressure Chemistry"; Kelm, H., Ed.; Reidel: Dordrecht, 1978, p. 435.
[217] Palmer, D. A.; Kelm, H. *Coordin. Chem. Rev.* **1981**, *36*, 89.
[218] van Eldik, R.; Kelm, H. *Rev. Phys. Chem. Jap.* **1980**, *50*, 185.
[219] Asano, T.; le Noble, W. J. *Chem. Rev.* **1978**, *78*, 407.
[220] Swaddle, T. W. *J. Chem. Soc. Chem. Commun.* **1982**, 832.
[221] Hamann, S. D. "The Physico-Chemical Effects of Pressure"; Butterworths: London, 1957, pp. 195–196.
[222] Hepler, L. G. *J. Phys. Chem.* **1965**, *69*, 965.
[223] Twigg, M. V. *Inorg. Chim. Acta* **1977**, *24*, L84.
[224] Iwata, M.; Saito, Y. *Acta Cryst.* **1973**, *B29*, 822.
[225] Ohba, S.; Toriumi, K.; Sato, S.; Saito, Y. *Acta Cryst.* **1979**, *B34*, 3535.
[226] Johnson, S. A.; Basolo, F.; Pearson, R. G. *J. Amer. Chem. Soc.* **1963**, *85*, 1741.
[227] Zipp, S. G.; Madan, S. K. *Inorg. Chem.* **1976**, *15*, 587.
[228] Chatterjee, C.; Basak, A. K. *Bull. Chem. Soc. Jap.* **1979**, *52*, 2710.
[229] Poë, A.; Vuik, C. P. J. *Inorg. Chem.* **1980**, *19*, 1771.
[230] Borghi, E.; Monacelli, F. *Inorg. Chim. Acta* **1977**, *23*, 53.
[231] Thirst, A. J.; Vaughan, D. H. *J. Inorg. Nucl. Chem.* **1981**, *43*, 2889.
[232] Spees, S. T.; Perumareddi, J. R.; Adamson, A. W. *J. Amer. Chem. Soc.* **1968**, *90*, 6626.
[233] Fleischer, E. B.; Krishnamurthy, M. *J. Amer. Chem. Soc.* **1971**, *93*, 3784.
[234] Ashley, K. R.; Leipoldt, J. G.; Joshi, V. K. *Inorg. Chem.* **1980**, *19*, 1608.
[235] O'Brien, P.; Sweigart, D. A. *Inorg. Chem.* **1982**, *21*, 2094.
[236] Prasad, D. R.; Ramasami, T.; Ramaswamy, D.; Santappa, M. *Inorg. Chem.* **1980**, *19*, 3181; **1982**, *21*, 850.
[237] Ogino, H.; Watanabe, T.; Tanaka, N. *Chem. Lett.* **1974**, 91; *Inorg. Chem.* **1975**, *14*, 2093.
[238] Sulfab, Y.; Taylor, R. S.; Sykes, A. G. *Inorg. Chem.* **1976**, 15, 2388.
[239] Ogino, H.; Shimura, M.; Tanaka, N. *Inorg. Chem.* **1979**, *18*, 2497.
[240] Guardalabene, J.; Gulnac, S.; Keder, N.; Shepherd, R. E. *Inorg. Chem.* **1979**, *18*, 22.
[241] Gerdom, L. E.; Baenziger, N. A.; Goff, H. M. *Inorg. Chem.* **1981**, *20*, 1606.
[242] Matsubara, T.; Creutz, C. *J. Amer. Chem. Soc.* **1978**, *100*, 6255.
[243] Coggon, P.; McPhail, A. T.; Mabbs, F. E.; Richards, A.; Thornley, A. S. *J. Chem. Soc. Dalton Trans.* **1970**, 3296.

Rapid-Reaction Techniques and Bioinorganic Reaction Mechanisms

R. G. Wilkins

Department of Chemistry,
New Mexico State University

I. INTRODUCTION

The 1950s saw the birth of many rapid reaction techniques which are now playing an important role in interpreting the complexities of chemical reactions. For recent reviews see references [1–9]. Many chemical processes are rapid, by which we mean that they are complete within a few seconds. Even slow reactions, easily measurable without recourse to specialized techniques, often contain a rapid component or components, the investigation of which is

139

essential for a complete accounting of the kinetic data. Furthermore, slow reactions will be pushed into the rapid time domain if large concentrations of protein (e.g. enzymes) are used, these large concentrations more closely simulating the biological conditions. Rapid reaction techniques are necessary for measuring the rates of many fundamental reactions, including acid-base reactions, interaction of ligands with metalloproteins (a vast area including enzyme catalysis), electron transfer processes and spin-state changes, protein conformational changes, protein-protein interactions and protein unfolding and refolding, all of which will be alluded to in this review. The time range will span relatively slow processes comparable with the blink of an eyelid (~ 0.2 s[10]) to such short times (10^{-12} s) that light travels only 0.03 cm in that time interval! It is still true, however, that "The use of rapid reaction techniques is a tool which should supplement the general chemical study of any problem and cannot profitably be promoted to be an end in itself".[11] Therefore, the rate of a chemical reaction, is as important for determining the use of rapid techniques for producing sizable amounts of reactive intermediates for kinetic and structural characterization. These and other applications to bioinorganic reactions will be emphasized in the review which will also survey the techniques at our disposal.

A. Abbreviations

τ = relaxation time

LADH = liver alcohol dehydrogenase

NADH = reduced nicotinamide adenine dinucleotide

Hb(Mb) = hemoglobin (myoglobin)

Mns   = mansyl

Cbz   = carbobenzoxy

HRP   = horseradish peroxidase

TPP   = meso-$\alpha,\beta,\gamma,\delta$-tetraphenylporphine

MP-11 = microperoxidase—the heme portion of the cytochrome c molecule with aminoacids 11 through 21 still attached; it has peroxidase activity

EDTA = ethylenediamine-N,N,N',N'-tetraacetate

SF   = stopped flow

TJ   = temperature jump

EJ   = electric field jump

CD   = circular dichroism

CIDNP = chemically-induced dynamic nuclear polarization

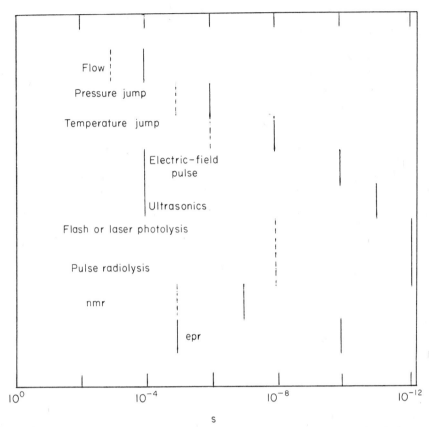

Fig. 1. Time coverage for various rapid-reaction techniques. The shorter time limit of the method, as generally employed, is indicated by a broken line, while that currently obtained in some laboratories is shown by a full line. The longer time limit is sometimes unlimited, but it may depend on the inherent instability of the system over long times.

II. RAPID REACTION MEASUREMENT

There are a variety of methods available for the study of rapid reactions. Figure 1 shows the reaction time range for the various techniques.[1,2,4-6] It can be seen that reaction times as short as 10^{-12} s (ps) are now measurable (but not easily). The complete equipment to apply some of the methods is commercially available but some of the techniques are highly specialized and therefore much less accessible to the investigator. A technique and/or a particular associated monitoring method may have been applied, at present, only to inorganic or organic reactions. Their extension to bioinorganic systems may not be a trivial problem, but is undoubtedly being considered.

A. Flow methods

The principles of the flow method are well documented.[12-14] In essence, they extend the shortest time range of observation from approximately some 10 s normally allowable by ordinary mixing and monitoring methods to 10^{-3} s or even shorter by using specialized mixing techniques. Usually a rapidly responding monitor is also necessary.

1. Stopped flow

This is by far the most used of the flow methods.[12,14,15] The reactant solutions in two syringes are rapidly mixed and abruptly stopped, and subsequent progress of the reaction is monitored at a point very near the mixer. The method uses small volumes of solution (as low as 0.2 ml per run) and provides easily analysed data. The limiting time resolution of a ms, or so, still allows the determination of large second-order rate constants in certain favorable conditions.[16] A number of stopped-flow systems are commercially available.[17]

Nearly all the usual monitoring methods have been employed, the applications of which will be deferred until Section III, but some are quite difficult to apply in practice. A beautifully detailed account of the stopped-flow technique is available.[15] The use of syringes of different volumes, e.g. 5.0 and 0.1 ml, allows the study of reactants in non-aqueous solution (water unstable) reacting with a much larger volume of an aqueous solution of reactant. The final mixture is predominantly an aqueous solution ($\sim 98\%$ H_2O) and applicable to the normal biochemical conditions. The method has been used to study the reaction of O_2^- [18] and characterize the reactive form of acetaldehyde in enzyme-catalysed reactions,[19] see Section IV.A.1. If large ratios of enzyme/substrate solution volumes (~ 100) are mixed, the enzyme is available for reuse, and a number of heme enzyme catalysed reactions have been thus studied.[20]

2. Continuous flow

The continuous-flow method avoids the time-limiting stopping feature of the stopped-flow technique but larger amounts of material are required.[13,14] By using a very fast jet mixer and incorporating the mixing chamber into the observation tube half-lives of observation can be reduced to approximately 50 μs and high second-order rate constants, near to diffusion-controlled values, are measurable.[21,22] Large amounts of material are still needed (at least 5 ml per run) and the treatment of kinetic data is complex.[21-23] If the monitoring is sluggish the continuous-flow method allows the resolution of much shorter reaction times than the stopped-flow technique. This applies, for example, in the study of rapid reactions involving O_2 using an O_2 electrode.[24]

3. Quenched flow

In particular instances the quenched-flow method is useful. The reactant solutions are rapidly mixed, and after a predesigned incubation time the reaction mixture is quenched (rapid cooling, precipitation, etc.) and analysed at leisure. Simple mixing equipment can be used[3] or a commercial stopped-flow apparatus converted into a double mixer arrangement.[25] Electron paramagnetic resonance monitoring of rapidly mixed solutions quenched by freezing has been very effective in studying rapid reactions of molybdenum enzymes[26] and iron proteins.[27,28] When separation of reactants is essential, as in the study of rapid exchange reactions, the quenched-flow method must be utilized.[29] The double mixer arrangement can also be used for studying the reactions of transients produced in mixer 1 with reactants in mixer 2, after an aging interval (20 ms to 11 s) for the transient.

B. Relaxation methods: small perturbations

Relaxation methods circumvent the mixing time limitation of the flow methods. The amounts of species present in a chemical equilibrium can be altered by a variety of methods. The rate of change of the system from the old to the new equilibrium (relaxation) is dictated by (and therefore a measure of) the rate constants linking the species at equilibrium.[4] Since equilibrium perturbation can be imposed very rapidly, it is possible to measure very short reaction times (Fig. 1). The method is limited to reversible reactions (i.e. with equilibrium constants not far removed from unity), the perturbation of which will produce a measurable change in the concentration of one of the reactants. Any perturbation which changes concentrations can in principle be used. Concentration, ionic strength and pH changes have all been utilized, and these can be imposed by flow methods, if necessary.[30,31] The acid-base properties of organic molecules may be modified in the excited state.[32] Thus large pH changes (10^{-4}–10^{-5} M [H^+]) can be initiated within 50 ns by electronically exciting certain naphthol derivatives. The ground state pK (~ 7) is lowered (pK^* ~ 0.5) on excitation.[33] Although the relaxation techniques are not as generally applicable as the flow methods, they *only* can be used to measure large first-order rate constants associated with many fundamental elementary reactions.[34] Further, regardless of the complexity of the reaction a set of first-order equations is always obtained.[3,4,8,35]

1. Temperature jump

This is undoubtedly the most versatile and useful form of the relaxation method. Commercially available apparatus[17] employs electric heating, giving temperature jumps of 3–15 °C within ms. Using coaxial cable as capacitor, machine times as short as 10–100 ns have been obtained.[36,37] Microwave heating has been applied, not only to aqueous solutions, but also to non-electrolytes in non-aqueous polar solvents. Only a small temperature jump is obtained, but repetitive jumps with computer collection improves the sensitivity of the method.[38] Flowing solutions must be used in conjunction with repetitive jumps for temperature control. For the shortest relaxation times (several degrees rise in < 30 ns) either direct heating using an I_2 laser[39] or Raman laser heating[40–42] have been used, to study a variety of biochemical reactions including conformational equilibria and stacking processes, which are both very rapid and attended by very small absorbance changes. The combination of temperature jump with stopped flow for the study of relaxation behavior of transients has not yet been extensively applied.[43–45] With rapid temperature-jump equipment, return of the pulsed solution to the ambient temperature after about 1 s limits the slow times measurable.

2. Pressure jump

In the usual form a perturbation of 50–150 bar is applied and spectral or conductivity monitoring is used. Small pressure changes (0.01–5 bar) can be effected if voltage pulses are repetitively applied to a stack of piezoelectric crystals for compression of a solution.[46,47] The pressure-jump method has nothing like the versatility of temperature jump and has a limiting resolution time of ms. However, it can be used for slower reactions and in a wider range of solvents.[48] The method has been applied recently to the study of protein association using light scattering[49] or turbidity monitoring,[48–50] see also reference [51], and in rare cases may replace temperature jump when ΔH for the reaction is near zero.[52] For full reviews of the pressure-jump technique see references [4, 5, 48, 53 and 54].

3. Electric-field jump

The equilibrium constant of a reaction occurring with a change in electric moment will be modified by a high electric field. The measurement of very short relaxation times are possible by the electric-field jump method (Fig. 1) but the technique is complicated and mainly restricted to ionic equilibria.[4,55–57] Kinetics of helix-coil transition of polypeptides has been studied by E-jump with conductimetric detection.[58] Recently a number of new techniques based on electric-field effects for study of reactions in very low dielectric media has been promoted, but their application is not straightforward.[4,57]

4. Ultrasonic techniques

Ultrasonic absorption involves *oscillating* perturbations by pressure and temperature of a chemical equilibrium. When the frequency of the reaction (i.e. 1/relaxation time, $1/\tau$) is comparable with the frequency of the sound wave, concentration changes lag behind the perturbation changes, power is absorbed from the wave and the resultant loss of amplitude of the signal can be used to determine the relaxation time of the chemical system. A variety of techniques must be used to cover the 10^4–10^{10} Hz (= cycles/s) sound frequency range but the resultant relaxation time range measurable (10^{-5}–10^{-11} s) is a very important one and the method, although not generally applicable, is a powerful one in specific instances. Large volumes must be used at the lower frequencies, but smaller ones (5 ml) can be employed at the highest frequency range and the material is recoverable.[4,59-62] The method played a major role in the early studies of metal ion–sulfate interaction.[63] More recently it has been used to study the labile alkali metal ion reactions with macrocycles[61] and has been applied to stacking and helix-coil transitions of biopolymers.[62]

C. Large perturbations

The relaxation methods discussed above involve small perturbations of the system and in fact the simple kinetic treatment of a single relaxation depends on this small deviation from equilibrium.[4,35] The perturbation of a chemical system at equilibrium, however, by an intense pulse of light (flash or laser *photolysis*) or a high energy electron pulse (*radiolysis*) can have profound effects on the system. Radiolysis induces oxidation-reduction changes while photolysis involves substitutional and redox changes. A number of highly reactive radicals can be generated by photolysis or radiolysis and their reactions with added substrates can be examined (in competition with other reactions of the radical, e.g. with H_2O, disproportionation, etc.). Some radicals which can be generated by radiolysis are shown in Table 1.[64-74] The radiolysis of water can be described approximately by equation (1).[64]

$$4H_2O \rightarrow 2.6e_{aq}^- + 2.6OH + 0.6H + 2.6H^+ + 0.4H_2 + 0.7H_2O_2 \qquad (1)$$

Addition of simple molecules can remove all but one of the radicals to allow study of the remaining radical (Table 1). Usually μM concentrations of radicals are generated in the 0.2–2.0 μs range using MeV electron pulses. Both radiolysis[75] and laser photolysis[76] methods can allow the visualization of

TABLE 1

Some radicals generated by radiolysis

Radical	Production (added substances underlined)[a]	Remarks
e_{aq}^-	$CH_3OH^{(b)} + OH \rightarrow CH_2OH + H_2O$ $CH_3OH^{(b)} + H \rightarrow CH_2OH + H_2$	Powerful reducing agent ($E^0 = -2.9$ V). Reacts diffusion controlled with many substrates.[64,65] Important for generating non-equilibrium reduced proteins (Section IV.B.2)
CO_2^-	$N_2O + e_{aq}^- \rightarrow N_2 + OH^- + OH$ $HCO_2^- + OH \rightarrow CO_2^- + H_2O$ $HCO_2^- + H \rightarrow CO_2^- + H_2$	$E^0 = -2.0$ V; reactivity often intermediate between e_{aq}^- and SO_2^{-}[66,67]
O_2^-	$O_2 + H \rightarrow O_2^- + H^+$ $O_2 + e_{aq}^- \rightarrow O_2^-$ $HCO_2^- + OH \rightarrow CO_2^- + H_2O$ $O_2 + CO_2^- \rightarrow O_2^- + CO_2$	Often acts as one-electron reductant ($E^0 = -0.33$ V).[68] Relatively slow, e.g. toward cyt c(III), $k = 1.5 \times 10^6$ M^{-1} s^{-1} at pH = 7[69,70]
OH	$N_2O + e_{aq}^- \rightarrow N_2 + OH^- + OH$ $N_2O + H \rightarrow N_2 + OH$	Strong oxidant ($E^0 = 1.9$ V).[71] Gives hydroxyl free radical adducts with certain amino acids[72]
$(SCN)_2^-$	$N_2O + e_{aq}^- \rightarrow N_2 + OH^- + OH$ $2SCN^- + OH \rightarrow (SCN)_2^- + OH^-$	Reference [73]. Useful in probing protein active site (Section IV.C.2)
Br_2^-	$N_2O + e_{aq}^- \rightarrow N_2 + OH^- + OH$ $2Br^- + OH \rightarrow Br_2^- + OH^-$	Reference [73]. Strong oxidant (Section IV.C.2)
N_3	$N_2O + e_{aq}^- \rightarrow N_2 + OH^- + OH$ $N_3^- + OH \rightarrow N_3 + OH^-$	Reference [73]. Reaction with yeast ADH goes via long range intramolecular charge transfer between tyrosine and tryptophan[74]

[a] Usually 1–10 μM radical generated in 0.2–2.0 μs. 1% methanol or saturated N_2O or ~ 0.1 M HCO_2^- or halide used. Phosphate buffers.

[b] $(CH_3)_3COH$ also used to scavenge. Radicals produced are relatively unreactive.

processes as short as a few picoseconds. For example, a Nd laser can deliver a single 6 ps pulse, well defined in band width, energy and time duration.[76] More usually the nanosecond or longer time frame is examined. Very specialized nanosecond and picosecond radiation sources and fast optical detectors and flashes of analysing light must be used for examination of process in the 10^{-8} to 10^{-12} s range.[77] These techniques allow for the very rapid generation of reactive protein transients and their spectral and kinetic characterization. Rapid fundamental conformational changes of the heme proteins have been observed *only* by these techniques, see Section IV. Full accounts of the techniques are given in references [78–80]. Pulse radiolysis[81] and laser photolysis[82] have been linked to the stopped-flow method.

D. Competition methods

The remaining rapid reaction techniques may be classified as competitive, where the reaction under study competes with a fast process which may be spin relaxation (nmr and epr), fluorescence or diffusion towards an electrode (electrochemical).[83] Monitoring of the process is generally internal, making use of the characteristics of the process itself.

1. Magnetic resonance

The determination of the rates of fast exchange processes by utilizing nmr line broadening is a powerful rapid reaction technique for systems at equilibrium.[84] It is being increasingly used, with the proliferation of sensitive equipment and computerized manipulation of data. One drawback is the relatively large concentrations ($\sim$ mM) of reactants that are still necessary.

A nucleus in different chemical environments A and B will generally have nuclear magnetic resonances at different frequencies. If the exchange of the nuclei between A and B (by a chemical process) is sufficiently slow, sharp lines corresponding to A and B will be recorded. As the exchange rate increases, there is first initial broadening of the signals (slow-exchange region), then coalescing of the signals and finally at high exchange rates narrowing of the single signal occurs (fast-exchange region). Eventually there is a very sharp signal with no contribution to the line width from exchange. All regions can be used to evaluate exchange rate constants but the most reliable method involves matching the observed spectra with a series of computer-calculated spectra using input data, chemical shift, relaxation time, etc.[85] There may very well be a complex relation between the relaxation time and the rate constants of the system.[86]

When one of the environments A or B is close to a paramagnetic ion, the paramagnetic contribution to relaxation is extremely useful for determining exchange rates. This approach has been used for studying exchange of solvent between metal-coordinated and free (bulk) solvent[87] and is increasingly used for probing the rate characteristics of interaction of small molecules with proteins, see Section IV.A.1.[88,89]

Electron paramagnetic resonance linewidth broadening can also give information about radical life-times and kinetic data[90] but appears to have been barely applied to biological systems.

2. Time-resolved fluorescence

Time resolution of the fluorescence decay and its anisotropy (using polarized light) have greater potential for probing structural features of proteins than even steady-state fluorescence measurements. The measurement of fluorescence life-times requires more expensive and specialized equipment than fluorescence spectrometers since *very* rapid extinction of the exciting light must be effected (e.g. using a nanosecond pulse) and rapid decay of the emission ($\tau \sim$ 0.4–200 ns) must be measured.[91,92] The tryptophan fluorescence decay of LADH, with excitation at 295 nm is biphasic with τ = 3.9 and 7.2 ns (Fig. 2). These decay times are assigned to buried Trp-314 and exposed Trp-15, respectively.[92]

3. Electrochemical

Many of the proteins with which we are concerned in this review undergo non-ideal behavior at electrode surfaces because of severe adsorption or insulation of the redox center from the electrode by protein. Kinetic studies using cyclic voltametry and polarography must therefore focus on the non-protein reactant.[93] Chronoamperometry has the advantage of *in situ* generation of a strong reductant in anaerobic conditions. The faradaic current will be increased in the presence of an added oxidant and this can be related to the rate constant for the redox process. The reaction of FeEDTA^{2-} and reduced viologens with cytochrome c(III) was studied by this means and the rate constant was found to be in good agreement with that determined by spectral stopped flow.[94] The method can obviously be used in situations where spectral monitoring is difficult.

High-pressure forms of stopped flow,[95] temperature jump,[96–98] laser photolysis[99] and nmr[100] equipment are now available. These allow the determination of volumes of activation, another kinetic parameter helpful in mechanism elucidation.[101]

E. Circumventing rapid reaction techniques

It is possible to circumvent (to a limited extent) rapid reaction techniques by working at lowered temperatures (even down to 4 K) when the reaction rate is sufficiently slowed down to measure it by conventional methods. Enzyme intermediates with normal life-times of milliseconds may be stable for hours at low temperatures. Mixed aqueous solvents must be employed and the solvent mixture must be tested for no adverse effects on the catalytic or structural properties of the enzyme.[102,103] Lowered temperature, combined with one of the rapid-reaction techniques, flow,[104] temperature jump,[105] photolysis[106]

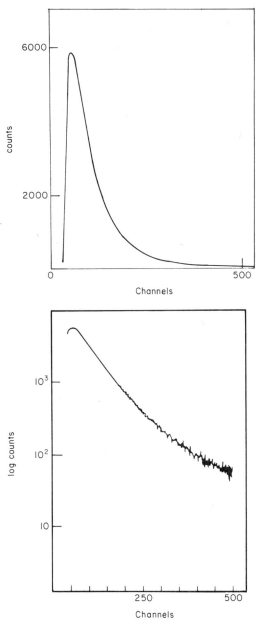

Fig. 2. Fluorescence decay for 80 μM LADH in 0.1 M sodium phosphate buffer at 10 °C. Excitation is at 295 nm and monitoring is at 350 nm. The decay curve (top Fig.) corresponds exactly to a double exponential with τ_1 = 3.9 ns and τ_2 = 6.9 ns. This is shown in the semi-log plot in the bottom Fig. A single exponential with τ = 5.4 ns fails to fit the data over long periods. Decay of the lamp is taken into account. Reprinted, in part, with permission from reference [92].

or nmr is a particularly effective method for probing reaction mechanisms. Structural properties of the frozen solutions are also an important result of this rapidly developing area of cryoenzymology.

III. RAPID-REACTION MONITORING

There are a large number of methods available to monitor the progress of a chemical reaction. The application of these to rapid reactions is not always simple. As important then, as the development of the various rapid-reaction techniques outlined in Section II, is the increased types of monitoring methods which have been applied to these techniques. A list of the monitoring methods which have been applied to more than one rapid-reaction technique is shown in Table 2, the references being to reviews or recent papers, which contain entry into the literature. Monitoring methods which have been used with flow techniques are listed in references [5, 12 and 13].

TABLE 2
Monitoring methods applied to rapid-reaction techniques

Monitoring method	Technique					
	Flow	T-jump	P-jump	E-jump	Photolysis	Radiolysis
uv and vis spectrophotometry	(a)	[107]	[48, 52]	[108]	[109]	[110]
fluorescence	[111]	[112]	[113]			
circular dichroism	[114]	[115]	[116]	[117]	[118]	
resonance Raman	[119]				[120]	[36, 121]
light scattering	[122]	[36, 123]	[46, 49, 124]			
nmr	[125]				[126]	[127]
epr	[26, 128]				[129]	[130]
conductivity	[131]	[132]	[46]	[133]	[134]	[135]

(a) The most versatile of the monitoring probes linked to flow methods.

The availability of a number of monitoring techniques to the investigator is important for a complete description of the reaction scheme, since different parts of the overall mechanism may respond to different physical probes. In addition, the characterization of transients in terms of different spectral properties is important for their structural determination.

A. Spectral monitoring

Ultra-violet and visible spectral monitoring remains the most important general method for determining the rates of rapid reactions both linked to flow and perturbation techniques. Even the small absorbance changes sometimes attending the flow and relaxation methods can be measured accurately with the sensitive detectors and associated data acquisition apparatus now available.* Small spectral changes may be amplified by the introduction of a chromophoric group into one of the reactants,[136-138] see Section IV.A.1. Introduction of mansyl or dansyl groups into ester and peptide substances can allow fluorescence-stopped flow characterization of substrate exo and endo-peptidases.[136,137] The modification may, however, alter the kinetic characteristics of the unmodified reactant and this has to be considered.[139,140] Other methods of producing enhanced spectral changes are to add indicators, to monitor pM[141] or pH[142] changes which often arise from reaction of metal ions (M) and of protic substrates or proteins. An indicator may react preferentially with reactant or product.[143]

Rapid scan spectrophotometry is valuable for measuring a series of spectra following mixing [144] or perturbation (in radiolysis[145] or photolysis[146]). The occurrence and number of intermediates in the reaction may be more easily assessed than by wavelength point-by-point analysis. For example, the occurrence of an isosbestic point at 435 nm strongly suggests that compound I is the sole product of the reaction between catalase and methyl-hydroperoxide or peracetic acid (Fig. 3).[147] Compound I is only stable for a few hundred milliseconds.[147] The accumulation of kinetic differential spectra by a series of runs at different wavelengths can still, however, provide valuable information on the progress of a reaction.[148] *Dual detector* accessories eliminate artifacts due to particles, bubbles, etc. by simultaneous observation of a reaction with two detector systems and by computer subtracting the two absorbances. They can be affixed to stopped flow in the spectral, fluorescent or light scattering mode or to T-jump equipment. By this means, the oxygen uptake by human red cells has been measured spectrally and shown to be 20–40 times slower than *in vitro*, using dual-detector stopped flow.[149] Flow and relaxation-based apparatus with absorption spectral monitoring can, with little or fairly little adaptation be used to follow *light scattering*[122-124] or *fluorescence*[36,111,112] changes. Fluorescence is a particularly sensitive monitor, allowing for the use of quite dilute solutions (μM) and thus the measurement of large second-order rate constants.[16] Even slight impurities (fluorescent) in the reagents may cause problems.[150]

---

* A wide variety of data acquisition arrangements are described in the literature. In our laboratories, the OLIS system linked to stopped flow and temperature jump has proved very satisfactory.

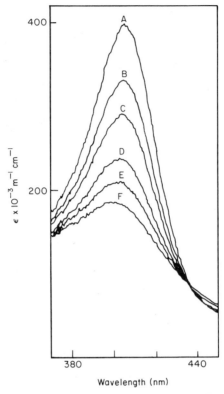

Fig. 3. Rapid scan spectrophotometry of the reaction of catalase (1.5 μM) with methyl hydroperoxide (100 μM) at pH 7.1 and 25 °C. All spectra had 1 ms scanning times. Curves show catalase before reaction (A), at stop of flow (B), 2 ms after stop of flow (C), 7 ms after stop of flow (D), 12 ms after stop of flow (E) and 47 ms spectrum (F).[147]

Circular dichroism has now been linked to flow and relaxation techniques and promises to be a powerful method for studying a number of types of reactions involving chiral reactants and intermediates.[114] The sensitivity of the method at present is much smaller than with the absorption or emission spectral techniques (Fig. 4) and resolution times are relatively long even linked to perturbation methods. Nevertheless, CD monitoring can provide information particularly on intermediates additional to that by other sensing.[151] In the unfolding of apomyoglobin, for example, changes monitored by CD are more rapid than fluorescence changes. This is ascribed to α-helical structural changes (CD) being faster than changes in the local environment of tryptophans and/or tyrosines (fluorescence).[152] Time resolved *resonance Raman* detection of excited states as well as intermediates have been

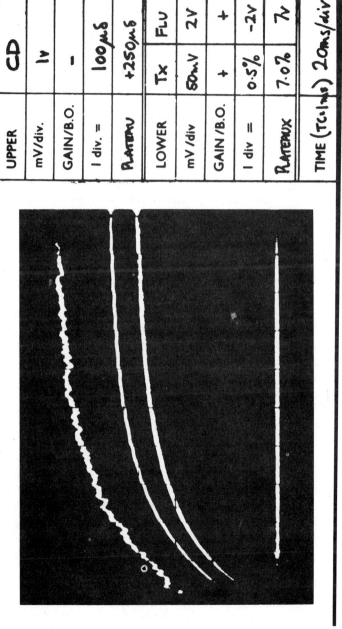

UPPER	CD	
mV/div.	1v	
GAIN/B.O.	–	
1 div. =	100μδ	
ᴘʟᴀᴛᴇᴀᴜ	+250μδ	

LOWER	Tx	Flu
mV /div	50mV	2V
GAIN /B.O.	+	+
1 div =	0·5%	–2v
ᴘʟᴀᴛᴇᴀᴜx	7·0%	7v

TIME (Tc·1ns) 20ms/div

Fig. 4. Simultaneous observations of CD (C), absorbance (A) and fluorescence (F) changes when the Mg^{2+} (52 mM), tetracycline (72 μM) complex is treated with Ca^{2+} ions (59 mM) in 50% methanol at pH 8. These traces correspond to rate constants of 22.6 (C), 23.4 (A) and 24.2 s^{-1} (F) and indicate a single process is involved. Reprinted with permission from Bayley, P. M. *Prog. Biophys. Molec. Biol.* **1981**, 37, 149–180. I am indebted to the author for a copy of the original photograph.

demonstrated in the millisecond,[119,153] micro and nanosecond[120] and even the picosecond[154] time scale! Infrared monitoring has not found extensive application in bioinorganic reactions. Nuclear magnetic resonance observation has been successfully linked to stopped and continuous flow. Shorter resolution times are possible but larger volumes are used with the latter.[125] A useful rapid injection probe which can be installed in a 60 MHz FT spectrometer allows the acquisition of up to eight spectra in less than one second. Concentrations of 10 mM must be used, however, at present.[155] In the CIDNP mode (which is much faster responding than the normal nmr) nmr has been used with perturbation methods.[126,127] The method has been mainly applied to inorganic and organic systems. Electron paramagnetic resonance combined with quenched flow represents a powerful combination for detecting paramagnetic intermediates in rapid reactions. In its original form, the reaction was quenched by rapid freezing into isopentane chilled with liquid nitrogen. The frozen solution was packed into an epr tube for examination.[26]

B. Non-spectral monitoring

Thermal changes (microcalorimetry)[156,157] and O_2,[24] pH and CO_2-selective electrodes[158-160] have been incorporated in flow apparatus. The instrument dead-time is usually somewhat longer (~ 10 ms) than with spectral monitoring but the methods can sometimes provide data not otherwise attainable. Conductivity monitoring, which is very sensitive, has been successfully associated with flow, relaxation, laser photolysis and pulse radiolysis techniques (Table 2). It has been most usefully applied, so far, to inorganic reactions which have large proton but small spectral changes in the reactions following perturbation.[134,161] Finally, a novel use of magnetic susceptibility monitoring linked to photolysis has been reported.[162]

It should be noted that relative rates of two fast processes may be measured by competition methods, avoiding rapid reaction techniques altogether, although care has to be exercised in their use.[163] The competition method is also an important method for measuring the rate constant for reaction of a "colorless" reactant in competition with that of a "colored" analog.[164] This approach is necessary in the study of radicals such as OH[165] or CO_2^-[166] which have small absorbance coefficients in the visible.

IV. APPLICATIONS OF RAPID-REACTION METHODS

Although this account of the applications of rapid-reaction techniques is not meant to be exhaustive, an attempt will be made to cover all the methods which are at the disposal of the "fast" kineticist by choosing appropriate reaction systems. Examples will be chosen to illustrate the multivaried approaches which can be used to measure rapid rates, elucidate structural features of the protein, characterize transients and shed light on proposed reaction schemes.

A. Measurement of rate

1. Small molecule interaction with protein

Stability constants (K) of protein-ligand complexes range from about 10^2 to 10^{15} M^{-1}. Since the various association rate constants k_{on} are often similar and near the diffusion controlled value (10^8–10^9 M^{-1} s^{-1}) the variation in K must reside largely in the dissociation rate constant (k_{on}/K). The latter will therefore vary from about 10^6 to 10^{-7} s^{-1} and be determined by functional requirements.[167] The association of protein (P) with a small molecule (L) is often not a simple overall biomolecular reaction but is rather of the form (2)

$$P + L \rightleftharpoons PL^* \rightleftharpoons PL \tag{2}$$

including a protein-promoted isomerization of the initially formed adduct PL^* to the final species PL.[168] This situation can be shown either by the observation of biphasic kinetics (rarely) or, more usually, by deviations from linearity of the plot of the pseudo first-order rate constant k_{obs} vs $[L]$, used in excess. The limiting value of k_{obs} will measure the $PL^* \rightleftharpoons PL$ transformation rate constant.[4,5] Flow or relaxation techniques are invariably required to resolve the constituent rate constants of scheme (2). Metal ion or ions which are usually at or near the active site of the protein are useful markers for probing the function of the protein. The general scheme (3) applies to a large number of ligand-metal site interactions:

$$PM + L \rightleftharpoons PML \rightleftharpoons P + ML \tag{3}$$
$$\updownarrow$$
$$PM + L'$$

The ligand L coordinates to the metal site of the protein (PM) to form a ternary complex.[169] The adduct may be stable and undergo no further reaction (at least over short times). Such a situation holds with slow-reacting substrates and inhibitors of enzyme action, and with small molecules (O_2, CO, NO) reacting with heme-containing proteins. The determination of rate constants for the formation and dissociation of the adduct PML usually requires direct examination by rapid-reaction techniques[170] and for enzyme systems, the data may complement that obtained by the overall steady-state treatment.[171] Two or more steps may be involved in the production of PML. The ternary complex PML may transform, possibly in a number of stages and involving other reactants, to the final product L' with regeneration of PM. The product L' may coordinate to PM. This, in simplified form, is the basis of enzyme-catalysed reactivity.

If the complex ML is stronger than PM, then PML will proceed to apoprotein P and ML. This process probably underlies most productions of apoprotein.[172-174] The reverse reaction, the interaction of ML with apoprotein has been usually studied for ML = aquated metal ion. These various aspects will be considered.

The kinetic analysis is simplified if intrinsic spectral changes in the system can be utilized. The zinc-containing *liver alcohol dehydrogenase* (LADH = E) catalyses the interconversion of aldehydes and alcohols by a compulsory ordered mechanism (4)

$$
\begin{array}{c}
\text{NADH} \qquad\qquad \text{Ald} \\
E \xrightleftharpoons[k_{-2}]{k_2} E^{\text{NADH}} \rightleftharpoons E^{\text{NADH}}_{\text{Ald}} \rightleftharpoons E^{\text{NAD}^+}_{\text{Alc}} \rightleftharpoons E^{\text{NAD}^+} \xrightleftharpoons[k_1]{k_{-1}} E \\
\qquad\qquad\qquad\qquad\qquad \downarrow \qquad\qquad\qquad \downarrow \\
\qquad\qquad\qquad\qquad\qquad \text{Alc} \qquad\qquad\quad \text{NAD}^+
\end{array} \tag{4}
$$

Steady-state kinetic studies[175,176] showed that the rate-determining step in the reduction of aliphatic aldehydes is the dissociation of the enzyme-NAD^+ complex, E^{NAD^+}. This is supported by agreement between the calculated (from steady state[176]) values of k_{-1} and k_1 and the directly measured values by stopped-flow spectral and fluorescence methods.[177,178] The $E^{\text{NAD}^+} \leftrightarrow E + \text{NAD}^+$ step was further resolved from results using pressure relaxation with fluorescence monitoring.[179] The non-linear dependence of the single relaxation rate constant on the concentration of NAD^+ was interpreted in terms of binding and isomerization, equation (5)[179]

$$
E^{\text{NAD}^+} \xrightleftharpoons[k_c]{k_a} {}^*E^{\text{NAD}^+} \xrightleftharpoons[k_d]{k_b} E + \text{NAD}^+ \tag{5}
$$

The value of k_a could be further equated to k_{-1} at three pHs (Fig. 5)[51] and thus the isomerization of the enzyme-NAD^+ complex is the rate-determining step for the enzyme-catalysed reduction of acetaldehyde, a quite unusual occurrence with enzymes.

To simulate coenzyme binding, the chelation of zinc in LADH by 1,10-phenanthroline and 2,2'-bipyridine was measured by stopped-flow spectral and fluorescence monitoring.[177,180-182] A limiting rate constant $(\sim 2 \times 10^2 \text{ s}^{-1})$[180-182] at high bipyridine concentration was interpreted as arising from rate-controlling dissociation of zinc-bound water in the enzyme. Its lowered value compared with that of the aquated zinc ion, $3 \times 10^7 \text{ s}^{-1}$[3]

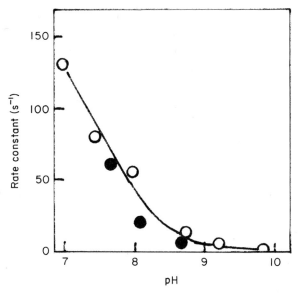

Fig. 5. Comparison of values of k_a[179] (●) and k_{-1}[178] (○) indicating that the isomerization of the enzyme NAD^+ complex controls the NAD^+ dissociation. The full line is the theoretical one for a pH-dependent dissociation (and isomerization), $pK_a = 7.6$ and k_a(max) $= 160$ s^{-1}.[51]

arises from a different geometry (distorted tetrahedron) and hydrophobic environment for zinc in the protein and points out the difficulty of extrapolating water exchange rate constants for metal ions to their values in metalloproteins.[181] By contrast temperature jump using circular dichroism on the LADH/auramine-O (a chromophoric inhibitor) system shows a two-step relaxation ascribed to ligand-induced isomerization.[183] The value of k_{-2} in equation (4) is best determined by displacement of NADH from E^{NADH} by added NAD^+. The process monitored spectrally,[178] by fluorescence[177] and CD stopped-flow[114c] leads to values of k_{-2} of 4–6 s^{-1}.

Finally, differential mixing stopped-flow techniques indicate that acetaldehyde and not the hydrate is the reactive substrate. The aldehyde is an equilibrium mixture with 55% hydrate in water, but is present as all carbonyl form in tetramethylurea. By mixing one part of acetaldehyde in tetramethylurea with 50 parts of a LADH/NADH mixture in aqueous buffer, the steady-state kinetics can be performed within 0.5 s *on the aldehyde*, before hydration equilibration can occur.[19]

A protein may be modified by introduction of a chromophoric group. As an example, the arsanilazo labelled tyrosine-248 in carboxypeptidase has proved ideal for exploring the catalytic activity and local structure of the enzyme both in the solid state[184] and in solution.[185] The red azoTyr–Zn complex (I) is at pH 8.0, an intramolecular coordination complex between arsanilazotyrosine-248 and the zinc atom of carboxypeptidase. The derivatized enzyme (E) is

(I)

disrupted (slightly) by an increase of temperature to given an additional amount of yellow (unliganded) derivative. This occurs extremely rapidly ($k = 2.9 \times 10^4 \text{ s}^{-1}$). In the presence of substrate [S] or product [P] temperature jump gives an additional slower relaxation. A curvature for k (relaxation) vs ([E] + [S]) or ([E] + [P]) leads to the full reaction scheme (6) shown for Gly-L-Phe(S) and L-Phe(P).

$$E + S \underset{}{\overset{K = 21\,\text{mM}}{\rightleftharpoons}} ES \underset{1.0 \times 10^3 \text{ s}^{-1}}{\overset{3.3 \times 10^3 \text{ s}^{-1}}{\rightleftharpoons}} ES^* \overset{0.01\,\text{s}^{-1}}{\rightleftharpoons}$$

$$EP^* \underset{1.2 \times 10^3 \text{ s}^{-1}}{\overset{1.8 \times 10^3 \text{ s}^{-1}}{\rightleftharpoons}} EP \overset{K = 10\,\text{mM}}{\rightleftharpoons} E + P \quad (6)$$

The turnover rate is sufficiently slow that the ES* → EP* transformation does not interfere with observations on the E–S system. With more rapidly hydrolysed peptide substrates, e.g. Cbz-Gly-Gly-Phe ($k_{cat} = 55 \text{ s}^{-1}$), it is necessary to use a stopped-flow, temperature-jump combination.[186]

Finally, modification of a substrate, particularly by fluorescent marking, can allow the observation of sensitive fluorescence changes when enzyme-substrate adduct formation occurs.[136,137] In this way the kinetic data for the formation and breakdown of the adduct can be accumulated (for example, see Fig. 6 and Table 3).

There have been a very large number of studies of enzyme-substrate and enzyme-inhibitor systems. Only rarely are all the rate constants for the reaction scheme (2) obtained.[5] Table 3 shows a representative selection of metalloproteins whose interaction with ligands have been determined directly by a variety of rapid-reaction techniques.

The interaction of apoprotein with metal ion is usually slow and may be studied by conventional or flow techniques.[196] The complete restoration of function of the protein may, however, require a first-order conformational

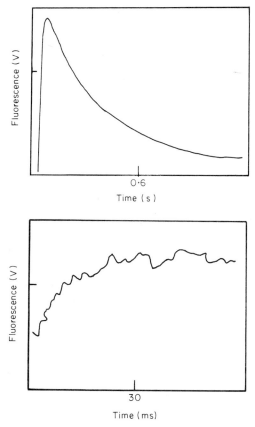

Fig. 6. Time course of the change of fluorescence during cleavage of Mns-Phe-Leu-Ala by thermolysin. Total enzyme = 27.4 μM. Initial substrate = 1.25 μM at pH 8.5 and 25 °C. Upper Fig. shows very rapid increase in fluorescence due to formation of enzyme-substrate complex, followed by a first-order decrease related to the breakdown of complex. The lower Fig. resolves the rapid formation (enzyme = 19.3 μM). The ordinate denotes the fluorescence as photomultiplier voltage. Reprinted, in part, with permission from reference [136].

change following the second-order incorporation of metal ion. This has been thoroughly investigated for concanavalin A which is a lectin isolated from jack bean. It binds saccharides, thereby exhibiting properties of considerable biological interest. Addition of Mn^{2+} and Ca^{2+} ions to apoconcanavalin A results in rapid uptake of the metal ions. Firm coordination of the metal ions and setting up of the sugar binding site (some 10–12 Å from the metal ions site) takes several minutes ($k \sim 0.01\,s^{-1}$).[197] The value of multimonitoring is shown in the stopped-flow study of the combination of ferric heme-containing fragments of cytochrome c with apofragments to form ordered complexes

TABLE 3

Kinetic studies of direct binding of ligands to metalloproteins

Protein	Ligand	k_{on} M⁻¹ s⁻¹	k_{off} s⁻¹	Remarks	Reference
Thermolysin	Mns-Phe-Leu-Ala	3×10^6	55	fluorescence s.f. Fluorescence increase (formation of ES) followed by decrease (breakdown of ES, 4.0 s^{-1}) cleavage at Phe-Leu bond	[136]
Carbonic anhydrase	p-NO$_2$C$_6$H$_4$SO$_2$NH$_2$	1.5×10^6	0.049	fluorescence s.f. Illustrative of behavior of large number of sulfonamide inhibitors[188]	[187]
Zinc insulin hexamer	2,2',2''-terpyridine	5.1×10^3	2.4	spectral s.f. Formation of ternary complex followed by breakdown to apoprotein	[189]
Aldolase (Zn²⁺ replaced by Mn²⁺)	CH$_3$COCH$_2$PO$_4$	6.1×10^7	1.1×10^5	³¹P nmr. $k_{off} \gg k_{cat}$ (20 s^{-1}) means ternary species feasible in catalysis	[89, 190]
Concanavalin A	manno and glucopyranosides	7×10^4– 1.3×10^5	4–220	nmr line broadening, fluorescence and spectral s.f. and T.j. competition, T.j.	[138, 164, 191–194]
Carboxypeptidase	O-(trans-p-chlorocinnamoyl) L-β-phenylacetate	—	—	spectral s.f. at -45 to $+25$ °C in MeOH, H$_2$O, ethylene glycol	[195]

resembling native horse heart cytochrome c.[198] The initial step is the second-order formation of an intermediate ($k = 1 \times 10^5$–3.2×10^6 M^{-1} s^{-1}) similar to native protein in exhibiting tryptophan-59 fluorescence, but lacking the native coordination. There is then a subsequent first-order change showing absorbance changes in the Soret region at 695 nm which is similar in rate to that for refolding of intact cytochrome c (Section IV). Absorbance at 695 nm arises from coordination of Met-80 sulfur binding to iron (Met-80 S—Fe bonding). Fluorescence quenching monitoring shows only the first phase while spectral observations at a variety of wavelengths show only the slower, further ordering of the proteins.

Proton transfer reactions are an intimate part of protein reactions and require the whole armory of rapid-reaction techniques for their measurement.[199] The rates of proton transfer reactions at oxygen or nitrogen centers are generally diffusion controlled. Steric, electronic effects, hydrogen bond rupture or conformational changes may introduce a slow down in the acid-base reaction.[7]

2. Redox reactions

Redox reactions of both the outer-sphere and inner-sphere type,[3] can be envisioned as proceeding through adducts, these latter acting as vehicles for the intramolecular electron transfer process. Cytochrome c contains a single heme in a chain of 104 amino acids and transports electrons from cytochrome c_1 to cytochrome oxidase. The most studied redox reaction of cytochrome c is undoubtedly that with the iron hexacyanides (7), for earlier literature see references [200 and 201]

$$\text{cyt } c(\text{II}) + \text{Fe(CN)}_6^{3-} \underset{k_{\text{red}}}{\overset{k_{\text{ox}}}{\rightleftharpoons}} \text{cyt } c(\text{III}) + \text{Fe(CN)}_6^{4-} \tag{7}$$

Stopped flow,[201] continuous flow,[202] temperature jump,[203–206] nmr line broadening[207] and pulse-radiolytically generated reactants ("instant mixing")[200] (see later) techniques have all been used to measure the kinetics of the reaction. The rapidity of the reaction at high Fe(CN)_6^{3-} concentrations precludes the use of stopped flow, and specialized continuous flow or relaxation methods must therefore be used. The deviations of k_{obs} vs $[\text{Fe(CN)}_6^{3-}]$ plots from linearity at high concentrations of the inorganic oxidant, used in excess, Fig. 7,[200] is the sole reason for suggesting intermediates as in equation (8)

$$\text{cyt } c(\text{II}) + \text{Fe(CN)}_6^{3-} \underset{k_{-1}}{\overset{k_1}{\rightleftharpoons}} \text{cyt } c(\text{II}). \text{Fe(CN)}_6^{3-} \underset{k_{-2}}{\overset{k_2}{\rightleftharpoons}} \text{cyt } c(\text{III}). \text{Fe(CN)}_6^{4-}$$

$$\underset{k_{-3}}{\overset{k_3}{\rightleftharpoons}} \text{cyt } c(\text{III}) + \text{Fe(CN)}_6^{4-} \tag{8}$$

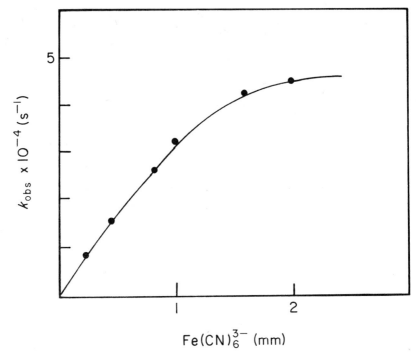

Fig. 7. Dependence of pseudo first-order rate constant (k_{obs}) on the concentration of $Fe(CN)_6^{3-}$ in the oxidation of cyt $c(II)$. The latter is produced in situ by e_{aq}^- reduction of cyt $c(III)$, 20 μM at pH 7.1. The oxidation was followed at 550 nm.[200]

Binding of cyt $c(II)$ with $Fe(CN)_6^{4-}$ and of cyt $c(III)$ with $Fe(CN)_6^{3-}$ can, however, be detected by equilibrium dialysis and temperature jump.[204] Values of rate and equilibrium constants suggest a common binding site for all combinations of reduced and oxidized protein and inorganic complexes.[200] Latest values for the rate and equilibrium constants for (7) and (8) are shown in Table 4.

In alkaline solution (pH >9) an additional effect is observed related to alkaline isomerization (see Section IV.B.1).[208,209] *After* oxidation of cyt $c(II)$ by $Fe(CN)_6^{3-}$ to cyt $c(III)$, two first-order transformations are observed (34.0 s^{-1}, 8.1 s^{-1} at pH 11.6 and 25 °C) by spectral stopped flow.[208] Using difference spectra, the product of the first isomerization is considered a high/mixed spin cyt $c(III)$ form which then changes to the alkaline form of cyt $c(III)$, Section IV.B.1. In the high/mixed spin state form it is conjectured that there is substantial displacement of the heme iron from the porphyrin plane, and with it increased conformational lability of the protein and thus

TABLE 4

Data for reaction (7) and scheme (8) at 25°C, I = 0.02 M[a] and neutral pH

k_{ox} M⁻¹ s⁻¹	k_{red} M⁻¹ s⁻¹	$K^{[a]}$ —	k_1 M⁻¹ s⁻¹	k_{-1} s⁻¹	$K_1^{[b]}$ M⁻¹	k_2 s⁻¹	k_{-2} s⁻¹	$K_3^{[c]}$ M⁻¹
4 × 10⁷[a,g]		2.2–3.4 × 10²[e,f,g]	2.5 × 10⁷[b]	7.6 × 10²[b]	3.3 × 10⁴[b,h]	4.6 × 10⁴[a,g]	3.3 × 10²[a,e]	4 × 10²[d]
1.3 × 10⁷[b]					8.7 × 10²[a,g]	1.9 × 10³[b]	1.0 × 10²[c]	15[c]
2.5 × 10⁶[c]	1.6 × 10³[c]	1.6 × 10³[c]			1.2 × 10³[c]	3.5 × 10³[c]	2.1 × 10²[d]	
						2 × 10⁴[d]		

(a) Reference [200]; (b) Reference [202] (I = 0.07 M); (c) Reference [203] (I = 0.3 M, T = 18 °C); (d) Reference [204]; (e) Reference [207]; (f) Reference [205]; (g) Reference [206]; (h) Value appears high, see reference [201].

facilitated final ligand interchange.[208] The existence of an alkaline form of cyt c(III) is important since it is less redox reactive. Reduction by catechol, for example, at pH 9 shows a fast step (reactive form) and slow step (limited by inactive → active transformation).[210]

The power of the nmr method for measuring rapid exchange rates is well illustrated by the study of reaction (9), R = CH_2Ph, p-C_6H_4Me:

$$Fe_4S_4(SR)_4^{2-} + Fe_4S_4(SR)_4^{3-} \rightleftharpoons Fe_4S_4(SR)_4^{3-} + Fe_4S_4(SR)_4^{2-} \qquad (9)$$

From line shape analysis, the value of k is 10^6–10^7 M^{-1} s^{-1} in CH_3CN. This indicates that the much lower corresponding self-exchange rate constant deduced for the oxidized and reduced ferredoxins which contain $Fe_4S_4(SR)_4$ cores arises from the protein moiety and not the $Fe_4S_4(SR)_4$ core.[211]

Redox reactions involving proteins and inorganic reactants (many of them rapid) have been comprehensively studied in recent years.[201,212,213] The reasons for this are clear. Using inorganic reactants, one can introduce a variety of charges, hydrophilic character, electron transfer abilities and free energies of reaction. The effect of these important properties on the ability of the protein to transfer electrons can be assessed. Some success for these systems can be claimed in understanding the accessibility of the protein to electron attack, effective charge of the protein and the relation of distance for electron transfer and rate. Extrapolation to protein/protein redox behavior is, however, still tenuous.[214]

3. Spin state changes

The interchange of low-spin and high-spin metal ion states may represent the simplest electron transfer process and provided that these are unattended by radical coordination changes they are likely to be very rapid. Spin equilibrium for iron(III) of the type (10)

$$^2T(S = 1/2) \underset{k_{-1}}{\overset{k_1}{\rightleftharpoons}} {}^6A(S = 5/2) \qquad (10)$$

has been reported for cytochrome P-450, catalase, myoglobin and hemo-globin.[215] The rate constants have been measured for horse ferric myoglobin hydroxide using laser stimulated Raman TJ[215] and human methemoglobin azide using cable TJ.[37] The values are not particularly different from those observed with a number of simple iron(III) (and iron(II) and cobalt(II)[216]) complex systems, Table 5.[215,217-220] The large values for k_1 and k_{-1} indicate that intramolecular spin multiplicity changes do not rate limit the second-order electron transfer reactions involving the spin-equilibria enzyme centers. The spin state relaxation rate of cytochrome P-450$_{cam}$ is much slower (Table 5) although even here it does not apparently limit the overall redox rates, for

TABLE 5

Rate constants (s^{-1}) for intersystem-crossing process in Fe(III) complexes 25 °C

System	k_1	k_{-1}	Technique	Reference
Fe acac$_2$ trien$^+$	1.6×10^8	3.2×10^8	ultrasonics and laser Raman T-j	[217]
Fe sal$_2$ trien$^+$	6.1×10^7	1.3×10^8	ultrasonics	[218]
Metmyoglobin hydroxide	$3.9 \times 10^{7(a)}$	$2.8 \times 10^{7(a)}$	laser Raman T-j	[215]
Cytochrome	4.6	53	T-j	[219]
P-450$_{cam}$	$342^{(b)}$	$23^{(b)}$		
	$52^{(b)(c)}$	$7^{(b)(c)}$	stopped flow (pH jump, spin change is proton coupled)	[220]

(a) 1 °C; (b) +camphor; (c) 4 °C.

example of cytochrome P-450 with putidaredoxin, its normal reductant protein.[219] This slowness may reflect a metal coordination number change or protein conformational change,[220] although not likely with metmyoglobin.[215] The same type of explanation probably applies to the (relatively) slow $\sim 100\,\mu s$ relaxation observed in temperature jump experiments with cytochrome c in acid.[221]

4. Protein folding

Many proteins can be reversibly unfolded by denaturing with urea or guanidine. Dilution of the solution results in refolding of the protein and (usually) recovery of the original properties of the protein. At least part of these processes are rapid and stopped-flow techniques must be used. Recently CD linked to stopped-flow[222] and pressure jump[116] have been added to the armory. A double mixing apparatus is useful for characterizing intermediates.

. The metal ion can have a major influence on the mechanism of folding of metalloproteins.[223,224] It is also a useful monitoring center and this is well illustrated with cytochrome c, where observations at 361 nm, 528 nm and 695 nm give information, during the folding, on (respectively) the coordination site of the heme iron, the spin state and the presence of Met-80-S iron linkage. Although the kinetics of folding of cyt c(III) have been comprehensively studied there is still disagreement on the mechanism.[224-226] Recent experiments[225] suggest that there are two forms of unfolded cyt c, U_f and U_s, each folding to native cyt c(N), scheme (11)

$$U_f \leftrightarrow U_s$$
$$U_s \rightarrow N; U_f \rightarrow N \tag{11}$$

This would account for the fast and slow refolding reactions of cyt c(III) originally observed by Ikai *et al.*[227] This is admitted, however, to be a simplified explanation since folding intermediates can be detected and other processes are also involved.[224-227]

There are at least three steps in the unfolding of myoglobin in acid solution ⁾ (pH <4.2), with release of heme. The fastest step, or steps, is complete within mixing time, the other two may be measured by spectral stopped-fow methods. Only the first and third steps are observed by SFCD and are associated with reduction in the α-helix content.[228] Reference [229] gives a recent summary of these findings.

B. Rapid generation of species

This aspect represents a very important application of rapid-reaction technique and methodology to the study of kinetics and mechanism. A species may be generated, with increasing rapidity, by flow, radiolysis and photolysis methods. The rapid production of even a *stable* species may be useful in the study of its fast reactions. Thus the reaction of a mixture of cyt c(III) and $Fe(CN)_6^{3-}$ with a pulse radiolytically produced e_{aq}^- leads, under the appropriate conditions, to the very rapid ($<1\,\mu s$) production of cyt c(II). Its subsequent rapid oxidation by the $Fe(CN)_6^{3-}$ present can be observed spectrally, even at high concentrations of $Fe(CN)_6^{3-}$ when flow methods are too slow and relaxation methods are inappropriate to an irreversible reaction. Alternatively, an appropriate mixture of cyt c(II) and $Fe(CN)_6^{4-}$ irradiated with a small amount of OH radicals can lead to preferential oxidation of the cyanide complex with *in situ* production of the desired reactants [cyt c(II) + $Fe(CN)_6^{3-}$]. In these ways the time-limiting mixing process is circumvented ("instant mixing").[200,206]

In the most interesting cases examined, however, the species produced is *unstable*. It will exist for a short time in much larger concentrations than it normally occurs and will be free of other species to which it will more slowly equilibrate. The spontaneous reactions of this species may be examined, including isomerization and conformational changes, self-combination, reaction with solvent, etc. Alternatively, its reactions with other materials may be studied. These can be added (by flow methods) or be present in the original solutions. A variety of spectral properties of the transients have been accumulated including uv and visible, fluorescence, resonance Raman, epr and nmr. This has been important for characterizing the transient and for studying the kinetics of its subsequent reactions.

Metal-containing proteins, and in particular those containing heme iron have played an important role in examining non-equilibrium states and their subsequent transformations. After perturbation, a number of events may occur at the metal; its oxidation state or the extent of its ligand binding may change, or the ground state may be excited. The structure of the protein and that of the metal site will momentarily be at nonequilibrium, and the protein will undergo a relaxation to the stable structure of the new state. There are three distinct types of perturbations that are used, giving in general, different or overlapping information on the subsequent processes.

1. Flow generation of transients

Metal-ligand bond breakage and formation may in certain instances be sufficiently slow that it may be observed in a transient following flow generation of that transient. Rapid reduction of cyt c(III) by dithionite at pH ~ 9 produces a non-equilibrium form of cyt c(II) which transforms slowly $(\sim 7\,\mathrm{s}^{-1})$ to the stable form. The transient has been characterized by spectral,[209] CD stopped-flow experiments[230] and resonance Raman-continuous flow[119] and its relatively long half-life is attributed to slow recombination of Met-80 as the sixth ligand to the heme iron (II), Met-80 being unbound to heme iron (III) in alkaline solution. The ligand replaced was considered to be lysine-72 or -79, but this is now unlikely.[231]

The "pulsed" techniques generate partially reduced or partially liganded species. Deoxyhemoglobin solutions containing dithionite are mixed with oxygen in a stopped-flow apparatus. Oxygen reacts rapidly with dithionite and with deoxyhemoglobin. By this means, hemoglobin is exposed *briefly* to oxygen and partially oxygenated intermediates are formed. Their subsequent dissociative behavior (by reaction with dithionite still present) can be kinetically assessed. It is not possible to produce such partially oxygenated intermediates since at equilibrium hemoglobin will be present as $\mathrm{Hb(Fe^{II})_4}$ and $\mathrm{Hb(Fe(II)O_2)_4}$ as a result of the cooperativity of the system. This experiment showed large and unsuspected differences between the reactivity toward O_2 of α- and β-chains.[232] Other examples of this approach and of flow-generated transients are shown in Table 6.[233-241]

2. Pulse radiolytic generation of transients

Pulse radiolysis can produce rapidly a powerful oxidizing or reducing radical. This radical will effect a *one* electron oxidation or reduction even of a substrate which can exist in more than two oxidation states. Thus reduction of methemoglobin, signified as $\mathrm{Hb(Fe^{III})_4}$ by electrons ($k = 1.6 \times 10^{10}\,\mathrm{M^{-1}\,s^{-1}}$) *must* lead to $\mathrm{Hb(Fe^{III})_3}$ $(\mathrm{Fe^{II}})$ as the sole product, if, as usually the case, the radical is in large deficiency.[110,242,243] The reactions of this unique transient may then be examined. It undergoes small spectral changes with a first-order rate constant $\sim 10^5\,\mathrm{s}^{-1}$, independent of heme concentration. This change is

TABLE 6

Examples of flow generation of transients

Protein	Perturbation	Results and product	Monitor	Reference
Cyt c(III)	s.f., pHnjump (7 → 11.6)	Neutral form (low spin) transformed to intermediate (high spin), $k = 25$ s^{-1} which transforms to final alkaline form (low spin), $k = 5.5$ s^{-1}	Spectral and CD. Rapid scan	[151, 208, 233, 234]
Cyt c-551 oxidase	s.f., Fe(CN)$_6^{3-}$	Oxidation of c(II) center ($k = 9.6 \times 10^4$ M^{-1} s^{-1}), d_1(II) center ($k = 1.5 \times 10^4$ M^{-1} s^{-1}) and conformational change (0.17 s^{-1})	Kinetic difference spectra	[148]
Hb(Fe^{II})$_4$ ($+S_2O_4^{2-}$)	s.f., Fe(CN)$_6^{3-}$	Partially oxidized intermediates of Hb (T-state) bound by Fe(CN)$_6^{4-}$. Reduction with $S_2O_4^{2-}$ monitored	Spectral	[235]
Fully or partially reduced cyt c oxidase	s.f., O$_2$	"Pulsed" cyt-c oxidase has different properties (i.e. towards cyt-c) than resting oxidase (from preparation). Pulsed form may play an important role in catalytic mechanism[237–239]	Spectral	[236–239]
Mb(III)—CN$^-$	s.f., $S_2O_4^{2-}$	Mb(II)—CN$^-$ immediate product which dissociates (0.10 s^{-1})		[240, 241]
Hb(Fe^{II}) (stripped)	s.f. and quenched flow, NO	Binding to α- and β-subunits equal rate constant. In presence of IHP (T-state favored) additional slow structural change ($t_{1/2} \sim 0.4$ s) arising from cleavage of iron-proximal histidine bond	EPR spectral	[28]

ascribed to a low-spin to high-spin (R state) transformation.[242,243] The spectrum of the transient is similar to that obtained by γ-irradiation of $Hb(Fe^{III})_4$ in H_2O/ethyleneglycol at liquid N_2 temperatures, in which conditions the transient is stabilized.[244] The reaction of the transient with CO or with O_2 may be examined by carrying out the e^-_{aq} reduction in the presence of these ligands. The high rate constants for reaction of $Hb(Fe^{III})_3$ (Fe^{II}) with CO[245-247] and with O_2[247-249] ($k = 4.1 \times 10^6$ and $\sim 3 \times 10^7$ M^{-1} s^{-1} respectively at pH ~ 7 using stripped hemoglobin) strongly suggests that the transient is in the high affinity (R) state, from comparison of data for reaction of deoxyhemoglobin with these ligands from flash photolysis, stopped-flow and temperature-jump experiments. Some other metalloproteins to which this approach has been applied are shown in Table 7.[250,252-259] It should be emphasized that assignment of spectral changes, following e^-_{aq} irradiation, to processes can be difficult.[260] These conformational relaxations may play a role in enzyme catalytic stages, biological energy conversion systems and the modulation of binding affinities.[250] It is also increasingly clear that proteins undergo a wide variety of molecular motions as shown by experimental and theoretical considerations,[251] and definition of the rapid conformational changes may help an understanding of these motions. Many slow reactions incorporate rapid steps in suggested mechanisms. The examination of the rapid step separately may yield supporting evidence for the mechanism. The oxidation of vitamin B_{12r} by bromine is second order and the rate-limiting step is assigned to (12)

$$Co(II) + Br_2 \rightarrow Co(III) + Br_2^- \text{ (or } Co(III)-Br + Br^-) \tag{12}$$

This is followed by either (13) or (14)

$$Co(II) + Br_2^- \rightarrow Co(III)-Br + Br^- \tag{13}$$

$$2Br_2^- \rightarrow Br_2 + 2Br^- \tag{14}$$

By examining the reaction of B_{12r} with Br_2^- (pulse radiolysis) it was shown that the second-order rate constant was 3.4×10^9 M^{-1} s^{-1} and that a complex $Co(III)-Br$ was formed and hydrolysed rapidly ($t_{1/2} \sim 1$ ms). Therefore this reaction proceeds by an inner-sphere mechanism and that with the conditions of the $Co(II)/Br_2$ reaction, 99.7% of Br_2^- produced in equation (12) reacts by equation (13).[261]

3. Flash and laser photolytic generation of transients

Flash or laser photolysis of an adduct may often promote photochemical dissociation via excited states. The subsequent (dark) recombination process can be examined spectrally. The product of the photolysis will be in a non-

TABLE 7

Some transients generated by hydrated electron reduction

Protein	Rate constants	Products	Remarks	Reference
HIPIP$_{reduced}$	1.8×10^{10} M^{-1} s^{-1} at pH = 7.0	HIPIP super-reduced	First production in aqueous solution of super-reduced species with spectrum similar to that of reduced ferredoxin	[252]
cyt c(III)	1.8×10^{10} M^{-1} s^{-1} at pH $\sim 9, 2 \times 10^4$ s^{-1}, 10^3 s^{-1}, 7 s^{-1}	Number of reduced, non-equilibrium forms of cyt c(II) reported. Final change is alkaline isomerization missing in neutral pH (latter also observed with CO$_2^-$ and O$_2^-$ reaction)[69,70]	Resonance Raman reported of long lasting ($k \sim 7$ s^{-1}) transient[259]	[250, 253–259]
Hb(Fe^{III}CN$^-$)$_4$	$\sim 4 \times 10^{10}$ M^{-1} s^{-1}, pH 6.2	Hb(Fe^{III}CN$^-$)$_3$ (Fe^{II}CN$^-$) slow changes, release of CN$^-$		[243, 250]
Hb(Fe^{III}N$_3^-$)$_4$	$\sim 4 \times 10^{10}$ M^{-1} s^{-1}, pH 6.2	Hb(Fe^{III})$_3$(Fe^{II})	Series of intermediates arising from ligand dissociation and/or conformation changes in reduced heme subunit	[243, 250]

equilibrium state and will transform faster than, during, or slower than the recombination and this can be disentangled kinetically. The reactivity of the transient is, as a rule, enhanced. The method, more than any other, has been used to generate transients over a very wide range of times (micro- to picoseconds). Multivaried information on a system may thus be obtained and this is well illustrated by the extensive research on the globin adducts.

In the first experiments on $Hb(Fe^{II}CO)_4$, it was shown that full removal of CO was possible by flash photolysis, and that the (dark) second-order recombination with CO involved both the R and T forms of the deoxy as well as their interconversion ($k_{R \to T} = 920 \ s^{-1}$ at 3 °C).[262,263] At the other end of the time scale, picosecond spectroscopy provides kinetic data on the initial events in ligand dissociation without protein movement.[264,265] Processes can be examined in which the ligand is removed from the iron but does not reach the outside solution. Within 3 ps of excitation at 353 nm, MbCO and MbO_2 are bleached and it is believed that ligand dissociation has occurred. Transient absorption spectra in the Soret region are observed within 50 psec and data obtained are interpreted in terms of the scheme (15).[264]

$$MbX^{**}$$

$$MbX \rightleftharpoons MbX^* \rightsquigarrow Mb^* + X \qquad (15)$$

$$Mb + X$$

Photodissociation of MbO_2 proceeds through an excited state of Mb (Mb^*) whereas MbCO is believed to produce the ground state (Mb) directly. Difference spectra taken at 200 ps after excitation indicates the product from MbO_2 and MbCO is very similar, if not identical, with deoxy Mb.[265] There is no evidence for sub-nanosecond geminate recombination with either MbCO or MbO_2. Up to 10 ns some recombination of MbO_2 but none of MbCO occurs.[264,265] Geminate recombination (a fraction of photolysed ligand rebinding very rapidly to heme before escaping to solution) is observed as fast spectral changes, following nanosecond laser photolysis of Hb adducts at room temperature.[266] These results have implications in the definition of quantum yields.[267]

Picosecond resonance Raman of photolysed HbCO shows three bands, distinct from HbCO and 4–7 cm^{-1} lower than in deoxy Hb. The product is regarded as Fe(II), in or close to the heme plane, but with a spin state, S = 2. The spin transformation within 30 ps (from S = 0 in HbCO) must occur in the excited state, since $S = 0 \leftrightarrow S = 2$ changes are in the 10^7–10^8 s^{-1} range (Section IV.A.3). This intermediate (with Raman frequencies lowered relative to deoxy Hb) must persist for at least 20 ns[120] and it is uncertain when iron, and proximal imidazole ligand, move away from the heme plane to its characteristic position in deoxy Hb. This slow relaxation may reflect the time constant for protein tertiary structural change, since nuclear motions *per se* would be expected to be very rapid ($<$ps).[154] The initial spectral changes following HbCO dissociation to 3 ns are significantly different from those of MbCO or related protoheme CO models. These recent picosecond photolysis experiments indicate that the tertiary heme structure has a major effect on the photodissociation.[268]

By combining lowered temperatures (down to 140 K) with flash photolysis (down to 2 μs), it has been observed how CO (and O$_2$) compete for the globin within the protein (IN) and from the solvent (OUT) [Scheme (16)]. Extensive studies lead to a model of the ligand approaching the bonding site by a few well defined pathways[269]

$$\overset{(+O_2)}{\text{MbCO}} \xrightarrow{h\nu} \text{Mb} + \text{CO}(+O_2)$$

$$
\begin{array}{c}
\overset{\text{IN}}{\diagup}\ \ \text{MbCO} + O_2 \\
\text{Mb} \hspace{4cm} \diagup \rightarrow \text{MbCO} + O_2 \hspace{2cm} (16) \\
\diagdown \rightarrow \text{Mb} + \text{CO} + O_2 \diagup \\
\underset{\text{OUT}}{} \hspace{4cm} \diagdown \rightleftharpoons \text{MbO}_2 + \text{CO}
\end{array}
$$

Laser photolysis of a weak acid can produce, in the excited state, a strong acid with rapid concomitant production of protons. The effect can be used for example to produce a rapid pH perturbation (e.g. 7.0 to 4.0)[33] or to probe the environment of a protein-fluorescent substrate site of interaction (Section IV.C.3). A few representative examples of the use of photolytic generation of transients for probing mechanism are shown in Table 8.[270–274] The advantages of the photochemical relaxation method over temperature and pressure-jump have been outlined.[270] In particular, if light is absorbed by a specific chemical species in a reaction system then selected intermediates may be generated.

C. Probing structural features and active site of metalloproteins

Although a number of the foregoing studies have been directly or indirectly concerned with elucidating protein structural features, it seems appropriate to devote a small section specifically to the topic.

TABLE 8

Some transients generated by photolytic methods

Substrate	Perturbation	Transient products	Remarks	Reference
Horseradish peroxidase C.NO adduct (HRP.NO)	Second-order recombination (2×10^5 M^{-1} s^{-1}) after 400 μs xenon flash at pH >11	HRP + NO	Alkaline form of HRP not produced because isomerization (~ 70 s^{-1}) slower than HRP + NO recombination. Shows Fe(III) state also photodissociable	[271]
[structure: N=N—C$_6$H$_4$—N(CH$_3$)$_2$, Ni^{2+} (H$_2$O)$_4$]	Biphasic relaxation after 3 μs laser pulse	Ni(PAD)(H$_2$O)$_5^{2+}$ (PAD, unidentate)	Allows direct determination of ring closure, not possible by T- or P-jump	[270, 272]
Hemochromes (L)Fe^{II}TPP-Py six-coordinated L covalently linked to TPP macrocycle	20 ns Q-switched Nd laser	Five-coordinated complex (L)Fe^{II}TPP	Allows direct determination of 5 → 6 (Py back on)	[273]
MbCO, MbO$_2$, HbCO, HRP-CO, MP-11-CO	Dye laser and flash photolysis down to −90 °C	Photodissociated proteins	Recombination kinetics followed in solvent mixtures. Interpreted as caged geminate transient diffusion-controlled reaction at −90 °C	[274]

1. Hydrogen exchange characteristics

The kinetics of hydrogen exchange reactions of peptide NH and side chain hydrogen atoms in proteins with D_2O have been useful for structural characterization.[275] Exchange times can range from seconds to years, so that rapid reaction techniques are of peripheral value. The H exchange rates of two of the six tyrosines in bovine pancreatic ribonuclease A are rapid at 25 °C ($k \sim 120$ s^{-1}, quite close to the value found for free tyrosine). They are thus considered to be fully exposed.[276]

2. Pulse radiolytic inactivation of enzymes

Powerful radicals such as e_{aq}^- and OH tend to indiscriminately attack amino acids, although the aromatic and heterocyclic amino acids are more reactive than the aliphatic, non-sulfur containing amino acids. Other radicals may react more readily with specific amino acids. Thus it is found that $(SCN)_2^-$ attacks tryptophan with a rate constant at least 10^3 larger than that for any other amino acid. Since $(SCN)_2^-$ inactivates, for example, lysozyme this constitutes excellent evidence for a crucial role for a tryptophan at the active site of the enzyme, consistent with the known structure.[277] This approach, the use of radical anions to probe the essential residues of enzymes, has been extended to a number of enzymes using pulsed and steady-state irradiation techniques.[278,279] Thus Tyr and Trp are implicated in carboxypeptidase A (using $(SCN)_2^-$ and Br_2^-),[280] His involved in superoxide dismutase (using Br_2^-),[281] His and Tyr in bovine carbonic anhydrase (using $(SCN)_2^-$ and Br_2^-)[282] and Cys, His in yeast alcohol dehydrogenase (using I_2^-, $(SCN)_2^-$ and Br_2^-).[283] In addition, the radicals $(SCN)_2^-$, Br_2^-, Cl_2^- and CO_3^- all give a common transient spectrum on reacting with tryptophan (and with tyrosine) in neutral solution, this also aiding the identification of the key targets in the various enzymes.[284]

However, metalloproteins with strongly reactive metal sites (e.g. porphyrins) may not be susceptible to this approach. Ferrocytochrome c is oxidized to ferricytochrome c by $(SCN)_2^-$, Br_2^- or N_3 radicals with 100% yield, without sign of an intermediate. The rate constants ($\sim 10^9$ M^{-1} s^{-1}) are apparently sufficiently higher than those for reaction with the latter and attacks the partially exposed region of the heme.[72]

3. Fluorescence characteristics

Fluorescence characteristics have been used to probe structural features of proteins. The fluorescence quenching of tryptophan residues in a stopped-flow apparatus can be used to study their reactivity and distribution in the protein matrix.[285] The tryptophan fluorescence decay of LADH, with excitation at 295 nm is biphasic with $\tau = 3.8$ and 7.2 ns (Fig. 2). These decay times are assigned to buried Trp-314 and exposed Trp-15 respectively.[92] As a final example, time-resolved fluorimetry has been used to probe the micro-environment of a binding site. Excitation of 8-hydroxypyrene-1,3,6-tri-sulfonate converts the weak acid ($pK = 7.7$) into a strong acid ($pK = 0.5$). The concomitant proton dissociation can be measured by time-resolved fluorim-etry. The rate constant, 1×10^{10} s^{-1}, is reduced in concentrated salt solution, and is an exponential function of the chemical activity of water in the solution. The proton dissociation of the probe found to bovine serum albumin is bi-phasic with $k = 3 \times 10^9$ s^{-1} and 1.4×10^8 s^{-1}. The rapid phase represents proton dissociation taking place in the binding site and correlates to a salt solution with water activity of 0.85. The slower phase represents the escape of proton from the binding site.[286]

V. CONCLUSIONS

It will be apparent from the contents of this review that no reaction in solution is too fast to be measurable. The elucidation of the reaction mechanism may be much more difficult, particularly with the enzyme-catalysed redox reactions, only briefly alluded to. It is clear that rapid reaction techniques allow for the observation of ephemeral transients and their characterization, without which the complete understanding of many fundamental processes will be im-possible. Nowhere is this more evident than in the current research on the photo-synthesis mechanism.[287] It is therefore more than a little surprising that many of the aspects raised in this review are given such scant attention in recent reviews and books devoted to kinetics, inorganic and bioinorganic chemistry, an omission commented on elsewhere.[288] An increase in the research and the number of researchers in this area, as the potential of the techniques becomes clear, will likely redress the imbalance. Certainly, the future of rapid-reaction technique applications looks very bright.

Acknowledgement

The writing of this review was made possible, in part, by the support of National Science Foundation and National Institutes of Health Grants. These are gratefully acknowledged.

REFERENCES

[1] Hague, D. N. "Fast Reactions"; Wiley-Interscience: New York, 1971.
[2] Hammes, G. G. (Ed.) "Investigation of Rates and Mechanisms of Reactions,

Part II: Investigation of Elementary Reaction Steps in Solution and Very Fast Reactions"; Wiley: New York, 1974.

[3] Wilkins, R. G. "The Study of Kinetics and Mechanism of Reactions of Transition Metal Complexes"; Allyn and Bacon: Boston, 1974, Chapters 3 and 5.

[4] Bernasconi, C. F. "Relaxation Kinetics"; Academic Press: New York, 1976.

[5] Hiromi, K. "Kinetics of Fast Enzyme Reactions"; Wiley: New York, 1979.

[6] Gettins, W. J.; Wyn-Jones, E. (Eds) "Techniques and Applications of Fast Reactions in Solution"; D. Reidel: Boston, 1979.

[7] Jones, J. R.; Crooks, J. E. *Ann. Rep. Chem. Soc. London (C)* **1979**, *76*, 131–159.

[8] Cantor, C. R.; Schimmel, P. R. "Biophysical Chemistry. Part III"; Freeman: San Francisco, 1980, Chapter 16.

[9] Hammes, G. G. *In* "Methods for Determining Metal Ion Environments in Proteins"; Darnall, D. W.; Wilkins, R. G., Eds; Elsevier/North-Holland: New York, 1980, Chapter 9.

[10] Kennard, D. W.; Smyth, G. L. *Nature* **1963**, *197*, 50–52.

[11] Gibson, Q. H. *Ann. Rev. Biochem.* **1966**, *35*, 435–456.

[12] Gibson, Q. H. *Methods Enzym.* **1969**, *16*, 187–228.

[13] Gutfreund, H. *Methods Enzym.* **1969**, *16*, 229–249.

[14] Chance, B. *In* "Investigation of Rates and Mechanisms of Reactions, Part II: Investigation of Elementary Reaction Steps in Solution and Very Fast Reactions"; Hammes, G. G., Ed.; Wiley: New York, 1974, Chapter 2.

[15] Hiromi, K. "Kinetics of Fast Enzyme Reactions"; Wiley: New York, 1979, pp. 68–121.

[16] Capelle, N.; Barbet, J.; Dessen, P.; Blanquet, S.; Roques, B. P.; Le Pecq, J-B. *Biochemistry* **1979**, *18*, 3354–3362.

[17] Hiromi, K. "Kinetics of Fast Enzyme Reactions"; Wiley: New York, 1979, p. 159.

[18] McClune, G. J.; Fee, J. A. *FEBS Lett.* **1976**, *67*, 294–296.

[19] Abdallah, M. A.; Biellmann, J-F.; Lagrange, P. *Biochemistry* **1979**, *18*, 836–838.

[20] Chance, B.; Devault, D.; Legallais, V.; Mela, L.; Yonetani, T. *In* "Fast Reactions and Primary Processes in Chemical Kinetics"; Claesson, S., Ed.; Wiley: New York, 1967, pp. 437–468.

[21] Holzwarth, J. F. *In* "Techniques and Applications of Fast Reactions in Solution"; Gettins, W. J.; Wyn-Jones, E., Eds; D. Reidel: Boston, 1979, pp. 13–23.

[22] Owens, G. D.; Taylor, R. W.; Ridley, T. Y.; Margerum, D. W. *Anal. Chem.* **1980**, *52*, 130–138.

[23] Gerischer, H.; Heim, W. *Z. Phys. Chem. (N.F.)* **1965**, *46*, 345–352.

[24] Luzzana, M. R.; Penniston, J. T. *Biochem. Biophys. Acta* **1975**, *396*, 157–164.

[25] Chock, S. P.; Eisenberg, E. *J. Biol. Chem.* **1979**, *254*, 3229–3235.

[26] Bray, R. C. *Biochem. J.* **1961**, *81*, 189–193; Bray, R. C.; Pettersson, R. *Biochem. J.* **1961**, *81*, 194–195; Bray, R. C. *Adv. Enzymol.* **1980**, *51*, 107–165.

[27] Thorneley, R. N. F.; Yates, M. G.; Lowe, D. J. *Biochem. J.* **1976**, *155*, 137–144.

[28] Ballou, D. P.; Palmer, G. *Anal. Chem.* **1974**, *46*, 1248–1253; Hille, R.; Palmer, G.; Olson, J. S. *J. Biol. Chem.* **1977**, *252*, 403–405.

[29] Gamsjäger, H.; Baertschi, P. *J. Chem. Soc. Dalton Trans.* **1976**, 1683–1686.

[30] Peterman, B. F.; Wu, C-W. *Biochemistry* **1978**, *17*, 3889–3892.

[31] Schelly, Z. A. *In* "Techniques and Applications of Fast Reactions in Solution"; Gettings, W. J.; Wyn-Jones, E., Eds; D. Reidel: Boston, 1979, pp. 35–39.

[32] Ireland, J. F.; Wyatt, P. A. H. *Adv. Phys. Org. Chem.* **1976**, *12*, 131–221.

[33] Clark, J. H.; Shapiro, S. L.; Campillo, A. J.; Winn, K. R. *J. Amer. Chem. Soc.* **1979**, *101*, 746–748; Gutman, M.; Huppert, D.; Pines, E. *J. Amer. Chem. Soc.* **1981**, *103*, 3709–3713.

[34] Pecht, I.; Rigler, R. (Eds) "Chemical Relaxation in Molecular Biology"; Springer-Verlag: New York, 1977. Application of relaxation techniques to a number of important topics including H-bond formation, protein folding and a number of interactions involving protein.

[35] Eigen, M.; de Maeyer, L. *In* "Investigations of Rates and Mechanisms of Reactions, Part II: Investigation of Elementary Reaction Steps in Solution and Very Fast Reactions"; Hammes, G. G., Ed.; Wiley: New York, 1974, Chapter 3.

[36] Porschke, D. *Rev. Sci. Instrum.* **1976**, *47*, 1363–1365.

[37] Perutz, M. F.; Sanders, J. K. M.; Chenery, D. H.; Noble, R. W.; Pennelly, R. R.; Fung, L. W-M.; Ho, C.; Giannini, I.; Pörschke, D.; Winkler, H. *Biochemistry* **1978**, *17*, 3640–3652.

[38] Aubard, J.; Nozeran, J. M.; Levoir, P.; Meyer, J. J.; Dubois, J. E. *Rev. Sci. Instrum.* **1979**, *50*, 52–58.

[39] Frisch, W.; Schmidt, A.; Holzworth, J. F.; Volk, R. *In* "Techniques and Applications of Fast Reactions in Solution"; Gettins, W. J.; Wyn-Jones, E., Eds; D. Reidel: Boston, 1979, pp. 61–70.

[40] Aubard, J.; Meyer, J. J.; Nozeran, J. M.; Levoir, P. *In* "Techniques and Applications of Fast Reactions in Solution"; Gettings, W. J.; Wyn-Jones, E., Eds; D. Reidel: Boston, 1979, pp. 71–75.

[41] Dewey, T. G.; Turner, D. H. *In* "Techniques and Applications of Fast Reactions in Solution"; Gettings, W. J.; Wyn-Jones, E., Eds; D. Reidel: Boston, 1979, pp. 235–238.

[42] Turner, D. H.; Flynn, G. W.; Sutin, N.; Beitz, J. V. *J. Amer. Chem. Soc.* **1972**, *94*, 1554–1559.

[43] Hammes, G. G. "Principles of Chemical Kinetics"; Academic Press: New York, 1978, p. 234.

[44] Bernasconi, C. F.; Muller, M. C. *J. Amer. Chem. Soc.* **1978**, *100*, 5530–5533.

[45] Verkman, A. S.; Dix, J. A.; Pandiscio, A. A. *Anal. Biochem.* **1981**, *117*, 164–169.

[46] Clegg, R. M.; Maxfield, B. W. *Rev. Sci. Instrum.* **1976**, *47*, 1383–1393.

[47] Halvorson, H. R. *Biochemistry* **1979**, *18*, 2480–2487.

[48] Gruenewald, B.; Knoche, W. *In* "Techniques and Applications of Fast Reactions in Solution"; Gettins, W. J.; Wyn-Jones, E., Eds; D. Reidel: Boston, 1979, pp. 87–94.

[49] Kegeles, G. *Methods Enzym.* **1978**, *48*, 308–320. P-jump/light scattering arrangements are reviewed.

[50] Davis, J. S. *Biochem. J.* **1981**, *197*, 309–314.

[51] Hardman, M. J. *Biochem. J.* **1981**, *197*, 773–774.

[52] Murakami, K.; Sano, T.; Yasunaga, T. *Bull. Chem. Soc. Jap.* **1981**, *54*, 862–868.

[53] Knoche, W. *In* "Investigation of Rates and Mechanisms of Reactions, Part II: Investigation of Elementary Reactions Steps in Solution and Very Fast Reactions"; Hammes, G. G., Ed.; Wiley: New York, 1974, Chapter 5.

[54] Takahashi, M. T.; Alberty, R. A. *Methods Enzym.* **1969**, *16*, 31–55.

[55] de Maeyer, L. C. M. *Methods Enzym.* **1969**, *16*, 80–118.

[56] De Maeyer, L.; Persoons, A. *In* "Investigation of Rates and Mechanisms of Reactions, Part II: Investigation of Elementary Reaction Steps in Solution and Very Fast Reactions"; Hammes, G. G., Ed.; Wiley: New York, 1974, Chapter 6.

[57] Hemmes, P. *In* "Techniques and Applications of Fast Reactions in Solution"; Gettins, W. J.; Wyn-Jones, E., Eds; D. Reidel: Boston, 1979, pp. 95–98.

[58] Tsuji, Y.; Yasunaga, T.; Sano, T.; Ushio, H. *J. Amer. Chem. Soc.* **1976**, *98*, 813–818.

[59] Eggers, F.; Kustin, K. *Methods Enzym.* **1969**, *16*, 55–80.

[60] Stuehr, J. *In* "Investigation of Rates and Mechanisms of Reactions, Part II: Investigation of Elementary Reaction Steps in Solution and Very Fast Reactions"; Hammes, G. G., Ed.; Wiley: New York, 1974, Chapter 7.

[61] Eyring, E. M.; Farrow, M. M.; Rodriquez, L. J.; Lloyd, L. B.; Rohrbach, R. P.; Allred, E. L. *In* "Techniques and Applications of Fast Reactions in Solution"; Gettins, W. J.; Wyn-Jones, E., Eds; D. Reidel: Boston, 1979, pp. 355–361.

[62] Zana, R.; Lang, J.; Tondre, C.; Sturm, J.; Yiv, S. *In* "Techniques and Applications of Fast Reactions in Solution"; Gettins, W. J.; Wyn-Jones, E., Eds; D. Reidel: Boston, 1979, pp. 225–233.

[63] Eigen, M.; Tamm, K. *Z. Elektrochem.* **1962**, *66*, 93–106; 107–121.

[64] Buxton, G. V.; Sellers, R. M. *Coordin. Chem. Rev.* **1977**, *22*, 195–274.

[65] Anbar, M.; Bambenek, M.; Ross, A. B. National Bureau of Standards Publication NSRDS-NBS43, 1973 and Supplement, 1975.

[66] Swallow, A. J. *Prog. Reaction Kinetics* **1978**, *9*, 195–365. An account of reactions of free radicals (including CO_2^-) produced by irradiation of organic compounds.

[67] Harrington, P. C.; Wilkins, R. G. *J. Biol. Chem.* **1979**, *254*, 7505–7508.

[68] Fee, J. A.; Valentine, J. S. *In* "Superoxide and Superoxide Dismutases"; Michelson, B. M.; McCord, J. M.; Fridovich, L., Eds; Academic Press: New York, 1977, pp. 19–60.

[69] Simic, M. G.; Taub, I. A.; Tocci, J.; Hurwitz, P. A. *Biochem. Biophys. Res. Commun.* **1975**, *62*, 161–167.

[70] Koppenol, W. H.; Van Buuren, K. J. H.; Butler, J.; Braams, R. *Biochim. Biophys. Acta* **1976**, *449*, 157–168.

[71] Dorfman, L. M.; Adams, G. E. National Bureau of Standards Publication NSRDS-NBS 46, 1973.

[72] Seki, H.; Imamura, M. *Biochim. Biophys. Acta* **1981**, *635*, 81–89.

[73] Ross, A. B.; Neta, P. National Bureau of Standards Publication NSRDS-NBS65, 1979.

[74] Land, E. J.; Prütz, W. A. *Int. J. Radiat. Biol.* **1979**, *36*, 75–83.

[75] Jonah, C. D. *Rev. Sci. Instrum.* **1975**, *46*, 62–66.

[76] Netzel, T. L.; Rentzepis, P. M. *Chem. Phys. Lett.* **1974**, *29*, 337–342; Noe, I. J.; Eisert, W. G.; Rentzepis, P. M. *Proc. Nat. Acad. Sci. USA* **1978**, *75*, 573–577.

[77] Hunt, J. W. *Adv. Radiat. Chem.* **1976**, *5*, 185–315; Shapiro, S. L. (Ed.) "Ultrashort Light Pulses"; Springer: Berlin, 1977. Contains reviews of applications of picosecond techniques and measurement.

[78] Porter, G.; West, M. A. *In* "Investigation of Rates and Mechanisms, Part II: Investigation of Elementary Reaction Steps in Solution and Very Fast Reactions"; Hammes, G. G., Ed.; Wiley: New York, 1974, Chapter 10.

[79] Dorfman, L. M. *In* "Investigation of Rates and Mechanisms, Part II: Investigation of Elementary Reaction Steps in Solution and Very Fast Reactions"; Hammes, G. G., Ed.; Wiley: New York, 1974, Chapter 11.

[80] Baxendale, J. H.; Rodgers, M. A. J. *Chem. Soc. Rev.* **1978**, *7*, 235–263.

[81] Bielski, B. H. J.; Richter, H. W. *J. Amer. Chem. Soc.* **1977**, *99*, 3019–3023.

[82] Sawicki, C. A.; Gibson, Q. H. *J. Biol. Chem.* **1979**, *254*, 4058–4062.

[83] Caldin, E. F. *In* "Techniques and Applications of Fast Reactions in Solution"; Gettins, W. J.; Wyn-Jones, E., Eds; D. Reidel: Boston, 1979, pp. 1–11.

[84] Swift, T. J. *In* "Investigation of Rates and Mechanisms, Part II: Investigation of

Elementary Reaction Steps in Solution and Very Fast Reactions"; Hammes, G. G., Ed.; Wiley: New York, 1974, Chapter 12.

[85] Kaplan, J. I.; Fraenkel, G. "NMR of Chemically Exchanging Systems"; Academic Press: London, 1980.

[86] For example Zuiderweg, E. R. P.; Hamers, L. F.; Rollema, H. S.; de Bruin, S. H.; Hilbers, C. W. *Eur. J. Biochem.* **1981**, *118*, 95–104.

[87] Burgess, J. "Metal Ions in Solution"; Wiley: New York, 1978, Chapter 11.

[88] Lee, L.; Sykes, B. D. *In* "Methods for Determining Ion Environments in Proteins"; Darnall, D. W.; Wilkins, R. G., Eds; Elsevier/North Holland: New York, 1980, Chapter 7.

[89] Mildvan, A. S.; Granot, J.; Smith, G. M.; Liebman, M. N. *In* "Methods for Determining Metal Ion Environments in Proteins"; Darnall, D. W.; Wilkins, R. G., Eds; Elsevier/North-Holland: New York, 1980, Chapter 8.

[90] Chen, K. S.; Hirota, N. *In* "Investigation of Rates and Mechanisms of Reactions, Part II: Investigation of Elementary Reaction Steps in Solution and Very Fast Reactions"; Hammes, G. G., Ed.; Wiley: New York, 1974, Chapter 13.

[91] Badea, M. G.; Brand, L. *Methods Enzym.* **1979**, *61*, 378–425.

[92] Ross, J. B. A.; Schmidt, C. J.; Brand, L. *Biochemistry* **1981**, *20*, 4369–4377.

[93] Strehlow, H. *In* "Investigation of Rates and Mechanisms of Reactions, Part II: Investigation of Elementary Reaction Steps in Solution and Very Fast Reactions"; Hammes, G. G., Ed.; Wiley: New York, 1974, Chapter 8.

[94] Ryan, M. D.; Wei, J-F.; Feinberg, B. A.; Lau, Y-K. *Anal. Biochem.* **1979**, *96*, 326–333; Wei, J-F.; Ryan, M. D. *Anal. Biochem.* **1980**, *106*, 269–277.

[95] Heremans, K.; Ceuterick, F.; Snauwaert, J.; Wauters, J. *In* "Techniques and Applications of Fast Reactions in Solution"; Gettins, W. J.; Wyn-Jones, E., Eds; D. Reidel: Boston, 1979, pp. 429–432.

[96] Caldin, E. F.; Grant, M. W.; Hasinoff, B. B.; Tregloan, P. A. *J. Phys. E* **1973**, *6*, 349–354.

[97] Jost, A. *Ber. Bunsenges. Phys. Chem.* **1974**, *78*, 300–303.

[98] Fitos, I.; Heremans, K.; Loontiens, F. G. *React. Kinet. Catal. Lett.* **1979**, *12*, 393–397.

[99] Hasinoff, B. B. *Biochemistry* **1974**, *13*, 3111–3117.

[100] Vanni, H.; Earl, W. L.; Merbach, A. E. *J. Magn. Reson.* **1978**, *29*, 11–19.

[101] Morild, E. *Adv. Protein Chem.* **1981**, *34*, 93–166.

[102] Douzou, P. *Adv. Enzymol.* **1980**, *51*, 1–74.

[103] Fink, A. L. *Acc. Chem. Res.* **1977**, *10*, 233–239.

[104] Auld, D. S. *Methods Enzymol.* **1979**, *61*, 318–335.

[105] Douzou, P. "Cryobiochemistry: An Introduction"; Academic Press: New York, 1977, Chapter 4.

[106] Austin, R. H.; Beeson, K. W.; Eisenstein, L.; Frauenfelder, H.; Gunsalus, I. C. *Biochemistry* **1975**, *14*, 5355–5373.

[107] Verkman, A. S.; Pandiscio, A. A.; Jennings, M.; Solomon, A. K. *Anal. Biochem.* **1980**, *102*, 189–195.

[108] Olsen, S. L.; Holmes, L. P.; Eyring, E. M. *Rev. Sci. Instrum.* **1974**, *45*, 859–861.

[109] Sawicki, C. A.; Morris, R. J. *Methods Enzym.* **1981**, *76*, 667–681. A flash photolysis apparatus with time resolution of about 5 ms and two laser systems, 1 μs and 30 ns, are described.

[110] Raap, A.; Van Leeuwen, J. W.; Rollema, H. S.; de Bruin, S. H. *Eur. J. Biochem.* **1978**, *88*, 555–563.

[111] Dunn, S. M. J.; Batchelor, J. G.; King, R. W. *Biochemistry* **1978**, *17*, 2356–2364.

180   R. G. Wilkins

Adaptation of commercial apparatus for fluorescence.

[112] Rigler, R.; Rabl, C-R.; Jovin, T. M. *Rev. Sci. Instrum.* **1974**, *45*, 580–588.

[113] Davis, J. S.;Gutfreund, H. *FEBS Lett.* **1976**, *72*, 199–207.

[114] Anson, M.; Bayley, P. M. *J. Phys. E.* **1974**, *7*, 481–486; Bachinger, H. P.; Eggenberger, H. P.; Hanish, G. *Rev. Sci. Instrum.* **1979**, *50*, 1367–1372; Bayley, P. M. *Prog. Biophys. Molec. Biol.* **1981**, *37*, 149–180.

[115] Anson, M.; Martin, S. R.; Bayley, P. M. *Rev. Sci. Instrum.* **1977**, *48*, 953–962.

[116] Gruenewald, B.; Knoche, W. *Rev. Sci. Instrum.* **1978**, *49*, 797–801.

[117] Cummings, A. L.; Eyring, E. M. *Biopolymers* **1975**, *14*, 2107–2114.

[118] Ferrone, F. A.; Hopfield, J. J.; Schatterly, S. E. *Rev. Sci. Instrum.* **1974**, *45*, 1392–1396.

[119] Forster, M.; Hester, R. E.; Cartling, B.; Wilbrandt, R. *Biophys. J.* **1982**, *38*, 111–116.

[120] Lyons, K. B.; Friedman, J. M.; Fleury, P. A. *Nature* **1978**, *275*, 565–566; Dallinger, R. F.; Woodruff, W. H.; Rodgers, M. A. *J. Appl. Spectros.* **1979**, *33*, 522–523.

[121] Hansen, K. B.; Wilbrandt, R.; Pagsberg, P. *Rev. Sci. Instrum.* **1979**, *50*, 1532–1538.

[122] Hofmann, K. P.; Emeis, D. *Biophys. Structure Mech.* **1981**, *8*, 23–34; Brouwer, M.; Bonaventura, C.; Bonaventura, J. *Biochemistry* **1981**, *20*, 1842–1848; Wei, G. J.; Bloomfield, A.; Resnick, R. M.; Nelsestuen, G. L. *Biochemistry* **1982**, *21*, 1949–1959.

[123] Thusius, D.; Dessen, P.; Jallon, J. M. *J. Mol. Biol.* **1975**, *92*, 413–432; Thusius, D. *In* "Chemical Relaxation in Molecular Biology"; Pecht, I.; Rigler, R., Eds; Springer-Verlag: New York, 1977, pp. 339–370.

[124] Kegeles, G.; Ke, Ch. H. *Anal. Biochem.* **1975**, *68*, 138–147.

[125] Couch, D. A.; Howarth, O. W.; Moore, P. *J. Phys. E.* **1975**, *8*, 831–833; Fyfe, C. A.; Cocivera, M.; Domji, S. W. H. *Acc. Chem. Res.* **1978**, *11*, 277–282; Sykes, B. D.; Grimaldi, J. J. *Methods Enzym.* **1978**, *49*, 295–321.

[126] Closs, G. L.; Miller, R. J. *J. Amer. Chem. Soc.* **1979**, *101*, 1639–1641; *Rev. Sci. Instrum.* **1981**, *52*, 1876–1885.

[127] Trifunac, A. D.; Johnson, K. W.; Lowers, R. H. *J. Amer. Chem. Soc.* **1976**, *98*, 6067–6068.

[128] Claiborne, A.; Fridovich, I. *Biochemistry* **1979**, *18*, 2324–2329; Kertesz, J. C.; Wolf, W. *J. Phys. E.* **1973**, *6*, 1009–1014.

[129] King Wong, S. *J. Amer. Chem. Soc.* **1979**, *101*, 1235–1239.

[130] Fessenden, R. W. *In* "Fast Processes in Radiation Chemistry and Biology"; Adams, G. E.; Fielden, E. M.; Michael, B. D., Eds; Wiley: New York, 1975, pp. 60–75.

[131] Okubo, T. *Biophys. Chem.* **1980**, *11*, 425–431; Cox, B. G.; Schneider, H. *J. Amer. Chem. Soc.* **1977**, *99*, 2809–2811; Okubo, T.; Kitano, H.; Ishiwatari, T.; Ise, N. *Proc. Roy. Soc. London Ser. A* **1979**, *366*, 81–90.

[132] Hoffman, H.; Yaeger, E.; Stuehr, J. *Rev. Sci. Instrum.* **1968**, *39*, 649–653.

[133] Sano, T.; Yasunaga, T. *Biophys. Chem.* **1980**, *11*, 377–386.

[134] Lilie, J. *J. Amer. Chem. Soc.* **1979**, *101*, 4417–4419.

[135] Beck, G. *Int. J. Radiat. Phys. Chem.* **1969**, *1*, 361–371; Asmus, K-D. *Int. J. Radiat. Phys. Chem.* **1972**, *4*, 417–438.

[136] Morgan, G.; Fruton, J. S. *Biochemistry* **1978**, *17*, 3562–3568.

[137] Lobb, R. R.; Auld, D. S. *Proc. Nat. Acad. Sci. USA* **1979**, *76*, 2684–2688.

[138] Clegg, R. M.; Loontiens, F. G.; Jovin, T. M. *Biochemistry* **1977**, *16*, 167–175.

[139] Malencik, D. A.; Anderson, S. R.; Shalitin, Y.; Schimerlik, M. I. *Biochem. Biophys. Res. Commun.* **1981**, *101*, 390–395.
[140] Neurohr, K. J.; Young, N. M.; Smith, I. C. P.; Mantsch, H. H. *Biochemistry* **1981**, *20*, 3499–3504.
[141] Scarpa, A.; Brinley, F. J., Jr; Dubyak, G. *Biochemistry* **1978**, *17*, 1378–1386. For example, for monitoring calcium ion.
[142] Koren, R.; Hammes, G. G. *Biochemistry* **1976**, *15*, 1165–1171.
[143] Boeker, E. A. *Biochemistry* **1978**, *17*, 258–269.
[144] Milano, M. J.; Pardue, H. L.; Cook, T.; Santini, R. E.; Margerum, D. W.; Raycheba, J. M. T. *Anal. Chem.* **1974**, *46*, 374–381; Papadakis, N.; Coolen, R. B.; Dye, J. L. *Anal. Chem.* **1975**, *47*, 1644–1649. A number of commercial models are now available.
[145] Sullivan, J. C.; Deutsch, E.; Adams, G. E.; Gordon, S.; Mulac, A. W.; Schmidt, K. H. *Inorg. Chem.* **1976**, *15*, 2864–2868. Quite difficult but can obtain three-dimension computer trace of spectra recorded after the pulse, and at intervals up to 200 μs thereafter.
[146] Tsuda, M. *Biochim. Biophys. Acta* **1979**, *545*, 537–546.
[147] Paleic, M. M.; Dunford, H. B. *J. Biol. Chem.* **1980**, *255*, 6128–6232.
[148] Barber, D.; Parr, S. R.; Greenwood, C. *Biochem. J.* **1978**, *173*, 681–690.
[149] Coin, J. T.; Olson, J. S. *J. Biol. Chem.* **1979**, *254*, 1178–1190.
[150] York, S. S.; Lawson, R. C., Jr; Worah, D. M. *Biochemistry* **1978**, *17*, 4480–4486.
[151] Hasumi, H. *Biochim. Biophys. Acta* **1980**, *626*, 265–276.
[152] Kihara, H.; Takahashi, E.; Yamamura, K.; Tabushi, I. *Biochem. Biophys. Res. Commun.* **1980**, *95*, 1687–1694.
[153] Terner, J.; Campion, A.; El-Sayed, M. A. *Proc. Natn. Acad. Sci. USA* **1977**, *74*, 5212–5216.
[154] Terner, J.; Stong, J. D.; Spiro, T. G.; Naguno, M.; Nicol, M.; El-Sayed, M. A. *Proc. Natn. Acad. Sci. USA* **1981**, *78*, 1313–1317.
[155] McGarrity, J. F.; Prodolliet, J.; Smyth, T. *Org. Magn. Reson.* **1981**, *17*, 59–65.
[156] Bowen, P.; Balko, B.; Blevins, K.; Berger, R. L.; Hopkins, H. P., Jr *Anal. Biochem.* **1980**, *102*, 434–440; Balko, B.; Berger, R. L.; Anderson, K. *Rev. Sci. Instrum.* **1981**, *52*, 888–894.
[157] Nakamura, T. *J. Biochem. Jap.* **1978**, *83*, 1077–1083.
[158] Crandell, E. D.; Obaid, A. L.; Forster, R. E. *Biophys. J.* **1978**, *24*, 35–42.
[159] Berger, R. L. *Biophys. J.* **1978**, *24*, 2–20.
[160] Gros, G.; Forster, R. E.; Lin, L. *J. Biol. Chem.* **1976**, *251*, 4398–4407.
[161] Lilie, J.; Shinohara, N.; Simic, M. G. *J. Amer. Chem. Soc.* **1976**, *98*, 6516–6520.
[162] Philo, J. S. *Proc. Natn. Acad. Sci. USA* **1977**, *74*, 2620–2623.
[163] Ogino, H.; Kikkawa, E.; Shimura, M.; Tanaka, N. *J. Chem. Soc. Dalton Trans.* **1981**, 894–896.
[164] Clegg, R. M.; Loontiens, F. G.; Van Landschoot, A.; Jovin, T. M. *Biochemistry* **1981**, *20*, 4687–4692.
[165] Boucher, H.; Sargeson, A. M.; Sangster, D. F.; Sullivan, J. C. *Inorg. Chem.* **1981**, *20*, 3719 3721.
[166] Hoffman, M. Z.; Simic, M. *Inorg. Chem.* **1973**, *12*, 2471–2472.
[167] Weber, G. *Adv. Protein Chem.* **1975**, *29*, 1–83.
[168] Citri, N. *Adv. Enzymol.* **1973**, *37*, 397–648.
[169] Mildvan, A. S. *In* "The Enzymes" Vol. II; Boyer, P. D., Ed.; Academic Press: New York, 1970, Chapter 9. Here the types of ternary complexes, their occurrence and properties are discussed.

[170] Hammes, G. G.; Schimmel, P. R. *In* "The Enzymes" Vol. II; Boyer, P. D., Ed.; Academic Press: New York, 1970, Chapter 2.

[171] Cleland, W. W. *In* "The Enzymes" Vol. II; Boyer, P. D., Ed.; Academic Press: New York, 1970, Chapter 1.

[172] Kidani, Y.; Hirose, J. *Biochem. Biophys. Res. Commun.* **1978**, *82*, 506–513.

[173] Harrington, P. C.; Wilkins, R. G. *J. Inorg. Biochem.* **1980**, *12*, 107–118.

[174] Rogers, R. J.; Billo, E. J. *J. Inorg. Biochem.* **1980**, *12*, 335–341.

[175] Theorell, H.; Chance, B. *Acta Chem. Scand.* **1951**, *5*, 1127–1144.

[176] Dalziel, K. *J. Biol. Chem.* **1963**, *238*, 2850–2858.

[177] De Traglia, M. C.; Schmidt, J.; Dunn, M. F.; McFarland, J. T. *J. Biol. Chem.* **1977**, *252*, 3493–3500.

[178] Kvassman, J.; Pettersson, G. *Eur. J. Biochem.* **1979**, *100*, 115–123.

[179] Coates, J. H.; Hardman, M. J.; Shore, J. D.; Gutfreund, H. *FEBS Lett.* **1977**, *84*, 25–28.

[180] Gilleland, M. J.; Shore, J. D. *Biochem. Biophys. Res. Commun.* **1970**, *40*, 230–235.

[181] Evans, S. A.; Shore, J. D. *J. Biol. Chem.* **1980**, *255*, 1509–1514.

[182] Frolich, M.; Creighton, D. J.; Sigman, D. S. *Arch. Biochem. Biophys.* **1978**, *189*, 471–480.

[183] Bayley, P. M.; Martin, S. R.; Anson, M. *Biochem. Biophys. Res. Commun.* **1975**, *66*, 303–308.

[184] Scheule, R. K.; Van Wart, H. E.; Vallee, B. L.; Scheraga, H. A. *Biochemistry* **1980**, *19*, 759–766.

[185] Johansen, J. T.; Vallee, B. L. *Biochemistry* **1975**, *14*, 649–660.

[186] Harrison, L. W.; Vallee, B. L. *Biochemistry* **1978**, *17*, 4359–4363.

[187] King, R. W.; Burgen, A. S. V. *Proc. R. Soc. London Ser. B* **1976**, *193*, 107–125.

[188] Coleman, J. E. *Ann. Rev. Pharmacol.* **1975**, *15*, 221–242.

[189] Dunn, M. F.; Pattison, S. E.; Storm, M. C.; Quiel, E. *Biochemistry* **1980**, *19*, 718–725.

[190] Smith, G. M.; Mildvan, A. S.; Harper, E. T. *Biochemistry* **1980**, *19*, 1248–1255.

[191] Brewer, C. F.; Marcus, D. M.; Grollman, A. P.; Sternlicht, H. *In* "Lysozyme"; Osserman, E.; Canfield, R.; Beychok, S., Eds; Academic Press: London, 1972, pp. 239–250.

[192] Lewis, S. D.; Shafer, J. A.; Goldstein, I. J. *Arch. Biochem. Biophys.* **1976**, *172*, 689–695.

[193] Harrington, P. C.; Wilkins, R. G. *Biochemistry* **1978**, *17*, 4245–4250.

[194] Farina, R. D.; Wilkins, R. G. *Biochim. Biophys. Acta* **1980**, *631*, 428–438.

[195] Makinen, M. W.; Kuo, L. C.; Dymowski, J. J.; Jaffer, S. *J. Biol. Chem.* **1979**, *254*, 356–366; Makinen, M. W.; Fukuyama, J. M.; Kuo, L. C. *J. Amer. Chem. Soc.* **1982**, *104*, 2667–2669.

[196] For example, Billo, E. J.; Brito, K. K.; Wilkins, R. G. *Bioinorg. Chem.* **1978**, *8*, 461–475.

[197] Harrington, P. C.; Moreno, R.; Wilkins, R. G. *Israel J. Chem.* **1981**, *21*, 48–51. When a mixture of Ca^{2+} and Mn^{2+} is added to demetallated concanavalin A, a rapidly formed mixed species $(MnCaP)_l$ is slowly converted irreversibly to the stable equilibrium form. This has been shown by nmr, and stopped-flow methods.

[198] Parr, G. R.; Taniuchi, H. *J. Biol. Chem.* **1979**, *254*, 4836–4842; *J. Biol. Chem.* **1980**, *255*, 8914–8918.

[199] Schuster, P.; Wolschann, P.; Tortschanoff, K. *In* "Chemical Relaxation in Molecular Biology"; Pecht, I.; Rigler, R., Eds; Springer-Verlag: New York, 1977, pp. 107–190.

[200] Ilan, Y.; Shafferman, A. *Biochim. Biophys. Acta* **1979**, *548*, 161–165.
[201] Butler, J.; Davies, D. M.; Sykes, A. G. *J. Inorg. Biochem.* **1981**, *15*, 41–53.
[202] McCray, J. A.; Kihara, T. *Biochim. Biophys. Acta* **1979**, *548*, 417–426.
[203] Kihara, H. *Biochim. Biophys. Acta* **1981**, *634*, 93–104.
[204] Brandt, K. G.; Parks, P. C.; Czerlinski, G. H.; Hess, G. P. *J. Biol. Chem.* **1966**, *241*, 4180–4185.
[205] Zabinski, R. M.; Tatti, K.; Czerlinski, G. H. *J. Biol. Chem.* **1974**, *249*, 6125–6129.
[206] Ilan, Y.; Shafferman, A.; Stein, G. *J. Biol. Chem.* **1976**, *251*, 4336–4345.
[207] Stellwagen, E.; Shulman, R. G. *J. Mol. Biol.* **1973**, *80*, 559–573.
[208] Saigo, S. *J. Biochem. Jap.* **1981**, *89*, 1977–1980.
[209] Lambeth, D. O.; Campbell, K. L.; Zand, R.; Palmer, G. *J. Biol. Chem.* **1973**, *248*, 8130–8136.
[210] Saleem, M. M. M.; Wilson, M. T. *Biochem. J.* **1982**, *201*, 433–444.
[211] Reynolds, J. G.; Coyle, C. L.; Holm, R. H. *J. Amer. Chem. Soc.* **1980**, *102*, 4350–4355.
[212] Butler, J.; Davies, D. M.; Sykes, A. G.; Koppenol, W. H.; Osheroff, N.; Margoliash, E. *J. Amer. Chem. Soc.* **1981**, *103*, 469–471.
[213] Mauk, A. G.; Scott, R. A.; Gray, H. B. *J. Amer. Chem. Soc.* **1980**, *102*, 4360–4363.
[214] Chance, B.; de Vault, D. C.; Frauenfelder, H.; Marcus, R. A.; Schieffer, J. R.; Sutin, N. (Eds) "Tunneling in Biological Systems"; Academic Press: New York, 1979.
[215] Dose, E. V.; Tweedle, M. F.; Wilson, L. J.; Sutin, N. *J. Amer. Chem. Soc.* **1977**, *99*, 3886–3888. And references therein.
[216] Dose, E. V.; Hoselton, M. A.; Sutin, N.; Tweedle, M. F.; Wilson, L. J. *J. Amer. Chem. Soc.* **1978**, *100*, 1141–1147.
[217] Binstead, R. A.; Beattie, J. K.; Dewey, T. G.; Turner, D. H. *J. Amer. Chem. Soc.* **1980**, *102*, 6442–6451.
[218] Binstead, R. A.; Beattie, J. K.; Dose, E. V.; Tweedle, M. F.; Wilson, L. J. *J. Amer. Chem. Soc.* **1978**, *100*, 5609–5614.
[219] Cole, P. E.; Sligar, S. G. *FEBS Lett.* **1981**, *133*, 252–254.
[220] Lange, R.; Hui Bon Hoa, G.; Debey, P.; Gunsalus, I. C. *Eur. J. Biochem.* **1979**, *94*, 491–496.
[221] Dyson, H. J.; Beattie, J. K. *J. Biol. Chem.* **1982**, *251*, 2267–2273.
[222] Luchins, J.; Beychok, S. *Science* **1978**, *199*, 425–426.
[223] Ko, B. P. N.; Yazgan, A.; Yeagle, P. L.; Lottich, S. C.; Henkens, R. W. *Biochemistry* **1977**, *16*, 1720–1725.
[224] Henkens, R. W.; Turner, S. R. *J. Biol. Chem.* **1979**, *254*, 8110–8112.
[225] Ridge, J. A.; Baldwin, R. L.; Labhardt, A. M. *Biochemistry* **1981**, *20*, 1622–1630.
[226] Myer, Y. P.; Pande, A.; Saturno, A. F. *J. Biol. Chem.* **1981**, *256*, 1576–1581.
[227] Ikai, A.; Fish, W. W.; Tanford, C. *J. Mol. Biol.* **1973**, *73*, 165–184.
[228] Kihara, H.; Takahashi, E.; Yamamura, K.; Tabushi, I. *Biochim. Biophys. Acta* **1982**, *702*, 249–253.
[229] Kim, P. S.; Baldwin, R. L. *Ann. Rev. Biochem.* **1982**, *51*, 459–589.
[230] Tabushi, I.; Yamamura, K.; Nishiya, T. *Tetrahedron Lett.* **1978**, *49*, 4921–4924.
[231] Bosshard, M. R. *J. Mol. Biol.* **1981**, *153*, 1125–1149.
[232] Gibson, Q. H. *Proc. Natn. Acad. Sci. USA* **1973**, *70*, 1–4.
[233] Davis, L. A.; Schejter, A.; Hess, G. P. *J. Biol. Chem.* **1974**, *249*, 2624–2632.
[234] Kihara, H.; Saigo, S.; Nakatani, H.; Hiromi, K.; Ikeda-Saito, M.; Tizuka, T. *Biochim. Biophys. Acta* **1976**, *430*, 225–243.
[235] Salhany, J. M. *Biochim. Biophys. Acta* **1978**, *534*, 239–245.
[236] Greenwood, C.; Gibson, Q. H. *J. Biol. Chem.* **1967**, *242*, 1782–1787.

184   R. G. Wilkins

[237] Brunori, M.; Colosimo, A.; Rainoni, G.; Wilson, M. T.; Antonini, E. *J. Biol. Chem.* **1979**, *254*, 10769–10775.
[238] Antonini, E.; Brunori, M.; Colosimo, A.; Greenwood, C.; Wilson, M. T. *Proc. Natn. Acad. Sci. USA* **1977**, *74*, 3128–3132.
[239] Colosimo, A.; Brunori, M.; Sarti, P.; Antonini, E.; Wilson, M. T. *Israel J. Chem.* **1981**, *21*, 30–33.
[240] Olivas, E.; de Waal, D. J. A.; Wilkins, R. G. *J. Biol. Chem.* **1977**, *252*, 4038–4042.
[241] Cox, R. P.; Hollaway, M. R. *Eur. J. Biochem.* **1977**, *74*, 575–587.
[242] Raap, A.; Van Leeuwen, J. W.; Rollema, H. S.; de Bruin, S. H. *FEBS Lett.* **1977**, *81*, 111–114.
[243] Clement, J. R.; Lee, N. T.; Klapper, M. H.; Dorfman, L. M. *J. Biol. Chem.* **1976**, *251*, 2077–2082.
[244] Blumenfeld, L. A.; Davydov, R. M.; Maganov, S. N.; Vilu, R. O. *FEBS Lett.* **1974**, *49*, 246–248.
[245] Rollema, H. S.; Scholberg, H. P. F.; de Bruin, S. H.; Raap, I. A. *Biochem. Biophys. Res. Commun.* **1976**, *71*, 997–1003.
[246] Ho, K.; Klapper, M. H.; Dorfman, L. M. *J. Biol. Chem.* **1978**, *253*, 238–241.
[247] Ilan, Y. A.; Samuni, A.; Chevion, M.; Czapski, G. *J. Biol. Chem.* **1978**, *253*, 82–86.
[248] Chevion, M.; Ilan, Y. A.; Samuni, A.; Navok, T.; Czapski, G. *J. Biol. Chem.* **1979**, *254*, 6370–6374.
[249] Raap, A.; Van Loeuwen, J. W.; Van Eck-Schouten, T.; Rollema, H. S.; de Bruin, S. H. *Eur. J. Biochem.* **1977**, *81*, 619–626.
[250] Blumenfeld, L. A.; Davidov, R. M. *Biochim. Biophys. Acta* **1979**, *549*, 255–280.
[251] Karplus, M.; McCammon, J. A. *CRC Crit. Rev. Biochem.* **1981**, *9*, 293–349.
[252] Butler, J.; Sykes, A. G.; Buxton, G. V.; Harrington, P. C.; Wilkins, R. G. *Biochem. J.* **1980**, *189*, 641–644.
[253] Land, E. J.; Swallow, A. J. *Arch. Biochem. Biophys.* **1971**, *145*, 365–372; *Biochim. Biophys. Acta* **1974**, *368*, 86–96.
[254] Pecht, I.; Feraggi, M. *Proc. Natn. Acad. Sci. USA* **1972**, *69*, 902–906.
[255] Lichtin, N. N.; Shafferman, A.; Stein, G. *Biochim. Biophys. Acta* **1973**, *314*, 117–135.
[256] Wilting, J.; Van Buuren, K. J. H.; Braams, R.; Van Gelder, A. F. *Biochim. Biophys. Acta* **1975**, *376*, 285–297.
[257] Shafferman, A.; Stein, G. *Biochim. Biophys. Acta* **1975**, *416*, 287–317.
[258] Blumenfeld, L. A.; Davydov, R. M.; Kuprin, S. P.; Spenanov, S. V. *Biophysics USSR* **1977**, *22*, 977–994.
[259] Cartling, B.; Wilbrandt, R. *Biochim. Biophys. Acta* **1981**, *637*, 61–68.
[260] Adzamli, I. K.; Ong, W. K.; Sykes, A. G.; Buxton, G. V. *J. Inorg. Biochem.* **1982**, *16*, 311–317.
[261] Meyerstein, D.; Espenson, J. H.; Ryan, D. A.; Mulac, W. A. *Inorg. Chem.* **1979**, *18*, 863–864.
[262] Gibson, Q. H. *Biochem. J.* **1959**, *71*, 293–303.
[263] Sawicki, C. A.; Gibson, Q. H. *J. Biol. Chem.* **1976**, *251*, 1533–1542.
[264] Cornelius, P. A.; Steele, A. W.; Chernoff, D. A.; Hochstrasser, R. M. *Proc. Natn. Acad. Sci. USA* **1981**, *78*, 7526–7529.
[265] Reynolds, A. H.; Rand, S. D.; Rentzepis, P. M. *Proc. Natn. Acad. Sci. USA* **1981**, 78, 2292–2296; Reynolds, A. H.; Rentzepis, P. M. *Biophys. J.* **1982**, *38*, 15–18.
[266] Albert, B.; Mohsni, S. El.; Lindquist, L.; Tfibel, F. *Chem. Phys. Letts.* **1979**, *64*, 11–16; Duddell, D. A.; Morris, R. J.; Richards, J. T. *Biochem. Biophys. Acta* **1980**, *621*, 1–8; Friedman, J. M.; Lyons, K. B. *Nature* **1980**, *284*, 570–572.

[267] Duddell, D. A.; Morris, R. J.; Muttucumaru, N. J.; Richards, J. T. *Photochem. Photobiol.* **1980**, *31*, 479–484.

[268] Hutchinson, J. A.; Traylor, T. G.; Noe, L. J. *J. Amer. Chem. Soc.* **1982**, *104*, 3221–3223.

[269] Alberding, N.; Chan, S. C.; Eisenstein, L.; Frauenfelder, H.; Good, D.; Gunsalus, I. C.; Nordlund, T. M.; Perutz, M. F.; Reynolds, A. M.; Sorensen, L. B. *Biochemistry* **1978**, *17*, 43–51.

[270] Greenwood, R. C.; Robinson, B. H.; White, N. C. *In* "Techniques and Applications of Fast Reactions in Solution"; Gettins, W. J.; Wyn-Jr nes, E., Eds; D. Reidel: Boston, 1979, pp. 321–327.

[271] Kobayashi, J.; Tamura, M.; Hayashi, K. *Biochemistry* **1982**, *21*, 729 732.

[272] Robinson, B. H.; White, N. C. *J. Chem. Soc. Faraday Trans. I* **1978**, *74*, 2625–2636.

[273] Lavalette, D.; Tetreau, C.; Momenteau, M. *J. Amer. Chem. Soc* **1979**, *101*, 5395–5401.

[274] Hasinoff, B. B. *J. Phys. Chem.* **1981**, *85*, 526–531.

[275] Woodward, C. K.; Hilton, B. D. *Ann. Rev. Biophys. Bioeng.* **1979**, *8*, 99–127.

[276] Nakanishi, M.; Tsuboi, M. *J. Amer. Chem. Soc.* **1978**, *100*, 1273–1275.

[277] Aldrich, J. E.; Cundall, R. B.; Adams, G. E.; Willson, R. L. *Nature* **1969**, *221*, 1049–1050; Adams, G. E.; Aldrich, J. E.; Bisby, R. H.; Cundall, R. B.; Redpath, J. L.; Willson, R. L. *Radiat. Res.* **1972**, *49*, 278–289.

[278] Grossweiner, L. I. *Curr. Topics Radn. Res. Quart.* **1976**, *11*, 141–199.

[279] Adams, G. E.; Wardman, P. *In* "Free Radicals in Biology" Vol. III; Pryor, W. A., Ed.; Academic Press: London, 1977, pp. 53–95.

[280] Roberts, P. B. *Int. J. Radiat. Biol.* **1973**, *24*, 143–152.

[281] Roberts, P. B.; Fielden, E. M. *In* "Fast Processes in Radiation Chemistry and Biology"; Adams, G. E.; Fielden, E. M.; Michael, B. D., Eds; Wiley: New York, 1975, pp. 319–326.

[282] Redpath, J. L.; Santus, R.; Ovadia, J.; Grossweiner, L. I. *Int. J. Radiat. Biol.* **1975**, *28*, 243–253.

[283] Badiello, R.; Tamba, M.; Quintiliani, M. *Int. J. Radiat. Biol.* **1974**, *26*, 311–319.

[284] Posener, M. L.; Adams, G. E.; Wardman, P.; Cundall, R. B. *J. Chem. Soc. Faraday Trans. I* **1976**, *72*, 2231–2239.

[285] Peterman, B. F.; Laidler, K. J. *In* "Techniques and Applications of Fast Reactions in Solution"; Gettins, W. J.; Wyn-Jones, E., Eds; D. Reidel: Boston, 1979, pp. 419–422.

[286] Gutman, M.; Huppert, D.; Nachliel, E. *Eur. J. Biochem.* **1982**, *121*, 637 642.

[287] Baum, R. M. *Chemical and Engineering News* **1982**, *60*, 21–25.

[288] Swallow, A. J. *Ann. Rep. Chem. Soc. London (C)* **1980**, *77*, 145–171.

Do Binucleating Ligands have a Biological Relevance?

David E. Fenton

Department of Chemistry,
University of Sheffield

A decade ago Richard Robson introduced the term *binucleating ligands*[1] to describe a group of compounds which were to be used in attempts to construct synthetic systems capable of binding and possibly activating molecular nitrogen. The concept was that by securing two metal ions at an appropriate distance a bridging position would be left between the two metals allowing for entry of the dinitrogen (Fig. 1). The complexes could be regarded as

D. E. Fenton

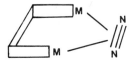

Fig. 1. Schematic representation of dinitrogen trapping by binucleated metals.

geometrical models for potential nitrogen-fixing systems.[2] The study of nitrogen fixation has, of course, evolved into a fascinating area of chemistry involving multicentred metalloproteins and a plethora of synthetic simulations.[3] Binucleating ligands and their metal complexes have also developed into a research area and the original thesis of the activation of small molecules persists as a central theme, although it is now dioxygen which is at the focal point.

This review is concerned with binucleating ligands and their relationship with metallobiomolecules containing bimetallic centres, as there is currently much interest in the use of metal complexes of such ligands as models for the coordination environment of the metals at the bio-site. It will discuss the evolution of binucleating ligands, the motivation for studying binuclear complexes and the application of the complexes in a biological context.

In "The Tin Drum", Gunther Grass suggested that one stratagem for novel writing is to put aside all mention of time and distance allowing for solution of the space-time problem.[4] This approach has great appeal when considering an area where any causality has an imprecision, and has further imposed on it moving external constraints. This review will, necessarily, juxtapose time sequences as frequently moving constraints, such as the recent applications of the full armoury of contemporary X-ray structure determination, intervene and lead to direct observation of the bimetallic centre in the metallobiomolecule. This process can, by introducing new insights, short-circuit some of the studies made via the speculative use of binuclear model compounds.

The topical nature of the area, particularly with emphasis on copper, is reflected in the very recent appearance of several texts,[5-8] and in that a discussion of Inorganic and Biochemical Perspectives in Copper Coordination Chemistry was held at SUNY at Albany in June, 1982.[9]

I. NAMING OF PARTS

The term *binucleating ligands* was defined as "polydentate chelating ligands capable of simultaneously binding two metal ions".[1] The definition was later refined to present macrocyclic binucleating ligands as macrocyclic ligands capable of securing two metal ions in close proximity.[10]

Model compounds are generally used in attempts to reproduce some feature of the structure or function of a metallobiomolecule in order to make comparisons which will aid in identification procedures. They have been designated as *speculative*, where the structure of the microenvironment of the metal ion in the metallobiomolecule is unknown, or *corroborative*, where the structure of the microenvironment is known and so a direct analogue may be synthesised.[11] In the first case a simple complex is generally used to reproduce some physical property of the metal centre and so the model is structurally, rather than functionally orientated. In the second case it is possible to carry out an extensive study of the metal centre in isolation through use of the model and to relate this study to the biomolecule. This is exemplified by Holm's work on the synthetic iron-sulphur cluster complexes directly related to ferredoxins.[12] In contrast work on the iron-sulphur-molybdenum cluster species may be regarded as speculative modelling of Mo–Fe protein of nitrogenase.[13]

II. THE EVOLUTION OF BINUCLEATING LIGANDS

Many coordination compounds have been found in which more than one metal is present. These range in type and character from the mixed metal salts of polyacids such as ethylenediaminetetraacetic acid to polynuclear organometallic species such as metal carbonyl cluster compounds. Both homo- and hetero-polynuclear species are observed but the metals are not bound within a single ligand framework. In addition there are many binuclear complexes derived from Schiff base and polyketonate precursors. Again there is no single encapsulating ligand present to give a species M_2L, but compounds of the general formula M_2L_2 are found, an associative process having brought two essentially monomeric subunits together to produce a binuclear product, structures **1–3**.[14–16] Complexes of this origin will be mentioned in this review when they relate to the M_2L series.

Impetus for the study of binucleating ligands and their complexes has come from several areas. Multidentate ligands which incorporate two metal atoms have value in studying the magnetic interactions between the metal ions. Binuclear complexes are also of interest as potential homogeneous catalysts capable of carrying out multi-step or different successive processes. Both of these aspects have relevance in the further application of homo- and heterobimetallic complexes as models for certain metallobiomolecules.

Since Robson introduced the term binucleating ligand, in 1970, there has been a steady increase in the number and type of such ligands synthesised. Their complexes fall into two general classes.[17] The first group consists of those complexes in which the metals share at least one donor atom in species containing adjacent sites in which the central donor atom(s) provide a bridge ("bridging donor sets"). The ligands giving these complexes have been collectively termed *compartmental ligands*.[18] The second group consists of those complexes in which donor atoms are not shared and so *isolated donor sets* exist. Selected examples of these types of ligands will be given to illustrate the number and variety of binucleating ligands.

A. Compartmental ligands

The ligands in this class are predominately Schiff bases derived from 2,6-disubstituted phenols and thiophenols, 1,3,5-triketones and β-ketophenols. In these the central phenolic, the central keto-oxygen or the thiophenolic sulphur atoms can act as the bridging donor atom. There are three types of these ligands, the macrocycle form, (A), derived from a "2 + 2" condensation reaction, an "end-off" acyclic form, (B), in which one donor bridge is removed and a "side-off" acyclic form, (C), in which one non-donor bridge is removed, see Fig. 2. In the metal complexes derived from (B), Y provides an endogeneous bridge, and a further exogeneous bridge may be provided by an anion.

1. Macrocyclic compartmental ligands

The macrocycles (A) may be either symmetrical, structures **4–6**, or non-symmetrical, structures **7–10**, in nature. In the non-symmetric macrocycles

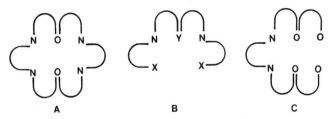

Fig. 2. Schematic representation of compartmental ligands. A, macrocycle (N_4O_2); B, "end-off" $(N_2YX_2$: X = N, OSi; Y = O, S); C, "side-off" (N_2O_4).

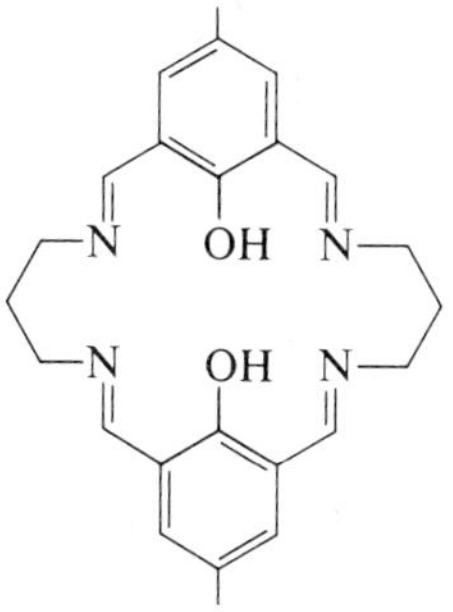

4[10,19]

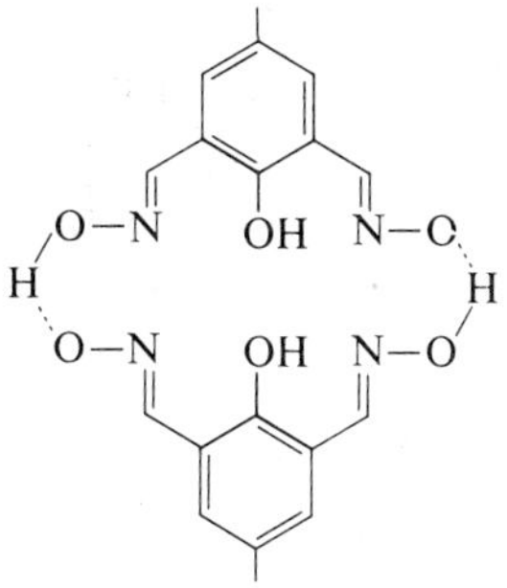

5[20]

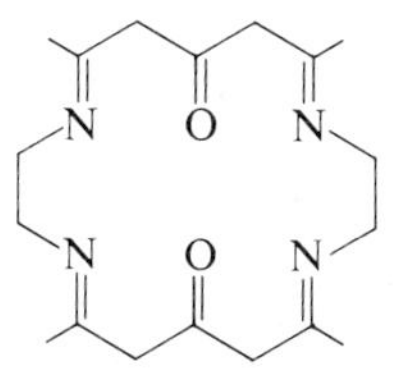

6[21]

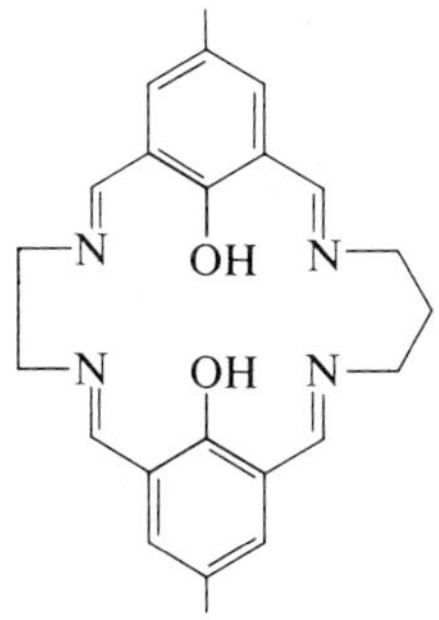

7[19]

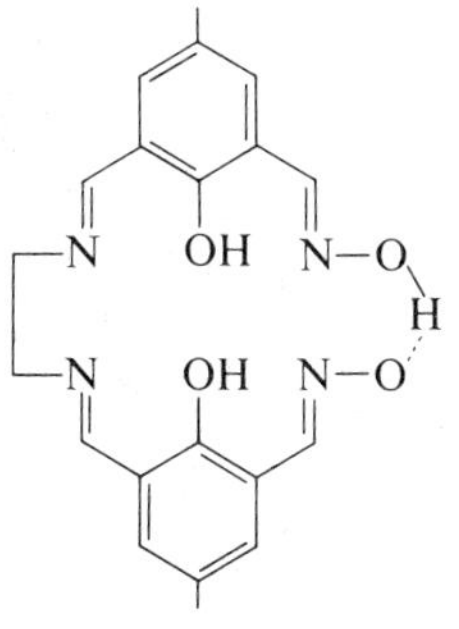

8[20]

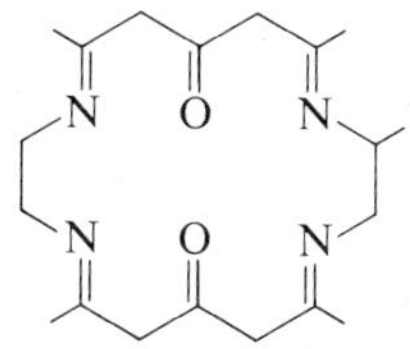

9[22]

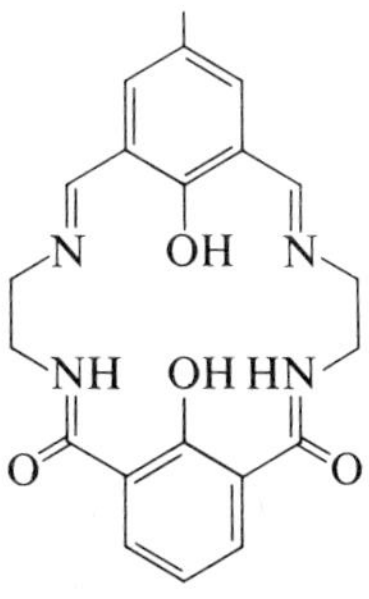

10[23]

spatial differences may occur in the coordination sites but the donor sets remain equivalent.

The macrocycles and their complexes are prepared by three different strategies: (1) direct synthesis of the free macrocycle followed by metal incorporation;[21,22] (2) a template reaction involving condensation of the precursors in the presence of the required metal salt;[10,19] and (3) a sequential route in which the mononuclear complex of the appropriate "end-off" or the binuclear complex of the "side-off" precursor is first formed and then treatment with a second equivalent of the appropriate amine or keto-precursor gives the macrocyclic system.[19,20,23] The second metal is then added as required. The sequential route is appropriate to the synthesis of non-symmetric species, and heterobinuclear metal complexes. Macrocycles derived from the diketo-analogue of 3-formyl-5-methylsalicylaldehyde have been reported in a preliminary communication.[24]

Using **6** as a ligand, mononuclear complexes of Cu(II), Ni(II) and Co(II) have been reported;[21,22] complexes of the type L(CuBr)$_2$ and L(CoCl)$_2$ have also been prepared for this ligand.[25] Although generally homobinuclear complexes of the macrocycles derived from 3-formyl-5-methylsalicyclaldehyde have been synthesised, with a predominate interest in copper(II), Robson's macrocycle **4** has also been used to generate mixed-valence metal complexes (Co^{III}–Co$^{II[26]}$ and Cu^{II}–Cu$^{I[27-28]}$), complexes of metals in low oxidation states (Cu^{I}–Cu$^{I[28,29]}$), and a range of heterobinuclear metal complexes (CuM, M = Mn(II), Fe(II), Co(II), Ni(II) and Zn(II).[30,31] Interest in the potential role of these complexes in modelling biometallosites has led to extensive electrochemical, spectral and magnetic studies being carried out.[27-33] X-ray crystallographic studies have confirmed the binuclear nature of the homobinuclear species derived from **4** and having Cu^{II}Cu^{II},[35] Cu^{II}Cu^{I},[34] Co^{II}Co^{II},[36] Co^{II}Co$^{III[26]}$ and Fe^{II}Fe$^{II[31]}$ centres present.

2. "End-off" acyclic compartmental ligands

The "end-off" ligands provide only one endogeneous bridging donor and so have a labile bridging site available between the metal sites into which a variety of anions (X$^-$) can be introduced as exogeneous bridges. This subclass gives a wide range of donor atom combinations with essentially the same basic structural framework, and has, in principle, the potential to bind molecules such as dioxygen, or dinitrogen, at the exogeneous bridging site.

The complexes are generally prepared by template procedures, or where possible by prior formation of the ligand followed by metal incorporation. Homobinuclear species have been synthesised and are almost exclusively complexes of copper(II). 3-formyl-5-methylsalicylaldehyde has been condensed with a range of amines including dialkylalkanediamines,[37-39] amino acids,[40,41] 2-aminoalkylpyridines,[29,42] histamine,[29,42] amino-phenols,[1,2,43] amino-thiophenols[44] and thiosemicarbazide.[49] Robson has synthesised species derived from disubstituted thiophenols.[45-47] Mixed valence state (Cu^{II}Cu^{I}) and low oxidation state (Cu^{I}Cu^{I}) complexes of **13** and **14** have also been prepared.[29] As with the macrocycles, extensive physico-chemical studies have been carried out, and the nature of the homobinuclear compounds verified by crystal structure determinations for [**15** (R = H,

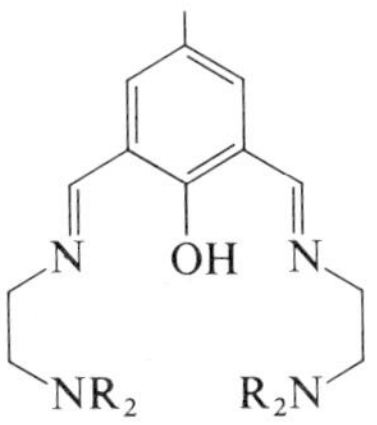

11 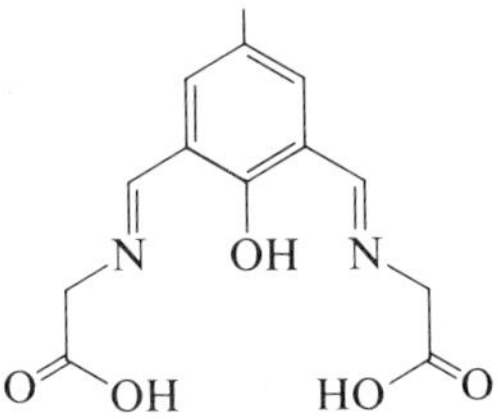   12 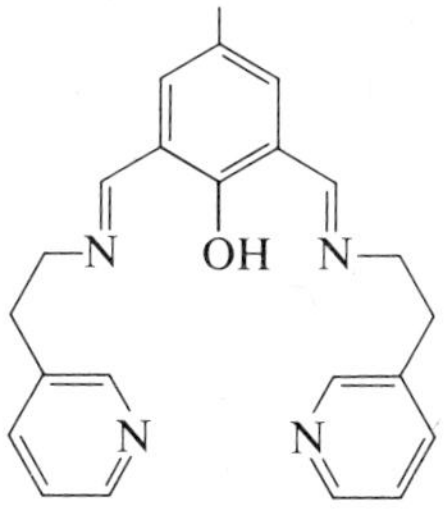   13

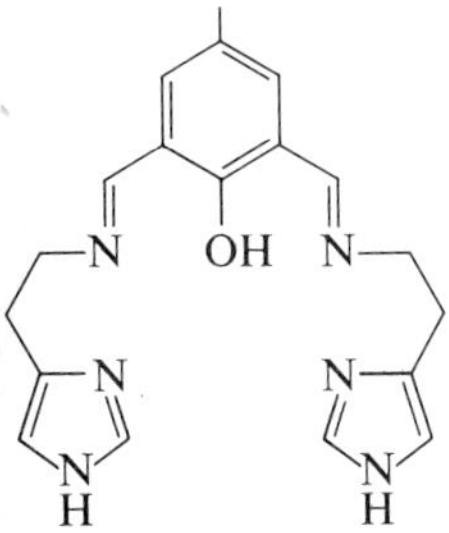

14   15   16

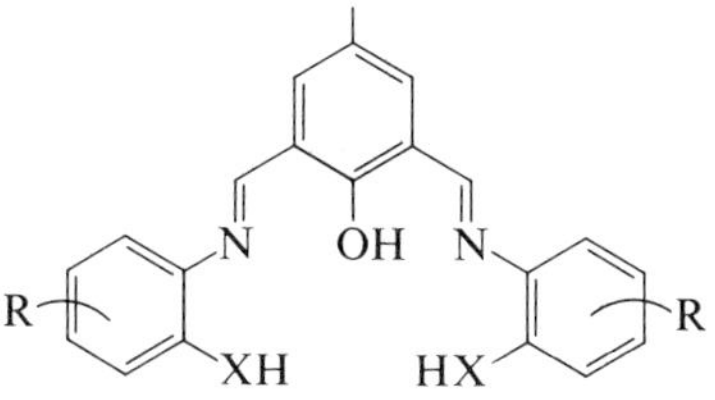

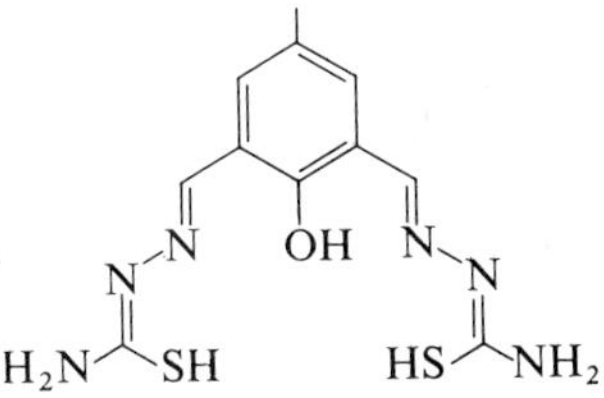

$X = O$), $Cu_2(N_2C_3H_3)]^{[48]}$ in which there is a pyrazole bridge; [16 $Ni_2(OEt)_2$, 2DMF][49] and [11 (R = H), $Cu_2Br_2ClO_4$, MeOH][39] in which the two copper ions are five-coordinated but in different environments; there is a bridging bromide anion and one copper has bromide as its fifth ligand, the other has methanol.

The viability of adding small molecules across the exogeneous bridging site has been demonstrated in the use of pyrazole, **17a** 3,5-dimethylpyrazole, **17b**, and azaindole, **18**, as ligands.[2,29] The addition of these molecules as anions

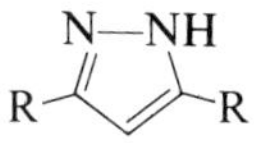

17: a, R = H   **18**
        b, R = CH$_3$

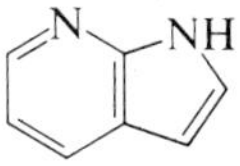

has been confirmed by X-ray crystal structure analysis of the bis-copper(II) complex **19**,[2] and the bis-copper(I) complex **20**,[29] both with a pyrazolate-bridge present.

3. "Side-off" acyclic compartmental ligands

The "side-off" ligands have been the subject of a recent review.[18] They are derived from a "2 + 1" condensation of a 1,3,5-triketone, β-ketophenol, or 3-

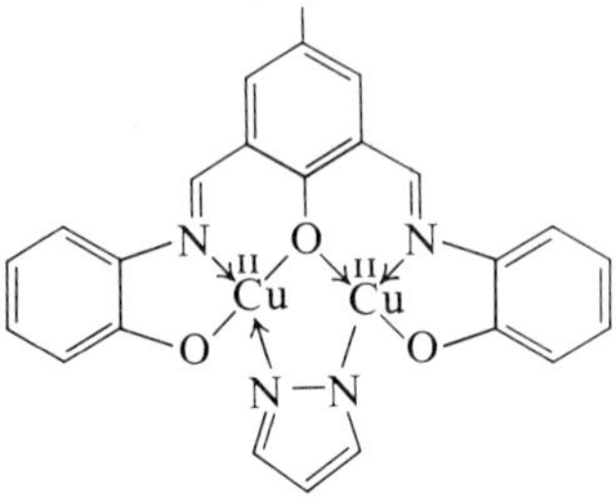

19

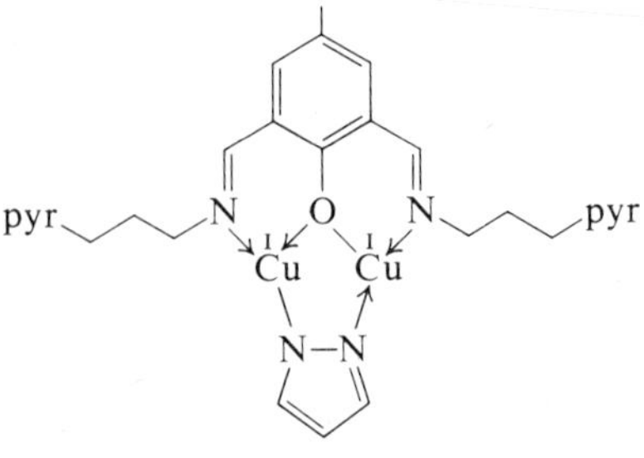

20

formylsalicyclic acid with an α,ω-alkanediamine. Acyclic ligands are prepared which present adjacent, dissimilar coordination compartments, i.e. "O_2O_2" and "N_2O_2" donor sets, and are capable of homo- or heterobinuclear complexation. Symmetric and non-symmetric ligands are available.

The general preparative route for the bimetallic complexes is to prepare first a pure mononuclear positional isomer, preferably in the inner —N_2O_2 compartment. Addition of a second metal then gives either a homobinuclear, if the metals are the same, or a heterobinuclear complex, if the metals are different. Using this approach homobinuclear copper(II), nickel(II) and cobalt(II) complexes have been prepared. The bis-nickel(II) complexes of **21**

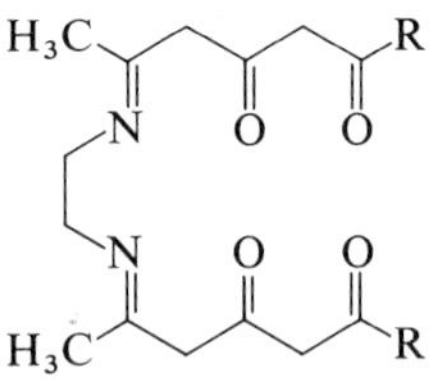

21[50-52]: R = CH_3, C_6H_4-, tBu-

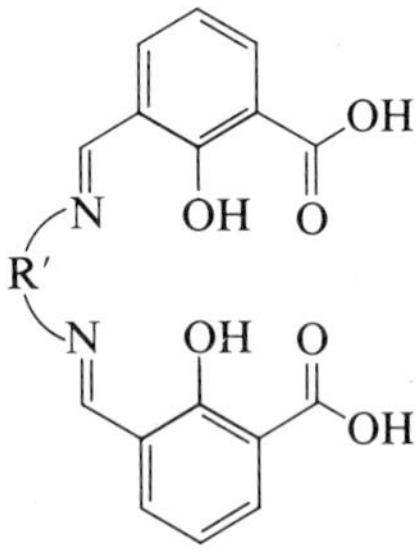

22[53,54]: R' = various bridging chains

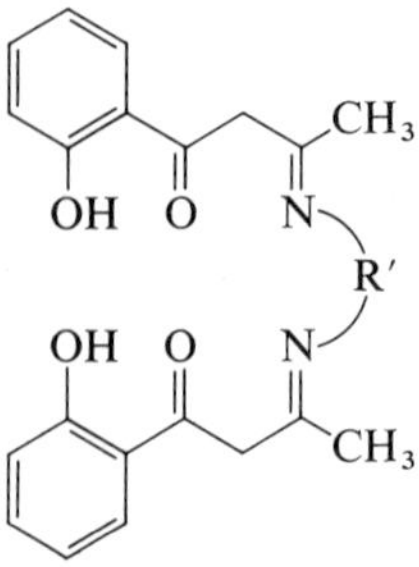

23[55,56]

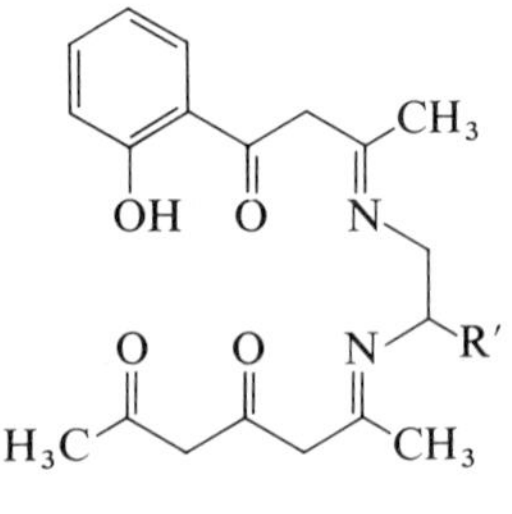

24[57]

are of interest in that the two nickel atoms are present in different spin-states and stereochemistries. The X-ray crystal structure of **25** shows the presence of square planar and octahedral nickel and the magnetic moment is solely that of high-spin, octahedral nickel(II).[58] A large range of heterobinuclear com-

25

plexes have also been prepared involving a transition metal, usually copper(II) or nickel(II), in the inner site and a range of metals—transition, alkali, alkaline earth, lanthanide or actinide—in the outer site.[18] The nature of the complexes has been confirmed by X-ray structures in several cases.[18] The magnetic properties of the bimetallic complexes have also been extensively studied as they bring into juxtaposition interesting pairs of atoms and so help in understanding exchange pathways.[59] One notable result has been the synthesis of a $Cu^{II}–V^{IV}$ complex of **22**, R $= CH_2CH_2$ in which there is an orthogonality of the magnetic orbitals centred on the two metal ions with a resulting net intramolecular ferromagnetism.[60]

B. Isolated donor sets

There now exists a wide variety of ligands in this category. In contrast to the compartmental ligands the isolated donor sets are not variations on a single theme but rather a number of different structural frameworks are utilised. Four general subclasses can be formulated with variations within each subclass:

1. Isolated donor sets within extendable macrocycles (Fig. 3).

2. Isolated donor sets within extendable macrobicycles (Fig. 4).

3. Isolated donor sets derived from planar macrocycles constrained to stack one above each other (Fig. 5).

4. Isolated donor sets separated by aromatic, or other, bridging functions (Fig. 6).

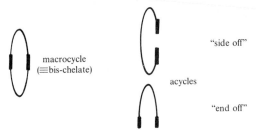

Fig. 3. Isolated donor sets within extendable macrocycles.

Fig. 4. Isolated donor sets within extendable macrobicycles.

Fig. 5. Isolated donor sets derived from planar macrocycles constrained to stack one above each other.

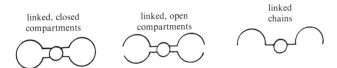

Fig. 6. Isolated donor sets separated by aromatic or other bridging functions.

Selected examples of each type of ligand will be given to illustrate the versatility of this general class.

1. Extendable macrocycles and related systems

The first macrocycle capable of circumscribing two metal ions completely was the octadentate macrocyclic thioether, **26**, reported by Busch in 1970.[61] Homobinuclear nickel(II) complexes of this ligand were reported and also of the macrocycle, **27**, derived from the template reaction of 1,4-dihydrazino-phthalazine with acetone in the presence of nickel(II) ions.[62] X-ray crystallo-

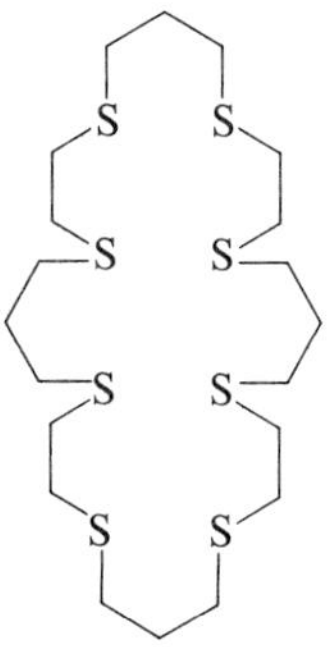

26

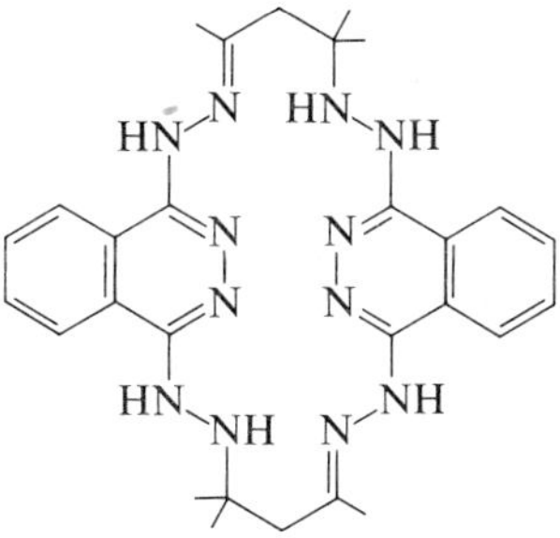

27

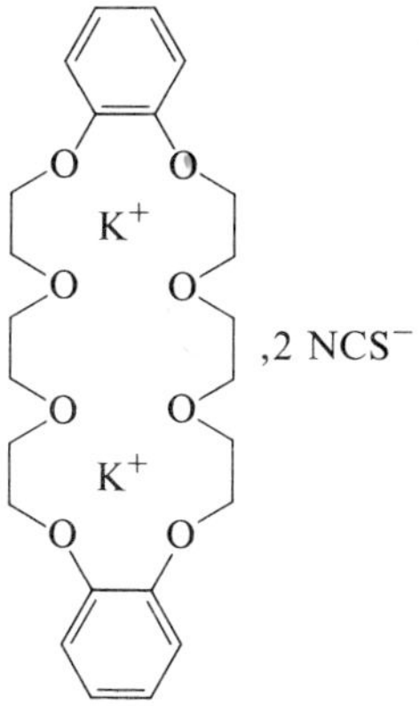

,2 NCS⁻

28

graphic evidence, confirming the ability of multidentate macrocycles to produce binuclear species, was provided in 1972 with the structure of the bis-potassium complex of the Pedersen cyclic polyether, dibenzo-24-crown-8, **28**.[63] Since then numerous examples of binucleating macrocycles have been produced based mainly on two sources, cyclic polyether related systems[64] and cyclic Schiff bases.[65]

Macrocyclic binucleating ligands based on two chelating subunits of the diethylene triamine type, **29**, and related ligands bearing two diagonally disposed pyridine groups, **30**, have been developed by Lehn and his coworkers.[64] All three form dinuclear copper(II) complexes in which the cations are within the ligand cavity. In the azide complexes each copper is bound to the three terminal N donors and two azide groups and the Cu—Cu distances are 5.98 and 4.79 Å in **29** and **30**, $n = 5$ respectively.[66]

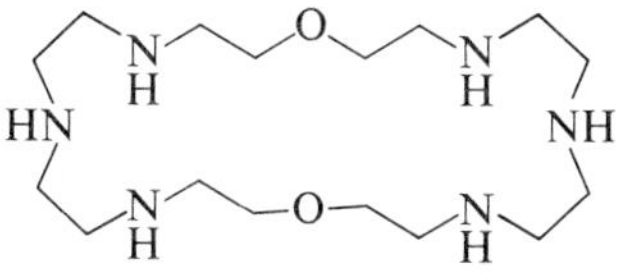

29 [24]—N₆O₂

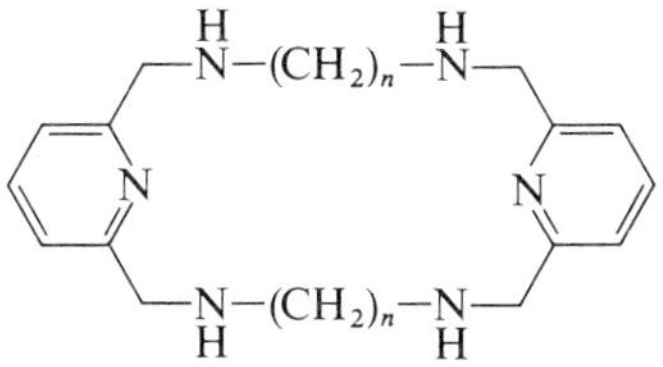

30; $n = 4$, [22]—N₄py₂
$n = 5$, [24]—N₄py₂

This type of binuclear ligand can dispose the metals in an arrangement suitable for bridging substrate addition. This has been an attraction in modelling metallobiosites as groups such as the imidazole group can, and have been introduced between the metal ions (*vide infra*).

Other related macrocycles and their binuclear copper complexes have been reported, **31**,[67] **32**[68] and **33**.[69] **31** provides a completely diamagnetic

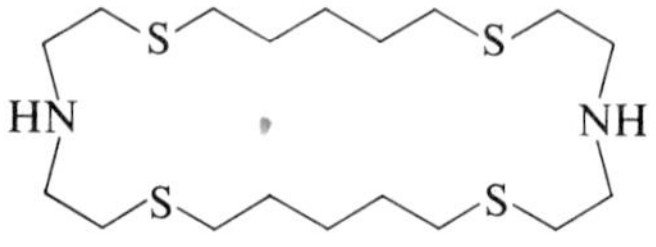

31 [24]—N₂S₄

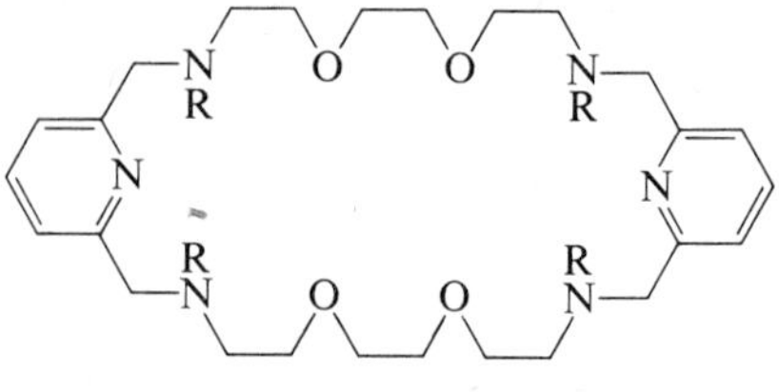

32 [30]—N₄O₄py₂
R = H, CH₃

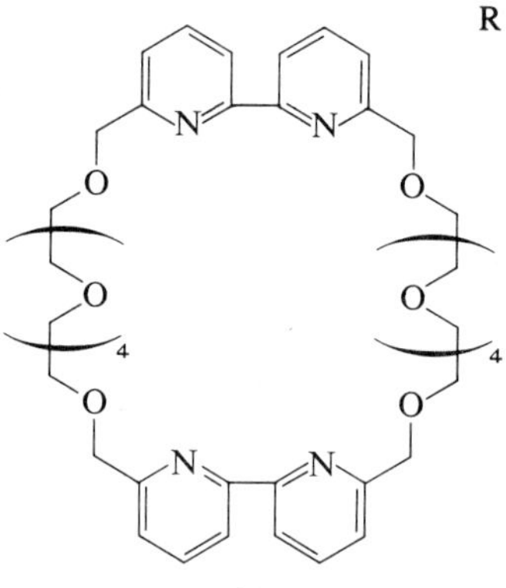

33

dicopper(II) complex when azide bridged[67] and **32** is involved in a dioxygen activation reaction, both of which will be discussed later.

Macrocyclic tetraimines, or "2 + 2" Schiff bases, **35**, have been synthesised and studied.[65] Such ligands evolved from studies on metal template induced syntheses of the mononuclear "1 + 1" pentadentate Schiff bases, **34**. The reaction of 2,6-diacetylpyridine with the α,ω-diamine, 1,10-diamino-4,7-dioxa-decane in the presence of small radius divalent cations such as Mg²⁺,[70] Fe²⁺,[71] Mn²⁺,[71] Co²⁺[65] and Cd²⁺[72] gave the "1 + 1" products, but if a larger radius metal such as Pb²⁺[73] was used a "2 + 2" condensation product, **35**, was isolated. Subsequent studies by Nelson[65] showed that the trans-metallation route could be used to synthesise the otherwise inaccessible dicopper(II) species. By utilising this technique with Ag⁺, Sr²⁺ and Ba²⁺, as

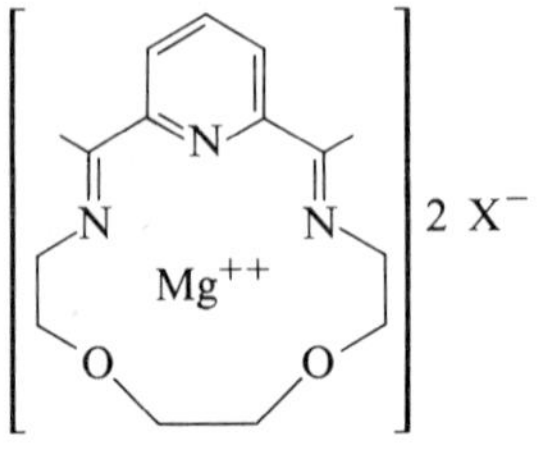

34, MgX₂

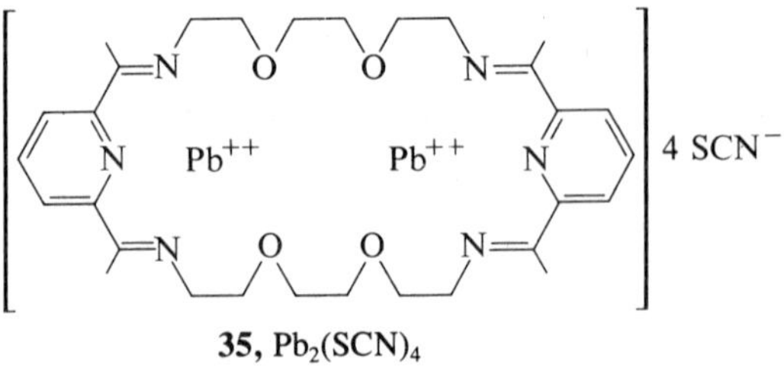

35, Pb₂(SCN)₄

the large radius templates, a wide range of macrocycles have been constructed. Representative examples of the ligands are given and reference made to the dicopper(II) complex. The binucleating nature has been verified by crystal structure studies in the cases of [36 (R = pd), $Cu_2(OH)(ClO_4)_3, 2H_2O$],[75] [36 (R = NSN), $Cu_2(imid)(ClO_4)_3$, H_2O],[76] [36 (R = NOON), $Cu_2(N_3)_3ClO_4$],[78] [36 (R = NOON), $Cu_2(OH)(ClO_4)_3$, H_2O],[79] [36 (R = NOON), $Cu_2(imid)(ClO_4)_3$, $2H_2O$][79] and [37, $Cu_2(NCS)_4$],[80] and one-, three- and four-atom bridging units ($-OH$, $-N_3$, imidazolate and pyrazole) may be introduced between the metals. The smaller rings are only expected to act as hosts for the smaller substrates. Heterobinuclear complexes of macrocyclic ligands have so far been restricted to two Cu(II)Ni(II) complexes of [36, R = NOON].[79]

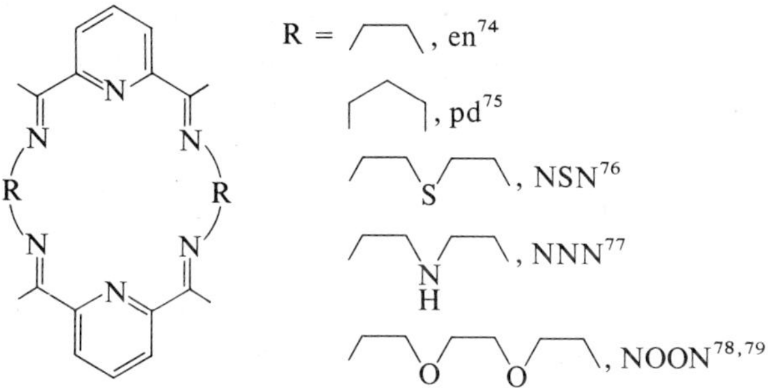

36

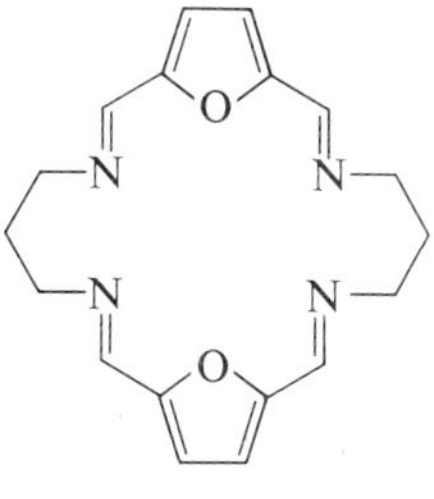

R = en[74], pd[75], NSN[76], NNN[77], NOON[78,79]

37[80]

In contrast to the pyridine- and furan-based tetraimine macrocycles, which have only been synthesised using template procedures, "2 + 2" Schiff base macrocycles, 38, derived from thiophen-2,5-dialdehyde and α,ω-diamino-polyoxaalkanes may be synthesised directly.[81] The X-ray crystal structures of 38 ($n = 0$), and of the di-silver(I)perchlorate complex of 38 ($n = 1$), show the nature of the ligands and that the silver ions are complexed only to the imine nitrogens. Each silver is complexed to one pair of lateral imines (N_aN_a, or N_bN_b), and rather remotely (at 2.71 Å) to a water molecule to give an

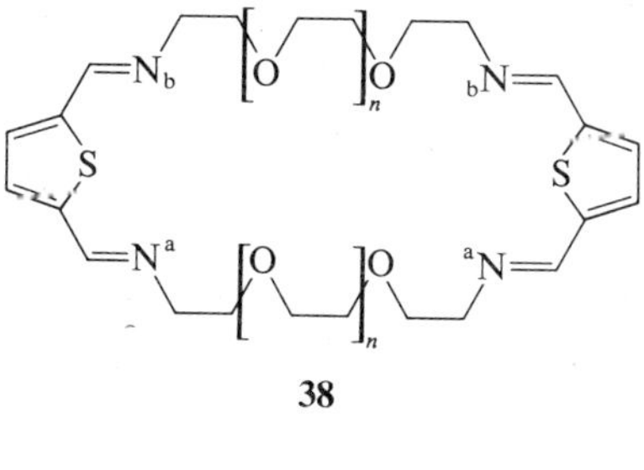

38

39

asymmetric silver environment. The thiophen sulphur atoms are at 3.10 Å and so appear to be non-coordinating.[81] Non-template procedures have also been used to prepare a series of binucleating octaazamacrocycles,[82] one of which, **39**, gives a binuclear copper complex $Cu_2L(ClO_4)_3$. The X-ray crystal structure of this complex shows that the ligand incorporates a symmetric Cu—Cu unit but with an unusually short Cu—Cu bond (2.445 Å).[83] It is proposed that the complex should be regarded as having a single electron delocalised over the two copper atoms, rather than having a mixed valence Cu(II)Cu(I) unit present.

"Side-off" and "end-off" acyclic binucleating ligands are available in this class. Rosen has prepared an "end-off" derivative of his phthalhydrazide macrocycle, **40**,[62] and Nelson has reported a hydroxy-bridged di-copper complex of the "side-off" ligand derived from 2,6-diacetylpyridine and triethylenetetramine, **41**.[84] Mononuclear barium complexes of the "end-off" ligand, **42**, have been prepared and used to prepare mononuclear barium complexes of the non-symmetric tetraimine macrocycle, **43**.[85] This ligand raises the intriguing possibility of tailoring macrocycles to have dissimilar donor arrangements leading to facile heterobinuclear complexation and so resembling the compartmental ligands.

2. Extendable macrobicycles

Axial macrobicycles. Extendable macrobicycles have been constructed from two relatively simple ligand combinations. Axial systems may be directly related to a combination of tripodal ligands, and lateral systems may be considered as a combination of a chelate and a macrocycle.[64]

Tren, $N(CH_2CH_2NH_2)_3$ is a tripodal ligand which readily complexes transition metal ions and can be used as a structural building block for the controlled arrangement of cations in space. By linking two tripodal units with chains of varying lengths a series of co-axial macrobicyclic ligands may be prepared.

The ligand **44**[86] has been synthesised, together with a series of derivatives, and provides an ellipsoidal cavity which is capable of binucleation. Binuclear Zn^{2+}, Cu^{2+} and Co^{2+} complexes have been prepared, but no X-ray structural data are yet available. The epr spectrum of the di-copper(II) species indicates that there is some interaction between the metals, and oxidation of the bis-cobalt(II) complex yielded a bridged μ-peroxo μ-hydroxo species indicating that substrate incorporation was possible, **45**. An analogous macrobicycle, the cryptand [3,3,3] containing two triethanolamine subunits has been reported during the extensive research carried out by Lehn into such ligands.[87]

The ligands mentioned above contain functionalised bridges; cryptands have also been prepared containing polymethylene chains. Bulkowski[88] has synthesised a series of "tren"-based macrobicycles of type **46** where *n* and *m* may vary.

44   **45**, 3 ClO₄⁻

These have been designed as tunable "open-face" ligands in which there is an accessible two-metal site as opposed to the hidden site in the cryptands. The site design is such that a *cis*-equatorial site arrangement is presented for substrate incorporation (Fig. 7). Variation of the bridge B–B results in a

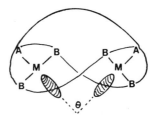

Fig. 7. Schematic representation of tuneable "open-face" ligand.

change of the metal–metal distance and variation of A–A leads to change in (L), the angle found by projection of the in-plane dx^2-y^2 lobes on the metal. This poised orbital arrangement is pertinent to substrate binding patterns in hemocyanin and tyrosinase. The bis-copper(II) complex of (**46**, $m = n = 4$) has been prepared. A related cryptand, **47**, based on tri-thioethanolamine has also been reported.[67]

46   **47**

Lateral macrobicycles. Lateral macrobicyclic systems may be prepared when a chelating subunit is bridged over a macrocycle. Such a system is **48** in which the 2,6-bis(aminomethyl)pyridine subunit is present together with the 12-membered diaza-dithia-macrocycle.[89]

The two copper atoms in the bis-copper(II) complex of **48** are expected to

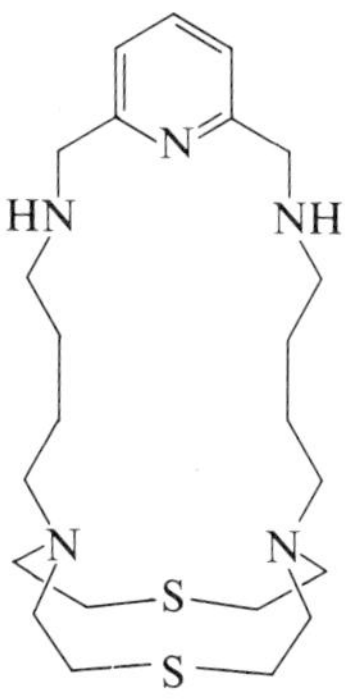

48

possess different redox properties as they are contained in markedly different coordination environments. Indeed the binuclear copper(II) complex undergoes monoelectronic reduction at about $+550$ mV (versus NHE in propylene carbonate), and this is believed to occur at the copper(II) in the $[12]$-N_2S_2 subunit allowing for facile formation of a Cu(II)Cu(I) mixed valence species. Such dissimilar donor sets should give heterobinuclear complexes.

Bridged porphyrins have been synthesised recently together with their bimetallic complexes. Gunter and his coworkers[90] have bridged 5,15-bis(*o*-aminophenyl)-2,3,7,8,12,13,17,18-octamethylporphyrin by condensing it with 2,6-pyridylbis(4′-thia-5′-pentanoyl chloride) to give the "strapped" porphyrin, **49**. The heterobinuclear complexes [Fe **49**-X-Cu(NS$_2$)OH]X, nH$_2$O (X$^-$ = ClO$_4^-$, BF$_4^-$, n = 0, 1) have been reported.[90]

Chang and his coworkers[91] have bridged mesoporphyrin XII diacid chloride by reaction with a diaminothiazole disulphide to give the thiazole "strapped" porphyrin, **50**. In this compound the bridging is via a β-

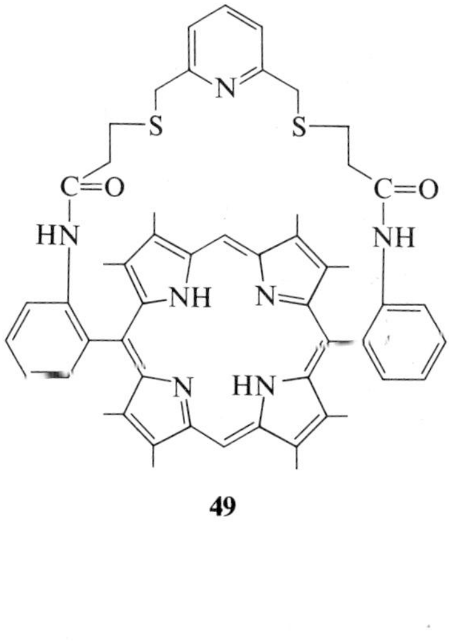

49

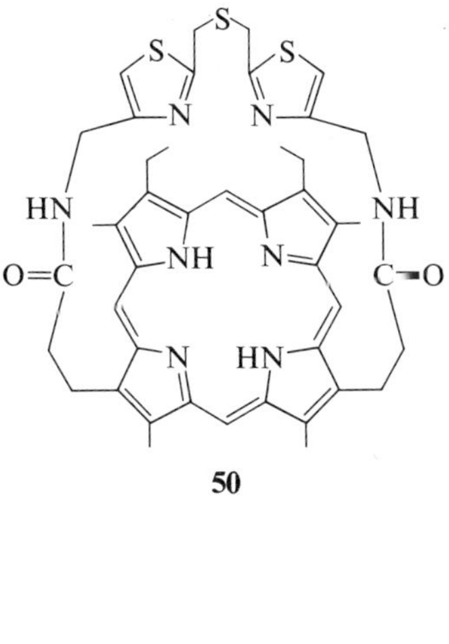

50

substitution and not α as in the previous example. Again an Fe^{III},Cu^{II} complex has been prepared, this time of formulation $FeCu(O)(H_2O)(OAc)$, **50**. The iron(III)–copper(II) complexes will be further discussed in Section IV.B.1.

C. Extendable macrotricycles and related compounds

1. Cylindrical macrotricycles

Cylindrical-macrotricyclic molecules can be devised by face to face linkage of two macrocycles by two bridges. Modification of the size of the macrocycles and the length of the bridges will change the size of the ligand cavities and so affect the coordination environment available to a metal. In addition to these changes the nature of any donor atoms can be varied. By carefully selecting structural fragments it should be possible to construct, and monitor the properties of, a wide range of potentially binucleating ligands, and to utilise the inner cavity of the ligand for substrate incorporation.

Much of the synthetic work carried out emanates from Strasbourg and the first cylindrical macrotricyclic ligands described were polyoxamacrotricycles, **51–55**.[64] The macrotricycle, **51**,[92] gave a bis-silver nitrate complex, the crystal structure of which showed that the silver atoms are inside the central

51

52 X = O

53 = CH$_2$

54 = *o*-phenylene

55 = NH

cavity, each on top of one of the terminal rings and at a distance of 3.88 Å.[92] The bis-copper(II) complex of **51** has also been prepared and its electro-chemical reduction to the bis-copper(I) complex occurs in two successive monoelectronic jumps at markedly positive potentials.[89] The remaining macrotricycles form dinuclear complexes with alkali, alkaline earth, silver and lead cations.[93,94] The crystal structure of the disodium iodide complex of **52** shows that the cations are located in each terminal macrocycle and are 6.40 Å apart.[95] This is a larger distance than for the two silver atoms in the disilver complex of **51**, and reflects the ability of the sodium to penetrate more deeply into the terminal macrocycles, even though the bridging units are the same.

The formation of heterobinuclear species has been detected in solution in the case of **52** where the silver(I)lead(II) complex is in equilibrium with the two homobinuclear species.[94]

56   57   58

Polythiamacrotricycles have been synthesised in order to capitalise further on the use of this type of ligand in coordinating transition metals. Most studies have been performed on the three ligands, **56–58**[96] all of which form binuclear cryptates by complexing two transition metals, one in each macrocyclic terminal subunit. Bis-copper(II) and bis-copper(I) complexes have been obtained for all three ligands, and a mixed valence copper(II)copper(I) complex has been found for the non-symmetric ligand **57**. The crystal structure of the dicopper(II) perchlorate complex of **56**[97] confirms that the metals are bound inside the terminal macrocycles with a copper–copper distance of 5.62 Å. This distance is expected to increase along the series **56–58**. The physicochemical studies carried out on the bis-copper complex of cryptand **56** have shown that it has features of interest in the mimicry of Type III copper centres.[98,99]

Perhaps more directly linked to biological molecules *per se* is the burgeoning area concerning co-facial ("face-to-face") porphyrins (FTF). The stimuli for study have come from two areas; the possibility that binuclear complexes derived from FTF might catalyse the four electron reduction of dioxygen to water, and the intention to seek a biomimetic system for chlorophyll pairs.

Collman, Chang and their coworkers have synthesised numerous FTF using two approaches. Collman has approached the problem by linking the porphyrins at the 5,15 positions, **59**, whereas Chang has utilised the 7,17 positions for his bridges.

59

Amide, amine, urea and polymethylene bridges have been used to bridge the 5,15 positions of octaalkyl[100] and octaphenyl[101] based porphyrins. Representative products are depicted below, **60–62**.

The ligand **60** is synthesised by the reaction of phosgene with the precursor diphenyldi(*o*-aminophenyl)porphyrin,[101] and **61** by the reaction of the relevant porphyrin diacid dichloride with the relevant diamino porphyrin.[100] These two methods have seen extensive application. The crystal structure of the dicopper(II) complex of **61** shows that the copper–copper distance is 6.33 Å,[100] within the range predicted by esr data for the systems such as **60**.[101] However, rather than a direct face-to-face environment there is a shear-like disposition of one porphyrin relative to the other to give a slipped

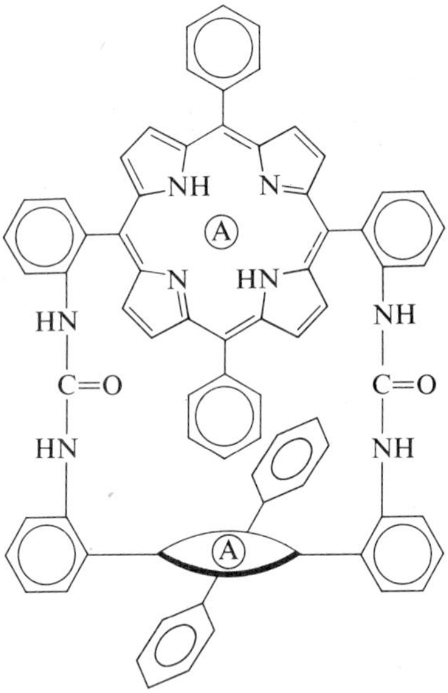

60 (A = A)

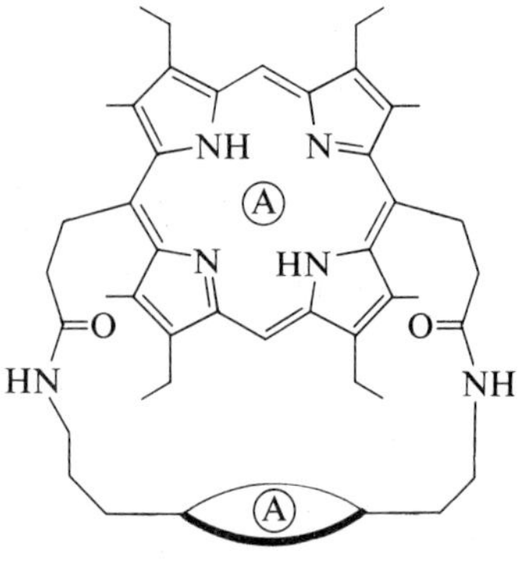

61 (A = A)

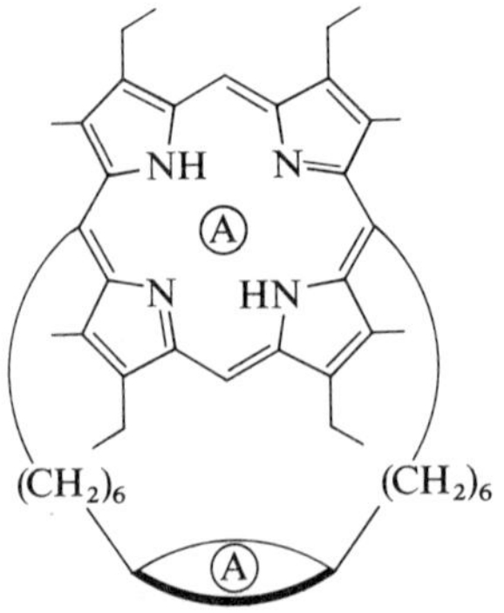

62 (A = A)

structure. It has been suggested that a less flexible chain would be required to inhibit this slippage.[100]

A slipped structure has also been detected by Chang[102] for the dicopper complex of the 7,17-bridged FTF hexyldiporphyrin, **63**. In this system the copper–copper distance is 5.22 Å. Chang has also prepared heterobinuclear iron(II)copper(II) FTF from the related pentyl-containing amido-bridged species.[103] As well as co-facial porphyrins, face-to-face species have been prepared in which a cyclic polyether, or polythiaether, caps the porphyrin structure,[104] to give a non-symmetrical arrangement, **64**. Other FTF systems

syn-**63** R = *n*-hexyl
R′ = *n*-butyl

64 R = *n*-hexyl

prepared include the "cyclophane" porphyrins, **65**, introduced by Ogoshi[105] from the condensation of the component diacid and dialcoholic porphyrins, and the "cyclophane" chlorophylls reported by Wasielewski, **66**.[106] This latter group have also synthesised selectively metallated doubly cofacial porphyrin trimers as models in the study of photoinduced electron transfer; the outer sandwich are mesoporphyrin II derivatives and the central portions are selectively functionalised porphyrins, **67**.

An interesting addition to this general class of ligands comes from the work of Busch.[108] Pairs of 16-membered macrocyclic ligating sites have been held in an approximately face-to-face orientation by various bridging groupings—$(CH_2)_n$, n = 2–8, m- and p-xylyl and duryl. The nature of the ligands has been confirmed by an X-ray crystal structure of a m-xylyl bridged di-nickel(II) complex, **68**, in which the metal separation is 13.6 Å. The two

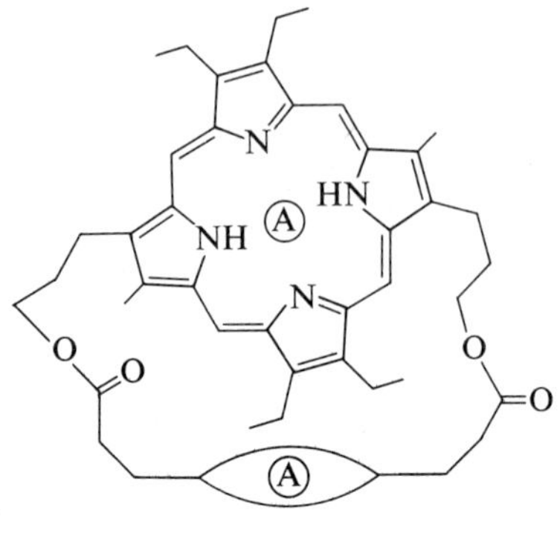

65 (A = A)

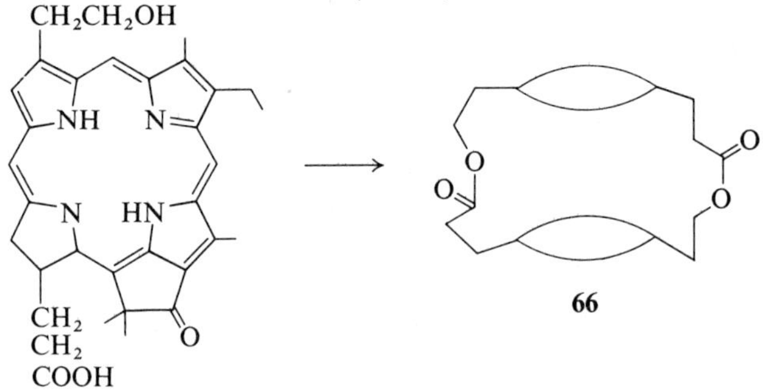

CH₂CH₂OH

→

66

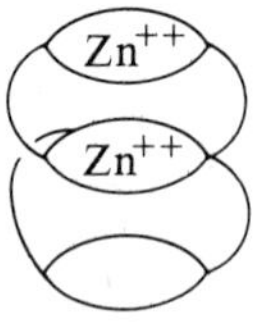

67

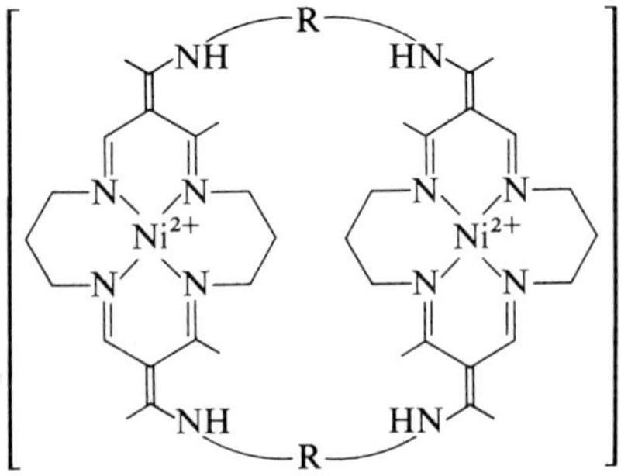

$(PF_6)_4$, 2(acetone)

68, R = *m*-xylyl

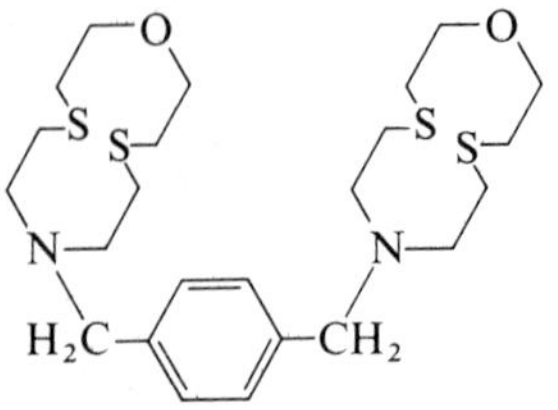

69

macrocyclic moieties are separated by a cavity, or "persistent void" into which smaller substrate molecules can enter.

2. Bis-macrocycles

Removal of one linking chain from the cylindrical macrotricycle leads to the formation of bis-macrocycles which may exist in one of the many orientations available between the extremes of *syn*- or *anti*-conformation. The ligand **69** has been reported by Osborn[109] and the crystal structures of two copper(II) complexes have been solved and discussed.[110] As these have bearing on the biomimicry of the hemocyanin site they will be discussed in Section IV.B.3.

Further synthetic bis-macrocycles are represented by **70**[111] and **71**.[112] Homobinuclear copper(II) complexes of **71** have been synthesised[112] and show some antiferromagnetic exchange, but only mononuclear alkali metal complexes of **70** have been reported.[111]

70, *n* = 2,3

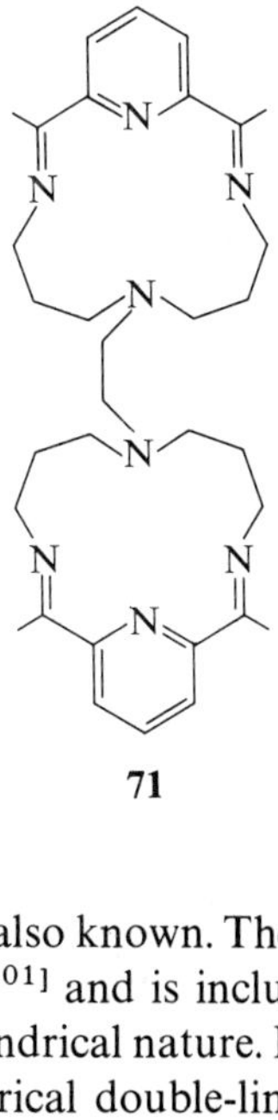

71

Bis(porphyrins) with single, or double bridges, are also known. The double-linked system, **72**, has been prepared by Collman,[101] and is included here rather than in the FTF section because of its non-cylindrical nature. Both *syn*- and *anti*-isomers have been prepared; non-symmetrical double-linked porphyrins are also available.[101] The single linked bis-porphyrin, **73**, has been prepared by reaction of the *o*-aminophenyl precursor with phosgene and verified by the crystal structure of the μ-oxo-bis-iron(III) complex, [Fe$_2$(**73**) O, H$_2$O, 2 toluene].[113] This species was conceived as producing an entropically favoured site for a ligand such as imidazole. The single ligand providing a rotational flexibility without hindering ligation ability.

72 *syn*   73

Bis(chlorophylls) have also been reported.[114-116] These, and **66**, exhibit several photochemical properties which mimic the *in vivo* special pair chlorophylls. By constructing the dimeric units it has been possible to adequately account for the redox and spin delocalisation properties of the pairs *in vivo*, but not yet to produce the unusually red-shifted optical spectrum. Such systems are of interest as evidence relating to the molecular organisation of chlorophyll in the photoreactive centres of green plants and photosynthetic bacteria suggest that special pairs of chlorophyll molecules are oxidised in the primary light conversion event in photosynthesis.

3. Polypodal ligands

By opening up each macrocycle in the bis-macrocycle, polypodal ligands, or "wishbones" have been constructed.

The work of Martell[117-120] showed that polypodal ligands based on the separation of two tridentate donor groups by a para-xylene bridge could be prepared incorporating nitrogen,[118,119] phosphorus[117] or arsenic[120] donor atoms. The ligand **74** readily complexes two metals, such as copper(II) or cobalt(II) and with the latter can act as an efficient dioxygen carrier.[119]

Karlin and his coworkers have utilised and extended this principle to include ortho-, meta- and para-xylene bridges in ligands of the general type **75**.[121-123] The crystal structure of the para-XYL(py)-di-copper(II) complex, $[Cu_2(L)Cl_4] \cdot 2H_2O$, shows the binucleating capability of the ligand, and a

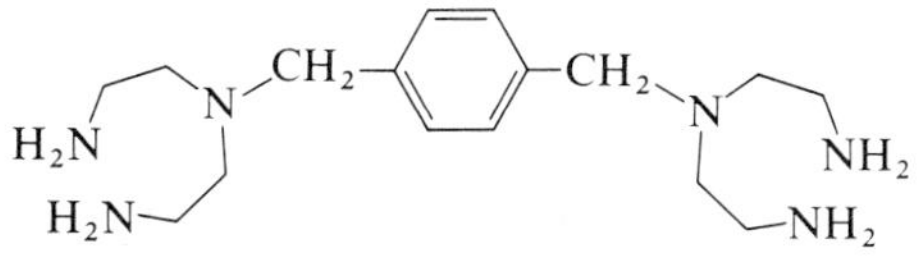

74

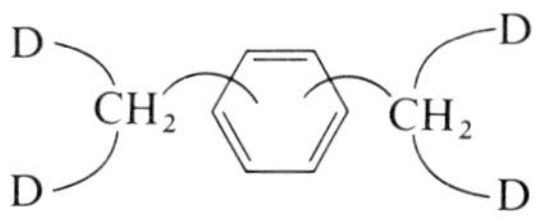

75; D = 2-pyridyl (XYL(py))
D = ethylthio (XYL(SEt))

large copper(II)–copper(II) separation of 11.71 Å. Preliminary electrochemical and esr studies were consistent with the maintenance of a large metal separation in solution.[112] The di-copper(I) complex of para-XYL(SEt), $[Cu_2^IL(PF_6)_2]$, however, is polymeric in the solid state.[123] The meta-XYL(py) ligand has given an interesting reaction in that oxidation of the di-copper(I) complex gave a di-copper(II) complex identified by X-ray analysis as **76**, and containing phenoxy- and methoxy-bridges.[121]

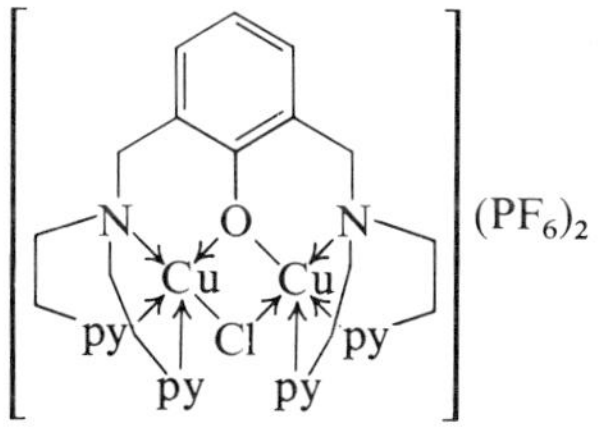

76

A variation of the pendant donors has been reported by Sorrell.[124] Reaction of bis(chloromethyl)-*p*-cresol, or of dibromo-*m*-xylene with pyrazole or 3,5-dimethyl pyrazole gives ligands providing N_2, N_3 or N_3O coordination units for each metal.

A bis-copper(I) complex of N,N,N′,N′-tetrakis-(2-pyridylmethyl)-ethylene-diamine, **77**, has been characterised.[125] The reaction of this complex with carbon monoxide gave a stable dicarbonyl adduct, and the X-ray crystal structure showed that one carbonyl was bound to each copper(I). The binding of carbon monoxide in solution was totally reversible and could be repeated at will. The structure of the bis-copper(I) complex, $Cu_2L(BF_4)_2$ has also been

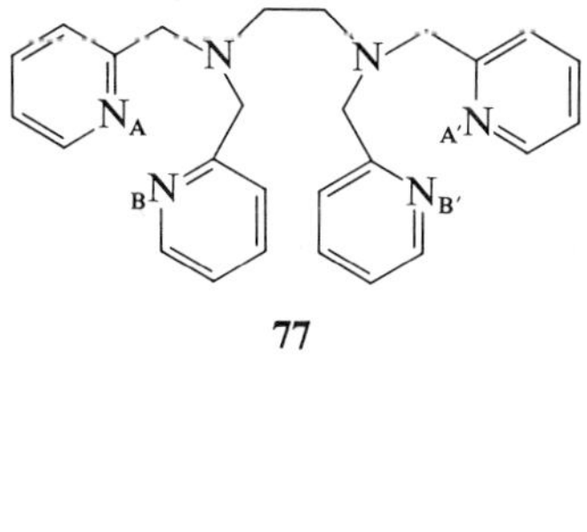

77

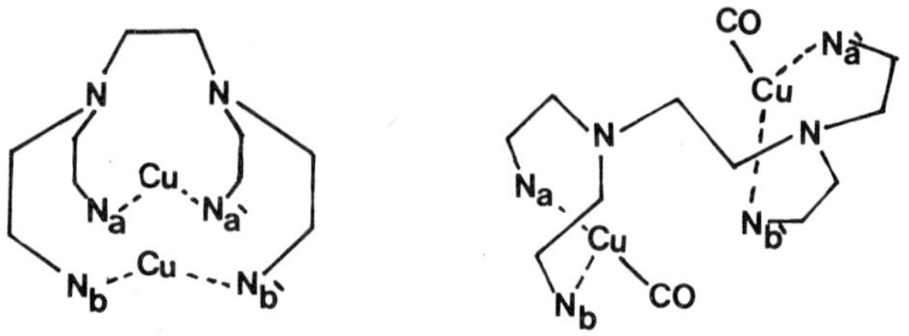

Fig. 8. Schematic representation of bonding modes of **77** in Cu$_2$(**77**)(BF$_4$)$_2$ and
Cu$_2$(**77**)(CO)$_2$(BF$_4$)$_2$.

determined and shows a Cu—Cu distance of 2.780 Å compared with 4.764 Å
in the dicarbonyl complex. In the former ligation of each copper(I) occurs via
pyridyl pairs at either end of the molecule (A, A' and B, B') whereas on addition
of CO extensive rearrangement occurs, the ligand flies open and coordination
occurs with donors from the same end of the bridge (AB and A'B') (Fig. 8).

A series of polypodes has evolved from the reaction of ethylenediamine
tetraacetic acid, and its related tetra-acids with 1,2-diaminobenzene to give
tetrakis-2'-benzimidazolylmethyl derivatives such as **78**. Reedjik and his

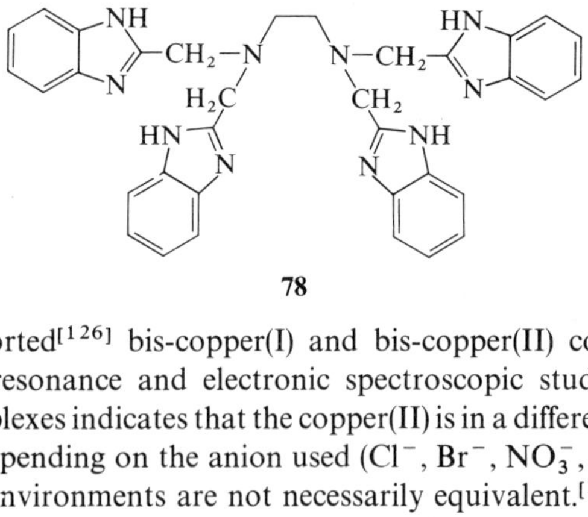

78

coworkers reported[126] bis-copper(I) and bis-copper(II) complexes of **78**.
Electron spin resonance and electronic spectroscopic studies on the bis-
copper(II) complexes indicates that the copper(II) is in a different coordination
environment depending on the anion used (Cl$^-$, Br$^-$, NO$_3^-$, ClO$_4^-$) and that
the copper(II) environments are not necessarily equivalent.[127]

The crystal structure of the bis-copper(I) perchlorate complex of **78** shows a
distinct similarity to that for the analogous complex of **77** in that the coppers
are bound to the AA' and BB' donor sets. The copper(I)–copper(I) distance is
3.043 Å, and reversible uptake of carbon monoxide has been detected.[128]

Methyl substituted analogues of **78** have been prepared with substitution
patterns as shown in **79** and the crystal structure of the bis-copper(II) nitrate
complex of **79a** has been solved.[129] The binuclear moiety exists as a
Cu$_2$L(NO$_3$)$_3^{2+}$ cation in which one nitrate anion bridges the copper centres,
the others being coordinated one to each copper atom. The copper atoms are

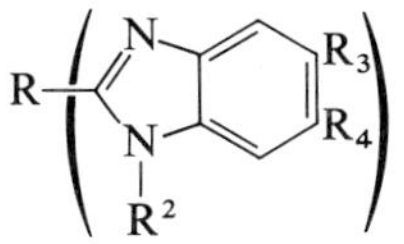

79; a, $R_2 = CH_3$; R_3, $R_4 = H$
b, $R_2 = R_3 = H$; $R_4 = CH_3$
c, $R_2 = H$; R_3, $R_4 = CH_3$

5.171 Å apart, and low temperature magnetic susceptibility studies show no copper–copper interaction.

An octadentate ligand, with five pendant benzimidazole groups has been derived from diethylenetriaminepentaacetic acid, and gave binuclear complexes with copper(II) and zinc(II),[130] and Kida and his coworkers have reported copper complexes of a group of pendant tetrakis-benzimidazole ligands in which the bridges are *m*- and *p*-xylyl and 1,3-cyclohexyl units, **80**. The ligand **80a** has been shown to reversibly interact with dioxygen.[131]

bz = 2'-benzimidazole

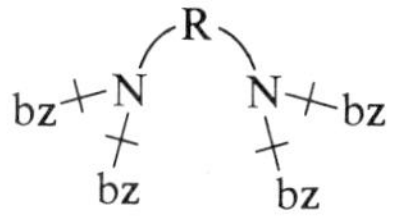

R =   (a);   (b);

bz N   N bz
   bz   bz
      80

(c);   (d);   (e)

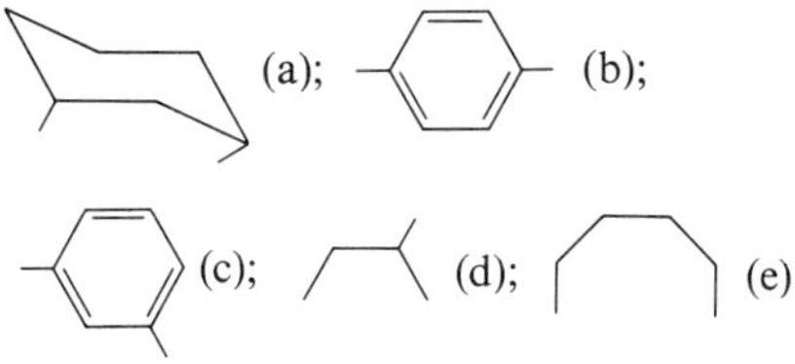

An interesting variation on this theme is found in the binucleating ligand **81** derived from the condensation of 2-hydroxy-1,3-diaminopropane-tetraacetic acid with four equivalents of 1,2-diaminobenzene, followed by N-alkylation with bromoethane.[132] The dicopper(II) complexes of this compound have been synthesised and species of the type $[Cu_2(\mathbf{81})X]^{2+}2Y^-$ have been found where $X^- = OAc^-$, N_3^- and $Y^- = ClO_4^-$, BF_4^-. These complexes utilise the hydroxo-group as an endogenous bridge and are discussed in Section IV.B.3.

Very recently homobinuclear copper(II), cobalt(II), iron(III) and nickel(II) complexes of **78**, **80d,e** and **81** have been added to the collection of bimetallic species derived from polypodal ligands.[133] In contrast to the previous work,

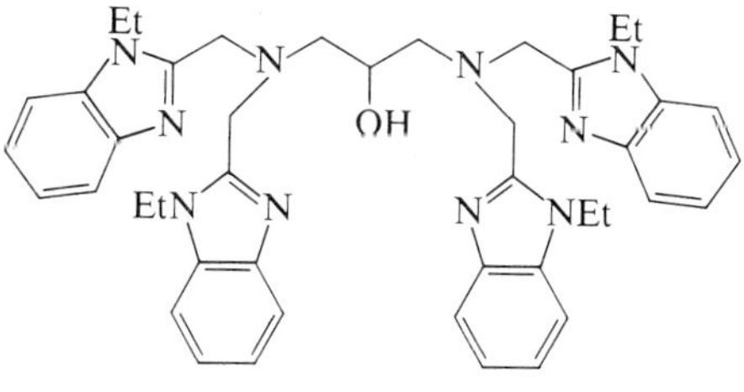

81

no use of the hydroxo-bridge is reported for the complexes $Cu_2(81)X_4$ ($X^- = ClO_4^-$, NO_3^-, Cl^-). A dinuclear iron(II) species is reported to pick up dioxygen before undergoing a sluggish irreversible oxidation reaction.

Further examples of polypodal ligands stem from the work of Hay, **82**,[134] and Kida, **83**,[135] **84**.[136] Binuclear copper(II) complexes have been prepared from these ligands and show little (L = **83**, **84**), or no (L = **82**) magnetic exchange properties.

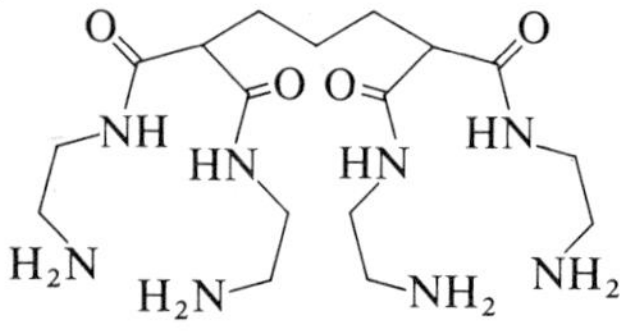

82

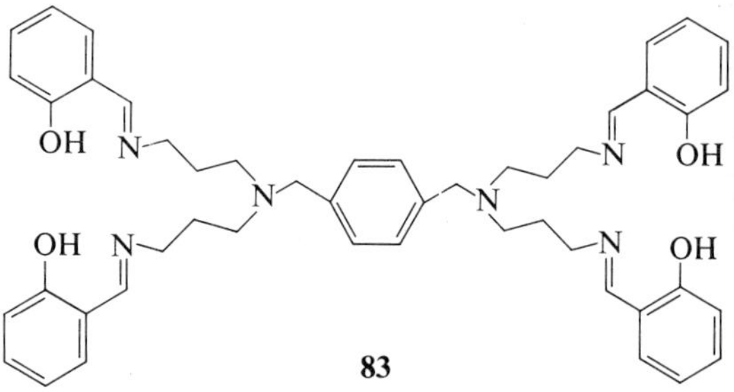

83

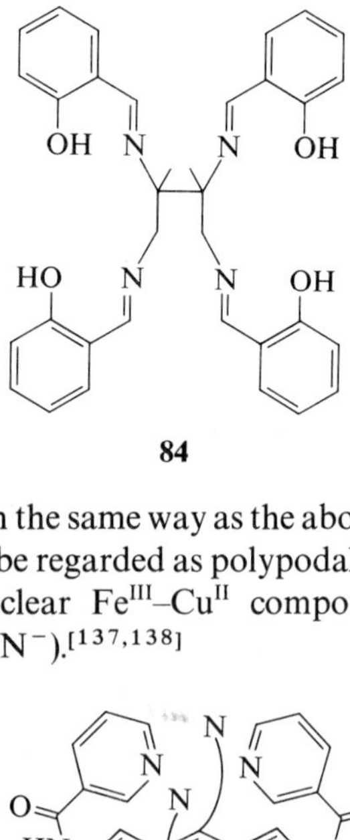

84

Although not derived in the same way as the above ligands, the "picket fence porphyrin", **85**, may also be regarded as polypodal, and it has been used in the synthesis of hetero-binuclear $Fe^{III}–Cu^{II}$ compounds, $[Fe(P)-X-Cu(N_4)]^{2+}$ ($X^- = Cl^-$, Br^-, N_3^-, SCN^-).[137,138]

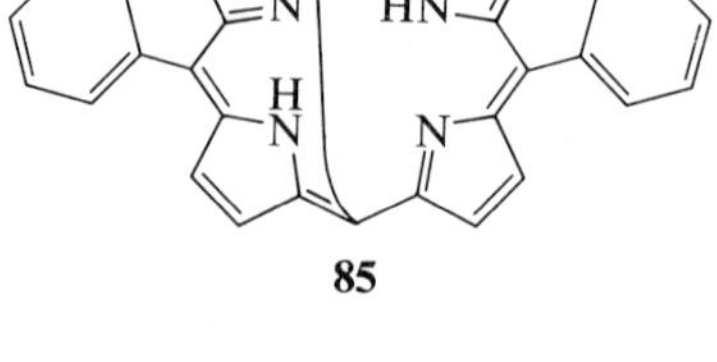

85

D. Separated donor sets

1. Linked-closed compartments

This class of compound has generally been designed to investigate the transmission of electronic effects through long conjugated bridging ligand systems.

The bicyclic octadentate ligand **86** consists of linked-closed compartments and is prepared by condensation of the components, tetraaminobenzene and 4,7-diaza-2,3,8,9-dibenzodecane-1,10-dione. Homobinuclear complexes of copper(II) and nickel(II) have been prepared from this ligand.[139] A second Schiff base system, **87**, was reported, by Black,[140] which gave di-nickel(II) complexes. No physical studies were, however, reported.

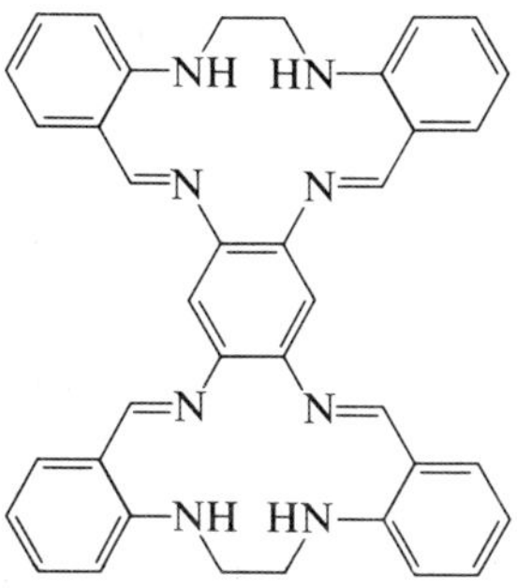

86

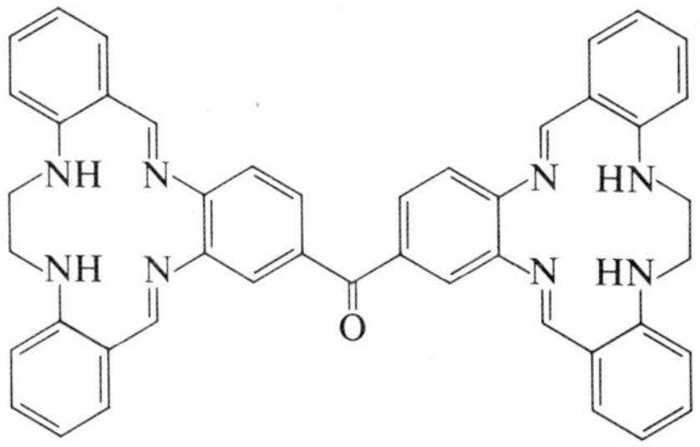

87

An interesting application of this type of compound can be found in the work of Redek.[141] The bis-cyclic polyether, **88**, provides the first synthetic compound in which "cooperativity" has been observed. On complexation with Hg(CN)$_2$ it is noted that the second metal is taken up at a rate 10-times faster than the first metal. The ligand is symmetrically disposed and has a conformational mechanism which allows for an enhanced receptivity at the second site after initial metal incorporation into the first.

Further examples of linked-closed compartments are found in a group of related bis-tetraazamacrocycles which arise from a coupling of the component macrocycles via carbon—carbon bond formation **89**,[142] **90**,[143] **91**,[144] **92**.[145]

2. Linked-open compartments

Related to the above subclass are linked-open compartments. Representative species are **93**,[146] **94**,[147] **95**[146] and **96**[148] and structural modifications have been made to **94** in order to make the homobinuclear metal complexes of

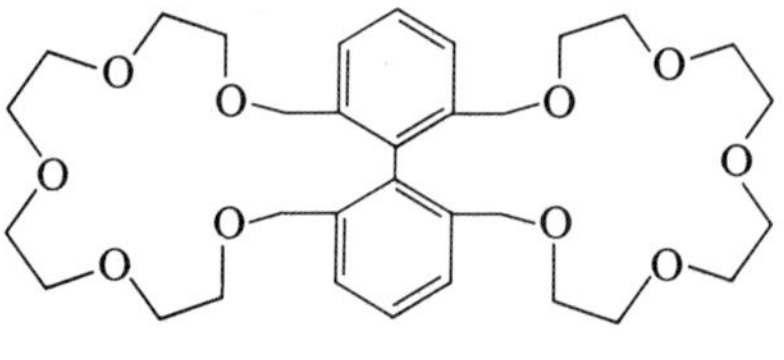

88

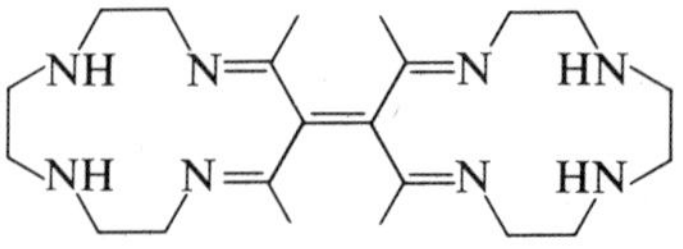

89

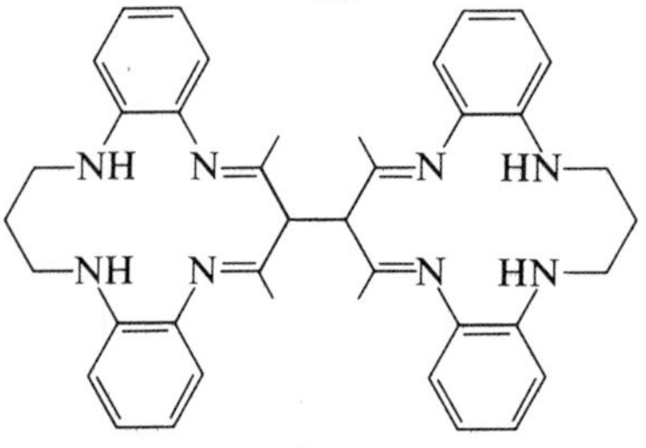

90

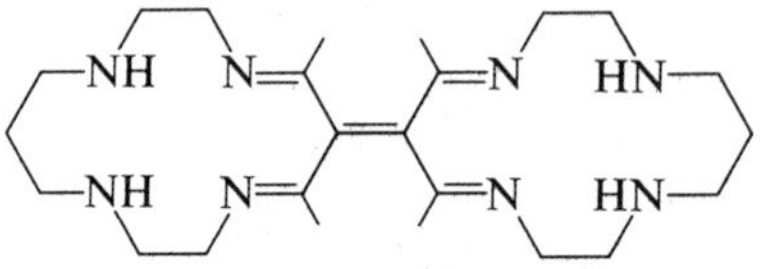

91

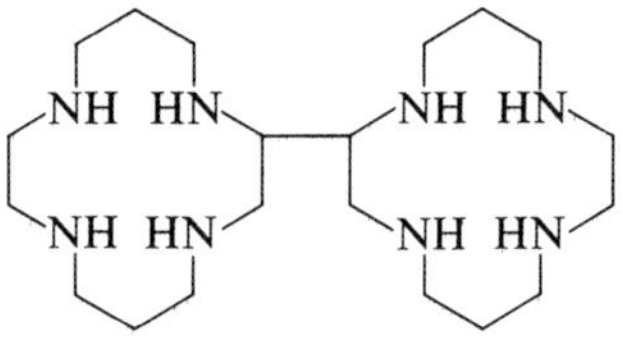

92

it more soluble; 2-isopropyl,[149] and 4-sulphito[150] substitutions have been made into the salicylaldehyde precursors.

Small antiferromagnetic exchange interactions have been detected in the binuclear complexes of **93** and **94** whereas no exchange was found in **95** where any through conjugation mechanism is broken at the biphenyl link.[146] Polarographic studies on **96** show two, one-electron reduction waves, and if *t*-butyl substituents are introduced then a single two-electron process is observed.[148]

Gagné[151] has reported mono- and dinuclear metal complexes of 1,3-bis-(2-pyridylimine)isoindoles, **97**. This bis-copper(II) species shows very slight antiferromagnetic coupling ($J = -1 \, cm^{-1}$), and electrochemical studies reveal a broad wave corresponding to two closely spaced one-electron reductions.

3. Linked-open chains

The final subclass, linked-open chains, covers a somewhat miscellaneous group of compounds some of which indicate that even the simplest of systems should not be discounted as potential binucleating ligands.

Imidazole-bridged binucleating ligands have been developed by Lippard and his coworkers.[152-154] The di-copper(II) complex **98** was prepared via a

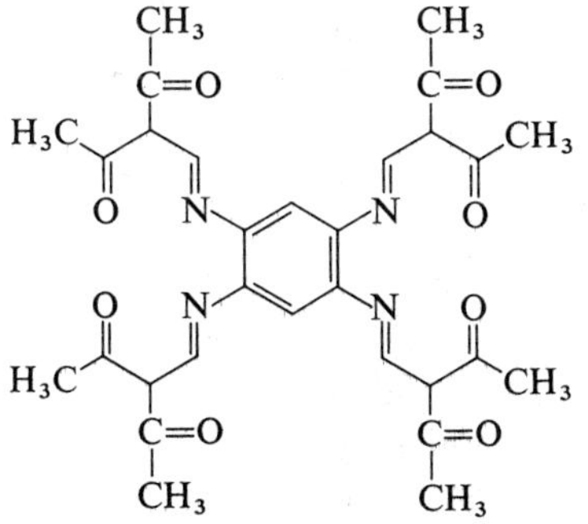

93

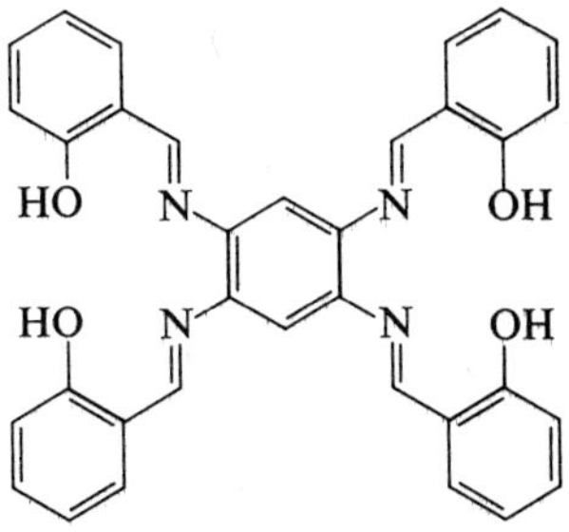

94

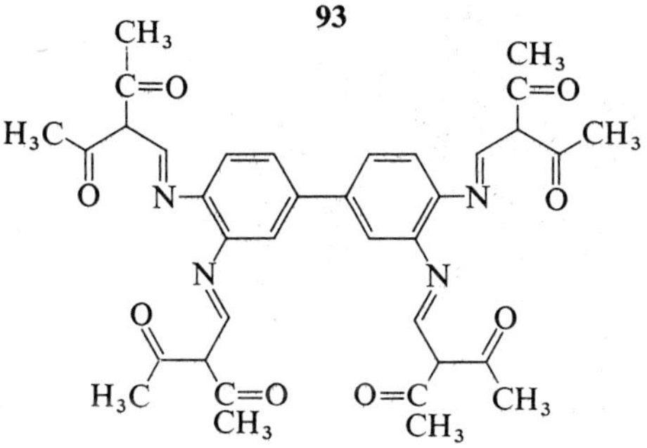

95

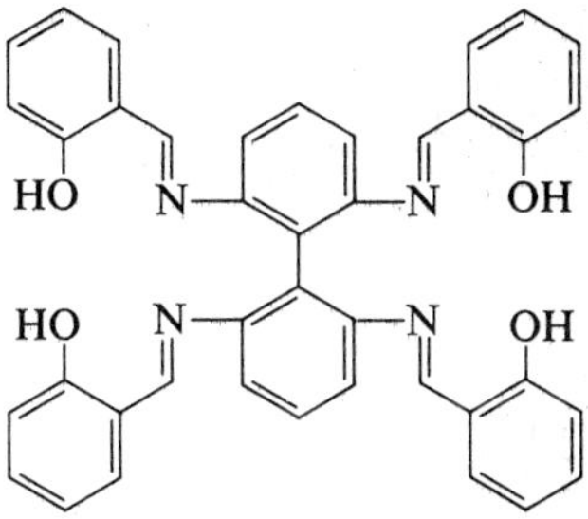

96

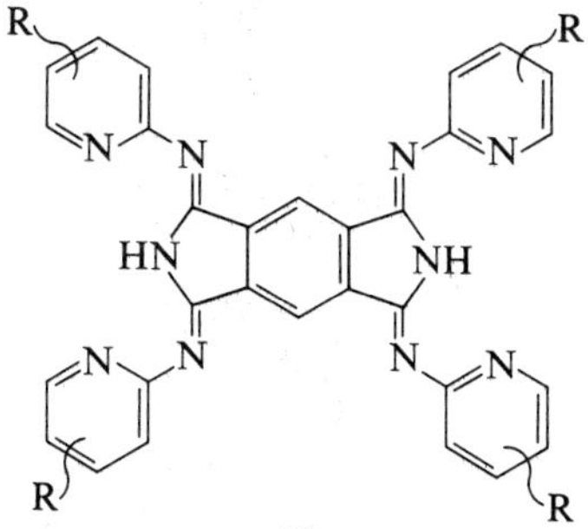

97

template procedure from imidazole-4,5-dicarboxaldehyde, 2-(2-aminoethyl-)pyridine and copper(II) nitrate. The crystal structure[153] verifies the formulation and reaction of **98** with imidazole give the bridged species $[Cu_2(L)imid]_2(NO_3)_4$, $4H_2O$, **99**. In this species the endogeneous bridging imidazoles lie parallel to the Cu–3N plane whereas the exogeneous, bridging imidazoles lie perpendicular to this plane.

A related pyrazine-bridged ligand, **100**, had been prepared earlier and the bis-copper(II) chloride complex prepared. Magnetic measurements indicate

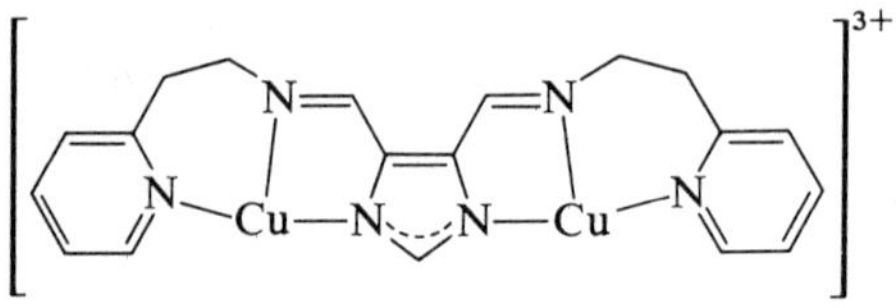

98

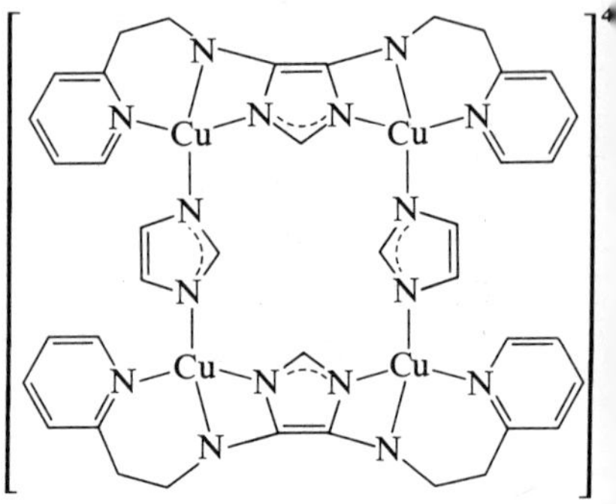

99

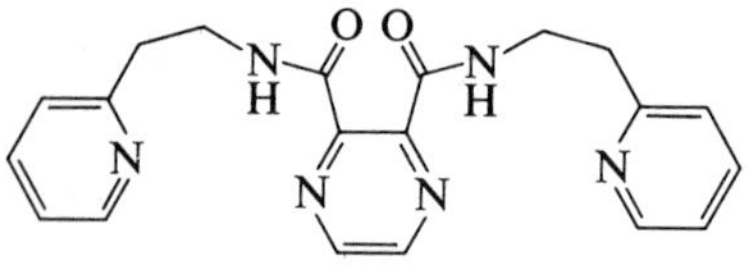

100

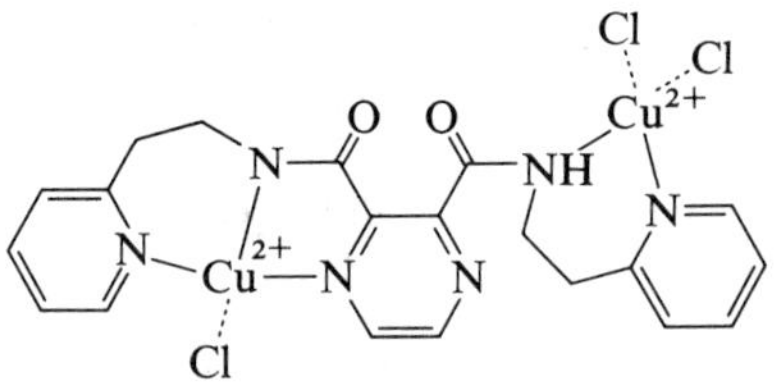

101

little metal–metal interaction and the postulated structure for the complex is as in **101**.[155]

Representative of binucleating ligands of this subclass, derived from 1,4-dihydrazinophthalazine, are **102**[156] and **103**.[157] Both have been shown to form μ-bridged bimetallic complexes, the former as the μ-chlorotetraaqua (L) di-nickel(II) chloride dihydrate, and the latter as a μ-chloro, μ-hydroxo (L) di-copper(II) dichloride. The latter complex has been used in studies on catecholase activity.[158]

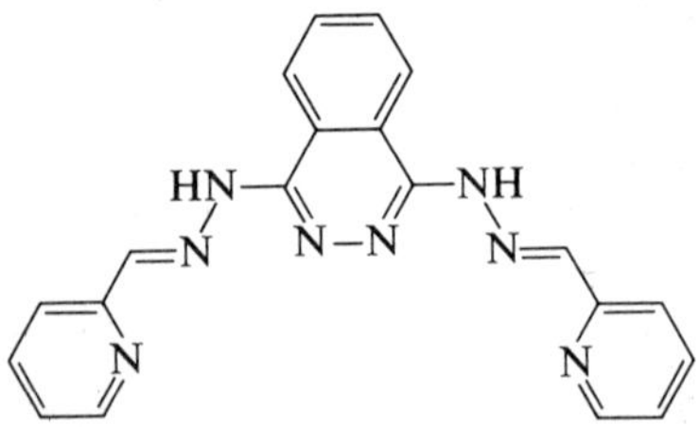

102

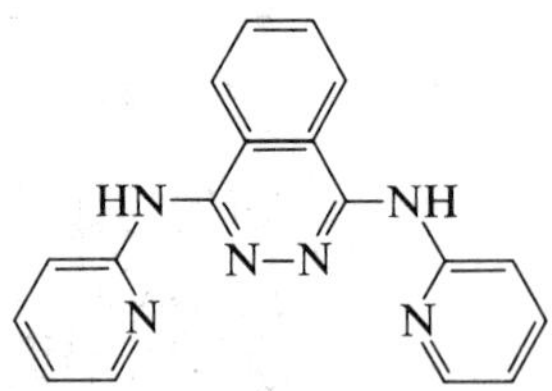

103

Amido-bridged ligands are also available and show antiferromagnetic coupling. The J values for one series of di-copper(II) complexes derived from **104**[159] are some of the largest known for Cu—Cu pairs bridged by multiatomic ligands (J $\sim -200\,\mathrm{cm}^{-1}$, c.f. J $\sim -150\,\mathrm{cm}^{-1}$ for carboxylate,

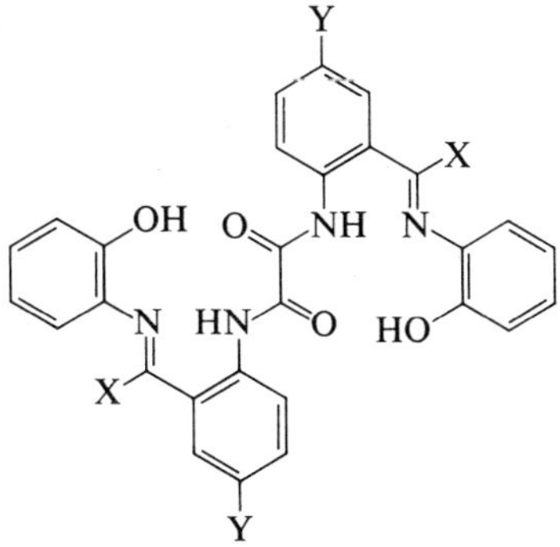

X	Y
H	H
 CON⟨⟩	H
,,	NO
,,	Cl
,,	F

104

$\sim 105 \ cm^{-1}$ for adenine, -26 to $-81 \ cm^{-1}$ for imidazolates and $0\text{--}37 \ cm^{-1}$ for oxalates). A second series of amido-bridged ligands, **105**, show subnormal magnetic moments at room temperature for all bis-copper(II) complexes, and the antiferromagnetic coupling increases with the size of the chelate rings (except six).[160]

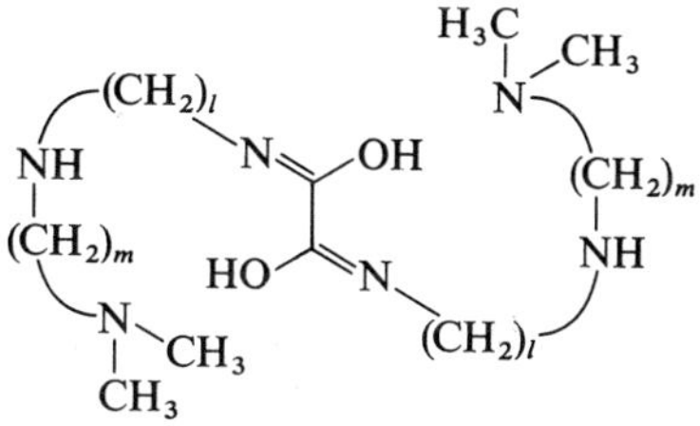

l	m
2	2
2	3
3	2
3	3
4	2
4	3

105

The di-nickel(II) complexes of 3,6-di(pyrid-2-yl)pyrazines, **106**, were proposed as being binuclear as a consequence of their magnetic properties.[161] A recent study on the complexes formed with copper(II) chloride has led to the isolation of $Cu_2(\textbf{106a})Cl_3(OH)(H_2O)$ and the crystal structure confirms the presence of a dinuclear complex in which the copper atoms are in different coordination environments, **107**.[162]

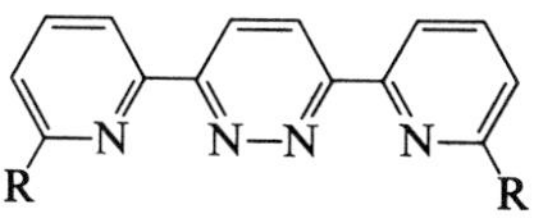

106; a, R = H
b, R = CH₃

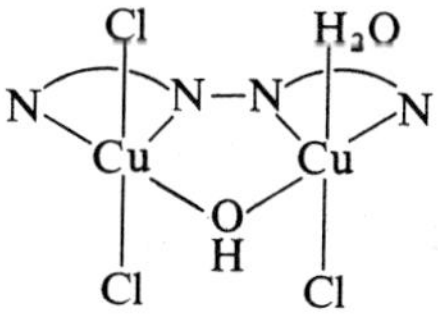

107

Open chain polydentate Schiff bases have been shown to act in a binucleating capacity. Kimura[163] has found that the hexadentate Schiff base derived from spermine and pyridine-2-aldehyde forms binuclear copper(II) complexes, **108**, which exhibit some antiferromagnetic coupling. The reaction of salicylaldehyde with triethylenetetramine leads to the Schiff base, **109**, which reacts with iron(III) chloride in the presence of traces of water to give crystals of the dinuclear iron(III) compound $Fe_2(109)Cl_2(OH)$, (solvent) for which the crystal structure shows the presence of a μ-hydroxy bridge. The formation of a binuclear rather than a mononuclear species is ascribed to steric constraints of the ligand.[164]

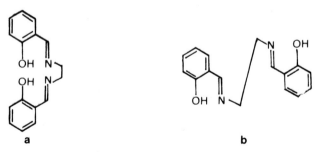

108 (X = Cl⁻, Br⁻, H₂O;
   Y⁻ = NO₃⁻, Br⁻)

109

The tetradentate Schiff bases N,N'-bis(salicylidene)-1,2-diaminoethane, (salen), and N,N'-bis(salicylidene)-1,2-diaminobenzene, (salophen), have been found to act in a bridging and binucleating capacity (Fig. 9) in their reaction with heavier transition metal organometallic species. Complexes such as dioxotetrachloro(salen)bis(triphenylphosphino)di-rhenium(V),[165] bis(1,5-cyclooctadienyl)(salophen)di-rhodium(I)[166] and bis(2-C,N-acetophenone-

Fig. 9. Bonding modes of *Salen*.

oxime)(salophen)di-palladium(II)[167] have been characterised by crystal structures. Further homobinuclear complexes have been prepared in which Ir(I),[169] Pt(II),[168] Au(I),[170] are present.

Even tetradentate tetramines have been found to give binuclear species in which the tetramine binds two metals. The reaction of triethylenetetramine with bis(hexafluoroacetylacetonate)copper(II), or iron(II) gives both 1:1 and 1:2 species: the crystal structure of the copper(II) complex shows that the tetramine acts as a binucleating ligand linking two *cis*-octahedral copper(II) cations.[171]

III. MOTIVATION FOR THE USE OF BINUCLEATING LIGANDS

There are many metalloproteins, or metalloenzymes, that possess functional centres containing two metal atoms held close together, less than 10 Å apart and often less than 5 Å apart.[172] The metal atoms often share a bridging ligand, or ligands, and the pairing of metals may be homobimetallic or heterobimetallic. The desire to understand the nature of these sites has led to the use of bimetallic complexes of binucleating ligands as speculative models for the metal environment. With time and the availability of more precise information from X-ray studies these have, in certain cases, approached corroborative status.

A brief description of the sites in selected bimetallobiomolecules is given below. The molecules under discussion herein are the homobimetallo-systems hemerythrin, hemocyanin, tyrosinase and the multicopper oxidases, and the heterobimetallo-species cytochrome *c* oxidase and superoxide dismutase.[7]

A. Copper-zinc superoxide dismutase (Cu^{II}, Zn^{II})[173–175]

Superoxide dismutases are metalloenzymes which combat the potentially toxic effects of superoxide ions, formed in one-electron oxidation reactions involving molecular oxygen, by catalysing the dismutation of the anion to dioxygen and hydrogen peroxide. Whether this is a real or artefactual

$$2O_2^- + 2H^+ \rightarrow O_2 + H_2O_2$$

biological function has been the subject of conjecture, nevertheless it is possible to discuss the structural features of the enzyme. Dismutases containing manganese, or iron, have been isolated but the copper–zinc protein from bovine tissues has been the most thoroughly studied.

The complete sequence of 150 residues in the polypeptide chain is known[176] and the three-dimensional X-ray structure has been determined to

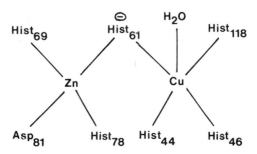

Fig. 10. Schematic representation of the bimetal site in Cu–Zn superoxide dismutase (reference [178]).

a resolution of 3 Å.[177] The protein consists of two identical, non-covalently associated subunits in each of which the metal binding sites are near the ends of the cylindrical arrangement. The essential features of the metal binding region are shown in Fig. 10.[178] Each copper(II) is coordinated to four histidines, one of which, histidine-61, acts as a bridge to the zinc and is deprotonated. The water molecule, predicted originally fron nmr relaxation studies,[179] is clarified by recent X-ray refinement and so each copper(II) is five-coordinate with an empty axial site. The zinc atom is coordinated to a further two histidines and one aspartic acid residue in an approximately tetrahedral geometry. The copper(II)–zinc distance is a ~5.4 Å. The zinc atom plays a structural role in that it helps the protein to preform the coordination environment around the copper, and the copper is the active catalytic centre.

It is possible to substitute the metal ions and this has been carried out to test structure–function relationships. The existence of an active form of superoxide dismutase with copper(II) substituted for the natural zinc[180] has led to the use of binuclear copper(II) complexes as models to probe the nature of the imidazolate bridge.[154]

B. Cytochrome c oxidase (Fe^{III}, Cu^{II})[181–182]

Cytochrome c oxidase is a complex enzyme which contains two heme units, low spin heme$_a$ and high spin heme$_{a3}$, and two copper(II) atoms. It is located as the terminal component of the mitochrondrial respiratory chain and has the important role of catalysing the rapid, four-electron reduction of molecular oxygen to water. The mechanism of this reduction is not clear but a body of

$$O_2 + 4H^+ + 4e^- \rightarrow 2H_2O$$

evidence has established that dioxygen interacts with one pair of heme and copper(II) only—heme$_{a3}$ and Cu$_{a3}$.

In the oxidised form heme$_{a_3}$ and Cu$_{a_3}$ exhibit properties which indicate that the two metal centres are strongly antiferromagnetically coupled, making the two metals epr invisible, or silent, and reducing their magnetic susceptibilities. This is evidenced by the exchange coupling constant, $-J$, of > 200 cm^{-1} for the oxidase. The heme$_{a_3}$ and Cu$_{a_3}$ were therefore assumed to be in close proximity and linked by a ligand which could mediate any magnetic exchange. Several potential links have been proposed, imidazolate,[183] carboxylate,[184] oxo-[185] and mercapto-[186] bridges, and criticised at length. An oxo-bridge was preferred as a working hypothesis for the site.[185]

No X-ray crystal structure is available for the bimetallic site of cytochrome c oxidase but EXAFS (extended X-ray absorption fine structure) studies have been reported. An investigation concerned with the copper(II)a$_3$ site was interpreted as showing that the metal is surrounded by a combination of sulphur and nitrogen (or oxygen) donors.[187] The Cu—S distance was 2.27, comparable with that found for the copper(II)–cysteine distance in the blue copper proteins,[188] and the Cu—N (or O) distance was 1.97 ± 0.2 Å. A more detailed investigation was concerned with both metal centres and led to a proposal for the fully oxidised heterobimetallic site (Fig. 1).[189]

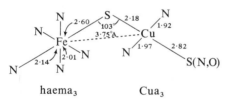

haema$_3$ Cua$_3$

Fig. 11. Proposed active site in cytochrome c oxidase (from EXAFS).

The active site proposed shows the copper atom to be surrounded by two nitrogens (at 1.97 Å), and a bridging sulphur (at 2.18 Å), with a further donor atom at 2.82 Å. This environment resembles the oxidised form of stella-cyanin.[190] The iron atom has four heme nitrogens at 2.01 Å, a proximal nitrogen at 2.14 Å and the octahedral coordination is completed by the bridging sulphur, shared with the copper atom, at 2.60 Å. This sulphur is believed to come from a cysteine, and the Fe—S—Cu angle is 103° consistent with sp^3. The Cu—Fe distance is 3.75 Å.

C. Hemerythrin (Fe, Fe)[191–194]

Hemerythrin has been designated an "alternative dioxygen carrier" and has a misleading name as it contains no heme unit. It is present in the red blood cells of some marine invertebrate phyla notably *Siphunculid* worms. The active centre is a pair of iron atoms about 3.5 Å apart and contained within a single polypeptide chain. Most hemerythrins are oligomeric, di-, tri-, tetra- and octameric forms are known, and although the dioxygen binding affinity for each iron is comparable with that for hemoglobin there is little cooperative action in hemerythrin. Myohemerythrin occurs as a monomeric unit and has a molecular weight comparable with a subunit of the octamer.

Deoxyhemerythrin is colourless and contains two high-spin iron(II) centres which can each add dioxygen to give oxyhemerythrin which is violet pink and involves two iron(III) centres and a peroxo-ligand. Both forms may be oxidised to methemerythrin which has iron(III) pairs. The low magnetic moment indicates strong antiferromagnetic coupling.

There now appears to be agreement with regard to the crystal structure of metazidohemerythrin, Fig. 12.[197] Recently (JACS, 1982)[264] from EXAFS

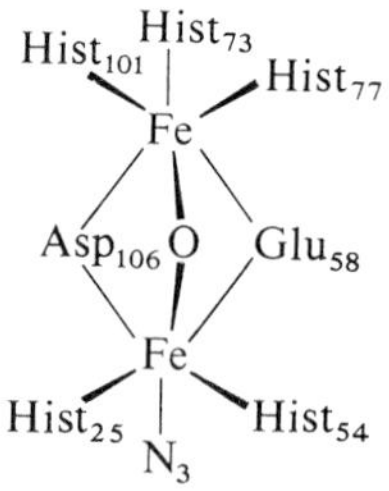

Fig. 12. Binuclear iron site in metaxidohemerythrin from *T. dyscritum*.

studies it has been concluded that the active site is very similar in the oxy and met forms, but distinctly different in deoxyhemerythrin. The binuclear iron centre in the oxy and met forms contains a μ-oxo bridge similar to that in μ-oxo diiron(III) complexes, and as in Fig. 12. Deoxyhemerythrin shows distinct changes and the Fe—Fe peak has disappeared indicating loss of the μ-oxo bridge upon reduction. For the oxy form the structure (Fig. 13) has been suggested, although this still does not fit all observations if the O_2^{2-} is bonded sideways on.

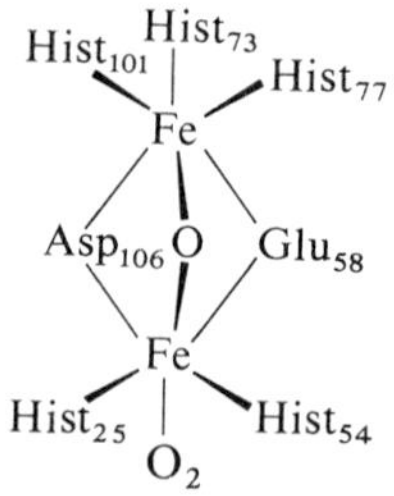

Fig. 13. Proposed iron site in oxyhemerythrin.

By treating the data for the metazido- and methydroxohemerythrins in the same way it is shown[197] that in the methydroxo-form the tyrosine molecule is too far from the iron and therefore that one iron is pentacoordinate. There is, however, some low site occupancy indicating that a fraction of the molecules do have a sixth (as yet unidentified) ligand. The worrying difference in the earlier crystallographic studies, although apparently now resolved, raises important questions concerning the possible extent of error in protein models originating from single source studies.[198]

An iron-containing enzyme believed to be related to hemerythrin is ribonucleotide reductase.[199] This enzyme catalyses the reduction of ribonucleotides to the corresponding deoxyribonucleotides and one subunit participates in the reaction via a tyrosyl free radical formed in conjunction with a binuclear iron centre. Moßbauer,[199] electronic spectra[200] and resonance Raman data[201] are indicative of the presence of an antiferromagnetically coupled, high-spin iron(III) pair with a μ-oxo-bridge as in hemerythrin.

D. Hemocyanin (Cu, Cu)[202–204]

Dioxygen for the metabolism of arthropods and molluscs is bound and transported by hemocyanin. The active centre is a pair of copper atoms capable of binding one dioxygen molecule. Deoxyhemocyanins are colourless, diamagnetic and epr inactive suggesting that a binuclear copper(I) site is present. On oxygenation a blue colour develops and an electronic spectrum characteristic of copper(II) is detected together with an intense charge transfer band, ca 345 nm, characteristic of a copper(II) dimer. The resonance Raman shows a band at 745 cm^{-1} indicating that a peroxide is formed (v, O—O) and it is consistent with two copper atoms binding one oxygen which acts as an exogeneous bridge. The binuclear site also requires an endogeneous bridge and there have been suggestions that this is an oxygen atom donor because of the 425 nm absorption in the uv-visible range.[205] Bridging ligands such as hydroxide, phenoxide or carboxylate have all been considered because of their ability to promote strong antiferromagnetic coupling. One important feature of oxyhemocyanin is that the binuclear copper(II) centre is strongly antiferromagnetically coupled with $-J > 550$ cm^{-1}.

EXAFS studies have indicated that the remaining ligands at the coppers are either two[206] or three[207] nitrogen or oxygen donors, two of which must be imidazoles from histidine. Use of an imidazole group fitting in the detailed analysis of oxyhemocyanin from *Megathura crenulata* leads to the proposal that the bimetallic site environment is as in Fig. 14.[206] The copper–copper distance is 3.55 Å and each copper is square planar; the nature of the endogeneous bridge remains elusive.

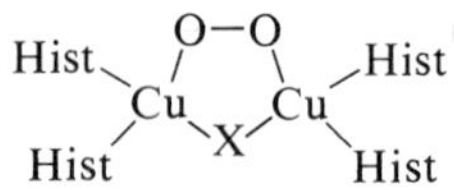

Fig. 14. Proposed binuclear site in oxyhemocyanin (from EXAFS).

The copper site of deoxyhemocyanin has also been studied by EXAFS[208] and shows that each copper(I) atom is coordinated to two or three imidazoles with an average copper–nitrogen distance of 1.95 Å. No evidence for a copper–copper interaction within 4 Å is observed and it is suggested that the two copper centres are coordinated only to the histidines leaving facial sides open for the attachment of dioxygen. On binding dioxygen the copper changes from copper(I) to copper(II), its coordination number changes from two to four, and the copper–copper distance is reduced suggesting that substantial rearrangement must occur in the protein structure.

E. Tyrosinase (Cu, Cu)[203–205]

Tyrosinase is a copper-containing mono-oxygenase found in many different micro-organisms, plants and animals, and is capable of catalysing the *o*-hydroxylation of monophenols and the oxidation of *o*-diphenols to *o*-quinones.

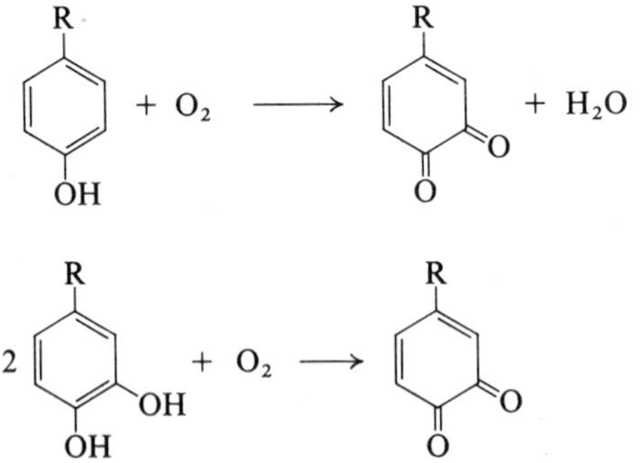

monophenolase (cresolase) activity

diphenolase (catecholase) activity

Comparisons of the chemical and spectral (epr, absorption and CD, resonance Raman) of tyrosinase derivatives with hemocyanin derivatives have shown a remarkable similarity between the two and led to the proposal that the binuclear site is comparable and contains antiferromagnetically coupled copper(II) pairs.[203] The structural representation of the metal centres has been proposed as shown in Fig. 15.

Tyrosinase has been isolated from a number of sources and the molecular properties vary. The copper content is not always precisely defined. However,

met (resting)   oxy

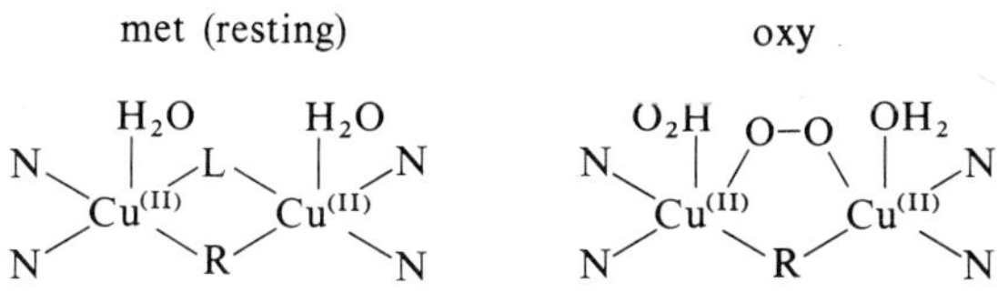

Fig. 15. Models for the bicopper site Met (resting) and oxy-tyrosinase.

recent biochemical studies by Lerch on a *Neurospora* tyrosinase have allowed for the first complete sequencing of a binuclear copper protein showing a molecular weight of 46 000 daltons, 407 amino acids and one binuclear copper unit.[210] The tentative proposal for the ligand environment shows at least four histidines to be involved (Fig. 16).[211] Binuclear copper units have been proposed for tyrosinases from bacteria, mushrooms, spinach beet and human malignant melanoma.

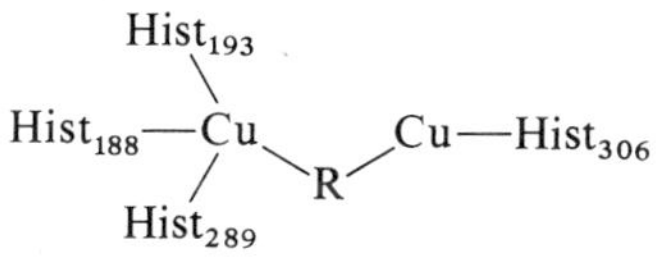

Fig. 16. Proposed metal environment of *Neurospora* tyrosinase.

A further copper monoxygenase is dopamine-β-hydroxylase[209,212] which catalyses the hydroxylation of dopamine to noradrenaline. It contains four magnetically isolated copper(II) atoms per tetramer and there have been differences of opinion as to whether a binuclear site is involved in its activity or not. A recent communication has revived the binuclear approach[213] and suggests that, from epr evidence, the two copper atoms involved in catalytic activity are quite close together and that a tyrosinase-like mechanism might apply to dopamine-β-hydroxylase.[214]

F. Multiple copper or "blue oxidases" (Cu, Cu)[215-217]

There are several proteins exhibiting oxidase activity which contain four, or more, copper atoms. Laccases, which catalyse the oxidation of *p*-diphenols to *p*-diquinones, with the accompanying four-electron reduction of dioxygen to water, contain four copper atoms. Ceruloplasmin, the major copper-containing protein from mammalian blood contains eight coppers; its precise role is conjectural although it catalyses the reduction of dioxygen to water and may act as a copper-carrying protein. Ascorbate oxidase also contains eight copper atoms. In each of these systems there are at least three coordination environments available to the metal and these have been designated as Types 1, 2 and 3.[216]

Type 1 copper is characterised by an intense absorption band near 600 nm and epr spectrum with an unusually small hyperfine coupling constant. Structural data is available for this site from X-ray crystallographic studies on plastocyanin[218,219] and azurin[220] both of which have their single copper atom in a severely distorted tetrahedral geometry. The presence of this site gives the oxidase an intense blue colour and leads to their term "blue oxidases".

Type 2 copper is present in all of the blue multi-copper oxidases and is characterised by lacking sufficient optical absorption to be observed above the other copper chromophores. The epr signal is similar to those exhibited by most small copper(II) complexes.

Type 3 coppers are a strongly antiferromagnetically coupled copper(II) dimer which can act as a two-electron donating system and is essential to the reduction of dioxygen. The site has absorption band, ca 330 nm, a lack of epr signal and is non-paramagnetic over a wide temperature range.

A recent article has suggested that these criteria be redefined so that Types 1–3 are replaced by Groups 1–3, and that Group IV, containing multi-copper proteins in which combinations of sites occur, be added.[221]

Laccase contains one each of Type 1 and Type 2, and two Type 3 coppers, and both ceruloplasmin and ascorbate oxidase contain two Type 1, two Type 2 and four Type 3 coppers. The problem in understanding the nature of the Type 3 site is that the oxidases contain all three types and so there can be problems for spectral data interpretation. In principle resting Type 3 copper can be equated with met-tyrosinase, and met-hemocyanin and there are limited spectral similarities.[203] However, the spectral changes associated with ligand binding to the met oxidases differ significantly from those observed for met-tyrosinase and met-hemocyanin. It is apparent that as the Type 3 unit in these oxidases may exhibit both similarities to and differences from the coupled site in hemocyanin and tyrosinase further chemical and spectral studies are required.[203]

Solomon[222] has demonstrated that the Type 3 site in Type 2 depleted Rhus laccase is, in fact, a reduced binuclear cuprous centre. This technique of type depletion shows great promise for further studies.

More detailed accounts of the information available for the nature of the coordination sites can be found in the references given. The challenge laid down to the chemist interested in binucleating ligands and their complexes is clearly evidenced, both from the past, and also for the future through the more unknown qualities of systems such as the homobinuclear iron sites, and the copper pairs in dopamine-β-hydroxylase and "blue" oxidases.

IV. METAL COMPLEXES OF BINUCLEATING LIGANDS AS MODELS FOR BIOSITES

Criteria for synthetic models of binuclear centres in metallobiomolecules have been reviewed[204] with particular reference to dicopper(II) centres. Synthetic binuclear metal complexes act as appropriate models for natural binuclear metal centres when they mimic some chemical or physical property of the biosite and so help improve our knowledge of it. In the main, studies on models have concentrated on physical properties such as magnetic susceptibilities, redox properties, optical and electron paramagnetic resonance spectral parameters. The imitation of the functional roles of the biosites is currently at a less well-advanced stage.

A. Physical properties of bimetallobiosites

1. Magnetic susceptibility and epr spectroscopy

The bimetallobiosites in cytochrome *c* oxidase, hemerythrin, ribonuclease reductase, oxyhemocyanin, tyrosinase and the blue oxidases (Type 3) all contain strongly antiferromagnetically coupled pairs of metal ions. The reproduction of such coupling has stimulated a large number of studies on the magnetic properties of a variety of binuclear compounds. The greater proportion of the work has centred on copper(II) because the diamagnetism of the last three biosites has given an especial challenge. There are relatively few binuclear compounds which are diamagnetic at ambient temperature and until recently the examples stemmed from bridged dimers. Some examples of dicopper(II) compounds exhibiting diamagnetism are given in Table 1.

The magnetic behaviour of a large number of dicopper(II) species has been studied in detail and there are excellent reviews available.[230,231] The magnetic exchange between two copper(II) ions is given by the Hamiltonian:

$$H = -2J.\hat{S}_1.\hat{S}_2$$

where $\hat{S}_1, \hat{S}_2$ are the spins of the ions and the interaction parameter 2J (in cm^{-1}) represents the separation of the singlet and triplet states, and is negative if the singlet level lies lowest. The strong antiferromagnetic interaction ($-2J > -500$ cm^{-1}) in the bimetallobiomolecules containing two copper(II) ions, and also in cytochrome *c* oxidase ($-2J > 200$ cm^{-1}) are most likely the consequence of a superexchange mechanism operating through bridging ligands.[175] One or more bridges may be present at the site, for example in oxyhemocyanin, a bound peroxide provides an exogeneous bridge and there is support for the presence of a μ-hydroxy, or -phenoxy, endogeneous bridge. Unfortunately there are no μ-peroxo-dicopper(II) model systems available, as

TABLE 1

Examples of dicopper(II) compounds exhibiting diamagnetism

Ligand	Complex	Reference
$C_6H_5-N\overset{N}{\underset{H}{=}}N-C_6H_5$	Cu_2L_4 (c.f. copper(II) acetate)	[223]
	$[CuL]_2(ClO_4)_2$ (oxybridged from ligand)	[224]
$(n = 2,3)$	$[CuL]_2(ClO_4)_2, 2H_2O$ (oxybridged from ligand)	[225]
	$(ClLCu)_2CO_3$ (carbonato-bridge)	[226]
	$[(LCu)_2CO_3](ClO_4)_2$ (carbonato-bridge)	[227]
31	$LCu_2(N_3)_4$ (azido-bridges)	[67]
81	LCu_2N_3 (alkoxo- and azido-bridges)	[132]
15 (R = H, X = S)	$LCu_2(OR)$ (phenoxo- and alkoxo-bridges)	[228]
	$LCu_2(OR)$ (phenoxo- and alkoxo-bridges)	[228]
21 (R = tBu)	LCu_2 (alkoxo-bridge)	[229]

yet, to test the superexchange potential of the system. The results with small molecules suggests that μ-carbonate bridges are potentially good superexchange bridges.[226,227]

It would not be too unkind to say, at this point, that the literature is replete with statements such as, the (magnetic) results suggest that this type of compound must be seriously considered as a possibility for the bimetallic site of a particular bimetallobiomolecule. Often the systems appear to have little obvious relevance to the site but that must be a reality of, and a problem associated with, any speculative model based on one technique. It is speculative and so can only be interpreted as reproducing the physical property of the site without necessarily approaching the real molecular environment. Nevertheless there is a validity in presenting suggestions, and there are often quite beneficial effects in other areas. For example the work of Kahn and his coworkers shows their utilisation of compartmental ligands in the molecular engineering of coupled polynuclear systems, particularly with reference to understanding the orbital mechanism of the exchange interaction.[59]

Electron paramagnetic resonance is also a valuable technique in examining the nature of binuclear sites. In the case of the binuclear copper centres this must apply to the oxidised centres as the reduced Cu(I)Cu(I) and the antiferromagnetically coupled forms give no epr signals as they are diamagnetic. Direct evidence for a binuclear site comes from the observation of triplet epr spectra for nitric-oxide-treated hemocyanin,[232] tyrosinase[232] and ceruloplasmin.[232] A metal separation of ~ 6 Å has been estimated for these modified forms.[232] The epr properties of dicopper(II) complexes[234] and of copper-containing proteins[235] have been reviewed in depth.

2. Optical spectroscopy

Optical spectra may be used to probe the nature of the bimetallobiosite by comparison of spectral data with that derived from simple model compounds in which the coordination geometry and donor environment of the metal are varied to give a range of possibilities.

The spectrum of oxyhemocyanin has bands at 345 ($\varepsilon = 20\,000$ M^{-1} cm^{-1}) and 570 ($\varepsilon = 1000$ M^{-1} cm^{-1}) nm with weaker transitions at 425 and ~ 700 cm^{-1}.[205] From detailed studies on oxy- and methemocyanin Solomon and his co-workers[203] have deduced that the strong bands may be assigned as peroxide to $Cu^{II}(d_{x^2-y^2})$ charge transfer (CT) transitions, and the band at 425 nm to an endogeneous ligand to Cu^{II} CT — where the ligand is probably tyrosine, or hydroxide. The lack of any significant intensity in the 300–400 nm region of the met-spectrum precludes sulphur ligation — as does the observation that hemocyanin can be reconstituted after RS-groups have been blocked in the apoenzyme.[236] The 700 nm band is associated with the ligand field transitions of the two tetragonal copper(II) ions. The presence of the peroxo-bridge is indicated by resonance Raman studies in which resonant enhancement of a peak at 744 cm^{-1} (*Cancer magister*) or 749 cm^{-1} (*Busycon canaliculatum*) occurs.[237] These bands are characteristic of the oxy-form, are sensitive to isotopic substitution of the dioxygen, and are on the fringe of the range associated with μ-peroxo-cobalt(III) complexes.

Tyrosinases show many spectral resemblances to the hemocyanins and so the copper sites are anticipated as being similar. Oxy-tyrosinase has a strong intensity band at 345 nm.[238] The chromophore responsible for the 330 nm band in Type 3 copper has not been established. The suggestion has been made that, from model studies involving α,ω-diaminopolythiaethanes, a thioether to copper(II) CT could be responsible as the band occurs at the appropriate energy and with the correct intensity.[239] A second group of workers has advocated that an imidazolato-bridge could be responsible as in studies on simple copper(II)-imidazole and copper(II)-imidazolato complexes a good spectral correlation occurs.[240] This difference of opinion is used here to illustrate the problems of extrapolation from a single physical source.

3. Redox behaviour

The naturally occurring binuclear compounds are capable of undergoing reversible two-electron transfer, and are characterised by high redox potentials relative to those for most simple copper(II) complexes. The values reported for fungal laccase, tree laccase and tyrosinase are $+782$ mV,[240] $+434$ mV[241] and $+360$ mV[242] respectively. No mixed valence intermediates resulting from one-electron processes have yet been detected in either the oxidation or reduction of Type 3 copper. In order to fully mimic the biosite a model system would need to incorporate both of these features, in addition to magnetic and spectral properties.

In simple copper(II) complexes high redox potentials have been achieved by distortion of the molecular shape towards tetrahedral geometry, or by incorporation of soft donor atoms in order to favour copper(I).[148] Two potential donor groups for involvement with tetragonal copper present in dicopper(II) sites are imidazole and thioether—both could arise from the protein chain through histidine and methionine entities. Imidazole has been implicated at the oxyhemocyanin site through EXAFS studies,[206-208] and the copper(II) ion in superoxide dismutase, which is bound to histidines, has a redox potential of $+420$ mV.[242] EXAFS has ruled out a thioether involvement in the first coordination shell of hemocyanin—optical spectra having previously provided an ambiguity showing the plausibility of either donor set in Type 3 centres.

From this brief account of some of the physical properties of the bimetallobiosites it is apparent that the construction of a model must incorporate all facets of these properties in order to be fully effective in a physical sense.

B. Models for heterobinuclear sites

1. Cytochrome *c* oxidase

Until the recent EXAFS[187,189] reports on this site it had remained elusive and posed many challenges. The paucity of available information on simple heterobinuclear systems had not helped in the solution of the problem and it was not until the 1980s that binucleating model compounds appeared. Prior to this, however, a hypothesis had been advanced for a bridged Fe^{III}—O—Cu^{II} site based on the probable efficacy of the catalytic cycle using this site and on the use of magnetic data.[185] The strength of the antiferromagnetic coupling in the oxidase is given by $-J > 200$ cm^{-1}; Fe^{III}—O—Fe^{III} dimers have $-J = 95$–146 cm^{-1} and, as has been commented on earlier, there are diamagnetic dicopper(II) complexes with oxygen in the bridge (as —OR, or carbonate). This suggested that the Fe^{III}—O—Cu^{II} moiety should be strongly coupled. An imidazolato model was disregarded as the Mn^{II}-imidazolato-Co^{II} complex of the bis-porphyrin, **73**, gave only $J = -5$ cm^{-1}. This system was seen as a good spin model for cytochrome *c* oxidase because it has potentially interacting $S = \frac{5}{2}$ and $S = \frac{1}{2}$ centres, and the unpaired electrons are in an orbital orientation likely to exist in the oxidase.[113] Furthermore the coupling in imidazolato-bridged dicopper(II) complexes is of the order $-J \sim 16$–87 cm^{-1}.[244] However, a better justification for dismissing the imidazole bridge on magnetic grounds would come from the synthesis and study of an iron(III) porphyrin-copper(II) complex. The structure of the Fe^{III}—O—Fe^{III} complex of **73** has been solved[113] and is seen as further suggestive of an oxo-bridged heterobinuclear moiety in cytochrome *c* oxidase: the exchange coupling was $-J = 107.5$ cm^{-1}.

A "picket fence porphyrin"-based model has been synthesised and studied (Fig. 17).[137–138] The long copper–chloride and iron–chloride bonds (average

Fig. 17. Schematic representation of the binucleated iron(III)–copper(II) complex of **85**.

2.47 Å) indicates a weak bridging between the metals. The temperature dependence of the magnetic moment is unusual and has been interpreted, with the aid of Moßbauer spectroscopy, in terms of a spin-equilibrium between high spin $(S = \frac{5}{2})$ and intermediate spin $(S = \frac{3}{2})$ iron(III). The spin-spin coupling between the iron(III) and copper(II) appears to be very small, or zero. A cyano-bridged derivative of the same system has magnetic properties indicative of a non-interacting Cu^{II} $(S = \frac{1}{2})$, Fe^{III} $(S = \frac{1}{2})$ system. Therefore although the components of the Fe^{III}—Cu^{II} pair have been assembled the magnetism has not been reproduced. This may be due to the long separation between the metal ions, or from a mismatch of orbitals denying a pathway for superexchange (Fig. 18a).

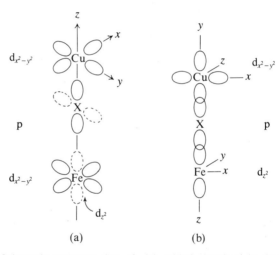

Fig. 18. Schematic representation of: (a) orbitals involved in the bridge of $[Fe(85)-X-Cu]^{2+}$; and (b) the orientation of orbitals predicted for significant exchange interaction between the metal centres.

In order to overcome this problem a strapped porphyrin, **49**, was synthesised to facilitate σ-overlap (via the p-orbitals of a bridging ligand) of the singly occupied $d_{x^2-y^2}$ Cu(II) with the d_{z^2} of the Fe^{III} (Fig. 18b).[90] Compounds of the type $[Fe(P)X$—$Cu(NS_2)Y]X$ were prepared where for example $X = ClO_4^-$ and $Y = {}^-OH$; $X = BF_4^-$ and $Y = {}^-OH$. The magnetic data again show that the exchange coupling effects are minimal.

In contrast to the lack of exchange shown here the Cu^{II}–Fe^{III} complex of the compartmental ligand, **22**, $R^1 = CH_2CH_2$, $CuFe(L)Cl$, H_2O, CH_3OH, was found to have $-J = 89.2$ cm^{-1} and using an orbital model the stabilisation of the spin quintet is ascribed to the overlap of orbitals built up from the $d_{x^2-y^2}$ metal orbitals pointing out along the equatorial bonds around the metal centres.[244] This appears to be a most efficient pathway for obtaining strong antiferromagnetic coupling between Cu^{II} and high-spin Fe^{III}.

A magnetically coupled heme-copper(II) species has been reported by Chang,[91] the Fe—O—Cu complex of the strapped porphyrin, **50**, having an antiferromagnetic coupling of $-J = 44$ cm^{-1}. FeCu(O)L(OAc), H_2O also has visible spectra similar to those for μ-oxo iron(III) dimers. This compound represents the first successful attempt at achieving any significant spin-coupling between Cu(II) and a high-spin Fe^{III} heme. The β-substitution of the bridge in the heme may be significant, and it is postulated that the system may also require an axial imidazole ligand. The EXAFS studies on the site in the oxidase have suggested a structure as in Fig. 11; the bridging moiety is given as a bridging cysteinyl S-atom.[189]

2. Superoxide dismutase (SOD)

This site has been established by X-ray crystallography[177] and therefore corroborative models can be sought. Although copper(II)–zinc hetero-bimetallic complexes have been isolated, none have been prepared with imidazolate bridges. Several dicopper(II) complexes with this bridge have been prepared. These are of value as derivatives may be made from (SOD) in which other metals are substituted for copper(II) and/or zinc(II). Thus the SOD protein which contains copper(II) in both binding sites exhibits a moderately strong antiferromagnetic coupling with $-J \sim 26$ cm^{-1}.[180]

In order to corroborate the nature of the homobinuclear site in Cu_2Cu_2SOD, and to show that it is similar to that in Cu_2Zn_2SOD, Lippard and his coworkers have investigated the properties of dicopper(II) imidazolate bridged complexes of **29**, **98** and a series of related bis-ligand binuclear complexes such as **110**.[152-154, 245-247] A study of the magnetic properties[245] reveals J values from -16 to -90 cm^{-1}. These values are environment sensitive: for the dicopper(II) complex of **98** $J = -81.8$ cm^{-1}, and for the dicopper(II) complexes, **110**, J ranges from -16 to -38 cm^{-1} paralleling the first pK_a of the free imidazole used in bridge formation.

These latter results are accounted for by a σ-exchange pathway, the electronic features that will stabilise the imidazolium cation will also enhance the interaction between the N lone pairs of the imidazole and the σ-symmetric $d_{x^2-y^2}$ orbitals of the copper(II). For the former results the larger value is rationalised on the basis of the near collinearity of the Cu—N (imidazole) bonds which increases the interaction of the N lone pairs with each other and leads to an increased antiferromagnetic coupling. The magnetic susceptibility data for **99** can be interpreted in terms of two J values: that for the copper pair linked by the binucleating ligand incorporated imidazole (parallel) is

imid $X = $ $(J = -38.1 \text{ cm}^{-1})$

$$\left[\text{[Cu complex structure 110]} \right]^{3+}$$

110

$= $ $(J = -16.9 \text{ cm}^{-1})$

$= $ $(J = -29.8 \text{ cm}^{-1})$

-87.6 cm^{-1} and that for the copper pair linked by the bridging imidazole (perpendicular) is -35.0 cm^{-1}.

The existence of an imidazole-bridged copper pair in Cu_2Cu_2SOD is therefore strongly supported by the above results, which also provide a basis for the identity of imidazole-bridged metal centres in other bimetallo-biomolecules.

Dicopper(II) complexes of extendable macrocycles have also been shown to incorporate imidazole into the cavity between the metals. The crystal structures of the imidazolate-bridged dicopper(II) complexes of the ligands **29**, **36** ((R = NOON) and **36** (R = NSN) have been solved. $[Cu_2(imH)_2(im)29](ClO_4)_3$ has two distorted trigonal-bipyramidal metal ions present circumscribed by the ligand and each bound to a terminal tripodal component, a bridging imidazolate and a neutral imidazole molecule.[245] No magnetic data were given. In $[Cu_2(im)36(R = NSN)](ClO_4)_3$,[76] and $[Cu_2(im)36(R = NOON)](ClO_4)_3, 2H_2O$,[79] the macrocycle encases the two copper ions which are internally bridged by the imidazolate anion. Each copper(II) has a square planar environment being also bound to the terminal three nitrogen atoms of the diimine moiety. The Cu—Cu distances are 5.87 Å and 5.99 Å respectively and the imidazolate anion intersects the two trimethine planes at angles (γ) of 88.6 and 90, and 68.8 and 79.1° respectively. The J values are -21.2 and -21.0 cm^{-1}, and it has been proposed[248] that a correlation can be made between the magnitude of the coupling constant and the Cu—N—C bond angle α (Fig. 19), rather than the dihedral angle (γ). In these compounds the α values are relatively constant; 128, 133° (R = NSN) and 131, 122° (R = NOON), whereas the dihedral angle changes markedly, and similar results have been observed for other dicopper(II) species.[248]

In addition to the magnetic studies the macrocycle, **29**, has been shown to convey an unusual stability, similar to that observed in forms of bovine erythrocyte SOD, to the imidazole-bridged copper(II) species in which the imidazole bridge is the major component in solution from pH 6 to 10.[247] This

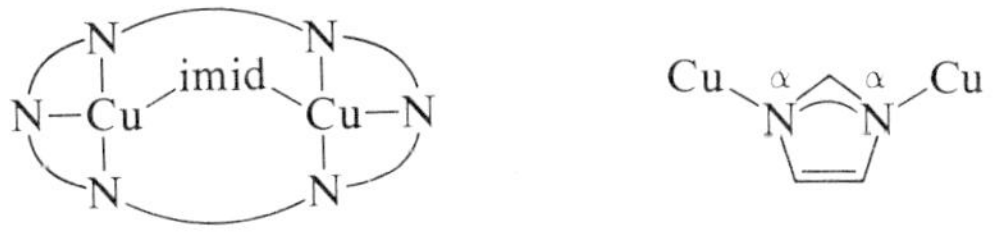

Fig. 19. Schematic representation of imidazole bridged dicopper(II) complex.

is in contrast with the acyclic bis-ligand complexes, **110**, in which the bridged species only predominates in solution over the narrow range $8.5 < pH < 9.5$.

C. Models for homobinuclear sites

The work so far reported using binucleating ligands as homobinuclear site models has centred on the mimicry of dicopper(II) sites. Latterly the focus has been on oxyhemocyanin analogues, stimulated by EXAFS information, but earlier studies were more catholic in nature seeking to find any points of comparison between the proposed model and the site. Many of the compounds described in Section B provide complexes having reduced magnetic moments or individual properties related to the biosites, and so the next section will concentrate on those results seen as being the most appropriate.

Compartmental ligands were first used and these gave several interesting results. Lintvedt and his coworkers have carried out an extensive study of a series of homobinuclear copper(II) complexes of β-triketones, **3**.[16] Although not strictly binucleating ligands, they are the parent compounds for the "side-off" acyclic compartmental ligands, **21**, and closely structurally related. The complexes have been shown to mimic the magnetic properties of the Type 3 sites in that they are heavily magnetically coupled, e.g. Cu_2BAA_2 (BAA = **3**, R = CH_3, $R^1 = C_6H_5$) is effectively diamagnetic at room temperature ($-2J = 740$ cm^{-1}). A further point of comparison was the unique electrochemical behaviour exhibited by five members of the series in that the binuclear copper(II) complexes may be reduced in two sequential, reversible one-electron steps having identical $E_{1/2}$ values. This ability to transfer two electrons at a given potential encourages the use of these compounds on simple site models but unfortunately low reduction potentials (-220 to -410 mV) are too low to make them effective models.[249]

Compound **111** is representative of a group of "end-off" compartmental ligands which provide examples of high redox potential binuclear copper(II) complexes which also have moderate to strong antiferromagnetic interactions.[204] The $\mu_{B.M.}$ at room temperature is 0.6 per copper(II) ion, and two overlapping reduction peaks are seen at $+329$ and $+209$ mV. Titration of this group of compounds with ascorbate monitoring shows that the complex acts as a 2e donor towards this reductant. The complexes also show an absorption

$$\left[\begin{array}{c} \text{structure 111} \end{array}\right]^{2+}$$

111

band in the region 317–335 nm assigned to a $s(\sigma) \rightarrow Cu(d_{x^2-y^2})$ ligand to metal CT band.

A second group of "end-off" compartmental ligands based on **13** and **14** has been shown by Gagné[29] to have redox potentials approaching those of the bimetallobiosites. However, the homobinuclear copper(I) derivatives of these complexes show no reactivity towards carbon monoxide as does hemocyanin. The oxidation/reduction of these complexes occurs in well-separated steps contrasting with the available information for the biosites.

Gagné has also shown[28] that in dicopper(II) complexes of the macrocycle **4** two well-separated quasi-reversible one-electron reductions (-523 and -913 mV) occur. No evidence for mixed valence forms of Type 3 sites has been reported. The Cu(II)–Cu(I) complex of **4** has been characterised by X-ray crystallography.

The dicopper(II) complex of the polythia-cylindrical macrotricycle **56** gives a high redox potential.[98] A detailed study shows that the two well-separated copper ions (5.62 Å apart) are reduced in separate monoelectronic steps at the same potential and so this complex represents a dielectronic receptor unit. There is essentially no antiferromagnetic coupling present in this molecule. The redox behaviour is attributed to the presence of the thioether donors and the distorted copper(II) geometry. In contrast the dicopper(II)-tetrazido complex of the polythia macrocycle, **31**, in which a di-azido bridge is present and the coppers are 5.14 Å apart is completely diamagnetic.[67]

Recent studies, linked with the available information from EXAFS, have shown that it is possible to set out on the route to a corroborative model for oxyhemocyanin.

Osborn, using the bis-macrocycle, **69**, synthesised the dicopper(II) complex $[Cu_2(OH)69](BF_4)_3$.[110] In this molecule a bridging hydroxide links two copper ions (Cu—Cu, 3.384 Å) and each copper is approximately square pyramidal with the macrocyclic donors providing the base and the bridging hydroxide the apex (Fig. 20). The $-2J$ value obtained from magnetic susceptibility data is 850 cm^{-1}, and the epr is characteristic of a dimeric unit. The very strong antiferromagnetic interaction is related to the large

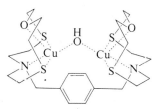

Fig. 20. Schematic representation of [Cu$_2$OH**69**]$^{3+}$.

Cu—O—Cu angle (132.2°) and to the presence of the bridging OH group in both basal planes of the binuclear unit allowing for good overlap with the Cu(d$_{x^2-y^2}$) orbitals. The ligand is also shown to be conformationally versatile as the dicopper(II) complex [Cu$_2$(NO$_2$)$_2$**69**](BF$_4$)$_4$ shows an opened structure (Fig. 21) in which the coppers are 11.26 Å apart.

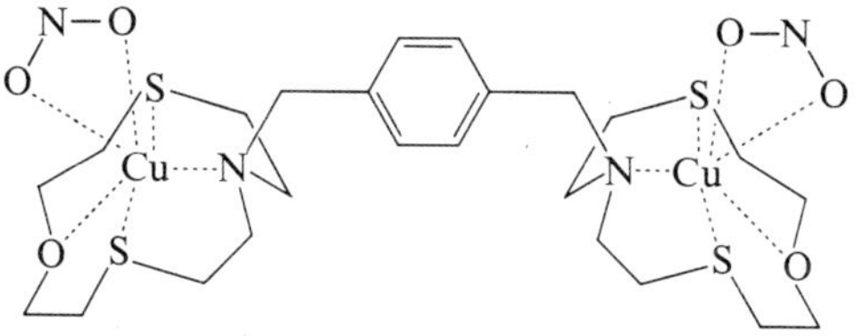

Fig. 21. Schematic representation of [Cu$_2$(NO$_2$)$_2$**69**]$^{4+}$.

The usefulness of a ligand with conformational flexibility is demonstrated in this work, and the proposal was made that, by analogy, a single-bridging phenolate from a tyrosine residue could satisfy the structural and magnetic requirements of a Type 3 site.

Lippard prepared the complex [Cu$_2$OH.ClO$_4$.L](ClO$_4$)$_2$.CHCl$_3$ from the extendable macrocycle, **39**.[250] In this complex (Fig. 22) the two copper atoms are coordinated to the diethylenetriamine poles of the macrocycle, and are

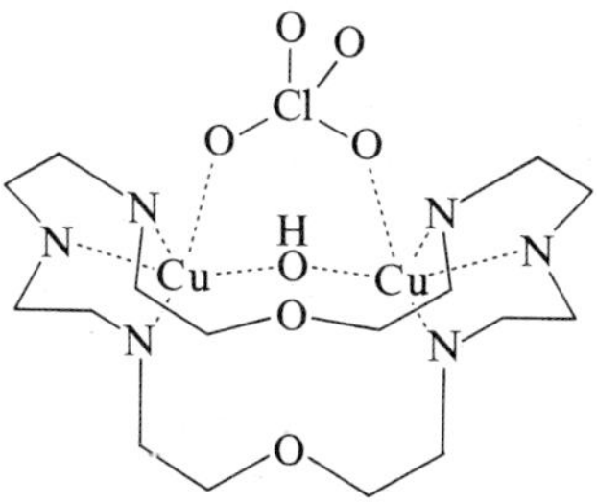

Fig. 22. Schematic representation of [Cu$_2$OH.ClO$_4$.**29**]$^{2+}$.

bridged by a single hydroxide ion at a distorted square planar site. The Cu—O—Cu angle is 143.7°, the coppers are 3.64 Å and a strong antiferromagnetic coupling is determined, $J \sim -500$ cm^{-1}. This large value may arise from the greater sp character of the bridging oxygen orbitals which arises on increasing the bond angle; it is unlikely to arise from the ClO_4^- presence as this is only very weakly coordinated to the copper. The stability of the bridge is demonstrated by the retention of the 637 nm visible absorption band over the pH range 6–11 in aqueous solution. There is also a band at 330 nm in the optical spectrum.

The remarkable similarity of the exchange coupling constant, the presence of the band at 330 nm, and the similarity of the Cu—Cu distance to that reported from EXAFS studies on oxyhemocyanin support the viability of a Cu—O(R)—Cu unit in the biological chromophore. The proposal that the endogeneous protein bridging unit might simply be the hydroxide ion is made as a consequence of the stability of the $[Cu_2OH]^{3+}$ unit.

A similar suggestion, namely that oxide or hydroxide might be the leading candidate for the bridging ligand in oxyhemocyanin comes from a recent study on the absorption and CD spectra of oxyhemocyanin from *Sepioteuthis lessonia*.[251] An absorption band, ca 650–700 nm, suggests that the copper(II) has a tetragonal geometry. No CT band was found in the 400–450 nm region implying that a tyrosine residue would not be involved as the bridging ligand as phenolate oxygen coordination would provide a band in this region.

Extendable macrocycles have provided further examples of $[Cu_2OH]^{3+}$ units. A hydroxy-bridged dicopper(II) complex of **36** (R = NOON) has been synthesised and the structure solved.[79] The complex $[Cu_2OH$ **36** (R = NOON)$](ClO_4)_3$, H_2O has each copper bound to the terminal diimine unit and the square plane is completed by the bridging hydroxy group *trans* to the pyridine. In addition each copper has an axial ligand, in one case a water molecule and in the other a perchlorate anion. The Cu—Cu distance is 3.57 Å and the Cu—O—Cu angle is 141.7°; an antiferromagnetic interaction with $J = -121.0$ cm^{-1} has been found, and the comment made that J might be sensitive not only to the Cu—O—Cu angle but also to non-bridging ligand modifications.

The crystal structure of $[Cu_2OH$ **36** (R = pd)$](ClO_4)_3$, $2H_2O$ has also been solved.[75] Again each copper is bound to the terminal unit and the square plane completed by a shared hydroxide. The two metals are also linked in a shared axial position by a second oxygen atom, presumably from a water molecule. The Cu—Cu distance is 3.145 Å and the Cu—O—Cu angles are 110.3° and 77.3° respectively. The J value is -32 cm^{-1} corresponding to the reduction in Cu—O—Cu angle. The analogous methoxy-bridged complex shows $J = -53$ cm^{-1}.

A further study on a potential model system for oxyhemocyanin was reported by Reed and coworkers[132] using the polypodal ligand **81**. The dicopper(II) complexes, $[Cu_2X \ 81]2Y^-$ were obtained.

Although the complex where $X^- = OAc^-$, $Y^- = ClO_4^-$ is essentially spin free, most derivatives $(X^- = NO_2^-$, pyrazolate, etc.) have reduced moments. The azide complex was found to be diamagnetic at room temperature $(X^- = N_3^-$, $Y^- = BF_4^-)$ and so, as azidomethemocyanin is also diamagnetic, a crystal structure was carried out. The copper atoms are each coordinated to a tertiary amine and to two N-ethylbenzimidazoles. The bridging alkoxide, and 1,3 azide bridge complete the five coordination and the coppers are 3.615 Å apart (Fig. 23).

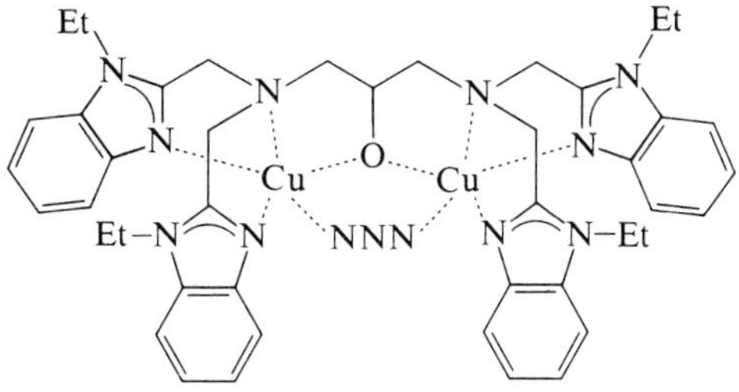

Fig. 23. Schematic representation of $[Cu_2(N_3)\textbf{81}]^{2+}$.

The alkoxide bridge, with a large Cu—O—Cu angle of 136.9°, is suggested as providing the major superexchange pathway, although azide is also known to act as a useful mediator of coupling.

The structural data and diamagnetism of this complex make it a useful model for oxy- and methemocyanin derivatives. There is a spectroscopic resemblance to azidomethemocyanin—in acetonitrile solution there is a uv maximum at 364 nm ($\varepsilon = 2380 \ M^{-1} \ cm^{-1}$) and a visible band at 695 nm ($\varepsilon = 195 \ M^{-1} \ cm^{-1}$), comparing with bands at 360 nm ($\varepsilon \sim 1500$) and 710 ($\varepsilon \sim 200$) in azidomethemocyanin (*B. canaliculatum*).[252] The ir shows an intense band in the region 2020–2040 cm^{-1} and this is assigned to $v_{asym} N_3^-$: in azidomethemocyanin this band is at 2042 cm^{-1}. The metal–metal distance, and metal–ligand bond lengths are also very comparable to the EXAFS data. These features led to a suggestion that alkoxide from serine or threonine becomes a viable candidate for the endogeneous bridge.

By using model systems in conjunction with EXAFS and other physical studies a picture is emerging for the dicopper site in oxyhemocyanin and related species. In contrast a recent review[193] notes the paucity of suitable model compounds for the confacial biooctahedral structure in hemerythrin, and comments on the difficulty in analysing the magnetic, spectroscopic and crystallographic properties of such a structure. This raises a challenge to the synthetic chemist for no one has yet developed a reversible dioxygen binding system devoid of heme, or utilising diiron centres within binucleating ligands.

D. Reactivity studies

It is apparent from the preceding discussion that a substantial effort has been made in synthesising and characterising binucleating ligands and their complexes, and in relating the physicochemical properties and structural features of the bimetal complexes to those of bimetallobiosites. In contrast there is, at present, a limited literature concerning the reactivity of complexes derived from binucleating ligands, and what there is is concentrated on dicopper(II) species.

Efforts have been directed towards the elucidation of the role of copper in catecholase and cresolase activity for which a mechanism involving a dicopper(II) intermediate such as **112** has been proposed.[253]

112

The work of Rogic has demonstrated that it is possible to efficiently catalyse the conversion of catechols with dioxygen to 1,2-benzoquinones using copper(II) chloride or $Cu_2(BAA)_2$ in the presence of triethylamine, or copper(II) species produced by the reaction of copper(I) chloride with oxygen in an aprotic solvent in the absence of added base.[254] The reaction sequence involves the formation of a dicopper(II) catecholate intermediate, electron transfer from the aromatic ring to two copper(II) centres in the intermediate giving two copper(I) centres and a 1,2-benzoquinone, irreversible reaction of the generated copper(I) species with dioxygen to give the active copper(II) reagent and reaction of this reagent with the catechol to give water and to regenerate the dicopper(II) catecholate (Fig. 24).

The conclusion drawn from detailed studies on these systems was that the premise that a specialist reagent in which the bimetal centre could be held in a highly organised environment in order to facilitate efficient electron transfer is too restrictive. The copper(II) centres present in the dicopper(II) catecholate intermediate generated *in situ* are quite effectively held by the substrate and allow for the occurrence of the electron transfer process. The suggestion was made that it is attractive to consider that Type 3 copper activity might occur via a similar mechanism, and that the role of the dioxygen in the catalytic cycle

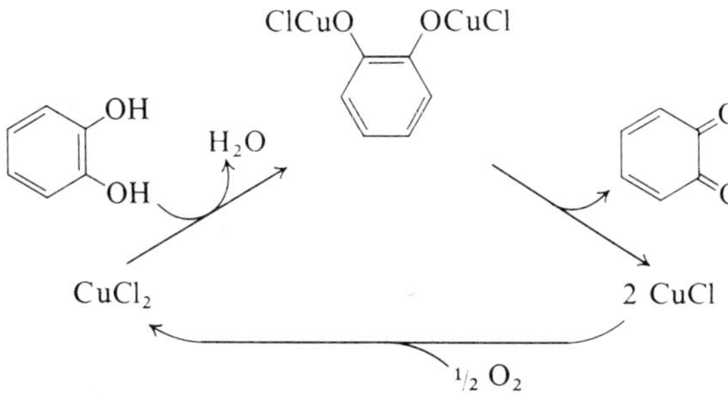

Fig. 24. Copper catalysed oxidation of catechol.

may also be to act as a thermodynamic driving force by reoxidising any generated copper(I) species back to active copper(II) species.

Lintvedt[255] has shown that the binuclear copper(II) complex, $Cu_2(BAA)_2$, catalyses the reaction of 3,5-di-*tert*-butylcatechol (DTBC) with oxygen in the presence of a molar equivalent of triethylamine, to give a near quantitative yield of 3,5-di-*tert*-butylbenzoquinone (DTBQ). The reaction is first order in catalyst and catechol, and zero order in dioxygen and base, with a rate constant of $10^{-1} M^{-1} s^{-1}$ consistent with a rate-determining catechol–catalyst association followed by electron transfer and reoxidation of the catalyst with dioxygen.

In contrast under anaerobic conditions little product was given in the reaction of catechols with $Cu_2(BAA)_2$;[254] however, if copper(II) chloride was added a small quantity of quinone was produced. This is seen to reflect the greater thermodynamic stability of the $Cu_2(BAA)_2$/CuCl pair relative to the Cu(HBAA)/$CuCl_2$ pair, as any copper(I) species resulting from the electron transfer from catechol to $Cu_2(BAA)_2$ must undergo an exchange with $CuCl_2$ present to give the $Cu_2(BAA)_2$/CuCl pair and so assist the conversion of the catechol to the quinone. Attempts to reduce $Cu_2(BAA)_2$ did not lead to a product having significant stability.

The catalytic oxidation of DBTC to DBTQ has been observed using dicopper complexes of the binucleating ligand, 103,[255] and putative intermediate steps have been identified spectroscopically. The binuclear copper(II) complexes, $(103)Cu_2^{II}X_3$ (X = Cl⁻, OAc⁻), may be reduced to the epr silent dicopper(I) complexes $(103)Cu_2^{I}QX$ (Q = DBTQ) on addition of one equivalent of catechol. Addition of excess catechol and dioxygen results in the catalytic oxidation of the excess catechol to quinone at a fast rate, and when all the catechol is consumed the complex $(103)Cu_2^{II}Q$ is detected. A tentative mechanism for the catecholase cycle has been presented (Fig. 25).

Complex (1) is rapidly converted to complex (3) via the transient copper(II)–catechol complex (2). The intermediate (4) is postulated such that

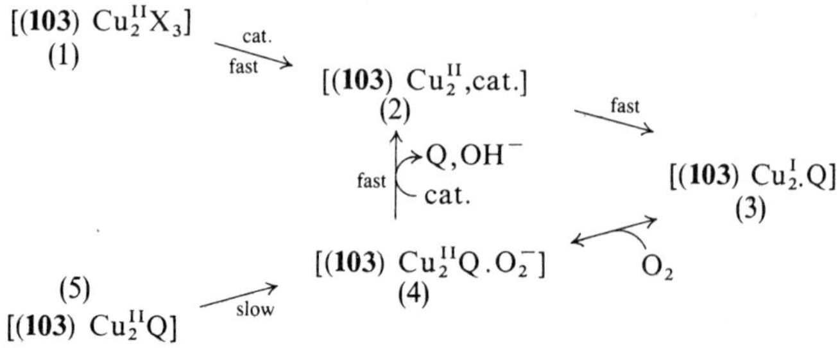

$$[(103) \ Cu_2^{II}X_3]$$
$$(1)$$
$\xrightarrow[\text{fast}]{\text{cat.}}$

$$[(103) \ Cu_2^{II},cat.]$$
$$(2)$$
$\xrightarrow{\text{fast}}$

$\text{fast} \left\{ \begin{array}{l} \nearrow Q,OH^- \\ \nwarrow cat. \end{array} \right.$

$$[(103) \ Cu_2^{I}.Q]$$
$$(3)$$

$$[(103) \ Cu_2^{II}Q.O_2^-]$$
$$(4)$$
$\swarrow \nearrow \quad O_2$

$$(5)$$
$$[(103) \ Cu_2^{II}Q] \xrightarrow{\text{slow}}$$

Fig. 25. Mechanism for catecholase reactivity involving [**103**, $Cu_2^{II}Cl_3$].

the cycle can proceed as oxidation of (3) to (5) is about five times slower than the catalytic rate, and (5) does not react significantly with the catechol. The rate-determining step is the conversion of (3) to (4) which is rapidly scavenged by the catechol to turn the cycle. (4) can also form the terminal product (5) at a slow rate. Complex (1) has also been stated to possess phenolase activity.

Further studies on the reaction of DBTC with binuclear copper complexes have been carried out by Kida[257] and by Vigee.[258,259] The former study concerned the reaction between a range of mono- and binuclear copper(II) complexes and both ascorbic acid and DBTC. Only one complex derived from a binucleating ligand was included, and the general conclusion was that mononuclear copper(II) complexes having distorted tetrahedral, or trigonal-bipyramidal copper present, and some binuclear complexes were readily reduced by the 2e donors. Square-planar mononuclear copper complexes were not reduced. The reactions were monitored spectrophotometrically; for ascorbic acid the loss of colour and spectral characteristics on reduction were observed, and for DBTC the ingrowth of the characteristic DBTQ band at 400 nm ($\varepsilon = 1900 \ M^{-1} \ cm^{-1}$) in ethanol was used. The binuclear complexes **113–116** showed reductions with ascorbic acid which could be reversed on exposure to the atmosphere, and served as good catalysts for the oxidation of DTBC giving results in line with those obtained for $Cu_2(BAA)_2$. In contrast the dicopper(II) complex of the binucleating ligand **105** (l = 3, m = 2) gave little or no activity. This was ascribed to the availability of a "steric match" between donor and acceptor in the series **113–116** (Fig. 26) which would not occur in **105** where the distance between the two copper atoms (> 5 Å) would inhibit this effect.

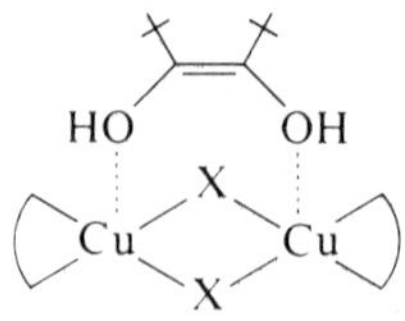

Fig. 26. "Steric match" between catechol and a binuclear centre.

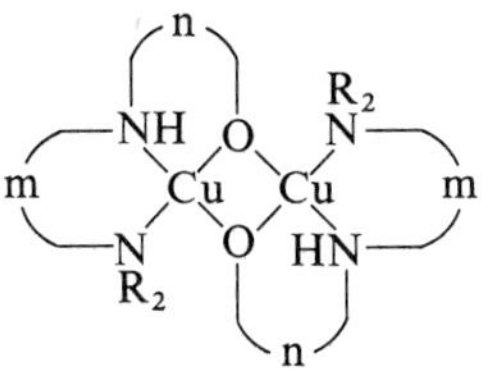

113

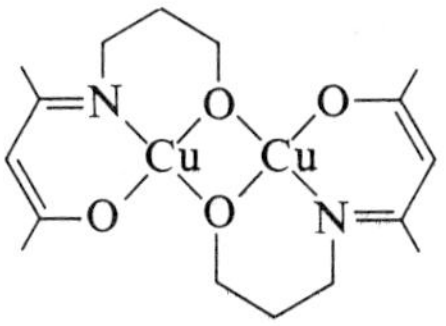

114

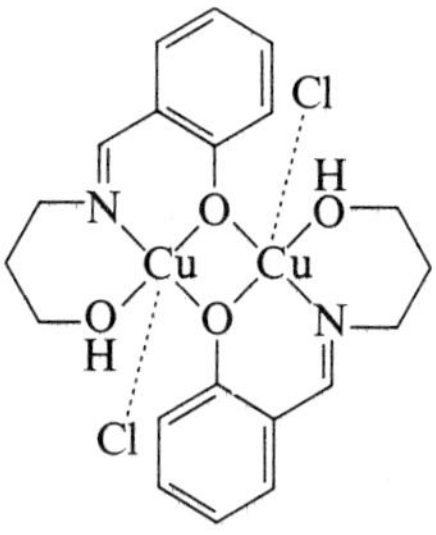

115

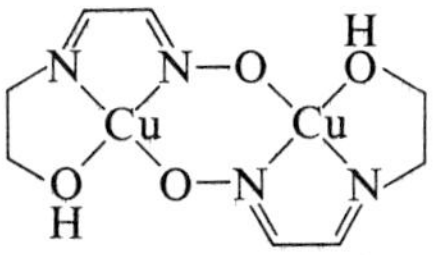

116

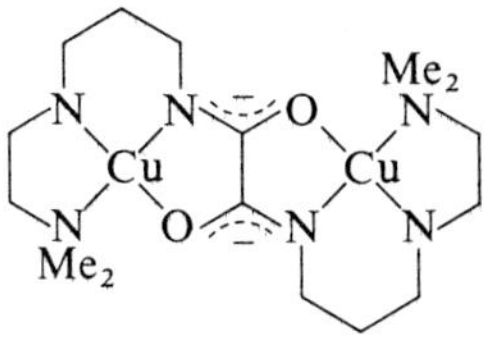

Cu$_2$ **105** (l = 3, m = 2)

Vigee has tested the catecholase activity of two groups of dicopper(II) complexes derived from binucleating ligands. The water-soluble binuclear complexes **117** were prepared and characterised and showed an ability to catalyse the oxidation of several substituted catechols.[258] The results showed that **117**-lys was about an order of magnitude more active than **117**-arg and two orders of magnitude more active than **117**-glu. This difference is not

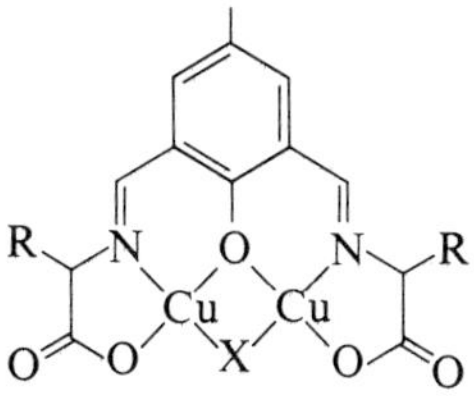

117

Lys R = $(CH_2)_4NH_2$, X = Cl
Glu R = $(CH_2)_2COOH$, X = OH
Arg R = $(CH_2)_3NHCNH_2$, X = Cl
$\qquad\qquad\quad \overset{\|}{NH}$

entirely understood and both steric and inductive contributions from the amino-acid centres could influence any activity, as could also the chloride bridge. Correlation of the rate of oxygen uptake to the moles of quinone formed shows that 4 mol of dioxygen are used for 1 mol of catechol oxidised. These results indicate an excessive uptake of dioxygen relative to the stoichiometry of the catecholase equation and may be accounted for by further reaction of the quinone with dioxygen.

A similar result had been found for a different group of complexes, **4** Cu$_2$Cl$_2$, 6H$_2$O; **12** Cu$_2$Cl; [**14** Cu$_2$OH](ClO$_4$)$_2$ and [**14**-red.Cu$_2$OH](ClO$_4$)$_2$, H$_2$O in which a decrease in the pH of the reaction media, precipitation of a black precipitate, and complex product spectra were observed.[259] Possible candidates for products included *cis, cis*-muconic acid, α-hydroxymuconic-ε-semi-aldehyde and oligomeric materials. A tentative scheme was presented,

and the conclusion drawn that the oxidation reaction is more complex than indicated by the simple catecholase equation. Similarities between the visible spectra of the models and the metalloenzymes were noted. A band, ca 600 nm, was detected for both systems and suggests a similar copper(II) coordination environment could exist for both species. However, there is a much enhanced catecholase activity for the enzyme over the model and this is presumed to result from factors ascribed mostly to the accompanying protein matrix. For example the matrix might induce a stereochemistry at the metal which would lead to a favourable redox potential, or to an enhanced metal–substrate interaction.

The reaction of ascorbate with a dicopper(II) complex has been noted by Urbach.[42] In the reaction of $[\mathbf{13}\ Cu_2OH](ClO_4)_2$ with sodium ascorbate an intense purple colour is observed, and this is ascribed to the formation of a weak adduct $[Cu_2L(OH)^{++}\ ascorbate^-]$ in which the colour stems from an intense charge transfer from the ligand to the metal. Addition of excess ascorbate to an air-saturated solution of the binuclear complex gives first the intense purple colour and this fades rapidly as the ascorbate is oxidised. The corresponding chloro-bridged species are more easily reduced and mono-nuclear copper(I) derivatives of the potentially binucleating ligand are found.[260]

The reaction of several binuclear copper(II) complexes with the one-electron donor N,N,N′,N′-tetramethyl-*p*-phenylenediamine (TMPD) has been discussed by Kida.[261,262] TMPD is a colourless compound but its oxidised form is blue and shows strong absorptions at 560 and 608 nm in alcohol. No remarkable changes in colour were detected when TMPD was mixed with planar mononuclear copper(II) complexes and allowed to stand at 20 °C for several hours under aerobic conditions. In contrast when TMPD and a binuclear complex were added together in methanol under aerobic conditions an intense blue colour developed immediately. If the same reaction was carried out under dinitrogen then little formation of $TMPD^+$ was detected. Consequently the results are seen to indicate that the oxidation of TMPD required both dioxygen and the binuclear complex to be present. A range of binuclear complexes was investigated (**113**–**116**, **105** (l = 3, m = 2), **21** (R = CH_3), **23** (R^1 = CH_2CH_2)) and their catalytic activity related to the reduction potential and molecular structure. The higher activity was found to correspond with the most positive reduction potential (**113**, Me-3-2) > (**113**, Et-2-3) > (**112**, H-3-3) > (**113**). The complexes derived from **105**, **21** and **23** showed practically no activity. This was attributed to the long copper–copper distance in **105**, and to the presence of dissimilar adjacent coordination sets in **21** and **23**.

The proposal is made that an intermediate complex **118** formed from TMPD, dioxygen and the dicopper(II) complex plays an important role in the

$$\begin{array}{c} TMPD-Cu\cdots O \\ | \quad\;\; | \\ TMPD-Cu\cdots O \end{array}$$

118

catalytic reaction by facilitating a two-electron transfer process as a concerted reaction. Such a mechanism would account for the high activity of those complexes having Cu—Cu distances in the range 3.0–3.5 Å. As this distance in **21** and **23** is ~3.0 Å factors other than simple structural parameters are probably involved.

Activation of dioxygen by binuclear copper(I) complexes has been observed. The reaction of dioxygen with the dicopper(I) complex of the polypodal ligand **75** (meta-XYL(py)) leads to the isolation of **76**[121] when methanol-$CHCl_3$ is the solvent; if methanol is absent the μ-hydroxy, μ-phenoxy derivative is formed. The incorporation of dioxygen into the xylyl moiety is important in terms of metal-catalysed oxygenation and because of the similarity of the action to that of copper mono-oxygenases such as tyrosinase. The μ-phenoxy bridges are also important because of the interest in establishing the role of a μ-phenoxy bridge in bimetallobiosites of oxyhemocyanin and Type 3 copper centres.

The extendable macrocycle **32** (R = H) is obtained by borohydride reduction of $Pb_2(35)(SCN)_4$.[68] The dicopper(I) complex, $Cu_2(32)(ClO_4)_2$ is a bright yellow diamagnetic solid which turns green on exposure to dioxygen in solution and, less rapidly, in the solid state. The rapid absorption of 1 mol of dioxygen by 1 mol of the binuclear copper(I) complex, in acetonitrile, is followed by a slower anaerobic oxidative dehydrogenation of the ligand by the bound dioxygen. This regenerates the copper(I) centres so that the cycle may

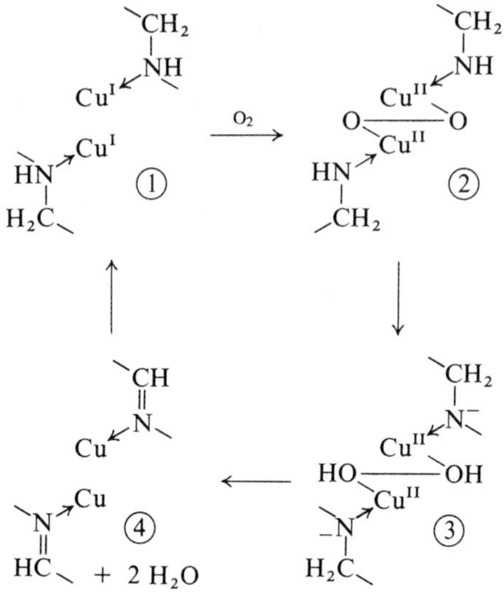

Fig. 27. Mechanism for activation of dioxygen by $Cu_2 33(ClO_4)_2$.

be repeated. A possible mechanism for the cycle has been proposed (Fig. 27). The formation of of a μ-peroxo-dicopper(II) intermediate is consistent with the observed stoichiometry.

The reaction of dioxygen with a dicopper(I)perchlorate complex of the polypodal ligand, **78**, in DMSO gives a green solution.[129] This colour is not removed completely on flushing with dinitrogen suggesting that the reaction is not completely reversible. If, however, ascorbic acid or hydrazine are added then the solution goes colourless and it is possible to effect several cycles. The uptake of ca 1 mmol O_2/Cu_2^I suggests the presence of a CuO_2Cu species but no Raman bands have been detected for coordinated dioxygen. The copper–copper distance in the complex is 3.04 Å[128] approximately 10% shorter than the 3.39 Å given by one EXAFS study for deoxyhemocyanin[207] and so it is proposed that such complexes might act as models for the hemocyanins.

This is further implied by the observation that in solution the dicopper(I) complex of **80a** undergoes a reversible (though not completely) colour change with alternate bubbling of dioxygen and dinitrogen.[131] Under N_2 a methanol–acetonitrile (1:14) solution of the complex was pale yellow, and on bubbling dioxygen a violet colour developed. When N_2 was bubbled through this solution the colour faded, and O_2 bubbling gave a brownish blue solution. The violet solution gave a broad band around 550–600 nm ($\varepsilon \sim 540$) and this resembles the spectrum oxyhemocyanin from *S. lessoma* where there is a broad band around 560–610 nm ($\varepsilon \sim 500$).[263] The violet species is believed to be due to the formation of a Cu_2—L—O_2 compound.

V. CONCLUSION

This review, which covers the literature available to me up to July, 1982, has as its title a question, "do binucleating ligands have a biological relevance?" From a subjective viewpoint the answer is yes. As has been demonstrated there is now available to the chemist an abundance of binucleating ligands and their bimetallic complexes. Their application to biology must surely be regarded as being relevant, particularly in their use as model systems, both speculative and corroborative, in attempts to understand the metal environments in bimetallobiomolecules. There is a greater difficulty in modelling the function of a site but the first steps have been taken along the path, particularly in the area of homobinuclear copper(II) chemistry.

An apposite concluding remark can be found in Jean-Marie Lehn's review of dimetallic macropolycyclic inclusion complexes;[64] "how promising the future of the chemistry of these systems appears and how much it gives room to the creative imagination and experimental skill of the chemist".

REFERENCES

[1] Robson, R. *Inorg. Nucl. Chem. Lett.* **1970**, *6*, 125.

[2] Robson, R. *Aust. J. Chem.* **1970**, *23*, 2217.

[3] Chatt, J.; Leigh, G. J. *Chem. Soc. Rev.* **1972**, *1*, 121; Newton, W.; Postgate, J. R.; Rodriguez-Barrueco, C. (Eds) *In* "Recent Developments in Nitrogen Fixation"; Academic Press: London, 1977.

[4] Grass, G. "The Tin Drum"; Hermann Luchtchard Verlag GmbH, 1959.

[5] Spiro, T. G. (Ed.) "Copper Proteins"; Wiley-Interscience: New York, 1981.

[6] Sigel, H. (Ed.) "Metals in Biology, No. 12, Properties of Copper"; Marcel Dekker: Basel, 1981; Sigel, H. (Ed.) "Metals in Biology, No. 13, Copper Proteins"; Marcel Dekker: Basel, 1981.

[7] Sykes, A. G. "Advances in Inorganic and Bioinorganic Mechanisms"; Academic Press: London, 1982.

[8] Lamy, J. N.; Lamy, J. (Eds) "Invertebrate O_2-binding Proteins"; Marcel Dekker: Basel, 1981.

[9] Karlin, K. D.; Zubieta, J. (Eds) "Abstracts of the 1st SUNYA Conversation in the Discipline; Inorganic and Biochemical Perspectives in Copper Coordination Chemistry", June 1–4, 1982.

[10] Pilkington, N. H.; Robson, R. *Aust. J. Chem.* **1970**, *23*, 2225.

[11] Hill, H. A. O. *Chem. Brit.* **1976**, *12*, 119.

[12] Holm, R. H. *Chem. Soc. Rev.* **1981**, *10*, 455.

[13] Coucouvannis, D. *Acc. Chem. Res.* **1981**, *14*, 201.

[14] Harris, C. M.; Sinn, E. *J. Inorg. Nucl. Chem.* **1968**, *30*, 2723.

[15] Barclay, G. A.; Hoskins, B. F. *J. Chem. Soc.* **1965**, 1979.
[16] Glick, M. D.; Lintvedt, R. L. *Progr. Inorg. Chem.* **1976**, *21*, 233.
[17] Groh, S. *Israel J. Chem.* **1976–7**, *15*, 277.
[18] Casellato, U.; Vigato, P. A.; Fenton, D. E.; Vidali, M. *Chem. Soc. Rev.* **1979**, *8*, 199.
[19] Okawa, H.; Kida, S. *Bull. Chem. Soc. Jap.* **1972**, *45*, 1759.
[20] Okawa, H.; Tokii, T.; Muto, Y.; Kida, S. *Bull. Chem. Soc. Jap.* **1973**, *46*, 2464.
[21] Fenton, D. E.; Gayda, S. E. *J. Chem. Soc. Chem. Commun.* **1974**, 960.
[22] Fenton, D. E.; Gayda, S. E. *J. Chem. Soc. Dalton Trans.* **1977**, 2095.
[23] Okawa, H.; Honda, M.; Kida, S. *Chem. Lett.* **1972**, 1027.
[24] Addison, A. W. *Inorg. Nucl. Chem. Lett.* **1976**, *12*, 899.
[25] Fenton, D. E.; Costes, J-P. Unpublished results.
[26] Hoskins, B. F.; Robson, R.; Williams, G. A. *Inorg. Chim. Acta* **1976**, *16*, 121.
[27] Gagné, R. R.; Koval, C. A.; Smith, T. J. *J. Amer. Chem. Soc.* **1977**, *99*, 8367.
[28] Gagné, R. R.; Koval, C. A.; Smith, T. J.; Cimolino, M. C. *J. Amer. Chem. Soc.* **1979**, *101*, 4571.
[29] Gagné, R. R.; Kreh, R. P.; Dodge, J. A. *J. Amer. Chem. Soc.* **1979**, *101*, 6917.
[30] Gagné, R. R.; Spiro, C. L.; Smith, T. J.; Hannam, C. A.; Thies, W. R.; Shienke, A. K. *J. Amer. Chem. Soc.* **1981**, *103*, 4073.
[31] Lambert, S. L.; Spiro, C. L.; Gagné, R. R.; Hendrickson, D. N. *Inorg. Chem.* **1982**, *21*, 68.
[32] Lambert, S. L.; Hendrickson, D. N. *Inorg. Chem.* **1979**, *18*, 2683.
[33] Spiro, C. L.; Lambert, S. L.; Smith, T. J.; Duesler, E. N.; Gagné, R. R.; Hendrickson, D. N. *Inorg. Chem.* **1981**, *20*, 1229.
[34] Gagné, R. R.; Henling, L. M.; Kistenmacher, T. J. *Inorg. Chem.* **1980**, *19*, 1226.
[35] Hoskins, B. F.; McLeod, N. J.; Schaap, H. A. *Aust. J. Chem.* **1976**, *29*, 515.
[36] Hoskins, B. F.; Williams, G. A. *Aust. J. Chem.* **1975**, *28*, 2593, 2607.
[37] Okawa, H.; Tokii, T.; Nonaka, Y.; Muto, Y.; Kida, S. *Bull. Chem. Soc. Jap.* **1973**, *46*, 1462.
[38] Ichinose, T.; Nishida, Y.; Okawa, H.; Kida, S. *Bull. Chem. Soc. Jap.* **1974**, *47*, 3045.
[39] Dickson, I.; Robson, R. *Inorg. Chem.* **1974**, *13*, 1301.
[40] Okawa, H.; Kida, S. *Bull. Chem. Soc. Jap.* **1971**, *44*, 1172.
[41] Okawa, H.; Kida, S.; Muto, Y.; Tokii, T. *Bull. Chem. Soc. Jap.* **1972**, *45*, 2480.
[42] Grzybowski, J. J.; Merrell, P. H.; Urbach, F. L. *Inorg. Chem.* **1976**, *17*, 3078.
[43] Okawa, H.; Ando, I.; Kida, S. *Bull. Chem. Soc. Jap.* **1974**, *47*, 3041.
[44] McFadyen, W. D.; Robson, R. *J. Coord. Chem.* **1976**, *5*, 49.
[45] Hughes, J. G.; Robson, R. *Inorg. Chim. Acta* **1979**, *36*, 237.
[46] Louey, M.; Nichols, P. D.; Robson, R. *Inorg. Chim. Acta* **1980**, *47*, 87.
[47] Robson, R. *Inorg. Chim. Acta* **1982**, *57*, 71.
[48] Vince, D. Unpublished results quoted in [26].
[49] Hoskins, B. F.; Robson, R.; Schaap, H. A. *Inorg. Nucl. Chem. Lett.* **1975**, *8*, 21.
[50] Lintvedt, R. L.; Glick, M. D.; Tomlonovic, B. K.; Gavel, D. P.; Kuszaj, J. M. *Inorg. Chem.* **1976**, *15*, 1633.
[51] Vidali, M.; Casellato, U.; Vigato, P. A.; Graziani, R. *J. Inorg. Nucl. Chem.* **1976**, *38*, 1453.
[52] Fenton, D. E.; Gayda, S. E. *J. Chem. Soc. Dalton Trans.* **1977**, 2101.
[53] Tanaka, M.; Kitaoka, M.; Okawa, H.; Kida, S. *Bull. Chem. Soc. Jap.* **1976**, *49*, 2469.
[54] Vidali, M.; Vigato, P. A.; Casellato, U. *Inorg. Chim. Acta* **1976**, *17*, L5.

[55] Fenton, D. E.; Gayda, S. E.; Casellato, U.; Vigato, P. A.; Vidali, M. *Inorg. Chim. Acta* **1978**, *27*, 9.

[56] Coombes, R. C.; Fenton, D. E.; Vigato, P. A.; Casellato, U.; Vidali, M. *Inorg. Chim. Acta* **1981**, *54*, L55.

[57] Bett, G.; Fenton, D. E.; Tate, J. R. *Inorg. Chim. Acta* **1981**, *54*, L101.

[58] Glick, M. D.; Lintvedt, R. L.; Anderson, T. J.; Mack, J. L. *Inorg. Chem.* **1976**, *15*, 2258.

[59] Kahn, O. *Inorg. Chim. Acta* **1982**, *62*, 3.

[60] Kahn, O.; Galy, J.; Journaux, Y.; Jaud, J.; Morgenstern-Badarau, I. *J. Amer. Chem. Soc.* **1982**, *104*, 2165.

[61] Travis, K.; Busch, D. H. *J. Chem. Soc. Chem. Commun.* **1970**, 1041.

[62] Rosen, W. *Inorg. Chem.* **1971**, *10*, 1832.

[63] Fenton, D. E.; Mercer, M.; Poonia, N. S.; Truter, M. R. *J. Chem. Soc. Chem. Commun.* **1972**, 66.

[64] Lehn, J-M. *Pure Appl. Chem.* **1980**, *52*, 2441.

[65] Nelson, S. M. *Pure Appl. Chem.* **1980**, *52*, 2461.

[66] Agnus, Y.; Louis, R.; Weiss, R. Unpublished results quoted in [64].

[67] Agnus, Y.; Louis, R.; Weiss, R. *J. Amer. Chem. Soc.* **1979**, *101*, 3381.

[68] Burnett, M. G.; McKee, V.; Nelson, S. M.; Drew, M. G. B. *J. Chem. Soc. Chem. Commun.* **1980**, 829.

[69] Newkome, G. R.; Kohli, D. K.; Fronczek, F. R.; Hales, B. J.; Case, E. F.; Chiari, G. *J. Amer. Chem. Soc.* **1980**, *102*, 7608.

[70] Cook, D. H.; Fenton, D. E.; Drew, M. G. B.; McFall, S. G.; Nelson, S. M. *J. Chem. Soc. Dalton Trans.* **1977**, 446.

[71] Drew, M. G. B.; Hamid bin Othman, A.; McFall, S. G.; McIlroy, P. D. A.; Nelson, S. M. *J. Chem. Soc. Dalton Trans.* **1977**, 1173; Drew, M. G. B.; Hamid bin Othman, A.; Nelson, S. M. *J. Chem. Soc. Dalton Trans.* **1976**, 1394; Drew, M. G. B.; Hamid bin Othman, A.; McIlroy, P. D. A.; Nelson, S. M. *J. Chem. Soc. Dalton Trans.* **1975**, 2507.

[72] Drew, M. G. B.; McFall, S. G.; Nelson, S. M. *J. Chem. Soc. Dalton Trans.* **1979**, 575.

[73] Cook, D. H.; Fenton, D. E.; Drew, M. G. B.; Rodgers, A.; McCann, M.; Nelson, S. M. *J. Chem. Soc. Dalton Trans.* **1979**, 414.

[74] Nelson, S. M.; Esho, F. S.; Drew, M. G. B. *J. Chem. Soc. Dalton Trans.* **1982**, 407.

[75] Drew, M. G. B.; Nelson, S. M. Personal communication.

[76] Drew, M. G. B.; Cairns, C.; Lavery, A.; Nelson, S. M. *J. Chem. Soc. Chem. Commun.* **1980**, 1122.

[77] Drew, M. G. B.; Nelson, J.; Nelson, S. M. *J. Chem. Soc. Dalton Trans.* **1981**, 1678.

[78] Drew, M. G. B.; McCann, M.; Nelson, S. M. *J. Chem. Soc. Chem. Commun.* **1979**, 481.

[79] Drew, M. G. B.; McCann, M.; Nelson, S. M. *J. Chem. Soc. Dalton Trans.* **1981**, 1868.

[80] Nelson, S. M.; Esho, F. S.; Drew, M. G. B. *J. Chem. Soc. Chem. Commun.* **1981**, 388.

[81] Bailey, N. A.; Eddy, M. M.; Fenton, D. E.; Jones, G.; Moss, S.; Mukhopadhyay, A. *J. Chem. Soc. Chem. Commun.* **1981**, 628.

[82] Dancey, K. P.; Dell, A.; Henrick, K.; Judd, P. M.; Owston, P. G.; Peters, R.; Tasker, P. A.; Turner, R. W. *J. Amer. Chem. Soc.* **1981**, *103*, 4952.

[83] Dancey, K. P.; Tasker, P. A.; Price, R.; Hatfield, W. E.; Brower, P. C. *J. Chem. Soc. Chem. Commun.* **1980**, 1248.

[84] Drew, M. G. B.; Knox, C. V.; Nelson, S. M. *J. Chem. Soc. Dalton Trans.* **1980**, 942.

[85] Nelson, S. M.; Knox, C. V.; McCann, M.; Drew, M. G. B. *J. Chem. Soc. Dalton Trans.* **1981**, 1669.

[86] Lehn, J-M.; Pine, S. H.; Watanabe, E-i.; Willard, A. K. *J. Amer. Chem. Soc.* **1978**, *99*, 6766.

[87] Dietrich, B.; Lehn, J-M.; Blanzat, J. *Tetrahedron* **1973**, *29*, 1629.

[88] Martin, A. E.; Bulkowski, J. E. *J. Amer. Chem. Soc.* **1982**, *104*, 1434.

[89] Comarmond, J.; Lehn, J-M. Unpublished results quoted in [64].

[90] Gunter, M. J.; Mander, L. N.; Murray, K. S.; Clark, P. E. *J. Amer. Chem. Soc.* **1981**, *103*, 6784.

[91] Chang, C. K.; Seokoo, M.; Ward, B. *J. Chem. Soc. Chem. Commun.* **1982**, 716.

[92] Wiest, R.; Weiss, R. *J. Chem. Soc. Chem. Commun.* **1973**, 678.

[93] Lehn, J-M.; Simon, J.; Wagner, J. *Angew. Chem. Intl. Ed.* **1973**, *12*, 579.

[94] Lehn, J-M.; Simon, J. *Helv. Chim. Acta* **1977**, *60*, 141.

[95] Fischer, J.; Mellinger, M.; Weiss, R. *Inorg. Chim. Acta* **1977**, *21*, 259.

[96] Alberts, A. H.; Annunziata, R.; Lehn, J-M. *J. Amer. Chem. Soc.* **1977**, *99*, 8502.

[97] Agnus, Y.; Louis, R. *Nouveau J. Chem.* **1981**, *5*, 105.

[98] Gisselbrecht, J. P.; Gross, M.; Alberts, A. H.; Lehn, J-M. *Inorg. Chem.* **1980**, *19*, 1386.

[99] Kahn, O.; Morgenstern-Badarau, I.; Audiere, J. P.; Lehn, J-M.; Sullivan, S. A. *J. Amer. Chem. Soc.* **1980**, *102*, 5935.

[100] Collman, J. P.; Chong, A. O.; Jameson, G. B.; Oakley, R. T.; Rose, E.; Schmittan, E. R.; Ibers, J. A. *J. Amer. Chem. Soc.* **1981**, *103*, 516.

[101] Collman, J. P.; Elliott, C. M.; Halbert, T. R.; Tovrog, B. S. *Proc. Natn. Acad. Sci. USA* **1977**, *74*, 18.

[102] Hatada, M. H.; Tulinsky, A.; Chang, C. K. *J. Amer. Chem. Soc.* **1980**, *102*, 7115.

[103] Ward, B.; Wang, C. B.; Chang, C. K. *J. Amer. Chem. Soc.* **1981**, *103*, 5236.

[104] Chang, C. K. *J. Amer. Chem. Soc.* **1977**, *99*, 2819.

[105] Ogoshi, K.; Sugimoto, H.; Yoshida, Z. *Tetrahedron Lett.* **1977**, 169.

[106] Wasielewski, M. R.; Svec, W. A.; Cope, B. T. *J. Amer. Chem. Soc.* **1978**, *100*, 1961.

[107] Wasielewski, M. R.; Nremczyk, N. P.; Svec, W. A. *Tetrahedron Lett.* **1982**, 3215.

[108] Busch, D. H.; Christoph, G. G.; Zimmer, L. L.; Jackels, S. C.; Grzybowski, J. J.; Callahan, R. C.; Kojima, M.; Holter, K. A.; Mocak, J.; Herron, N.; Chavon, M.; Schammel, W. P. *J. Amer. Chem. Soc.* **1981**, *103*, 5107.

[109] Bulkowski, J. E.; Burk, J. L.; Ludmann, M. F.; Osborn, J. A. *J. Chem. Soc. Chem. Commun.* **1977**, 498.

[110] Burk, P. L.; Osborn, J. A.; Youinou, M-T.; Agnus, Y.; Louis, R.; Weiss, R. *J. Amer. Chem. Soc.* **1981**, *103*, 1273.

[111] Calverley, M. J.; Dale, J. *J. Chem. Soc. Chem. Commun.* **1981**, 684.

[112] Murase, I.; Hamada, K.; Kida, S. *Inorg. Chim. Acta* **1981**, *54*, L171.

[113] Landrum, J. T.; Grimmett, D.; Haller, K. J.; Scheidt, W. R.; Reed, C. A. *J. Amer. Chem. Soc.* **1981**, *103*, 2640.

[114] Wasielewski, M. R.; Smith, M. H.; Cope, B. T.; Katz, J. J. *J. Amer. Chem. Soc.* **1977**, *99*, 4172.

[115] Wasielewski, M. R.; Studies, M. H.; Katz, J. J. *Proc. Natn. Acad. Sci. USA* **1976**, *73*, 4382.

[116] Boxer, S. G.; Closs, G. E. *J. Amer. Chem. Soc.* **1976**, *98*, 5406.

[117] Taqui Khan, M. M.; Martell, A. E. *Inorg. Chem.* **1975**, *14*, 676.

[118] Ng, C. Y.; Martell, A. E.; Motekaitis, R. J. *J. Coord. Chem.* **1979**, *9*, 255.

[119] Ng, C. Y.; Motekaitis, R. J.; Martell, A. E. *Inorg. Chem.* **1979**, *18*, 2982.
[120] Taqui Khan, M. M.; Martell, A. E.; Mohinddin, R.; Ahmed, M. *J. Coord. Chem.* **1980**, *10*, 1.
[121] Karlin, K. D.; Dahlstrom, P. L.; Cozzette, S. N.; Scensny, P. M.; Zubieta, J. *J. Chem. Soc. Chem. Commun.* **1981**, 881.
[122] Karlin, K. D.; Dahlstrom, P. L.; Dipierro, L. T.; Simon, R. A.; Zubieta, J. *J. Coord. Chem.* **1981**, *11*, 61.
[123] Karlin, K. D.; Hyde, J. R.; Zubieta, J. *Inorg. Chim. Acta* **1982**, *66*, L57.
[124] Sorrell, T. N.; Jameson, D. L.; Malachowski, M. R. *In* "Abstracts of the 1st SUNYA Conversation in the Discipline; Inorganic and Biochemical Perspectives in Copper Coordination Chemistry", June 1–4, 1982.
[125] Gagné, R. R.; Kreh, R. P.; Dodge, J. A.; Marsh, R. E.; McCool, M. *Inorg. Chem.* **1982**, *21*, 254.
[126] Hendriks, H. M. J.; ten Bokkel Huinink, W. O.; Reedjik, J. *Rec. Trav. Chim. Pays-Bas* **1979**, *98–9*, 499.
[127] Birker, P. J. M. W. L.; Hendriks, H. M. J.; Reedjik, J.; Verschoor, G. C. *Inorg. Chem.* **1981**, *20*, 2408.
[128] Birker, P. J. M. W. L.; Hendriks, H. M. J.; Reedjik, J. *Inorg. Chim. Acta* **1981**, *55*, L17.
[129] Hendriks, H. M. J. PhD Thesis, University of Leiden, 1981; and personal communication.
[130] Birker, P. J. M. W. L.; Schierbeek, A. J.; Verschoor, G. J.; Reedjik, J. *J. Chem. Soc. Chem. Commun.* **1981**, 1124.
[131] Nishida, Y.; Takahashi, K.; Kuramoto, H.; Kida, S. *Inorg. Chim. Acta* **1981**, *54*, L103.
[132] McKee, V.; Dagdigian, J. V.; Bau, R.; Reed, C. A. *J. Amer. Chem. Soc.* **1981**, *103*, 7000.
[133] Sakurai, T.; Kaji, H.; Nakahara, A. *Inorg. Chim. Acta* **1982**, *67*, 1.
[134] Hay, R. W.; Berubi, R.; McLaren, F. *Inorg. Chim. Acta* **1981**, *54*, L161.
[135] Oishi, N.; Nishida, Y.; Kida, A. *Chem. Lett.* **1981**, 1031.
[136] Izumitani, T.; Okawa, M.; Kida, S. *Chem. Lett.* **1981**, 483.
[137] Gunter, M. J.; Mander, L. N.; McLaughlin, G. M.; Murray, K. S.; Berry, K. J.; Clark, P. E.; Buckingham, D. A. *J. Amer. Chem. Soc.* **1980**, *102*, 1470.
[138] Berry, K. J.; Clark, P. E.; Gunter, M. J.; Murray, K. S. *Nouveau J. Chem.* **1980**, *4*, 581.
[139] Fleischer, E. B.; Sklar, L.; Kendall-Torry, A.; Tasker, P. A.; Taylor, F. B. *Inorg. Nucl. Chem. Lett.* **1973**, *9*, 1061.
[140] Black, D. St. C.; Bos Vanderzaln, C. H.; Wong, L. C. H. *Aust. J. Chem.* **1979**, *32*, 2303.
[141] Rebek, J., Jr; Wattley, R. V.; Costello, T.; Gadwood, R.; Marshall, L. *Angew. Chem. Intl. Ed.* **1981**, *20*, 605.
[142] Cunningham, J. A.; Sievers, R. E. *J. Amer. Chem. Soc.* **1973**, *95*, 7183.
[143] McElroy, F. C.; Dabrowiak, J. C. *J. Amer. Chem. Soc.* **1976**, *98*, 7112.
[144] Switzer, J. A.; Endicott, J. F. *J. Amer. Chem. Soc.* **1980**, *102*, 1181.
[145] Barefield, E. K.; Cheung, D.; van Derveer, D. G.; Wagner, F. *J. Chem. Soc. Chem. Commun.* **1981**, 302.
[146] Hasty, E. F.; Colburn, T. L.; Hendrickson, D. N. *Inorg. Chem.* **1973**, *12*, 2414.
[147] Merrell, P. H.; Osgood, P. A. *Inorg. Chim. Acta* **1975**, *14*, L33.
[148] Patterson, G. H.; Holm, R. H. *Bioinorg. Chem.* **1975**, *4*, 257.
[149] Merrell, P. H.; Maheu, L. J. *Inorg. Chim. Acta* **1978**, *28*, 47.

[150] Merrell, P. H.; Abrams, M. *Inorg. Chim. Acta* **1979**, *32*, 93.
[151] Gagné, R. R.; Marritt, W. A.; Marks, D. N.; Siegl, W. O. *Inorg. Chem.* **1981**, *20*, 3260.
[152] Kolks, G.; Frihart, C. R.; Rabinowitz, H. N.; Lippard, S. J. *J. Amer. Chem. Soc.* **1976**, *98*, 5720.
[153] Dewan, J. C.; Lippard, S. J. *Inorg. Chem.* **1980**, *19*, 2079.
[154] Kolks, G.; Frihart, C. R.; Coughlin, P. K.; Lippard, S. J. *Inorg. Chem.* **1981**, *20*, 2933.
[155] Fleischer, E. B.; Lawson, M. B. *Inorg. Chem.* **1972**, *11*, 2772.
[156] Sullivan, D. A.; Palenik, G. J. *Inorg. Chem.* **1977**, *16*, 1127.
[157] Thompson, L. K.; Chacker, V. T.; Elvidge, J. A.; Lever, A. B. P.; Parrish, R. V. *Can. J. Chem.* **1969**, *47*, 4141.
[158] Lever, A. B. P.; Ramaswamy, B. S.; Pickens, S. R. *Inorg. Chim. Acta* **1980**, *46*, L59.
[159] Berry, K. J.; Black, D. St. C.; Bos Vanderzaln, C. H.; Moss, G. I.; Murray, K. S. *Inorg. Chim. Acta* **1980**, *46*, L21.
[160] Nonoyama, K.; Ojima, H.; Nonoyama, M. *Inorg. Chim. Acta* **1982**, *59*, 275.
[161] Ball, P. A.; Blake, A. B. *J. Chem. Soc.* (A) **1969**, 1415.
[162] Ghedini, M.; de Munno, G.; Denti, G.; Manotto Lanfredi, A. M.; Tiripichio, A. *Inorg. Chim. Acta* **1982**, *57*, 87.
[163] Kimura, M.; Suzuki, S.; Mari, N.; Nakahara, A. *Inorg. Chim. Acta* **1981**, *56*, 83.
[164] Bailey, N. A.; McKenzie, E. D.; Worthington, J. M.; McPartlin, M.; Tasker, P. A. *Inorg. Chim. Acta* **1977**, *25*, L137.
[165] Bombieri, G.; Mazzi, U.; Gilli, G.; Hernandez-Cano, F. *J. Organometal. Chem.* **1978**, *159*, 53.
[166] Bonnaire, R.; Manoli, J. M.; Potvin, C.; Platzner, N.; Goasdoue, N.; Davoust, D. *Inorg. Chem.* **1982**, *21*, 2032.
[167] Fallon, G. D.; Gatehouse, B. M.; Reichert, B. E.; West, B. O. *J. Organometal. Chem.* **1974**, *81*, C28.
[168] Murray, K. S.; Reichert, B. E.; West, B. O. *J. Organometal. Chem.* **1973**, *63*, 461.
[169] Cozens, R. J.; Murray, K. S.; West, B. O. *J. Organometal. Chem.* **1971**, *27*, 399; Platzner, N.; Goasdoue, N.; Bonnaire, R. *J. Organometal. Chem.* **1978**, *160*, 455.
[170] Murray, K. S.; Reichert, B. E.; West, B. O. *J. Organometal. Chem.* **1973**, *61*, 451.
[171] Fenton, D. E.; Bailey, N. A. Unpublished results.
[172] Sadler, P. J. *Inorg. Perspect. Biol. Med.* **1978**, *1*, 233.
[173] Michelson, A. M.; McCord, J. M.; Fridovich, I. (Eds) "Superoxide and Superoxide Dismutases"; Academic Press: London, 1977.
[174] Valentine, J. S.; Pantoliano, M. W. *In* "Copper Proteins"; Spiro, T. G., Ed.; Wiley-Interscience: New York, 1981, Chapter 8.
[175] Fee, J. A. *In* "Metals in Biology, No. 13, Copper Proteins"; Sigel, H., Ed.; Marcel Dekker: Basel, 1981, Chapter 8.
[176] Steinman, H. M.; Naik, V. R.; Abernethy, J. L.; Hill, R. L. *J. Biol. Chem.* **1974**, *249*, 7326.
[177] Richardson, J. S.; Thomas, K. A.; Rubin, B. H.; Richardson, D. C. *Proc. Natn. Acad. Sci. USA* **1975**, *72*, 1349.
[178] Richardson, D. C.; Richardson, J. S. Personal communication quoted in [175].
[179] Gaber, B. P.; Brown, R. D.; Koenig, S. H.; Fee, J. A. *Biochim. Biophys. Acta* **1972**, *271*, 1; Boden, W.; Holmes, M. C.; Knowles, P. F. *Biochem. Biophys. Res. Commun.* **1974**, *57*, 845.
[180] Fee, J. A.; Briggs, R. G. *Biochim. Biophys. Acta* **1975**, *400*, 439.

[181] Erecinska, M.; Wilson, D. F. *Arch. Biochem. Biophys.* **1978**, *188*, 1.
[182] Wharton, D. C. *In* "Inorganic Biochemistry"; Eichhorn, G. L., Ed.; Elsevier: Amsterdam, 1973, Chapter 27.
[183] Palmer, G.; Babcock, G. T.; Vickery, L. E. *Proc. Natn. Acad. Sci. USA* **1976**, *73*, 2206.
[184] Seiter, C. H. A.; Angelos, S. G., Jr; Perreault, R. A. *Front. Biol. Energ.* **1978**, *2*, 897.
[185] Reed, C. A.; Landrum, J. T. *FEBS Lett.* **1979**, *106*, 265.
[186] Hemmerich, P. *In* "The Biochemistry of Copper"; Peisach, J.; Aisen, P.; Blumberg, W. E., Eds; Academic Press: New York, 1966.
[187] Scott, R. A.; Cramer, S. P.; Shaw, R. W.; Bernert, H.; Gray, H. B. *Proc. Natn. Acad. Sci. USA* **1981**, *78*, 664.
[188] Tullins, T. D.; Frank, P.; Hodgson, K. O. *Proc. Natn. Acad. Sci. USA* **1978**, *75*, 4069.
[189] Powers, L.; Chance, B.; Ching, Y.; Angiolollo, P. *Biophys. J.* **1981**, *34*, 465.
[190] Peisach, J.; Powers, L.; Blumberg, W. E.; Chance, B. *Biophys. J.* **1982**, *37*, 396a.
[191] Kurtz, D. M., Jr; Shriver, D. F.; Klotz, I. M. *Coord. Chem. Rev.* **1977**, *24*, 145.
[192] Stenkamp, R. E.; Jensen, L. H. *In* "Advances in Inorganic Biochemistry"; Vol. I. Eichhorn, G. L.; Marzilli, L. G., Eds; Elsevier-North Holland: New York, 1979, Chapter 8.
[193] Loehr, J. S.; Loehr, T. M. *In* "Advances in Inorganic Biochemistry"; Vol. I. Eichhorn, G. L.; Marzilli, L. G., Eds; Elsevier-North Holland: New York, 1979, Chapter 9.
[194] Hendrickson, W. A. *In* "Invertebrate O_2-binding Proteins"; Lamy, J. N.; Lamy, J., Eds; Marcel Dekker: Basel, 1981, p. 503.
[195] Hendrickson, W. A. *Naval Res. Rev.* **1978**, *31*, 1.
[196] Stenkamp, R. E.; Siecker, L. C.; Jensen, L. H. *Proc. Natn. Acad. Sci. USA* **1976**, *73*, 349.
[197] Stenkamp, R. E.; Siecker, L. C.; Jensen, L. H.; Sanders-Loehr, J. *Nature* **1981**, *291*, 263.
[198] Ibers, J. A.; Holm, R. H. *Science* **1980**, *209*, 223.
[199] Atkin, C. L.; Thelander, L.; Reichard, P.; Long, G. *J. Biol. Chem.* **1973**, *248*, 7464.
[200] Peterson, L.; Gräslund, A.; Ehrenberg, A.; Sjöberg, B-M.; Reichard, P. *J. Biol. Chem.* **1980**, *255*, 6706.
[201] Sjöberg, B-M.; Loehr, T. M.; Sanders-Loehr, J. *Biochemistry* **1982**, *21*, 96.
[202] Lontie, R.; Witters, R. *In* "Metals in Biology, No. 13, Copper Proteins"; Sigel, H., Ed.; Marcel Dekker: Basel, 1981, Chapter 7.
[203] Solomon, E. I. *In* "Copper Proteins"; Spiro, T. G., Ed.; Wiley-Interscience: New York, 1981, Chapter 2.
[204] Urbach, F. L. *In* "Metals in Biology, No. 13, Copper Proteins"; Sigel, H., Ed.; Marcel Dekker: Basel, 1981, Chapter 7.
[205] Eickman, N. C.; Himmelwright, R. S.; Solomon, E. I. *Proc. Natn. Acad. Sci. USA* **1979**, *76*, 2094.
[206] Co, M. S.; Hodgson, K. O.; Eccles, T. K.; Lontie, R. *J. J. Amer. Chem. Soc.* **1981**, *103*, 984.
[207] Brown, J. M.; Powers, L.; Kincaid, B.; Larrabee, J. A.; Spiro, T. G. *J. Amer. Chem. Soc.* **1980**, *102*, 4210.
[208] Co, M. S.; Hodgson, K. O. *J. Amer. Chem. Soc.* **1981**, *103*, 3200.
[209] Lerch, K. *In* "Metals in Biology, No. 13, Copper Proteins"; Sigel, H., Ed.;

Marcel Dekker: Basel, 1981, Chapter 5.

[210] Lerch, K. *Proc. Natn. Acad. Sci. USA* **1978**, *75*, 3635.

[211] Pfiffner, E.; Dietler, C.; Lerch, K. *In* "Invertebrate O_2-binding Proteins"; Lamy, J. N.; Lamy, J., Eds; Marcel Dekker: Basel, 1981, p. 541.

[212] Villafranca, J. J. *In* "Copper Proteins"; Spiro, T. G., Ed.; Wiley-Interscience: New York, 1981, Chapter 7.

[213] Blackburn, N. J.; Mason, H. S.; Knowles, P. F. *Biochem. Biophys. Res. Commun.* **1980**, *595*, 1275.

[214] Blackburn, N. J.; Sutton, J. *In* "Abstracts of 1st SUNYA Conversation in the Discipline; Inorganic and Biochemical Perspectives in Copper Coordination Chemistry", June 1–4, 1982.

[215] Reinhammer, B.; Malmström, B. G. *In* "Copper Proteins"; Spiro, T. G., Ed.; Wiley-Interscience: New York, 1981, Chapter 3.

[216] Fee, J. A. *Struct. Bonding* **1975**, *23*, 1.

[217] Laurie, S. H.; Mohammed, E. S. *Coord. Chem. Rev.* **1980**, *38*, 279.

[218] Colman, P. M.; Freeman, H. C.; Guss, J. M.; Murata, M.; Norris, V. A.; Ramshaw, J. A. M.; Venkatappa, M. P. *Nature* **1978**, *272*, 319.

[219] Freeman, H. C. *In* "Coordination Chemistry—21"; Laurent, J-P., Ed.; Pergamon: New York, 1981.

[220] Adman, E. T.; Jensen, L. H. *Israel J. Chem.* **1981**, *21*, 8.

[221] Cass, A. E. G.; Hill, H. A. O. *CIBA Found. Sym. 79; Excerpta Medica: Amsterdam*, 1980, 71.

[222] Lu Bien, C. D.; Winkler, M. E.; Thamann, T. J.; Scott, R. A.; Co, M. S.; Hodgson, K. O.; Solomon, E. I. *J. Amer. Chem. Soc.* **1981**, *103*, 7014.

[223] Harris, C. M.; Hoskins, B. F.; Martin, R. L. *J. Chem. Soc.* **1959**, 3728.

[224] de Courcy, J. S.; Waters, T. N.; Curtis, N. F. *J. Chem. Soc. Chem. Commun.* **1977**, 572.

[225] Bertrand, J. A.; Smith, J. H.; Eller, P. G. *Inorg. Chem.* **1974**, *13*, 1649.

[226] Churchill, M. R.; Davies, G.; El-Sayed, M. A.; El-Shazly, M. F.; Hutchinson, J. P.; Rupich, M. W.; Watkins, K. O. *Inorg. Chem.* **1979**, *18*, 2296.

[227] Davies, A. R.; Einstein, F. W. B.; Curtis, N. F.; Martin, J. W. L. *J. Amer. Chem. Soc.* **1978**, *100*, 6258.

[228] McFadyen, W.; Robson, R.; Schaap, H. *Inorg. Chem.* **1972**, *11*, 1777.

[229] Lintvedt, R. L.; Tomlonovic, B.; Fenton, D. E.; Glick, M. D. *Adv. Chem. Ser. No. 150* **1976**, 407.

[230] Gerloch, M. *Progr. Inorg. Chem.* **1980**, *26*, 1.

[231] Inoue, M.; Kibo, M. *Coord. Chem. Rev.* **1976**, *21*, 1.

[232] Schoot Uiterkamp, A. J. M.; van der Deen, H.; Berendsen, H. C. J.; Boas, J. F. *Biochim. Biophys. Acta* **1974**, *372*, 407.

[233] Van Leeuwen, F. X. R.; van Gelder, B. F. *Eur. J. Biochem.* **1978**, *87*, 305.

[234] Smith, T. D.; Pilbrow, J. R. *Coord. Chem. Rev.* **1974**, *13*, 173.

[235] Boas, J. F.; Pilbrow, J. R.; Smith, T. D. *In* "Biological Magnetic Resonance, 2"; Berliner, L. J.; Reuben, J., Eds; Plenum: New York, 1980, Chapter 7.

[236] Lontie, R.; Witters, R. *In* "Inorganic Biochemistry"; Eichhorn, G. L., Ed.; Elsevier: Amsterdam, 1973, Chapter 12.

[237] Freedman, T. B.; Loehr, J. S.; Loehr, T. M. *J. Amer. Chem. Soc.* **1976**, *98*, 2809.

[238] Deinum, J.; Lerch, K.; Reinhammer, B. *FEBS Lett.* **1976**, *69*, 161.

[239] Amundsen, A. R.; Whelan, J.; Bosnich, B. *J. Amer. Chem. Soc.* **1977**, *99*, 6730.

[240] Fawcett, T. G.; Bernaducci, E. F.; Krogh-Jespersen, K.; Schugar, H. J. *J. Amer. Chem. Soc.* **1980**, *102*, 2598.

[241] Reinhammer, B. R. M. *Biochim. Biophys. Acta* **1972**, *275*, 245.
[242] Makino, N.; McMahill, P.; Mason, H. S. *J. Biol. Chem.* **1974**, *249*, 6062.
[243] Fee, J. A.; Dicorletto, P. E. *Biochemistry* **1973**, *12*, 4893.
[244] Jaud, J.; Journaux, Y.; Galy, J.; Kahn, O. *Nouveau J. Chim.* **1980**, *4*, 629.
[245] Kolks, G.; Lippard, S. J.; Waszczak, J. V.; Lilienthal, H. R. *J. Amer. Chem. Soc.* **1982**, *104*, 717.
[246] Coughlin, P. K.; Dewan, J. C.; Lippard, S. J.; Watanabe, E-I.; Lehn, J-M. *J. Amer. Chem. Soc.* **1979**, *101*, 265.
[247] Coughlin, P. K.; Lippard, S. J.; Martin, A. E.; Bulkowski, J. E. *J. Amer. Chem. Soc.* **1980**, *102*, 7617.
[248] Drew, M. G. B.; Nelson, S. M.; Reedjik, J. *Inorg. Chim. Acta* **1982**, *64*, L189.
[249] Fenton, D. E.; Lintvedt, R. L. *J. Amer. Chem. Soc.* **1978**, *100*, 6267.
[250] Coughlin, P. K.; Lippard, S. J. *J. Amer. Chem. Soc.* **1981**, *103*, 3228.
[251] Kina, J.; Suzuki, S.; Mori, W.; Nakahara, A. *Inorg. Chim. Acta* **1981**, *56*, L33.
[252] Himmelwright, R. S.; Eickman, N. C.; Lu Bien, C. D.; Solomon, E. I. *J. Amer. Chem. Soc.* **1980**, *102*, 5378.
[253] Ochiai, E-I. *J. Inorg. Nucl. Chem.* **1975**, *37*, 1503.
[254] Demmin, T. R.; Swerdloff, M. D.; Rogic, M. M. *J. Amer. Chem. Soc.* **1981**, *103*, 5795.
[255] Tsuruya, S.; Lintvedt, R. L. "Abstracts 176th National Meeting, A.C.S."; Miami, September 1978, INORG 070.
[256] Lever, A. B. P.; Ramaswamy, B. S.; Pickens, S. R. *Inorg. Chim. Acta* **1980**, *46*, L59.
[257] Oishi, N.; Nishida, Y.; Ida, K.; Kida, S. *Bull. Chem. Soc. Jap.* **1980**, *53*, 2847.
[258] Moore, K.; Vigee, G. S. *Inorg. Chim. Acta* **1982**, *66*, 125.
[259] Bolus, D.; Vigee, G. S. *Inorg. Chim. Acta* **1982**, *67*, 19.
[260] Grzybowski, J. J.; Urbach, F. L. *Inorg. Chem.* **1980**, *19*, 2604.
[261] Nishida, Y.; Oishi, N.; Kida, S. *Inorg. Chim. Acta* **1980**, *46*, L69.
[262] Nishida, Y.; Oishi, N.; Kuramoto, H.; Kida, S. *Inorg. Chim. Acta* **1982**, *57*, 253.
[263] Mori, W.; Yamauchi, O.; Nakao, Y.; Nakahara, A. *Biochem. Biophys. Res. Commun.* **1975**, *66*, 725.
[264] Elam, W. T.; Stern, E. A.; McCallum, J. D.; Sanders-Loehr, J. *J. Amer. Chem. Soc.* **1982**, *104*, 6369.

Molybdenum Enzymes: A Survey of Structural Information from EXAFS and EPR Spectroscopy

Stephen P. Cramer

Corporate Research Science Laboratories,
Exxon Research and Engineering Company

I. INTRODUCTION

Rapid progress is being made toward unravelling the structure of molybdenum enzymes.[1,2] Most of the structural information about the molybdenum environments in these proteins has come from two spectroscopic techniques, X-ray absorption spectroscopy[3] and electron paramagnetic resonance.[4] Molybdenum enzymes have been examined by X-ray absorption spectroscopy since 1974,[5] and this work complements electron paramagnetic resonance studies in progress since 1959.[6] At this point in time, nearly every major type of molybdenum protein has been probed by both techniques; it is, therefore, appropriate to take stock of what has been learned. The focus of this review will be almost exclusively on the local molybdenum environment, with enough of the details about the catalytic activity and other protein properties required to put these results in context.

A major goal in the spectroscopic study of these enzymes has been a structural explanation for the diverse catalytic and electrochemical properties of the molybdenum centers. The reactions catalysed are summarized in Table 1; they range from the relatively facile oxidation of sulfite to the difficult reduction of dinitrogen. The molybdenum redox potentials vary from above 200 mV to below -500 mV versus the standard hydrogen electrode $E^{0\prime}$ at pH 7.

There is a unique feature in molybdenum biochemistry which suggests that a systematic structural survey might yield insights which are more than the sum of the individual studies. This is the existence of *cofactors*, namely the iron–molybdenum cofactor,[7] "Fe-Mo-co", of nitrogenase and the molybdenum cofactor,[8] "Mo-co", apparently common to all other molybdoenzymes. As illustrated in Fig. 1, these cofactors are small molecules containing molybdenum which can be released from one protein and then inserted into a second apo-protein structure to form an active enzyme. It is not

TABLE 1

Physical properties and reactions catalysed by molybdenum enzymes

Enzyme	Reaction catalysed	Prosthetic groups	Protein subunits
Nitrogenase (*C. pasteurianum*)	$N_2 + 6H^+ + 6e^- \rightarrow 2NH_3$	$2\ \{2[Fe_4S_4],\ FeMo\text{-}co\}$	$2 \times 50\ 000;\ 2 \times 60\ 000$
Xanthine oxidase (bovine milk)	$RH + H_2O \rightarrow ROH + 2H^+ + 2e^-$	$2 \left\{ \begin{array}{l} 2[Fe_2S_2], \\ FAD,\ Mo\text{-}co \end{array} \right\}$	$2 \times 150\ 000$
Sulfite oxidase (chicken liver)	$SO_3^- + H_2O \rightarrow SO_4^{2-} + 2e^- + 2H^+$	$2\ \{Fe\text{-}PPIX,\ Mo\text{-}co\}$	$2 \times 55\ 000$
Nitrate reductase (*E. coli*)	$NO_3^- + 2e^- + 2H^+ \rightarrow NO_2^- + H_2O$	$4\ Fe_4S_4$ $1\ Mo\text{-}co$	$1 \times 142\ 000;\ 1 \times 60\ 000;$ $1 \times 20\ 000$
Nitrate reductase (*Chlorella vulgaris*)	$NO_3^- + 2e^- + 2H^+ \rightarrow NO_2^- + H_2O$	$4 \left\{ \begin{array}{l} FAD,\ FePPIX \\ Mo\text{-}co \end{array} \right\}$	$4 \times 90\ 000$
CO_2 reductase (*C. pasteurianum*)	$HCOO^- \leftrightarrow CO_2 + H^+ + 2e^-$		

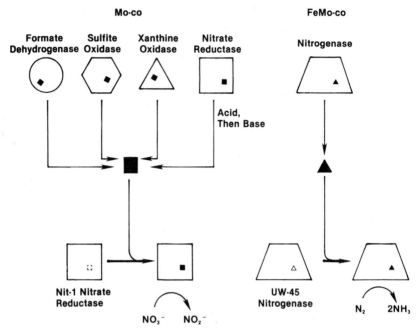

Fig. 1. Schematic illustration of the cofactor complementation process.

yet clear whether these cofactors ever exist as free entities *in vivo*, or whether they are always bound to carrier proteins. In the strict biochemical usage the application of the term "cofactor" is a misnomer, since these species do not form dissociable ternary complexes with enzyme and substrate in the manner of other cofactors.

The same molybdenum cofactor is common to at least four different types of molybdoenzymes, sulfite oxidase, xanthine oxidase, nitrate reductase and formate dehydrogenase, whereas the iron–molybdenum cofactor as yet has only been found in nitrogenase. Assuming that some of the molybdenum environment from the cofactor is preserved upon insertion into the protein complex, it appears that *dramatic changes in redox properties and catalytic activity can be achieved by systematic perturbation of the molybdenum environment.* Understanding the molybdenum environment of these two cofactors in their free forms as well as in a protein matrix will help reveal how modifications of the molybdenum coordination sphere alter its chemical reactivity. Ultimately, such knowledge should be applicable to the rational design of new types of molybdenum-based catalysts with controllable properties.

II. EXAFS VERSUS EPR

X-ray absorption and electron paramagnetic resonance are quite complementary spectroscopic tools for the structural study of molybdenum enzymes. EXAFS is less sensitive than EPR in terms of quantity of material required; yet, with fluorescence detection[9] and synchrotron radiation,[10] it is now possible to obtain EXAFS on 0.1 mM molybdenum in aqueous solution. EXAFS does not require a particular molybdenum oxidation state, whereas direct EPR study of non-nitrogenase molybdenum environments, to-date, has been restricted to the d^1 Mo(V) oxidation state. A major weakness of EXAFS is the difficulty in interpreting the spectra of mixtures, which is less of a problem for EPR. The Mo(V) oxidation state is typically present as an equilibrium mixture with Mo(VI) and/or Mo(IV), as illustrated schematically in Fig. 2. Almost all molybdenum EXAFS work has, therefore, been done on Mo(VI) and Mo(IV) oxidation states. Ligand identification using EPR nuclear hyperfine splittings can be unambiguous when the molybdenum site has

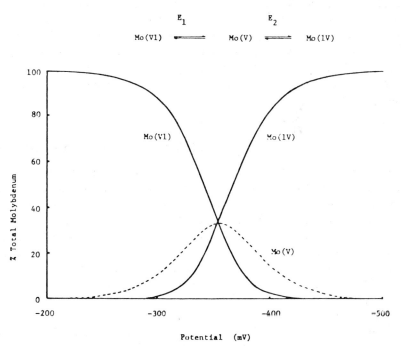

Fig. 2. Nernst curves for a molybdenum couple involving the formation of a stable one electron reduced intermediate. The curves are calculated for a system of $E_1 = E_2 = -355$ mV. The maximum formation of Mo(V), 33%, occurs at a potential $E = (E_1 + E_2)/2$ (reference [4]).

naturally abundant or artificially enriched nuclei with non-zero spin in its vicinity. EXAFS can also identify the atomic number of a particular donor, by using characteristic phase shift and amplitude properties. These methods are not precise, however, and although oxygen can easily be distinguished from sulfur, additional chemical information is required to distinguish say oxygen from nitrogen or sulfur from chlorine. In summary, EXAFS has given us a basic structural picture of fully oxidized or fully reduced enzyme forms, while EPR has revealed a host of Mo(V) intermediates whose nuances would not be observed with the former technique.

III. NITROGENASE

A. General properties

Nitrogenase catalyses the reduction of dinitrogen to ammonia, and it is indisputably the most important molybdenum-containing enzyme. Since the availability of chemically combined or "fixed" nitrogen is often the limiting factor in plant growth, the effects of the nitrogenase found in the symbiotic bacteria associated with plant root nodules are of enormous agricultural importance. The enzyme has been the subject of many review articles,[7,11-13] and there is a regular international symposium on nitrogen fixation.[14,15]

There is considerable complexity in the stoichiometry of the reaction catalysed by nitrogenase:

$$(6 + y)e^- + xMgATP + (6 + y)H^+ + N_2 \rightarrow$$
$$xMgADP + xP_i + (y/2)H_2 + 2NH_3 \quad (1)$$

The number of electrons consumed in hydrogen production (y) and the number of ATPs hydrolyzed (x) depends on the reaction conditions.[12] Two different proteins are involved in the reaction, an iron protein sometimes referred to as component II or azoferredoxin, and a molybdenum–iron protein alternatively called component I or molybdoferredoxin. Since kinetic evidence indicates that the iron protein reduces the molybdenum–iron protein which in turn reduces dinitrogen, still another proposed nomenclature calls the iron protein dinitrogenase reductase and reserves the term dinitrogenase for the molybdenum–iron protein alone.[16]

The *Clostridium pasteurianum* molybdenum–iron protein has a molecular weight of about 220 000 and contains $2 \times 50\,000$ and $2 \times 60\,000$ dalton subunits.[17] *Azotobacter vinelandii* Mo–Fe protein has a slightly higher molecular weight of about 245 000 and also contains two pairs of dissimilar subunits, each having a molecular weight of about 61 000.[18] The amino-acid sequence of an algeal Mo–Fe protein has recently been determined using DNA sequencing techniques.[19] Chemical analysis of crystalline protein from *Azotobacter vinelandii* gave 33 Fe and 2 ± 0.1 Mo atoms per molecule.[20] There has been a long debate over the prosthetic group composition of the Mo–Fe protein. One scheme, based on Mössbauer spectroscopy, proposes that 16 of the irons are present in $4Fe_4S_4$ cores referred to as "P-clusters", perhaps two irons occur in a separate spectral class S, while the remaining 10–14 Fe atoms are associated with the two iron–molybdenum cofactor sites which give the $S = 3/2$ EPR signal.[21] The presence of $4Fe_4S_4$ clusters has also been found chemically by extrusion methods.[22]

The Mo–Fe protein from *Clostridium pasteurianum* has recently yielded diffraction quality crystals, with a space group $P2_1$ and two molecules per unit cell of dimensions $70 \times 151 \times 122$ Å.[23] Preliminary studies reveal a molecular "pseudo-" two-fold axis, indicating a gross similarity between α and β subunits.[24]

B. EPR results

It has been known for years that the Mo–Fe protein exhibits an EPR signal with g-values near 4.3, 3.7 and 2.0, assignable to an $S = 3/2$ species.[25-27] Although Mo(III) could in principle yield such a signal, no detectable broadening was observed upon incorporation of enriched ^{95}Mo.[25] In contrast, the use of ^{57}Fe resulted in a 5–7 gauss broadening.[26,28]

The first evidence for molybdenum involvement with the $S = 3/2$ signal came from spin–echo experiments, in which the effect of ^{95}Mo on the relaxation curve of this signal can be seen (Fig. 3).[29] Recent ENDOR experiments have shown an effect from both ^{95}Mo (30) and ^{57}Fe (31) on the $S = 3/2$ signal. The conclusion from the ^{95}Mo ENDOR spectra was the presence of an *even* molybdenum oxidation state. The ^{57}Fe ENDOR spectrum reveals that there are six distinct iron environments associated with the $S = 3/2$ signal, which can be divided into two triplets of similar irons.

C. EXAFS results

Nitogenase was actually the first *enzyme* to be examined by X-ray absorption spectroscopy, although oxygen-binding proteins such as hemoglobin and hemocyanin, as well as electron-transport proteins such as rubredoxin and azurin, were studied earlier or at about the same time. The very first absorption edge results[32] were invalid because of the use of inactive protein, but the subsequent EXAFS data using the transmission mode on lyophilized protein[33] have since been reproduced on enzyme in solution by both transmission[34] and fluorescence detection techniques.[35,36]

Examination of the nitrogenase absorption edge region, Fig. 4, revealed

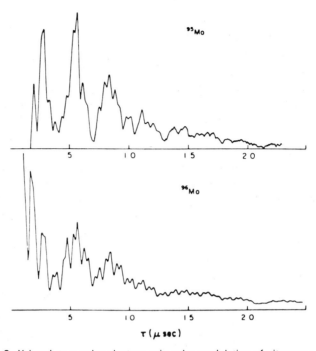

Fig. 3. X-band, two pulse electron spin echo modulation of nitrogenase MoFe protein. Samples were held at 2 °K and echoes were obtained at field and frequency appropriate to excitation at $g = 2.0$. Abscissa, interpulse interval; ordinate echo amplitude. Top panel: MoFe protein from *C. pasteuranium* grown on medium enriched ($\sim 90\%$) in ^{95}Mo ($I = 5/2$); bottom panel: MoFe protein from *C. pasteuranium* grown on medium enriched ($\sim 98\%$) in ^{96}Mo ($I = 0$) (unpublished work of Mims and Orme-Johnson).

some qualitative information about the nitrogenase molybdenum environment. The edge *position* is near the low end of the range observed for molybdenum, indicating a low oxidation state and/or a covalent environment. The edge *shape* shows only a single inflection point, whereas all terminal oxomolybdenum model compound edges had an additional low energy inflection arising from a bound state transition. Thus, it was concluded from the edge alone that the nitrogenase molybdenum was devoid of terminal oxo groups when active, and perhaps existed in a high sulfur environment.

From the split Fourier transforms in Fig. 5 and the beat pattern of the direct EXAFS in Fig. 6, it appears that two major components are required to explain the nitrogenase EXAFS. Based on comparison with model compounds as well as theoretically calculated EXAFS, the data were interpreted as the sum of Mo–S and Mo–Fe interactions. This led to the basic conclusion that nitrogenase contained a Mo,Fe,S cluster, and that the molybdenum–iron

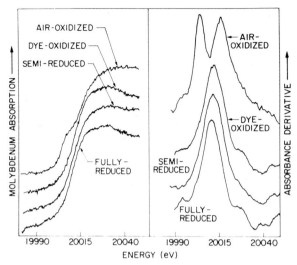

Fig. 4. Nitrogenase absorption edges (reference [33]).

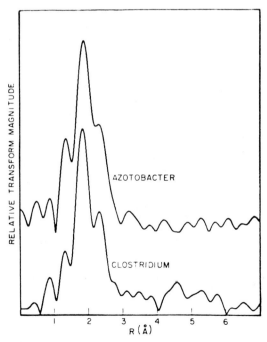

Fig. 5. Fourier transforms of nitrogenase Mo EXAFS (reference [34]).

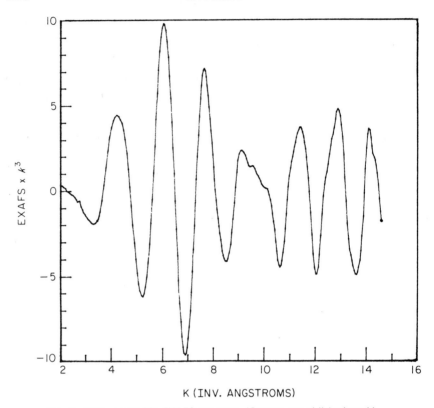

Fig. 6. Nitrogenase Mo EXAFS spectrum (Cramer, unpublished work).

distance was 2.72 ± 0.05 Å. Based on these results, a number of structural models have been proposed, and these are outlined in Scheme 1.

Two alternative structural models consistent with the EXAFS were originally suggested, one with a linear Fe-$(S)_2$-Mo-$(S)_2$-Fe cluster as in (II) and another model consisting of an MoFe$_3$S$_4$ cube (I). The subsequent synthesis of a double-cubane model compound and the similarity of its EXAFS to that of nitrogenase led Hodgson and coworkers to conclude that "the Mo–Fe protein possesses a structural fragment similar to the MoFe$_3$S$_4$ cube that constitutes one half of the complex $[Mo_2Fe_6S_9(SEt)_8]^{3-}$".[37] This conclusion was challenged by Teo and Averill,[38] who reinterpreted the original EXAFS data and found two rather than three Fe neighbors, and proposed model III for the Mo site. Teo later proposed model IV instead.[39] Other proposals include "string-bag" models as in V[40,41] and more extended arrays as in VI.[42]

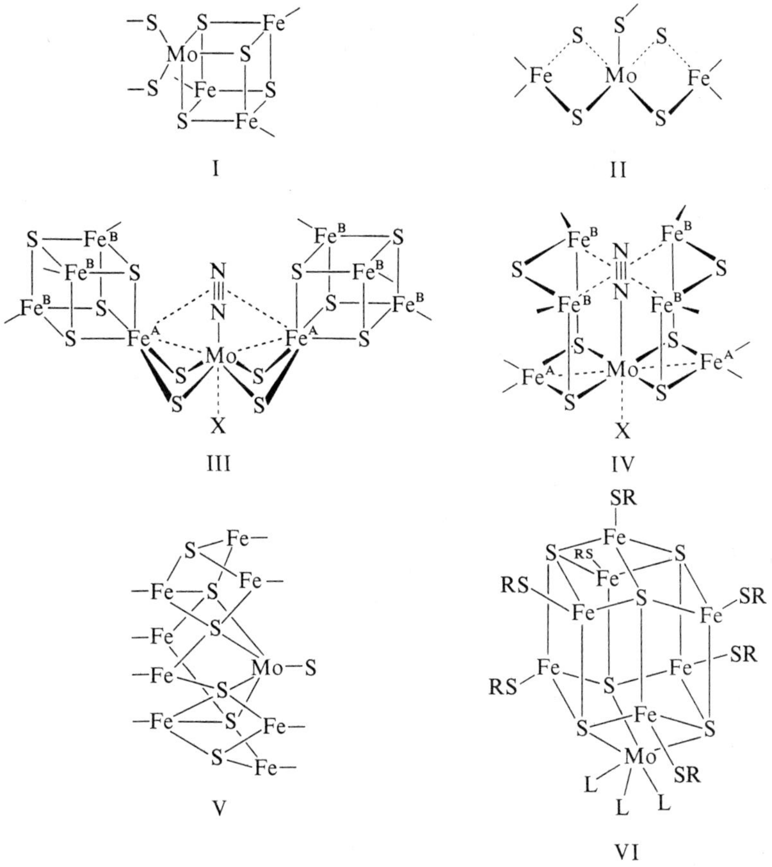

Scheme 1. Recent proposals for the structure of the nitrogenase molybdenum site.

IV. IRON-MOLYBDENUM COFACTOR

A. General properties

The iron–molybdenum cofactor, "FeMo-co", was first isolated by Shah and Brill in 1977.[20] The cofactor was separated from its protein matrix using N-methylformamide extraction on a pellet of citrate-acidified, neutralized MoFe protein, and it was assayed using reconstitution of the MoFe protein from a mutant *A. vinelandii* strain called UW45. Subsequent work by Yang *et al.* (1962) has shown that FeMo-co can be isolated by a variety of procedures.[43]

The original cofactor composition was reported as 1 Mo:8 Fe:6 (acid-labile) S. Spectroscopic work described above yields a minimum value of 6 irons, while more recent chemical analyses yield 7 irons per molybdenum.[43]

Sulfur analyses ranging from as low as 4 labile sulfides[43] to as high as 11.9 total sulfurs have been reported.[44] In the latter radiochemical analysis, 3.2 ± 2 sulfurs were ascribed to amino acid impurities. If 3 or 4 sulfurs remain bound as tri- as tetrathiomolybdate, the calculated number of remaining sulfurs is 6 or 5, which is close to the original values for acid-labile sulfide. The authors suggest a FeMo-co stoichiometry of $MoFe_6S_8$ or $MoFe_6S_9$. To-date, the only organic components identified in FeMo-co are NMF or other extrinsic ligands introduced during isolation. The report that FeMo-co contains acetyl-Co-A[45] was disproven.[43]

B. EPR results

The earliest EPR studies of FeMo-co in N-methylformamide revealed broad signals with g-values at 4.5, 3.3 and 2.01.[46] This signal was recognized as coming from the same $S = 3/2$ center which is observed in the intact MoFe protein, as shown in Fig. 7. The resemblance was even more striking upon addition of thiophenol. The initial report that FeMo-co binds CO under reducing conditions[46] appears to have been an artifact. Chelating agents such as EDTA and σ-phenanthroline abolish the FeMo-co EPR signal, whereas α,α'-bipyridal does not.[43]

The recent synthesis of capped $MoFe_3S_4$[47,48] cubes reveals that they also exhibit an $S = 3/2$ state when in the appropriate oxidation level, and as illustrated in Fig. 8, their EPR properties bear some resemblance to those of FeMo-co.[48] However, $Fe(MoS_4)_2^{3-}$ also has a similar EPR, as do other $S = 3/2$ systems.

C. EXAFS results

The initial work on FeMo-co molybdenum EXAFS established that the Mo,Fe,S cluster found in the intact protein was preserved during cofactor isolation.[34] More extensive studies have since been reported on both the molybdenum[35,49] and iron[50] EXAFS of FeMo-co. The picture that emerges involves a Mo,Fe,S cluster whose peripheral ligation can undergo extensive variation.

A preliminary report by Burgess et al.[35] predicted that the FeMo-co molybdenum was surrounded by 3–4 sulfurs at 2.35 Å, 2–3 irons at 2.66 Å and 2–3 oxygens or nitrogens at 2.10 Å. As illustrated in Fig. 9, the major difference with the Mo environment of the intact protein was the appearance of the oxygen/nitrogen ligand subset. A subsequent progress report[49] presented EXAFS spectra for FeMo-co "as isolated" as well as in the presence of thiol or selenol. Significant changes were found upon addition of the latter reagents. The authors hypothesize that FeMo-co as isolated has three oxygen and/or

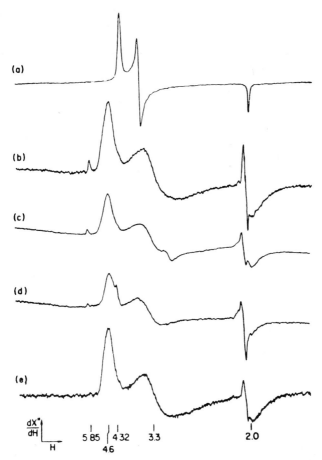

Fig. 7. FeMo-co EPR: (a) *A. vinelandii* Mo–Fe protein; (b) *A. vinelandii* FeMo-co; (c) *C. pasteurianum* FeMo-co; (d) *K. pneumoniae* FeMo-co; (e) *A. vinelandii* FeMo-co, 4 K (others 13 K) (reference [46]).

nitrogen ligands and three sulfur ligands around the Mo center, with more sulfur present upon addition of thiol, and still more sulfur present in intact MoFe protein. They also indicate that seven-coordinate molybdenum with 4Fe neighbors might occur in certain samples. This would certainly be an exciting structural finding, but further data collection and analysis are necessary to confirm these ideas.

FeMo-co has also been examined using the iron K-edge EXAFS,[50] but the large error estimates and large number of iron atoms allow for a wide range of structural interpretations. Four different components were used to fit the data, for which the Fourier transform is illustrated in Fig. 10. The fits predicted an

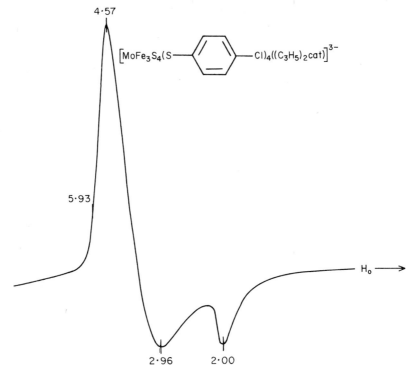

Fig. 8. MoFe$_3$S$_4$ cube EPR (reference [48]).

average Fe environment with 3.4 $\pm$ 1.6 S (Cl) atoms at 2.25(2) Å, 2.3 $\pm$ 0.9 Fe atoms at 2.66(3) Å, 0.4 $\pm$ 0.1 Mo atoms at 2.76(3) Å, 1.2 $\pm$ 1.0 O(N) atoms at 1.81(7) Å. The Mo–Fe distance is 0.1 Å longer than the value calculated from the Mo EXAFS by the Hodgson group.

D. Nitrogenase and FeMo-co summary

The current consensus is that the MoFe protein contains 4Fe$_4$S$_4$ clusters and 2FeMo-co clusters per $\alpha_2\beta_2$ tetramer. The presence of Mo–Fe interactions at about 2.7 Å has been demonstrated unambiguously. The recent EXAFS work[49] has clearly shown that the molybdenum environment changes when FeMo-co is removed from the enzyme, with the number of sulfur ligands being diminished. The chemical and EPR studies[43] provide strong evidence that the peripheral iron environment can also vary.

From a bioinorganic standpoint, the major structural problem in understanding nitrogenase remains the arrangement of metals and bridging ligands within the core of FeMo-co in the intact enzyme. Although a cubane-like

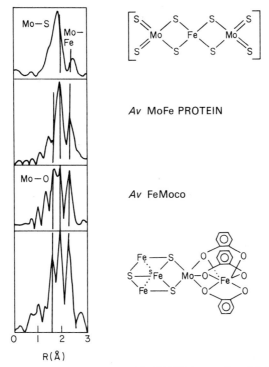

Av MoFe PROTEIN

Av FeMoco

Fig. 9. Fourier transforms of FeMo-co Mo EXAFS data and model data. The two main frequency components, Mo–S and Mo–Fe, clearly visible for nitrogenase and the $FeMo_2S_8$ model, are augmented in the catechol-capped model and native FeMo-co by a lower R peak assigned as O or N (reference [35]).

$MoFe_3S_n$ fragment might be a part of FeMo-co, the distribution of the three remaining irons remains a mystery, and non-cubane geometries for the molybdenum environment still need to be considered. As illustrated in Fig. 11, remarkable progress has been made in the synthetic chemistry of Mo,Fe,S clusters, but none of the models contains the correct metal stoichiometry. Clearly, questions about substrate interactions and the reaction mechanism of nitrogenase cannot be answered until the basic structure of FeMo-co is solved.

V. SULFITE OXIDASE

A. General properties

Sulfite oxidase catalyses the oxidation of sulfite to sulfate using cytochrome c as the physiological electron acceptor[51,52]

$$SO_3^{2-} + 2\text{cyt } c(\text{III}) + H_2O \rightarrow SO_4^{2-} + 2\text{cyt } c(\text{II}) + 2H^+ \tag{2}$$

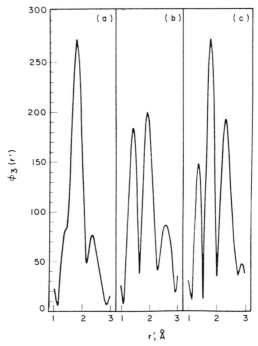

Fig. 10. Fourier transforms of the iron K edge EXAFS $k^3 \times x(k)$ versus k of (a) $[p\text{-}CH_3C_6H_4S)_2FeS_2FeS_2MoS_2]^{3-}$ (b) $[(C_6H_5O)_2FeS_2MoS_2]^{2-}$ and (c) the FeMo-co of nitrogenase (reference [50]).

It is the simplest molybdenum enzyme, and it typically exists as a dimer of equivalent 55 to 60 kdalton subunits,[53] each of which contains molybdenum and cytochrome b_5-like heme in covalently attached but distinct domains.[54] The enzyme has been crystallized in a variety of forms, but no structural data are yet available. As summarized in Table 4 (see p. 292), the redox potentials for sulfite oxidase molybdenum and heme[55] range from about -200 mV to $+100$ mV, significantly higher than the sulfate reduction potential.

B. EPR results

Although a variety of anion effects have been reported for the sulfite oxidase Mo(V) EPR signals,[56] it now appears that most of these changes are really pH effects, and that there are basically three types of spectra that can be elicited.[57] These are the low and high pH signals, which are interconvertible with pK_a of 8.2,[58] as well as a phosphate-bound signal. In all cases the signals are rhombic[57] rather than axial.[56] The various signals observed to-date are summarized in Figs 12 and 13.

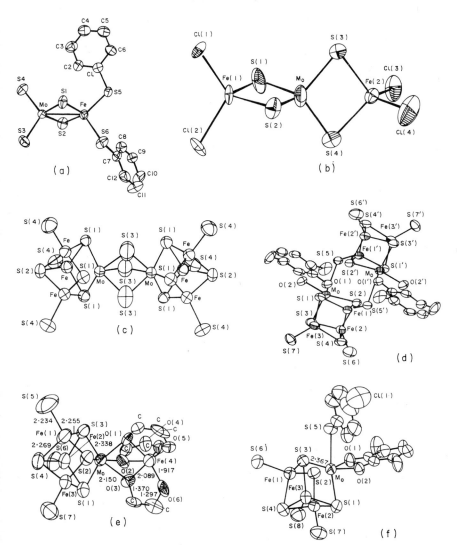

Fig. 11. Some recent Mo, Fe, S compounds with relevance for nitrogenase: (a) stereochemistry of the $[S_2MoS_2Fe(SPh)_2]^{2-}$ dianion. Hydrogen atoms are omitted for clarity;[134] (b) structure and labelling of the $[(FeCl_2)_2MoS_4]^{2-}$ anion;[135] (c) structure of $[Mo_2Fe_6S_9(SEt)_8]^{3-}$ as its Et_4N^+ salt; the two disordered ethyl groups in the $MoS(SEt)_2Mo$ bridge unit and those of the six terminal thiolate ligands are omitted;[37] (d) structure of $[Mo_2Fe_6S_8^*(SEt)_6(Pr_2cat)_2]^{4-}$ as its Et_4N^+ salt; shown are 50% probability ellipsoids and bridging and terminal ligand–metal bond distances (Å). Primed and unprimed atoms are related by an inversion center;[130] (e) structure of $[MoFe_4S_4(SEt)_3(C_6H_4O_2)_3]^{3-}$ as its Et_4N^+ salt. The ethyl groups of the three thiolate ligands and four ring carbon atoms of each of the three catecholate ligands are omitted;[47] (f) structure of $[MoFe_3S_4(S\text{-}p\text{-}C_6H_4Cl)_4((C_3H_5)_2cat)]^{3-}$. The $p\text{-}C_6H_4Cl$ groups of the terminal ligands and the $CH{=}CH_2$ portions of the catecholate ligand are omitted.[48]

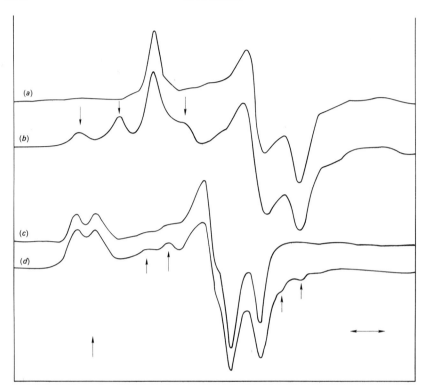

Fig. 12. ^{17}O effects on low and high pH sulfite oxidase EPR signal: (a) ^{16}O high pH; (b) 48% ^{17}O high pH; (c) low pH; and (d) 48% ^{17}O low pH.[61]

Garner and coworkers have reinvestigated the sulfite oxidase heme EPR signal at 20 degrees Kelvin.[59] They found no perturbation of the low spin Fe(III) by Mo(V) or vice versa, and concluded that the Mo–Fe separation was greater than 5 Å.

The low pH signal shows a proton splitting which is nearly isotropic and about 10 gauss (see Table 2), and this proton is rapidly exchangeable in D_2O.[58] Diluting the enzyme in ^{17}O-enriched water reveals ^{17}O hyperfine splittings of about 13 gauss.[60] At high pH values the proton splitting disappears, and an average ^{17}O splitting of 6 gauss is observed.

The phosphate complex of sulfite oxidase yields an EPR signal similar to the low pH signal, but without proton splitting.[57] It has, however, been found to exhibit ^{17}O effects.[61] As shown in Fig. 13, ^{17}O splittings appear when ^{17}O-enriched phosphate is used in ordinary water, whereas ^{17}O water does not introduce splittings in the presence of unlabelled phosphate. The authors interpret their results as indicating direct coordination of phosphate to

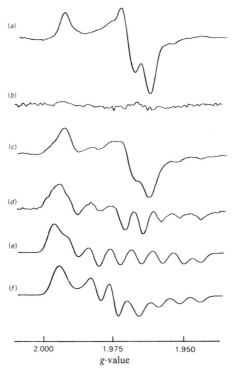

Fig. 13. [17]O effects on phosphate sulfite oxidase EPR signal: (a) sulfite-reduced in 25 mM phosphate in [17]O-enriched H_2O; (b) difference spectrum between and spectrum in normal H_2O; (c) spectrum with O-labelled phosphate; (d) 2 × [(c) - 0.65(a)]; (e, f) alternative simulations.[61]

molybdenum, via replacement of either a hydroxy group or a terminal oxygen atom.

C. EXAFS results

Sulfite oxidase X-ray absorption studies[62,63] reveal a dramatic difference in the absorption edges and EXAFS Fourier transforms for the oxidized and dithionite-reduced species, as illustrated in Figs 14 and 15. Curve-fitting analysis of the EXAFS data suggests that there are two oxo groups in the oxidized form of the enzyme, but only a single terminal oxo in the reduced enzyme, as shown in Scheme 2. This is consistent with the idea that an oxo group is protonated upon reduction of the enzyme at low pH, and that the proton on this hydroxyl is the source of the observed hyperfine splittings. It is also consistent with total removal of an oxo group. The former hypothesis

TABLE 2

Representative EPR parameters for molybdenum enzymes

Enzyme	g-values (±0.001)				Average A-values (gauss)			Reference
	g_1	g_2	g_3	g_{av}	^1G	^{17}O	^{33}S	
Nitrogenase (C. pasteurianum)	4.3	3.7	2.0					[25]
Xanthine oxidase								
"very rapid"	2.025	1.956	1.950	1.977		13.7	2	[79, 81–85]
"rapid type 1"	1.991	1.969	1.964	1.975	13.3, 3	14		[82, 108, 132]
"rapid type 2"	1.995	1.972	1.962	1.976	10.1, 10.1	10, 10		[82, 108]
"inhibited"	1.991	1.977	1.951	1.973		1.7, 1.4		[82]
"slow"	1.975	1.970	1.957	1.967	16.3, 1.6	10, 10		[79, 88]
Sulfite oxidase								
"high pH"	1.987	1.964	1.953	1.968		13		[58, 60, 82]
"low pH"	2.004	1.972	1.966	1.980	9.8	6		[58, 60, 82]
"phosphate"	1.992	1.969	1.961	1.974		9		[58, 60, 61]
Nitrate reductase								
E. coli low pH	1.999	1.985	1.963	1.982	9.2			[104]
Chlorella low pH[a]	1.994	1.969	1.967	1.977				
E. coli high pH	1.987	1.980	1.961	1.976				[104]
Chlorella high pH[a]	1.984	1.951	1.947	1.961				
Formate dehydrogenase	2.018	2.003	1.994	2.005	5.3, 5.3			[108]

[a] Unpublished results.

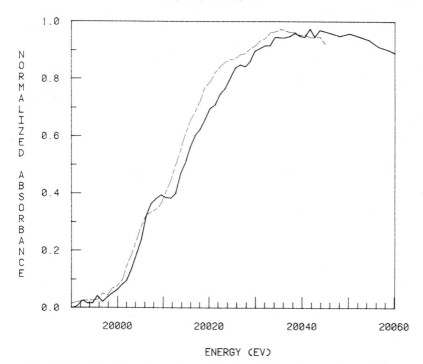

Fig. 14. Mo absorption edges for rat liver for sulfite oxidase. Oxidized(——),
H$_2$/H$_2$ase/MV-reduced (————) (Cramer, unpublished).

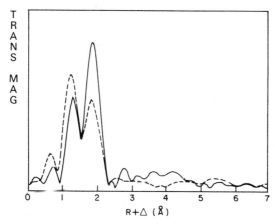

Fig. 15. Sulfite oxidase EXAFS Fourier transforms. Oxidized (————), reduced
(——).[63]

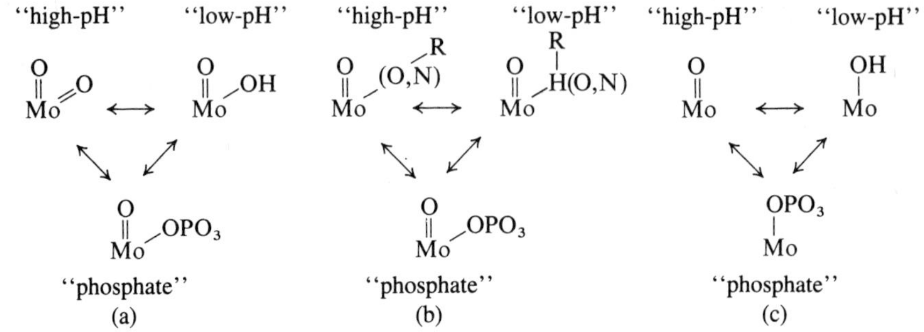

"high-pH"   "low-pH"   "high-pH"   "low-pH"   "high-pH"   "low-pH"

Scheme 2. Alternative interpretations of combined EXAFS and EPR results.

requires a dioxo Mo(V) species as the high pH form of the EPR active form of the enzyme. No model compounds for such a Mo(V) species are available, but this might be due to the rapid formation of oxo bridged dinuclear compounds, as in Scheme 3.

Scheme 2a appears at first to successfully combine the EXAFS and EPR results, and it was initially favored by Bray[64] and later Cramer et al.[63] However, on further inspection there are some divergences with the [17]O hyperfine results. The [17]O concentration dependence of the [17]O hyperfine splittings indicates that there is a strong interaction with only a single [17]O nucleus. Consequently, the hypothetical dioxo Mo(V) species of Scheme 2a must have a very large splitting for one terminal oxo and a very small splitting for the second oxo. Scheme 2b removes this difficulty, but in this case one would expect two different [17]O splittings in the phosphate spectrum when using both $H_2^{17}O$ and [17]O-labelled phosphate. Only a single splitting is observed. Scheme 2c is consistent with all the EPR data, but at first appears incompatible with the observation by EXAFS of a terminal oxo in the dithionite-reduced data. However, since the latter spectrum was recorded at pH 7.8, it is possible that a significant fraction of the proposed hydroxyl was in the deprotonated form. It is now clear that the pH dependence of the reduced EXAFS could help resolve this point.

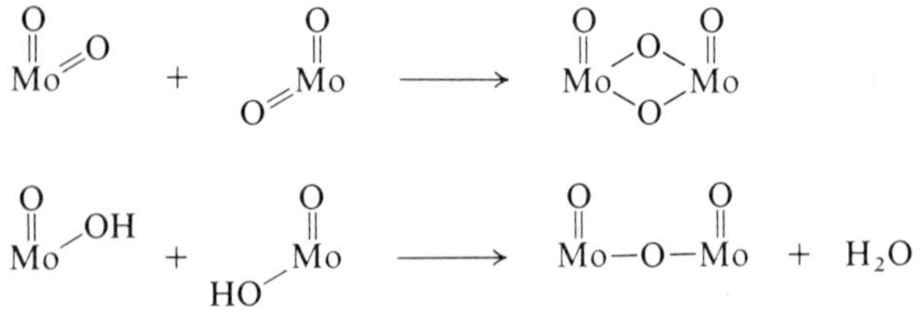

Scheme 3. Dimerization problem for dioxomolybdenum(V) model compounds.

The sulfite oxidase EXAFS also indicated a set of two or three sulfurs in the oxidized enzyme at 2.42 Å, shifting to 2.38 Å in the reduced enzyme with an amplitude best explained by 3 sulfurs. Combining there results with the information about oxo ligation yields a plausible structure for the sulfite oxidase molybdenum site, as shown in Scheme 4. It is unclear whether the postulated third sulfur ligand is bound to the molybdenum in the oxidized state, or simply close enough to bind upon reduction of the molybdenum.

$$Mo-OH + HO-Mo \longrightarrow Mo-O-Mo + H_2O$$

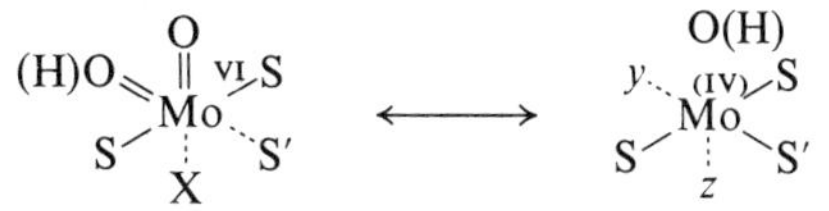

Scheme 4. Proposed molybdenum environments in oxidized and dithionite-reduced sulfite oxidase.

D. Sulfite oxidase summary

The EPR studies of sulfite oxidase have revealed the presence of exchangeable protons and oxygens close to the molybenum, while the EXAFS studies have revealed not only terminal oxo groups but sulfur donor ligands as well. This allows several precise structural questions to be posed about the sulfite oxidase molybdenum site. One point which needs clarification is the nature of proton equilibria with respect to the oxo groups. Although EPR studies have shown the presence of a proton with pK_a of 8.2 in the Mo(V) state, which is conceivably associated with a Mo–OH species, it is unclear what the corresponding behavior of the Mo(VI) and Mo(IV) states is. A second point to be clarified is the arrangement of sulfur ligands in the oxidized enzyme. It is also not known what additional ligands complete the coordination sphere. Finally, there is complete uncertainty as to which ligands, if any, are donated by the protein and which ligands are from the molybdenum cofactor.

V. XANTHINE OXIDASE

A. General properties

Xanthine oxidase belongs to a class of enzymes collectively known as molybdenum iron–sulfur flavin hydroxylases, which also includes aldehyde oxidase and xanthine dehydrogenase.[64,65] The reactions catalysed by these enzymes are quite numerous, involving a wide range of purines, pteridines, pyrimidines and aldehydes

$$RH + H_2O \rightarrow ROH + 2H^+ + 2e^- \tag{3}$$

These enzymes are closely related structurally and nearly identical from the molybdenum point of view. Conversion between oxidase and dehydrogenase activity apparently involves a thiol group[66,67] which is not at the molybdenum site. The comments made for xanthine oxidase should be considered as general for this class.

The molecular weight of milk xanthine oxidase is about 300 000, and the enzyme is a dimer of equivalent polypeptide subunits.[68] Each subunit contains one molybdenum, one FAD and two different (2Fe-2S) clusters.[70] As recorded in Table 4, the molybdenum redox potentials for active xanthine oxidase fall between -300 and -400 mV, which is considerably more negative than sulfite oxidase. They are also pH and temperature-dependent.[69] Similar redox potentials, molecular weights and prosthetic group compositions have been found for xanthine oxidase, xanthine dehydrogenase and aldehyde oxidase from a variety of sources.[71]

An important aspect of molybdenum hydroxylase chemistry is the conversion from active or "intact" to inactive "desulfo" forms, either gradually during storage or rapidly with cyanide.[72,73]

$$X.O.^{ox} + CN^- \rightarrow X.O.^{red} + SCN^- \qquad (4)$$
$$\text{active} \qquad\qquad \text{inactive}$$

The redox potentials for desulfo xanthine oxidase are an average of 40–100 mV lower than those found for intact enzyme.[74,75] Activity can be restored to some extent by treatment with sulfide.[72,73] Furthermore, active and desulfo forms can be resolved by affinity chromatography.[76]

B. EPR results

More molybdenum EPR signals are known for xanthine oxidase than for any other molybdenum enzyme. For the purposes of this review, four main types can be discerned,[64,65] namely the "very rapid", "rapid" and "inhibited" signals associated with active enzyme, and the "slow" signal from desulfo enzyme. The g-values and hyperfine splittings for these signals are summarized in Table 2, while the spectra themselves are presented in Fig. 16.

A large number of nuclear hyperfine interactions have been observed in the xanthine oxidase EPR, most of which have been summarized by Bray.[64,65] The best understood splittings are the proton interactions observed in most of the signals. An important mechanistic finding is that the proton causing the larger splitting in the "rapid" signal is abstracted from the C-8 position of xanthine and related substrates.[77,78] Splittings from ^{13}C have been observed in the inhibited signal when the enzyme is treated with [^{13}C]-methanol,[79] and in the very rapid signal when using xanthine having ^{13}C in the 8-position.[79] ^{17}O effects have been observed in the rapid signal of enzyme

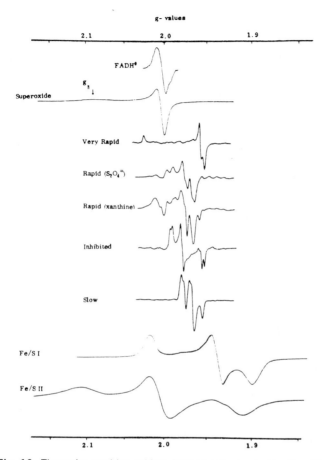

Fig. 16. The major xanthine oxidase EPR signals reported by Bray.[64]

equilibrated with $H_2{}^{17}O$,[60,80] as well as in the very rapid signal.[81] Very recently, Bray and Gutteridge have published an extensive study of ^{17}O effects on the xanthine oxidase signals, utilizing computer simulations and exploring the ^{17}O-concentration dependence.[82] ^{33}S splittings are observed when desulfo enzyme is reconstituted with $Na_2{}^{33}S$.[85] Finally, arsenite-inhibited xanthine oxidase has been reinvestigated recently and found to have very complicated ^{75}As splittings.[83,84] Representative nuclear hyperfine interactions are illustrated in Fig. 17.

The most important hyperfine splitting to explain is that arising from a strong proton interaction in the rapid signal (Scheme 5). Since a direct molybdenum hydride interaction as in I seems unlikely,[86,87] the question becomes the nature of the intervening atom X as in II. The nature of X is also

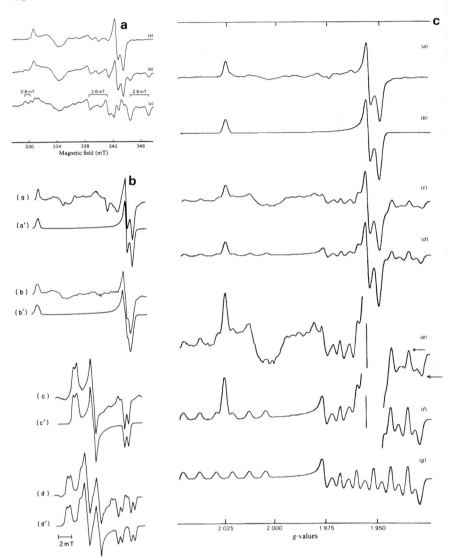

Fig. 17. Summary of types of nuclear hyperfine interactions observed in xanthine oxidase Mo(V) EPR. (a) ^{33}S effects. Top to bottom: Very rapid signal; very rapid signal after reactivation with 59% ^{33}S sodium sulfide; difference spectrum to yield pure ^{33}S spectrum;[85] (b) ^{13}C effects. Top to bottom: very rapid signal with ordinary xanthine, and simulation; very rapid signal with C-8 ^{13}C xanthine; simulation, inhibited signal with ordinary methanol, simulation; inhibited signal with ^{13}C methanol, simulation;[79] (c) ^{17}O effects. Top to bottom: very rapid signal in ordinary water, simulation; very rapid signal in 50% ^{17}O water, simulation; expanded scale, simulation; simulation for 100% ^{17}O;[81] (d) ^{75}As effects. Top to bottom: partially dithionite-reduced; arsenite-complexed, partially dithionite-reduced; arsenite-complexed partially-reduced, then plus 10 mM xanthine; same, but plus 3 mM salicylate instead of xanthine.[84]

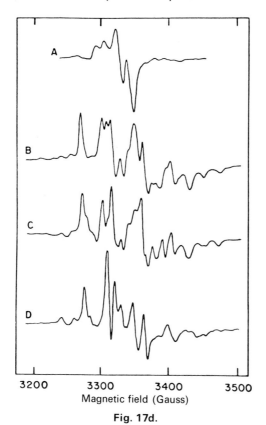

A

B

C

D

3200   3300   3400   3500

Magnetic field (Gauss)

Fig. 17d.

important mechanistically because it is presumably the proton-abstracting group.[77,78] In a proposal based on coupled electron proton transfer,[87] Stiefel favored a nitrogenous X as in III, although models IV and V were not ruled out. Earlier proposals favored structure VI, while the most recent work of Bray favors structure VII.[88]

One of the major structural questions arising from the chemical and

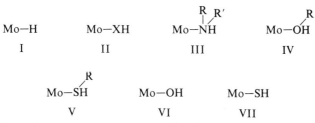

Scheme 5. Proposed sources of proton splitting in xanthine oxidase.

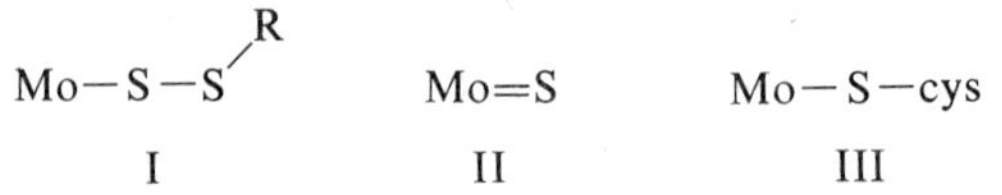

$$Mo-S-S\overset{\displaystyle R}{\diagup} \qquad Mo=S \qquad Mo-S-cys$$

I   II   III

Scheme 6. Possible sources of cyanolysable sulfur in xanthine oxidase.

spectroscopic studies of xanthine oxidase is the nature of the cyanolysable sulfur (Scheme 6). This was originally thought to be a persulfide sulfur as in I[89] although a terminal sulfur as in II was proposed quite early,[90] and even a cysteine sulfur as in III was considered.[91] The anisotropy of the [33]S splittings in the "very rapid" signal of [33]S-reactivated enzyme lends strong support to structure II.[85]

The [17]O hyperfine splittings of the xanthine oxidase EPR signals are more complicated than those found in sulfite oxidase. By analysing the [17]O-concentration dependence of the changes, Bray and Gutteridge[81] found evidence for a single exchangeable oxygen in the very rapid and rapid type 1 signals, and two exchangeable oxygens in the inhibited and rapid type 2 signals.

By combining all of the information known about ^{1}H, ^{13}C, [17]O and [33]S splittings, Bray and Gutteridge have formulated a fairly detailed picture of the terminal ligation in active xanthine oxidase.[82] Their proposal is reproduced in Scheme 7.

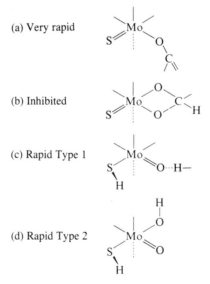

(a) Very rapid

(b) Inhibited

(c) Rapid Type 1

(d) Rapid Type 2

Scheme 7. Structures suggested by Bray and Gutteridge for Mo(V) species of active xanthine oxidase, based on EPR hyperfine interactions alone.[82]

Clearly, a wealth of structural questions were raised by the chemical and EPR studies. Some of these points have been clarified by EXAFS, while additional complications have arisen.

C. EXAFS results

The earliest EXAFS studies of xanthine oxidase[92,93] produced contradictory results. The analysis by Tullius *et al.* found 1.5 terminal oxygens at 1.71 Å, as well as 2.1 sulfurs at 2.54 Å. In contrast, Bordas *et al.* found 1 terminal oxygen at 1.75 Å, 2 sulfurs at 2.46 Å, and another Mo–S interaction at 2.25 Å. Both groups also found a long Mo–S at about 2.85 Å. A subsequent study by Cramer *et al.*[63] of chicken liver xanthine dehydrogenase yielded the values summarized in Table 3. The absorption edges observed for xanthine oxidase are shown in Fig. 18, the EXAFS Fourier transforms shown in Fig. 19 and the fits in Fig. 20.

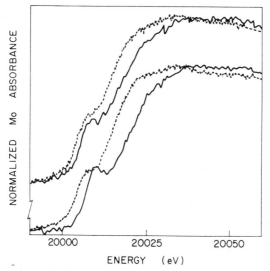

Fig. 18. Xanthine dehydrogenase absorption edges. Top, oxidized, intact XDH (——) vs reduced, intact XDH (----); bottom, oxidized, cyanolysed XDH vs reduced, cyanolysed XDH.[63]

All of the xanthine dehydrogenase absorption edges exhibited a pronounced low energy shoulder, and in the oxidized cyanalysed spectrum a separate peak was actually resolved. Most of the oscillator strength in these transitions is probably the result of a terminal Mo=O bond(s). However, the oxidized edges may also reflect a distorted molybdenum coordination sphere which is closer to tetrahedral than octahedral.

TABLE 3

Summary of EXAFS results on molybdenum enzymes and proteins

Enzyme	Conditions	Mo=O		Mo—S		Type	Mo—X		Reference
		Number	R (Å)	Number	R (Å)		Number	R (Å)	
Nitrogenase (C. pasteurianum)	lyophilized, "semi-reduced"	0	—	3–4	2.35	Mo—Fe Mo—S'	2–3 1–2	2.72 2.49	[33]
Nitrogenase (A. vinelandii)	25 mM Tris HCl, pH 7.4 "semi-reduced"	0		3–4	2.35	Mo—Fe Mo—S'	2–3 1–2	2.73 2.46	[34]
Sulfite oxidase (chicken liver)	50 mM KPi, pH 7.8, oxidized	2	1.68	2–3	2.41				
Sulfite oxidase (chicken liver)	50 mM KPi, pH 7.8, dithionite-reduced	1	1.69	3	2.38				
Xanthine dehydrogenase (chicken liver)	5 mM KPi, pH 7.8, oxidized, active	1	1.70	2	2.47	Mo=S	1	2.15	[63]
Xanthine dehydrogenase (chicken liver)	5 mM KPi, pH 7.8, reduced, active	1	1.68	3	2.38				[63]
Xanthine dehydrogenase (chicken liver)	5 mM KPi, pH 7.8, oxidized, desulfo	2	1.67	2	2.46				[63]
Xanthine oxidase (chicken liver)	5 mM KPi, pH 7.8, reduced, desulfo	1	1.66	2–3	2.33				[63]
Xanthine dehydrogenase (bovine milk)	5 mM KPi, pH 7.8, oxidized, active	1–2	1.75	2	2.49	Mo=S Mo—S'	1 1	2.25 2.89	[93]
Xanthine oxidase (bovine milk)	lyophilized, oxidized, desulfo	2	1.74	2	2.49	Mo—S''	1	2.91	[93]
Xanthine oxidase (bovine milk)	100 mM Tris-HOAc, pH 8.5, oxidized	1.5	1.71	2.1	2.54	Mo—S'	1.1	2.84	[92]

TABLE 3—*continued*

Enzyme	Conditions	Mo=O Number	Mo=O R (Å)	Mo—S Number	Mo—S R (Å)	Type	Mo—X Number	Mo—X R (Å)	Reference
Nitrate reductase (E. coli)	50 mM KPi, pH 7.0, oxidized	0		2	2.37	Mo—Fe Mo—O, N	1 2	2.78 2.12	[105]
Nitrate reductase (E. coli)	50 mM KPi, pH 7.0, reduced	0		2	2.36	Mo—Fe Mo—O, N	1 2	2.79 2.10	[105]
Nitrate reductase (Chlorella)	80 mM KPi, pH 7.6, oxidized	2	1.72	2–3	2.44				[105]
Nitrate reductase (Chlorella)	80 mM KPi, pH 7.6, reduced	1	1.67	3	2.38	Mo—O, N	1	2.07	[105]
Mo-(2Fe-2S) protein (D. gigas)	100 mM Tris HCl, pH 7.6, oxidized	2	1.68	2	2.47	Mo—O, N	1	1.90	[96]
Mo-(2Fe-2S) protein (D. gigas)	100 mM Tris HCl, pH 7.6, dithionite-reduced	1	1.68	2	2.38				[96]
CO_2 reductase (C. pasteurianum)	50 mM Tris HCl, pH 8, as isolated	3	1.74	0					[112]
Mo-binding protein (C. pasteurianum)	50 mM Tris HCl, pH 8, as isolated	3	1.74	0					[137]

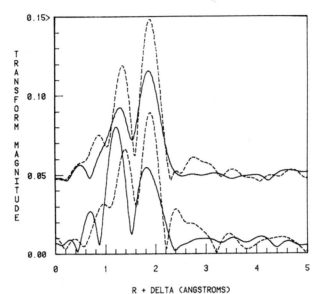

Fig. 19. Xanthine dehydrogenase Fourier transforms. Top to bottom: oxidized, intact XDH (– – – –) vs reduced, intact XDH (——), oxidized cyanolysed XDH (– – – –) vs reduced, cyanolysed XDH (——).[63]

Curve-fitting the xanthine dehydrogenase EXAFS confirmed the presence of a terminal Mo–S interaction at 2.15 Å in the oxidized active enzyme. This short bond disappeared upon dithionite reduction while the terminal Mo=O stayed in place. As expected, cyanolysed xanthine dehydrogenase showed no evidence for a short Mo—S bond. Rather, this species appeared to have two terminal Mo—O bonds in its oxidized form, and only a single oxo when reduced. Both forms of the enzyme had two sulfurs at about 2.47 Å in the oxidized forms, which shortened by about 0.1 Å upon reduction. An interpretation consistent with these data and the hyperfine splittings found by Bray is presented in Scheme 8.

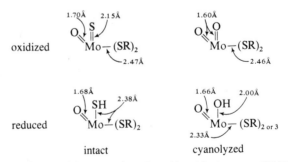

Scheme 8. Suggested interpretation of xanthine dehydrogenase EXAFS.

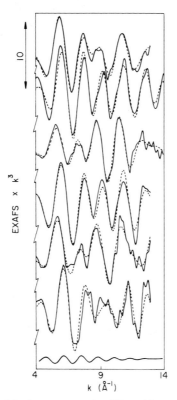

Fig. 20. Xanthine dehydrogenase and sulfite oxidase curve-fitting. Measured EXAFS (——) and best fit (– – – –). Top to bottom: oxidized SO, reduced SO, oxidized, intact XDH, reduced, intact XDH, oxidized, cyanolysed XDH, reduced, cyanolysed XDH. Bottom: simulation of 1 Mo–S at 2.85 Å.[63]

D. Xanthine oxidase summary

A valuable result from the xanthine oxidase EXAFS work is the confirmation of a terminal sulfide as the cyanolysable sulfur. Protonation of this sulfur, or of an oxo in the desulfo enzyme, upon reduction can account for the observed hyperfine interactions. Still, there remain questions about the more distant sulfur ligands. In particular, it is not clear why the xanthine oxidase Mo S bonds are about 0.05 Å longer than those in sulfite oxidase. This might reflect a *trans* effect in xanthine oxidase due to the terminal ligands. Alternatively, the sulfurs might interact with each other to form a disulfide, which tend to have longer Mo—S bond lengths. A combination of both effects might also be operative. The nature of the remaining ligands is still a mystery.

TABLE 4

Molybdenum redox potentials in molybdenum enzymes

Enzyme	Conditions	E_1 (mV) Mo(VI) → Mo(V)	E_2 (mV) Mo(V) → Mo(IV)	Reference
D. gigas Mo protein		−415	−530	[94]
Formate dehydrogenase				
(*M. formicicum*)	50 mM Bicine, pH 7.7	−330	−470	[108]
Aldehyde oxidase				
(rabbit liver, active)	50 mM KPi, pH 7.8	−359	−351	[108]
(rabbit liver, desulfo)	10 mM KPi, pH 7.8	−439	−401	[108]
Xanthine dehydrogenase				
(chicken liver, active)	50 mM KPi, pH 7.8	−357	−337	[75]
(chicken liver, desulfo)	50 mM KPi, pH 7.8	−397	−433	[75]
Xanthine oxidase				
(bovine milk, active)	50 mM KPi, pH 7.8	−355	−355	[108]
(bovine milk, desulfo)	50 mM KPi, pH 7.8	−354	−386	[108]
Sulfite oxidase	5 mM Tris-HCl, pH 8.0	38	−163	[108]
Nitrate reductase				
(*Chlorella vulgaris*)	100 mM MOPS, pH 7.1	− 34	− 54	[101]
(*E. coli*)		180	220	[102]

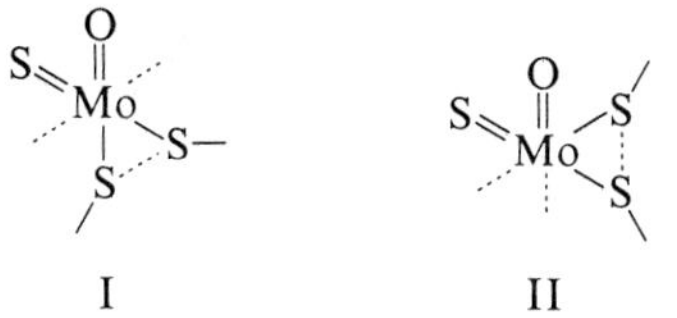

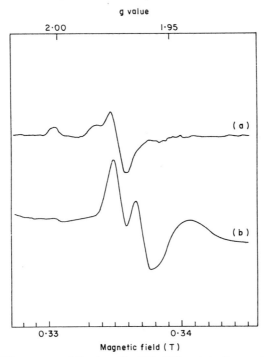

I   II

Scheme 9. Possible Mo—S bond lengthening interactions in xanthine oxidase.

VII. *D. Gigas* Mo-(2Fe-2S) PROTEIN

A. General properties

No enzymatic function is yet known for this molybdenum-containing protein isolated from *Desulfovibrio gigas*. It has a molecular weight of about 120 000, and contains one molybdenum and six irons, the latter as 2Fe-2S clusters.[94,95] The molybdenum protein redox potentials found in this enzyme are low, −415 mV for Mo(VI)-Mo(V) and −530 mV for Mo(V)-Mo(IV), Table 4.

B. EPR results

The molybdenum EPR spectra of the *D. gigas* protein is illustrated in Fig. 21.

Fig. 21. EPR spectrum of *D. gigas* Mo-(2Fe-2S) protein. Top: resting; bottom: partially reduced.[94]

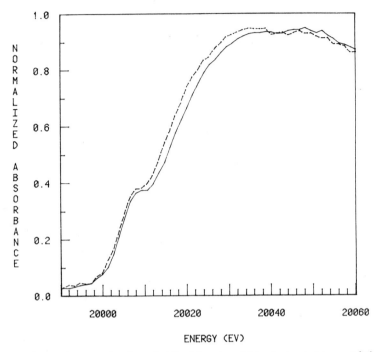

Fig. 22. *D. gigas* protein edges. Oxidized (———) vs dithionite-treated (– – – –).[96]

The resting enzyme exhibited a signal which integrated to about 11% of the total molybdenum. Upon dithionite reduction a different signal appeared which had a strong resemblance to that of desulfo xanthine oxidase.[94]

C. EXAFS results

As in all its other properties, the EXAFS of the *D. gigas* protein strongly resembles that of desulfo xanthine oxidase.[96] The edges shown in Fig. 22 and the Fourier transforms and curve-fitting shown in Figs 23 and 24 are all consistent with a primarily dioxo-Mo(VI) species as isolated which is converted to a mono-oxo species upon reduction. Two sulfur ligands are clearly present, and additional oxygen or nitrogen ligands presumably complete the coordination sphere. A plausible model for this molybdenum site is summarized in Scheme 10.

Scheme 10. Suggested partial structures for *D. gigas* protein molybdenum site.

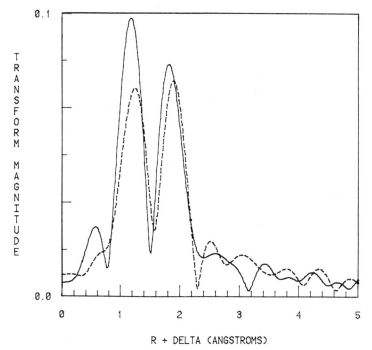

Fig. 23. *D. gigas* protein Fourier transforms. Oxidized (——) vs dithionite-treated (————).[96]

D. *D. gigas* protein summary

Certainly, the main question to be resolved about the *D. gigas* protein is its role in the biochemistry of this organism. In this regard, it would be interesting to see if the enzyme can be reacted with sulfide to yield a molybdenum environment more akin to active xanthine oxidase.

VIII. NITRATE REDUCTASE

A. General properties

There are two known types of nitrate reductase enzymes, both of which reduce nitrate to nitrite[97]

$$NO_3^- + 2e^- + 2H^+ \rightarrow NO_2^- + H_2O \tag{5}$$

Assimilatory nitrate reductases reduce nitrate to nitrite so that the nitrogen can ultimately be reduced to ammonia and then incorporated into amino acids. The physiological electron donor may be NAD(P)H. These enzymes

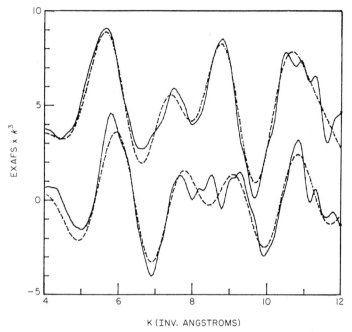

Fig. 24. *D. gigas* protein curve-fitting. Data (——) and fit (————). Top: oxidized; bottom: dithionite-treated.[94]

contain molybdenum, heme and FAD. A representative case is the enzyme from *Chlorella vulgaris*, which is a 360 000 dalton homotetramer[98] containing one of each prosthetic group per subunit. The *dissimilatory* or *respiratory* nitrate reductases use nitrate merely as terminal electron acceptor in the absence of dioxygen. An example is the *E. coli* enzyme, which has a molecular weight of 220 000 and contains one molybdenum and 16 iron atoms,[99] the latter as $4Fe_4S_4$ clusters.[100]

The molybdenum redox potentials have recently been determined for assimilatory nitrate reductase;[101] at pH 7 they are -34 mV for Mo(VI)-Mo(V) and -54 mV for Mo(V)-Mo(IV). These are similar to the sulfite oxidase values. Respiratory *E. coli* enzyme was found to have significantly higher potentials, a Mo(VI) $\rightarrow$ Mo(V) potential of $+180$ mV and a Mo(V) $\rightarrow$ Mo(IV) potential of $+220$ mV.[102]

B. EPR results

Relatively little EPR work has been done on the assimilatory nitrate reductases, but the signals are similar to sulfite oxidase with respect to pH

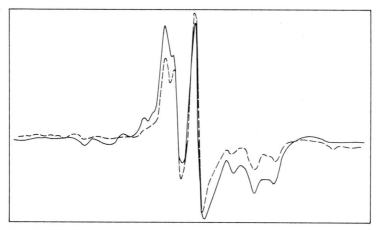

Fig. 25. [17]O effects on the *Chlorella* nitrate reductase EPR spectrum. Normal, low pH signal (——) vs same in 50% [17]O water.[103]

dependence and proton splittings.[100] As shown in Fig. 25, [17]O effects can be observed in these spectra.[103]

A more comprehensive analysis of the EPR from the *E. coli* enzyme has been carried out by Vincent and Bray.[104] They observed five EPR signals assignable to Mo(V), which they label the "low-pH", "high-pH", "nitrate complex", "nitrite-complex" and "non-functional" signals. The low and high pH forms, illustrated in Fig. 26, are related by a pK_a of 8.26, and the proton

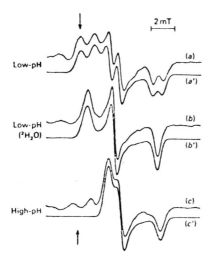

Fig. 26. *E. coli* nitrate reductase Mo EPR signals and simulations.[104]

which splits the low pH signals is rapidly exchangeable with D_2O. All of the spectra are rhombic in form, and the g-values are summarized in Table 3. [17]O effects have recently been observed on the *E. coli* nitrate reductase signals as well.[103]

C. EXAFS results

The molybdenum sites of the *Chlorella* and *E. coli* enzymes have been compared in an X-ray absorption study.[105] As illustrated in Fig. 27, the

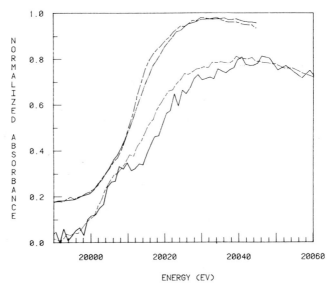

Fig. 27. Molybdenum absorption edges for nitrate reductase. Top (——), ferricyanide-oxidized *E. coli* enzyme (– – – –), dithionite-reduced *E. coli* enzyme, bottom (——), as isolated *Chlorella* enzyme; bottom (– – – –) NADH-reduced *Chlorella* enzyme.[105]

absorption edges for the two enzymes are quite different in appearance, and the same applies to the EXAFS Fourier transforms shown in Fig. 28.

The curve-fitting results (Fig. 29) indicate that the *Chlorella* enzyme molybdenum site is nearly identical to that of hepatic sulfite oxidase, whereas the *E. coli* enzyme might contain a novel site, as illustrated in Scheme 11.

The structural differences observed by EXAFS might have significant mechanistic implications, and a plusible explanation for the cumulative EXAFS and EPR data is presented in Scheme 12.

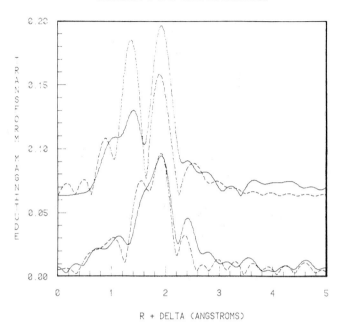

CHLORELLA & E.C. NITRATE REDUCTASE

R + DELTA (ANGSTROMS)

Fig. 28. EXAFS Fourier transforms for nitrate reductase. Top (————), as isolated *Chlorella* enzyme; bottom (————) NADH-reduced *Chlorella* enzyme; bottom (————) oxidized *E. coli* 3nzyme, (———) NADH-reduced *Chlorella* enzyme.

D. Nitrate reductase summary

Nitrate reductase enzymes are still incompletely understood. For the *Chlorella* enzyme, the structural questions appear to be the same as posed for sulfite oxidase. The *E. coli* enzyme site appears particularly enigmatic. It is not clear whether there are certain oxidizing conditions under which a dioxo-Mo(VI) species is produced, or whether there is something in the ligand arrangement which precludes such a species. A second question pertains to the possible Mo–Fe interaction. There are as yet no chemical models for molybdenum bridged to Fe_3S_4 or Fe_4S_4 clusters, and it is unclear what sort of bridging interaction might be present.

The nature of the EPR-active species in *Chlorella* and *E. coli* is also of interest. By analogy with sulfite oxidase, the *Chlorella* enzyme might exhibit a protonic equilibrium between species I and II (Scheme 13). The *E. coli* enzyme might exhibit a similar equilibrium. Further work with ^{17}O might help clarify this point.

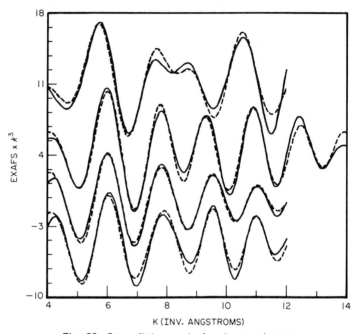

Fig. 29. Curve-fitting results for nitrate reductase.

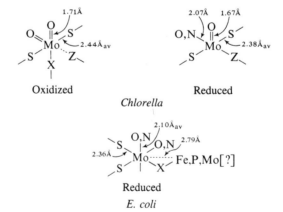

Scheme 11. Proposed structures for *Chlorella* and *E. coli* nitrate reductase molybdenum sites.

IX. FORMATE DEHYDROGENASE (CO₂ REDUCTASE)

A. General properties

Depending on the organism, the physiological role of formate dehydrogenase enzymes may be to oxidize formate or to reduce CO_2.[106,107] In the latter case,

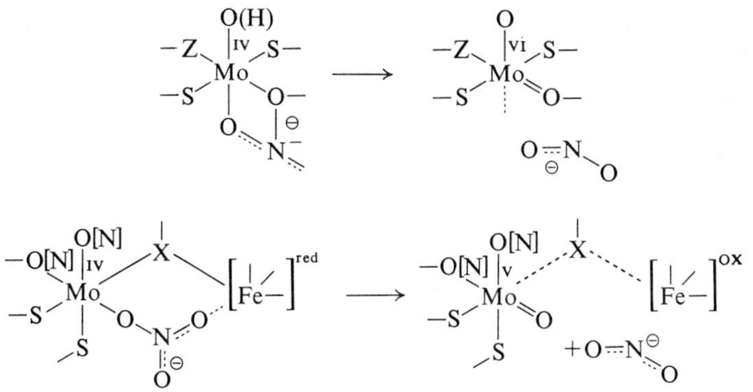

Scheme 12. Mechanistic possibilities derived from nitrate reductase structural results.

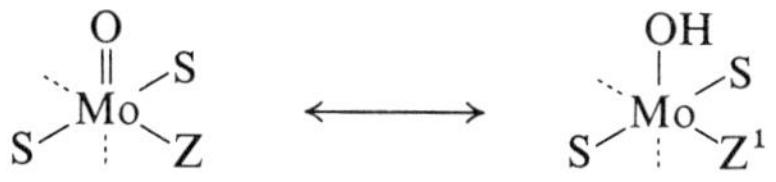

Scheme 13. Possible source of proton splittings in *Chlorella* nitrate reductase.

the CO_2 reductase activity is generally the first step in carbon fixation, since the formate produced can be further metabolized via the tetrahydrofolate pathway to one-carbon precursors for cell materials.

$$HCOO^- \leftrightarrow CO_2 + H^+ + 2e^- \qquad (6)$$

The size and prosthetic group composition of formate dehydrogenases varies enormously, as summarized in Table 5. In fact, some of the enzymes do not require molybdenum at all. The enzyme from *Clostridium thermoaceticum*

TABLE 5
Representative types of formate dehydrogenase [a]

Source	Electron acceptor	Molecular weight	Non-protein components
Escherichia coli	Quinone	590 000	Heme, Mo, Se, Fe/S
Clostridium thermoaceticum	NADP	300 000	Mo, W, Se
Clostridium pasteurianum	Ferredoxin	118 000	Mo, Fe/S
Methanococcus vannielii	F_{420}	200 000(?)	Mo, Se, Fe/S
Pseudomonas oxalaticus	NAD	315 000	FMN, Fe/S
Candida boidinii	NAD	74 000	—

[a] From reference [106].

works better with tungsten than with molybdenum,[110] while that from *Pseudomonas oxalaticus* appears to require neither metal.[111]

The reduction potentials reported for *Methanobacterium formicicum* formate dehydrogenase are low, -330 mV for Mo(VI)-Mo(V) and -470 mV for Mo(V)-Mo(IV).[108] Information on the Mo redox potentials of enzymes from other sources is not yet available.

B. EPR results

The only molybdenum EPR work reported to-date for formate dehydrogenase is the observation of a rhombic signal ($g_{av} = 2.005$) seen in the formate-reduced enzyme from *Methanobacterium formicicum*.[109] As illustrated in Fig. 30, this signal exhibits both proton and ^{95}Mo coupling. The

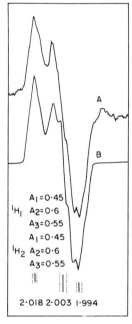

Fig. 30. EPR spectrum of *M. formicicum* formate dehydrogenase.[109]

investigators point out that the g-values are mugh higher than those found in other molybdenum enzymes, suggesting a significant difference in the Mo centers. The proton splitting pattern indicates the presence of two equivalent protons.

C. EXAFS results

Preliminary EXAFS results are available for the tungsten enzyme from *Clostridium thermoaceticum* and the molybdenum enzyme from *Clostridium pasteurianum*.[112] In Fig. 31 the Fourier transform of the tungsten L_{III} edge EXAFS is shown, in comparison with two tungsten compounds and the

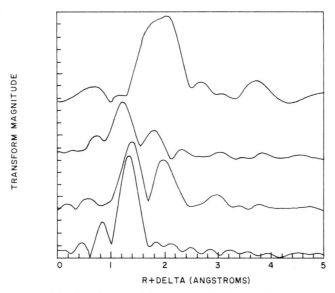

Fig. 31. Formate dehydrogenase Fourier transforms.

molybdenum enzyme. Clearly the tungsten site is not the dioxo type of species found in many molybdenum enzymes, nor is it similar to the cluster type site proposed for nitrogenase. Preliminary curve-fitting analysis indicates the presence of at least two sulfur ligands at about 2.35 Å as well as at least two oxygen or nitrogen ligands at about 2.10 Å.

In sharp contrast with the *C. thermoaceticum* tungsten enzyme, the CO_2 reductase molybdenum site in *C. pasteurianum* appears to have three oxo groups. This is indicated by the unique absorption edge (Fig. 32) and the Fourier transform (Fig. 31), which clearly shows a peak in the region characteristic of oxo ligation. Surprisingly, there is no evidence for coordination by sulfur ligands, which have been found in all other molybdenum enzymes examined to-date. Instead, additional oxygen or nitrogen ligands at 2.1 and 2.4 Å were found. The contrast between the two types of sites is shown in Scheme 14.

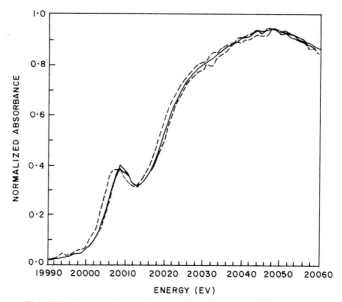

Fig. 32. *C. pasteurianum* formate dehydrogenase Mo edges.

C. pasteurianum *C. thermoaceticum*

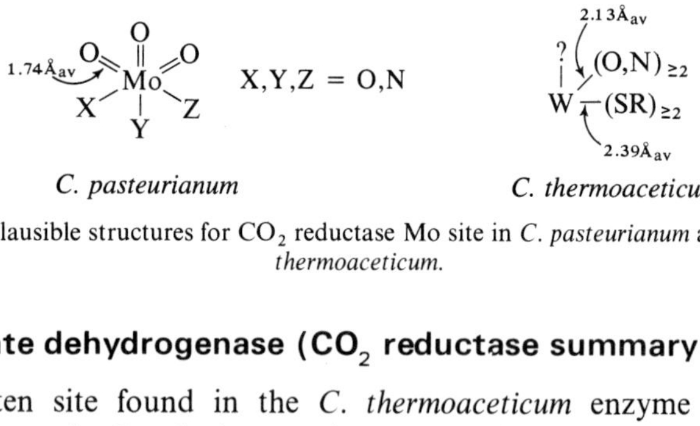

Scheme 14. Plausible structures for CO_2 reductase Mo site in *C. pasteurianum* and W site in *C. thermoaceticum.*

D. Formate dehydrogenase (CO_2 reductase summary)

The tungsten site found in the *C. thermoaceticum* enzyme bears some resemblance to the *E. coli* nitrate reductase molybdenum environment, since both enzymes appear to lack terminal oxo groups in the presence of dithionite. There might also be some similarity with the *M. formicicum* Mo site. Since two proton splittings were found, the latter might have 2Mo—OH bonds. A major unanswered question is whether or not a W–Se interaction exists. It is also unclear as to whether or not the tungsten is redox active during CO_2 reduction. Finally, it needs to be determined whether terminal oxo species, such as found in the other non-nitrogenase molybdenum enzymes, are ever present at the tungsten site.

The discovery of a tri-oxo molybdenum site in *C. pasteurianum* formate dehydrogenase poses an entirely new set of structural questions. The edge data indicate that the molybdenum site is not redox active, although binding of formate and/or carbonate cannot be ruled out. Furthermore, this is the only molybdenum enzyme whose EXAFS has failed to indicate sulfur ligation. This is consistent with tri-oxo ligation, since all known tri-oxo molybdenum compounds, apart from MoO_3S^{2-}, complete their coordination sphere with relatively hard ligands such as amines.[113] A possible role for molybdenum in the *C. pasteurianum* enzyme might therefore be as a binding site for formate and/or bicarbonate, with the actual electron transfer taking place through the iron–sulfur clusters. In fact, reduction of CO_2 catalysed by synthetic iron–sulfur clusters has recently been demonstrated.[114]

X. MOLYBDENUM PROCESSING PROTEINS

A. General properties

Almost all organisms which utilize metals for enzymatic purposes have evolved systems for transporting the metals across cell membranes, "permeases", as well as binding proteins to sequester the metal once inside the cell. For example, the protein ferritin is used to store iron,[115] and large amounts of zinc and copper are accumulated in metallothioneins.[116] In the case of molybdenum, these transport and storage processes are better understood genetically than structurally or mechanistically.

It is known that there are permease systems for transporting molybdate across cell membranes.[117] This system is relatively non-specific, since it also transports sulfate and tungstate.

Once inside the cell, molybdenum is stored in various precursors before being incorporated into active enzymes. For example, Johnson *et al.* have shown that in mammalian liver there is a pool of molybdenum in the form of molybdenum cofactor, and that the total molybdenum content of the cell is about evenly divided between this pool, that in sulfite oxidase, and that in xanthine dehydrogenase.[118] Rajagopalan has also observed a protein in *E. coli* which stores the molybdenum cofactor.[119] Brill and coworkers have described a set of mutants in *Klebsiella* which lack various precursors to nitrogenase.[120] A final example is the study of Hinton and Mortenson,[121] in which radioactive ^{99}Mo and electrophoresis was used to monitor the course of molybdenum after derepression for nitrogenase synthesis.

There is no molybdenum EPR data available on any of these molybdenum storage proteins, perhaps because the molybdenum is present as fully-oxidized Mo(VI). However, there are some preliminary EXAFS results on a low molecular weight molybdenum protein from *Clostridium pasteurianum*.

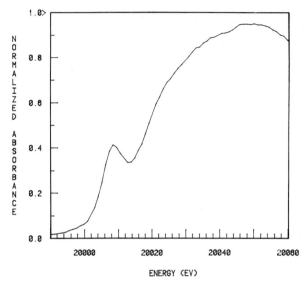

Fig. 33. *C. pasteurianum* Mo-binding protein Mo absorption edge.

B. EXAFS results

The molybdenum absorption edge of the *Clostridium* Mo-binding protein is illustrated in Fig. 33. The strong bound state transition is quite similar to that observed in CO_2 reductase, and the Fourier transform shown in Fig. 34 is also quite similar to the transform of the enzyme EXAFS.

Curve-fitting analysis of the Mo-binding protein EXAFS was consistent with a tri-oxo molybdenum site, with the remaining ligands most likely oxygen and/or nitrogen donors. A plausible model is shown in Scheme 15.

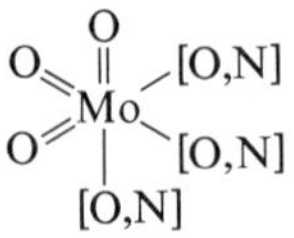

$$
\begin{array}{c}
\text{O} \\
\text{O} \diagdown \overset{\|}{\underset{|}{\text{Mo}}} \diagup \text{[O,N]} \\
\text{O} \diagup \quad \diagdown \text{[O,N]} \\
\text{[O,N]}
\end{array}
$$

Scheme 15. Proposed molybdenum environment for Mo-binding protein.

XI. MOLYBDENUM COFACTOR

The molecular structure of the molybdenum cofactor, "Mo-co", has been an elusive entity for nearly 20 years. The early genetic studies of Pateman *et al.* with *Aspergillus nidulans* mutants showed that nitrate reductase and xanthine

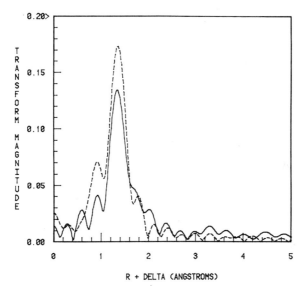

Fig. 34. Mo-binding protein EXAFS Fourier transform (——) compared with MoO_4^{2-} transform (————).

dehydrogenase contained a common genetic determinant.[122] Subsequent work by Nason *et al.* demonstrated that this species was a small molecule apparently common to all known Mo enzymes.[123] An important clarification was made by Pienkos, Shah and Brill,[124] who showed that the nitrogenase iron–molybdenum cofactor, FeMo-co, could be chromatographically resolved from Mo-co, and that neither had the biological activity of the other. However, complete purification and characterization of Mo-co has been hindered by low preparative yields, the instability of the cofactor,[124-129] and an imperfect assay.[130]

The exact nature of the organic part of Mo-co is still uncertain. It was originally thought to be a small polypeptide, and a preliminary report by Johnson listed 15 amino acids as being present.[8] A different group claimed the presence of aspartic acid, threonine, serine, lysine and alanine in the ratio of $2:1:5:3:1$.[125] The amino acid composition (if any) is currently in limbo.

A major breakthrough in Mo-co research was the discovery of the fluorescence properties of inactive cofactor.[8,126] As illustrated in Fig. 35, the absorption spectra of oxidized and inactivated Mo co are similar to biopterin. Based on this finding, it was suggested that Mo-co is a pterin derivative. Subsequently, two different oxidative degradation products of Mo-co were distinguished, as illustrated in Scheme 16. The ferricyanide-inactivated Mo-co derivative, form B, yielded a periodate-sensitive glycol upon alkaline phosphatase cleavage of its phosphate ester bond.

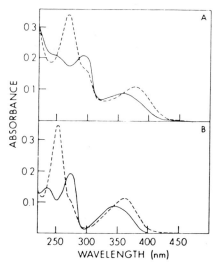

Fig. 35. Absorption spectra of inactive Mo cofactor (A) and biopterin (B). Spectra were recorded in H_2O (——) and 1 N NH_4OH (————).[126]

Oxidation with permanganate yielded a product similar to, if not the same as, pterin-6-carboxylic-7-sulfonylic acid.

The indication of sulfur in the cofactor pterin led Johnson and Rajagopalan to investigate possible relationships with other sulfur-containing pterins.[133] They discovered that the urinary excretion product urothione yielded oxidation products similar to those of dephospho Mo-co form B, and from as yet unpublished nmr data concluded that dephospho form B differs from

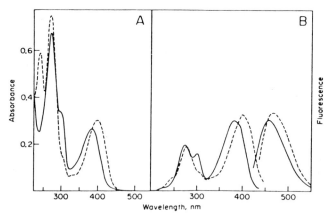

Fig. 36. Absorption (A) and fluorescence (B) spectra of form A (——) and form B (————) inactive derivatives of Mo cofactor.

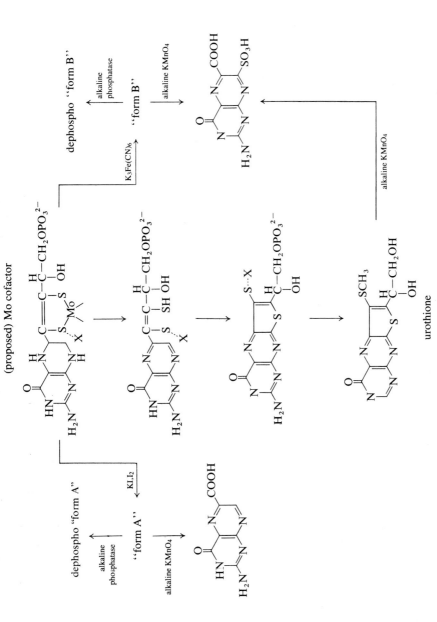

Scheme 16. Structure of Mo-co proposed by Rajagopalan, with related chemistry.

urothione merely by the absence of a —SCH$_3$ functionality. Possible relationships between all of these species are summarized in Scheme 16.

XII. SUMMARY

The most valuable insight gained from the study of molybdenum enzymes is an awareness of their structural diversity. This requires significant changes in the catalytic mechanisms proposed for these enzymes. Much of the early thought about molybdenum enzyme mechanisms was influenced by the notion of a universal molybdenum cofactor and the underlying assumption that the molybdenum environment in proteins is nearly invariant. Accordingly, these proposals sought to unify all of the reactions catalysed into a single scheme. The first major break in this simplistic view came with the discovery that the molybdenum in nitrogenase was contained in a unique polynuclear Mo,Fe,S cluster devoid of oxo groups. Since then mononuclear Mo-co molybdenum sites have been observed with one, two or three terminal oxo groups, in species such as reduced sulfite oxidase, oxidized sulfite oxidase and *Clostridial* CO$_2$ reductase, respectively, and an oxo-sulfido combination has been found in xanthine oxidase. Species with as many as three thiolate-like sulfur ligands have been found, as in reduced *Chlorella* nitrate reductase, and sites devoid of sulfur ligands have also been observed, as in the *Clostridial* Mo-binding protein. Finally, a second polynuclear Mo–Fe site may be present in *E. coli* nitrate reductase. A summary of the major structures observed to-date is presented in Scheme 17.

Despite the progress that has been made, a great deal of work is needed before the understanding of molybdenum enzymes is on a par with that of iron, copper and zinc proteins. By far the greatest step will be made when X-ray crystallographic structures become available for nitrogenase and the other proteins, as well as for the isolated cofactors. There is also the potential for significant progress by application of other types of spectroscopy. Infrared and Raman techniques might be useful probes of the terminal oxo and/or sulfido groups, while ENDOR spectroscopy might illuminate some of the complicated ^{1}H and ^{17}O hyperfine splittings.

Both xanthine oxidase and nitrogenase have been the subject of numerous kinetic and mechanistic studies. Application of similar techniques to the remaining enzymes should prove fruitful, especially in light of the new structural results.

One field which holds promise for longer range studies is the chemical modification of the molybdenum enzymes in order to probe the importance of particular structural features. For example, once the structure of FeMo-co is understood and a synthetic route to this cluster is established, it might be

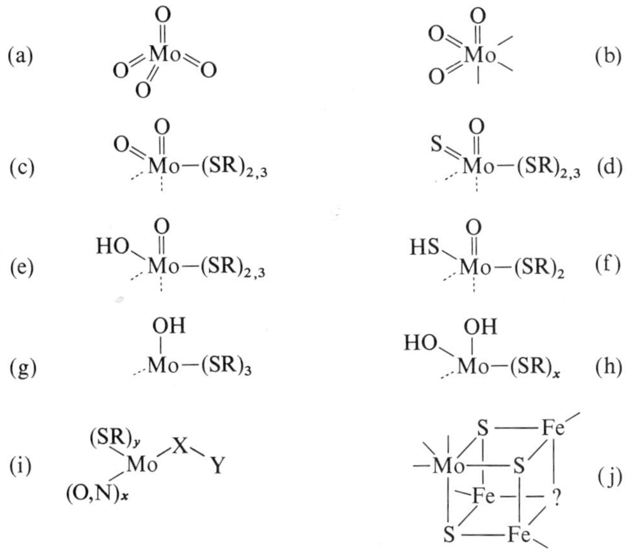

Scheme 17. Summary of Mo enzyme structures observed to-date.

possible to create slightly different clusters that would still occupy the FeMo-co site. In a similar vein, if a pterin structure is ultimately verified for Mo-co, modified pterins might still be able to complement nit-1 nitrate reductase or other apo-proteins. Application of genetic engineering techniques to change specific amino-acid residues in a molybdenum enzyme would allow perturbation of the protein receptor. Both types of modification would enhance understanding of the enzyme mechanism, and such studies might eventually yield modified enzymes with new catalytic activities. A legitimate goal in this process is the synthesis of molecules containing molybdenum which possess the same local structure as the enzymes and catalytic activity as well. The prospects look very good for rapid progress along all these fronts in the near future.

REFERENCES

[1] Coughlan, M. P. (Ed.) "Molybdenum and Molybdenum-Containing Enzymes"; Pergamon Press: New York, 1980.
[2] Newton, W. E.; Otsuka, S. (Eds) "Molybdenum Chemistry of Biological Significance"; Plenum Press: New York, 1980.
[3] Teo, B. K.; Joy, D. C. (Eds) "EXAFS Spectroscopy: Techniques and Applications"; Plenum Press: New York, 1981.

[4] Barber, M. J.; Salerno, J. C. "Molybdenum and Molybdenum-Containing Enzymes"; Coughlan, M. P., Ed.; Pergamon Press: New York, 1980, pp. 544–568.

[5] Cramer, S. P. PhD Thesis, Stanford University, 1977.

[6] Bray, R. C.; Malmstrom, B. G.; Vänngard, T. *Biochem. J.* **1959**, *81*, 178.

[7] Pienkos, P. T.; Shah, V. K.; Brill, W. J. "Molybdenum and Molybdenum-Containing Enzymes"; Coughlan, M. P., Ed.; Pergamon Press: New York, 1980, pp. 385–401.

[8] Johnson, J. L. "Molybdenum and Molybdenum-Containing Enzymes"; Coughlan, M. P., Ed.; Pergamon Press: New York, 1980, pp. 345–383.

[9] Cramer, S. P.; Scott, R. A. *Rev. Sci. Instrum.* **1981**, *52*, 395–399.

[10] Winick, H.; Doniach, S. (Eds) "Synchrotron Radiation Research"; Plenum Press: New York, 1980.

[11] Mortenson, L. E.; Thorneley, R. N. F. *Ann. Rev. Biochem.* **1975**, *48*, 387–418.

[12] Hageman, R. V.; Burris, R. H. "Molybdenum and Molybdenum-Containing Enzymes"; Coughlan, M. P., Ed.; Pergamon Press: New York, 1980, pp. 403–426.

[13] Orme-Johnson, W. H.; Münck, E. "Molybdenum and Molybdenum-Containing Enzymes"; Coughlan, M. P., Ed.; Pergamon Press: New York, 1980, pp. 427–438.

[14] Newton, W. E. and Nyman, C. J. (Eds) "Proceedings of the 1st International Symposium on Nitrogen Fixation"; Washington State University Press: Pullman, Washington, 1976; Newton, W. E.; Postgate, J. R.; Rodriguez-Barrueco, C. (Eds) "Recent Developments in Nitrogen Fixation"; Academic Press: New York, 1977; Newton, W. E.; Orme-Johnson, W. H. (Eds) "Nitrogen Fixation"; University Park Press: Baltimore, 1980.

[15] Gibson, A. H.; Newton, W. E. (Eds) "Current Perspectives in Nitrogen Fixation"; Australian Academy of Sciences: Canberra, 1981.

[16] Hageman, R. V.; Burris, R. H. *J. Biol. Chem.* **1979**, *254*, 11189–11192.

[17] Huang, T. C.; Zumft, W. G.; Mortenson, L. E. *J. Bact.* **1973**, *113*, 884–890.

[18] Swisher, R. H.; Landt, M.; Reithel, F. J. *Biochem. J.* **1977**, *163*, 427–432.

[19] Hazelcorn, A. B. Submitted for publication.

[20] Shah, V. K.; Brill, W. J. *Proc. Natn. Acad. Sci. USA* **1977**, *74*, 3249–3253.

[21] Münck, E.; Rhodes, H.; Orme-Johnson, W. H. *Biochim. Biophys. Acta* **1975**, *400*, 32–53.

[22] Kurtz, D. M.; McMillan, R S.; Burgess, B. K.; Mortenson, L. E.; Holm, R. H. *Proc. Natn. Acad. Sci. USA* **1979**, *74*, 3249–3253.

[23] Weininger, M. S.; Mortenson, L. E. *Proc. Natn. Acad. Sci. USA* **1982**, *79*, 378–380.

[24] Yamane, T.; Weininger, M. S.; Mortenson, L. E.; Rossman, M. G. *J. Biol. Chem.* **1982**, *257*, 1221–1223.

[25] Palmer, G.; Multani, J. S.; Cretney, W. C.; Zumft, W. G.; Mortenson, L. E. *Arch. Biochem. Biophys.* **1972**, *153*, 325–332.

[26] Smith, B. E.; Lowe, D. J.; Bray, R. C. *Biochem. J.* **0000**, *135*, 331–341.

[27] Orme-Johnson, W. H.; Hamilton, W. D.; Jones, T. L.; Tso, M-Y.; Burris, R. H.; Shah, V. K.; Brill, W. J. *Proc. Natn. Acad. Sci. USA* **1972**, *69*, 3142–3145.

[28] Orme-Johnson, W. H.; Davis, L. C. "Iron–Sulfur Proteins", Vol. 3; Lovenberg, W., Ed.; Academic Press: New York, 1977, p. 31.

[29] Mims, W. B.; Orme-Johnson, W. H. Unpublished results.

[30] Hoffman, B. M.; Roberts, J. E.; Orme-Johnson, W. H. *J. Amer. Chem. Soc.* **1982**, *104*, 860–862.

[31] Hoffman, B. M.; Venters, R. A.; Roberts, J. E.; Nelson, M.; Orme-Johnson, W. H. *J. Amer. Chem. Soc.* **1982**, *104*, 4711–4712.

[32] Cramer, S. P.; Eccles, T. K.; Kutzler, F.; Hodgson, K. O.; Mortenson, L. E. *J. Amer. Chem. Soc.* **1976**, *98*, 1287.

[33] Cramer, S. P.; Hodgson, K. O.; Gillum, W. O.; Mortenson, L. E. *J. Amer. Chem. Soc.* **1978**, *100*, 3398–3407.

[34] Cramer, S. P.; Gillum, W. O.; Hodgson, K. O.; Mortenson, L. E.; Stiefel, E. I.; Chisnell, J. R.; Brill, W. J.; Shah, V. K. *J. Amer. Chem. Soc.* **1978**, *100*, 3814–3819.

[35] Conradson, S. D.; Hodgson, K. O.; Burgess, B. K.; Newton, W. E.; Adams, M. W.; Mortenson, L. E. Stanford Synchrotron Radiation Laboratory, 1981, Activity Report, VIII-26-VIII-27.

[36] Cramer, S. P. Stanford Synchrotron Radiation Laboratory, 1981, Activity Report, VIII-24-VIII-25.

[37] Wolff, T. E.; Berg, J. M.; Warrick, C.; Hodgson, K. O.; Holm, R. H.; Frankel, R. B. *J. Amer. Chem. Soc.* **1978**, *100*, 4630–4632.

[38] Teo, B. K.; Averill, B. A. *Biochem. Biophys. Res. Commun.* **1979**, *88*, 1454–1461.

[39] Teo, B. K. "EXAFS Spectroscopy: Techniques and Applications"; Teo, B. K.; Joy, D. C., Eds; Plenum Press: New York, 1981, pp. 13–58.

[40] Lu, J. "Nitrogen Fixation"; Newton, W. E.; Orme-Johnson, W. H., Eds; University Park Press: Baltimore, 1980, pp. 343–371.

[41] Tsai, K. R. "Nitrogen Fixation"; Newton, W. E.; Orme-Johnson, W. H., Eds; University Park Press: Baltimore, 1980, pp. 373–387.

[42] Christou, G.; Hagen, K. S.; Holm, R. H. *J. Amer. Chem. Soc.* **1982**, *104*, 1744–1745.

[43] Yang, S-S.; Pan, W-H.; Friesen, G. D.; Burgess, B. K.; Corbin, J. L.; Stiefel, E. I.; Newton, W. E. *J. Biol. Chem.* **1982**, *257*, 8042–8048.

[44] Nelson, M. J.; Levy, M. A.; Orme-Johnson, W. H. *Proc. Natn. Acad. Sci. USA.* In press.

[45] Levchenko, L. A.; Roschupkina, O. S.; Sadkov, A. P.; Marakushev, S. A.; Mikhailov, G. M.; Borodko, Y. G. *Biochem. Biophys. Res. Commun.* **1980**, *96*, 1384–1392.

[46] Rawlings, J.; Shah, V. K.; Chisnell, J. R.; Brill, W. J.; Zimmerman, R.; Münck, E.; Orme-Johnson, W. H. *J. Biol. Chem.* **1978**, *253*, 1001–1004.

[47] Wolff, T. E.; Berg, J. M.; Holm, R. H. *Inorg. Chem.* **1981**, *20*, 174–180.

[48] Armstrong, W. H.; Mascharak, P. K.; Holm, R. H. *Inorg. Chem.* **1982**, *21*, 1701–1702.

[49] Burgess, B. K.; Yang, S-S.; You, C-B.; Li, J-G.; Friesen, G. D.; Pan, W-H.; Stiefel, E. I.; Newton, W. E.; Conradson, S. D.; Hodgson, K. O. "Current Perspectives in Nitrogen Fixation"; Gibson, A. H.; Newton, W. E., Eds; Australian Academy of Science: Canberra, 1981, pp. 71–74.

[50] Antonio, M. R.; Teo, B. K.; Orme-Johnson, W. H.; Nelson, M. J.; Groh, S. E.; Lindahl, P. A.; Kauzlarich, S. M.; Averill, B. M. *J. Amer. Chem. Soc.* **1982**, *104*, 4703–4705.

[51] Cohen, H. J.; Betcher-Lange, S.; Kessler, D. L.; Rajagopalan, K. V. *J. Biol. Chem* **1972**, *247*, 7759–7766.

[52] Oshino, N.; Chance, B. *Arch. Biochem. Biophys.* **1975**, *170*, 514–528.

[53] Rajagopalan, K. V. "Molybdenum and Molybdenum-Containing Enzymes"; Coughlan, M. P., Ed.; Pergamon Press: New York, 1980, pp. 241–272.

[54] Johnson, J. L.; Rajagopalan, K. V. *J. Biol. Chem.* **1977**, *252*, 2017–2025.

[55] Cramer, S. P.; Gray, H. B.; Scott, N. S.; Barber, M.; Rajagopalan, K. V.

"Molybdenum Chemistry of Biological Significance"; Newton, W. E.; Osaka, S., Eds; Plenum Press: New York, 1980, pp. 157–168.

[56] Kessler, D. L.; Rajagopalan, K. V. *Biochem. Biophys. Acta* **1974**, *370*, 389–398.

[57] Lamy, M. T.; Gutteridge, S.; Bray, R. C. *Biochem. J.* **1980**, *185*, 397–403.

[58] Cohen, H. J.; Fridovich, I.; Rajagopalan, K. V. *J. Biol. Chem.* **1971**, *246*, 367–373.

[59] Garner, C. D.; Buchanan, I.; Collison, D.; Mabbs, F. E.; Porter, T. G.; Wynn, C. H. Submitted for publication.

[60] Cramer, S. P.; Johnson, J. L.; Rajagopalan, K. V.; Sorrell, T. N. *Biochem. Biophys. Res. Commun.* **1979**, *91*, 434–439.

[67] Gutteridge, S.; Lamy, M. T.; Bray, R. C. *Biochem. J.* **1980**, *191*, 285–288.

[62] Cramer, S. P.; Gray, H. B.; Rajagopalan, K. V. *J. Amer. Chem. Soc.* **1979**, *101*, 2772–2774.

[63] Cramer, S. P.; Wahl, R.; Rajagopalan, K. V. *J. Amer. Chem. Soc.* **1981**, *103*, 7721–7727.

[64] Bray, R. C. "Advances in Enzymology and Related Areas of Molecular Biology"; Meister, A., Ed.; Wiley: New York, 1979, pp. 107–165.

[65] Bray, R. C. "The Enzymes", Vol. XII; Boyer, P. D., Ed.; Academic Press: New York, 1975, pp. 299–419.

[66] Wahl, W. R.; Rajagopalan, K. V. *Arch. Biochem. Biophys.* **1976**, *172*, 365–379.

[67] Kaminski, Z. W.; Jezewska, M. M. *Biochem. J.* **1982**, *207*, 341–346.

[68] Nelson, C. A.; Handler, P. *J. Biol. Chem.* **1968**, *243*, 5368.

[69] Porras, A. G.; Palmer, G. *J. Biol. Chem.* **1982**, *257*, 11617–11626.

[70] Massey, V.; Brumby, P. E.; Komai, H.; Palmer, G. *J. Biol. Chem.* **1969**, *244*, 1682.

[71] Coughlan, M. P. "Molybdenum and Molybdenum-Containing Enzymes"; Pergamon Press: New York, 1980, pp. 119–185.

[72] Massey, V.; Edmondson, D. *J. Biol. Chem.* **1970**, *245*, 6595–6598.

[73] Wahl, R. C.; Rajagopalan, K. V. *J. Biol. Chem.* **1982**, *257*, 1354–1359.

[74] Cammack, R.; Barber, M. J.; Bray, R. C. *Biochem. J.* **1976**, *157*, 469–478.

[75] Barber, M. J.; Coughlan, M. P.; Kanda, M.; Rajagopalan, K. V. *Arch. Biochem. Biophys.* **1980**, *201*, 468–475.

[76] Edmondson, D.; Massey, V.; Palmer, G.; Beacham, L. M.; Elion, G. B. *J. Biol. Chem.* **1972**, *247*, 1597–1604.

[77] Bray, R. C.; Knowles, P. F. *Proc. Roy. Soc. Ser. A* **1968**, *302*, 351–353.

[78] Gutteridge, S.; Tanner, S. J.; Bray, R. C. *Biochem. J.* **1978**, *175*, 869–878.

[79] Tanner, S. J.; Bray, R. C.; Bergmann, F. *Biochem. Soc. Trans.* **1978**, *6*, 1328–1330.

[80] Gutteridge, S.; Malthouse, J. P. G.; Bray, R. C. *J. Inorg. Biochem.* **1979**, *11*, 355–360.

[81] Gutteridge, S.; Bray, R. C. *Biochem. J.* **1980**, *189*, 615–623.

[82] Bray, R. C.; Gutteridge, S. *Biochemistry* **1982**, *21*, 5992–5999.

[83] Coughlan, M. P.; Rajagopalan, K. V.; Handler, P. *J. Biol. Chem.* **1969**, *244*, 2658–2663.

[84] Hille, R.; Stewart, R. C.; Fee, J. A.; Massey, V. *J. Biol. Chem.* **1983**, *258*, 4849–4856.

[85] Malthouse, J. P. G.; Bray, R. C. *Biochem. J.* **1980**, *191*, 265–267.

[86] Edmondson, D.; Ballou, D.; Van Heuvelen, A.; Palmer, G.; Massey, V. *J. Biol. Chem.* **1973**, *248*, 6135.

[87] Stiefel, E. I. *Proc. Natn. Acad. Sci. USA* **1973**, *70*, 988–992.

[88] Gutteridge, S.; Tanner, S. J.; Bray, R. C. *Biochem. J.* **1978**, *175*, 887–897.

[89] Massey, V.; Edmondson, D. *J. Biol. Chem.* **1970**, *245*, 6595–6598.

[90] Williams, R. J. P.; Wentworth, R. A. D. "Chemistry and Uses of Molybdenum"; Mitchell, P. C. H., Ed.; Climax Molybdenum Co.: London, 1973, pp. 212–215.
[91] Coughlan, M. P. *FEBS Lett.* **1977**, *81*, 1–6.
[92] Tullius, T. D.; Kurtz, D. M., Jr; Conradson, S. D.; Hodgson, K. O. *J. Amer. Chem. Soc.* **1979**, *101*, 2776–2779.
[93] Bordas, J.; Bray, R. C.; Garner, C. D.; Gutteridge, S.; Hasnain, S. S. *Biochem. J.* **1980**, *191*, 499–525.
[94] Moura, J. G. G.; Xavier, A. V.; Cammack, R.; Hall, D. O.; Bruschi, M.; LeGall, J. *Biochem. J.* **1978**, *173*, 419–425.
[95] Moura, J. G. G.; Xavier, A. V.; Bruschi, M.; LeGall, J.; Hall, D. O.; Cammack, R. *Biochem. Biophys. Res. Commun.* **1976**, *72*, 782–789.
[96] Cramer, S. P.; Moura, J. G. G.; Xavier, A. V.; LeGall, J. Manuscript in preparation.
[97] Hewitt, E. J.; Notton, B. A. *In* "Molybdenum and Molybdenum-Containing Enzymes"; Coughlan, M. P., Ed.; Pergamon Press: New York, 1980, pp. 273–325.
[98] Howard, W. D.; Solomonson, L. P. *J. Biol. Chem.* **1982**, *257*, 10243–10250.
[99] Adams, M. W. W.; Mortenson, L. E. *J. Biol. Chem.* **1982**, *257*, 1791–1799.
[100] Adams, M. W. W.; Mortenson, L. E. Personal communication.
[101] Barber, M. J.; Solomonson, L. S.; Rajagopalan, K. V. Manuscript in preparation.
[102] Vincent, S. P. *Biochem. J.* **1979**, *177*, 757–759.
[103] Cramer, S. P.; Solomonson, L. S.; Adams, M. W. W.; Mortenson, L. E. Manuscript in preparation.
[104] Vincent, S. P.; Bray, R. C. *Biochem. J.* **1978**, *171*, 639–647.
[105] Cramer, S. P.; Solomonson, L. S.; Adams, M. W. W.; Mortenson, L. E. *J. Amer. Chem. Soc.* Submitted for publication.
[106] Ljungdahl, L. *In* "Molybdenum and Molybdenum-Containing Enzymes"; Coughlan, M. P., Ed.; Pergamon Press: New York, 1980, pp. 463–486.
[107] Thauer, R. K.; Fuchs, G.; Jungermann, K. "Iron–Sulfur Proteins", Vol. 3; Lovenberg, W., Ed.; Academic Press: New York, pp. 121–156.
[108] Barber, M. J.; Siegel, L. M. *In* "The Chemistry and Uses of Molybdenum: Fourth International Conference".
[109] Barber, M. J.; Siegel, L. M.; Schauer, N. L.; May, H. D.; Ferry, J. G. *Fed. Abstr.*, No. 3632, **1982**.
[110] Ljungdahl, L. G.; Andreesen, J. R. *FEBS Lett.* **1975**, *54*, 279–281.
[111] Muller, V.; Willnow, P.; Ruschig, V.; Hopner, T. *Eur. J. Biochem.* **1978**, *83*, 485–498.
[112] Scherer, P. A.; Thauer, R. K. *Eur. J. Biochem.* **1978**, *85*, 125–135.
[113] Stiefel, E. I. *Prog. Inorg. Chem.* **1977**, *22*, 1–223.
[114] Tezuka, M.; Yajima, T.; Tsuchiya, A.; Matsumoto, Y.; Uchida, Y.; Hidai, M. *J. Amer. Chem. Soc.* **1982**, *104*, 6834–6836.
[115] Harrison, P. M.; Hoare, R. J.; Hoy, T. F.; Macara, I. G. "Iron in Biochemistry and Medicine"; Jacobs, A.; Worwood, M., Eds; Academic Press: New York, 1974, pp. 73–114.
[116] Kägi, J. H. R.; Himmelhoch, S. R., Whanger, P. D.; Bethane, J. L.; Vallee, B. L. *J. Biol. Chem.* **1974**, *249*, 3537–3542.
[117] Elliott, B. B.; Mortenson, L. E. *J. Bact.* **1976**, *127*, 770–779.
[118] Johnson, J. L.; Jones, H. P.; Rajagopalan, K. V. *J. Biol. Chem.* **1977**, *252*, 4994–5003.
[119] Amy, N. K.; Rajagopalan, K. V. *J. Bact.* **1979**, *140*, 114–124.

[120] Roberts, G. P.; MacNeil, T.; MacNeil, D.; Brill, W. J. *J. Bact.* **1978**, *13*, 267–279.

[121] Hinton, S. PhD Thesis, Purdue University, 1981.

[122] Pateman, A. J.; Cove, D. J.; Rever, B. M.; Roberts, D. B. *Nature* **1964**, *301*, 58–60.

[123] Nason, A.; Lee, K-Y.; Pam, S-S.; Lamberti, X.; Devries, J. *Proc. Natn. Acad. Sci. USA* **1971**, *68*, 3242–3246.

[124] Pienkos, P. T.; Shah, V. K.; Brill, W. J. *Proc. Natn. Acad. Sci. USA* **1971**, *74*, 5468–5471.

[125] Alikulov, Z. A.; L'vov, N. P.; Burikhanov, S. S.; Kretovich, V. L. *Izvestiya Akademii Nauk SSSR Seriya Biol.* **1980**, *5*, 712–718.

[126] Johnson, J. L.; Hainline, B. E.; Rajagopalan, K. V. *J. Biol. Chem.* **1980**, *255*, 1783–1786.

[127] Rajagopalan, K. V.; Johnson, J. L.; Hainline, B. E. *Fed. Proc.* **1982**, *41*, 2608–2612.

[128] Claassen, V. P.; Oltmann, L. F.; Van't Riet, J.; Brinkman, U. A. Th.; Stouthamer, A. H. *FEBS Lett.* **1982**, *142*, 133–137.

[129] Lee, K-Y. *Chinese J. Microbiol.* **1978**, *11*, 21–29.

[130] Ketchum, P. A.; Cambier, H. Y.; Frazier, W. A., III; Madansky, C. H.; Nason, A. *Proc. Natn. Acad. Sci. USA* **1970**, *66*, 1016–1023.

[131] Tanner, S. J.; Bray, R. C.; Bermann, F. *Biochem. Soc. Trans.* **1978**, *6*, 1328–1330.

[132] Gutteridge, S.; Tanner, S. J.; Bray, R. C. *Biochem. J.* *1978*, *175*, 879–885.

[133] Johnson, J. L.; Rajagopalan, K. V. *Proc. Natn. Acad. Sci. USA* **1982**, *79*, 6856–6860.

[134] Tieckelman, R. H.; Silvis, H. C.; Kent, T. A.; Huynh, B. H.; Waszczak, J. V.; Teo, B. K.; Averill, B. A. *J. Amer. Chem. Soc.* **1980**, *102*, 5550–5559.

[135] Coucouvanis, D.; Baenziger, N. C.; Simtson, E. D.; Stremple, P.; Swenson, D.; Kostikas, A.; Simopoulos, A.; Petrouleas, V.; Papaefthymiou, V. *J. Amer. Chem. Soc.* **1980**, *102*, 1732.

[136] Armstrong, W. H.; Holm, R. H. *J. Amer. Chem. Soc.* **1981**, *103*, 6246–6248.

[137] Cramer, S. P.; Hinton, S.; Mortenson, L. E. Unpublished results.

Oxygen-18 Exchange Studies of Aqua- and Oxo-ions

Heinz Gamsjäger and R. Kent Murmann

Institut für Physikalische Chemie
Montanuniversität Leoben and
Department of Chemistry, University of Missouri

I. INTRODUCTION

The oxygen exchange between solvent water and simple aqua–metal ions (1) or oxo-anions (2) is closely related since substitution occurs at either the M—O or the X—O bonds respectively.

$$n\text{H}_2{}^*\text{O} + [\text{M(OH}_2)_n]^{z+} \rightleftharpoons n\text{H}_2\text{O} + [\text{M}({}^*\text{OH}_2)_n]^{z+} \tag{1}$$

$$n\text{H}_2{}^*\text{O} + [\text{XO}_n]^{z-} \rightleftharpoons n\text{H}_2\text{O} + [\text{X}{}^*\text{O}_n]^{z-} \tag{2}$$

In some cases two or more non-equivalent M—O or X—O bonds are present as in polymeric aqua-metal ions and oxo-anions, and in monomeric oxo-metal ions. The substitution reactions of oxo-metal complexes have been reviewed in Volume 1 of this series.[1] A precise knowledge of the structural nature and exchange behaviour of aquated metal ions and oxo-anions is a prerequisite to the understanding of inorganic reaction mechanisms in aqueous media. In principle the determination of hydration numbers and rates of ^{18}O exchange with solvent is simple and straightforward, but definitive experiments have proven to be more difficult.

The exploratory experiments of Cohn and Urey in 1938[2] and those of Hall and Alexander,[3] on anion–water oxygen exchange, stand out as the forerunners in this area. In 1950 Taube and his coworkers[4–7] published the first of a number of classical papers in which the exchange of water between hydrated cations and solvent were studied using the ^{18}O tracer techniques. Since then this method has been applied for the investigation of comparatively slow isotopic exchange reactions of inorganic and in some cases organic systems. From these studies, quantitative information can be obtained on

1. the number of positions occupied by water, hydroxide and oxide ions around the central atom M or X;
2. the kinetic properties of aqua-cations and oxo-anions in aqueous solution;
3. the mechanism(s) by which these exchange processes occur.

II. DETERMINATION OF COORDINATION NUMBERS

The rate of isotopic water exchange with an aqua-cation or oxo-anion has to be relatively slow in order to allow the number of oxygens around M or X to be counted by ^{18}O tracer techniques. The data required for the determination of water holdback by the ion using water sampling to follow the ^{18}O level are:

1. an accurate knowledge of the chemical composition of the salt solution;
2. the isotopic composition of solvent oxygen after mixing but before exchange has taken place;

3. the isotopic composition of the solvent after isotopic equilibrium between solvent and solute oxygen has been attained.

Historically the first formula established by this method seems to have been that of the uranyl ion.[8] A weighed portion of pure uranyl chloride hydrate, $UO_2Cl_2 . 3H_3O$ was added to a known amount of water. Either the salt or the solvent was enriched in ^{18}O. Water was distilled from the solution and its $^{18}O/^{16}O$ ratio was determined following the method of Cohn and Urey,[2] i.e. carbon dioxide was isotopically equilibrated with purified liquid water samples and subsequently analysed by mass spectrometry. Various modifications of this original approach have been used and rapid sampling techniques have been developed. A common modification consists of converting oxo-ions to well-characterized solids, structurally and stoichiometrically, containing the original oxo-core. Using ^{18}O enriched solvent it can often be shown how many of the oxygens in the solid come from the inner coordination sphere of the aqueous species. Consequently structural information obtained in the solid state can be unambiguously extended to solution. In Table 1 a selection of formulae established by ^{18}O methods is given.

TABLE 1
Some formulae established by ^{18}O-methods

Formula	n_O/n_{CA} [a]	Sampling method	Reference
$Al(OH_2)_6^{3+}$	6.0 ± 0.5	H_2O	[9]
VO_{aq}^{2+}	1.0 ± 0.1	H_2O	[10]
VO_4^{3-}	4.0 ± 0.1	$Co(NH_3)_6VO_4 . 2H_2O$	[11]
$Cr(OH_2)_6^{3+}$	6.0 ± 0.2	H_2O	[6]
$[(H_2O)_4Cr(OH)_2Cr(OH_2)_4]^{4+}$	5.04 ± 0.07	H_2O	[12]
FeO_4^{2-}	4.0 ± 0.1	$BaFeO_4$	[13]
$Mo_2O_{4aq}^{2+}$	0.99 ± 0.02 (inert) 1.02 ± 0.03 (labile)	$[Pt(en)_2][Mo_2O_4 \ EDTA]$	[14]
$Mo_3O_{4aq}^{4+}$	1.33	$[Mo_3O_4(NCS)_9]^{5-}$	[15]
$Rh(OH_2)_6^{3+}$	5.9 ± 0.4	H_2O	[16]
$Ir(OH_2)_6^{3+}$	6.0 ± 0.2	H_2O	[17]
UO_2^{2+}	2	H_2O	[8]
NpO_2^+	2.1 ± 0.2	$NpO_2(OH)H_2O, H_2O$	[18]

[a] Ratio of the molar amounts of slowly exchanging oxygen and central atom in the oxo-ion investigated.

III. KINETICS OF OXYGEN EXCHANGE REACTIONS

Isotopic oxygen exchange between oxo-ions and solvent water proceeds via first-order processes provided only tracer quantities of ^{18}O labelled reactants are introduced into the chemically equilibrated solutions. The kinetic rate law relevant for exchange reactions is commonly referred to as the McKay equation.[19] Applied to reactions (1) and (2) this results in (3) and (4) respectively

$$-\ln(1-F) = Rt\left\{\frac{n[M(OH_2)_n^{z+}] + [H_2O]}{n[M(OH_2)_n^{z+}][H_2O]}\right\} \tag{3}$$

$$-\ln(1-F) = Rt\left\{\frac{n[XO_n^{z-}] + [H_2O]}{n[XO_n^{z-}][H_2O]}\right\} \tag{4}$$

where R is the overall rate of oxygen transfer between water and oxo-ion, t is time and F the fraction of exchange completed. F can be expressed as

$$F = (x_0 - x_t)/(x_0 - x_\infty) \tag{5}$$

where x_0, x_t and x_∞ are the mole fractions of ^{18}O in $[M(OH_2)_n]^{z+}$, $[XO_n]^{z-}$ or in the solvent water at times $t = 0$, $t =$ time of sampling and $t = \infty$ (at exchange equilibrium). Since usually $n[M(OH_2)_n^{z+}] \ll [H_2O]$ or $n[XO_n^{z-}] \ll [H_2O]$, equations (3) and (4) often reduce to (6) or (7)

$$-\ln(1-F) = Rt/n[M(OH_2)_n^{z+}] \tag{6}$$

or

$$-\ln(1-F) = Rt/n[XO_n^{z-}] \tag{7}$$

Finally R is related to the rate constant for exchange by the usual relationship relating the rate, R, with the concentrations of the reacting ions and the order with respect to each variable is determined by measuring R under differing solution conditions. Equations (3) and (4) have been derived neglecting kinetic isotope effects on the exchange rate.[20] This first-order simplification occurs because, in each elementary step, all but one of the concentrations are time independent and the labelled molecules enter the reaction with a molecularity of unity in elementary reaction steps.[21] If the molecularity with respect to labelled compounds is greater than unity in any elementary reaction step then the reaction need not appear first order. It was, however, shown that under most conditions likely to be realized in practice neither deviation from first-order kinetics as a result of isotopic fractionation nor difference in the kinetic form due to the mechanism of exchange should be observed.[22,23]

If α and β are the kinetic isotope effects in the two opposite transfer reactions then, $\alpha/\beta =$ isotope exchange equilibrium constant $= z_\infty/y_\infty$ where z and y are the atom fraction of the minor isotope in the two species. Assuming only one transferable oxygen atom per ion, equation (8) becomes:

$$-\ln(1 - F) = Rt\,\frac{\beta[\text{M—OH}_2] + \alpha[\text{H}_2\text{O}]}{[\text{M—OH}_2][\text{H}_2\text{O}]} \tag{8}$$

By means of the experimental slope and an experimental value for the isotope exchange equilibrium constant one can obtain values for αR and βR but they cannot be separated into their factors. Thus the absolute fundamental exchange rate cannot be obtained with only two isotopes. The magnitude of this error is, with $^{16}O{-}^{18}O$, probably never larger than 2%.[24]

IV. EXPERIMENTAL TECHNIQUES

A. Mass spectrometric ^{18}O determination

The most generally applicable ^{18}O analysis method has been mass spectrometric determination after converting the oxygen containing compound into a suitable gas either by equilibration or by decomposition.

1. ^{18}O content of water

The original method for the accurate determination of the ^{18}O content of solvent water was by equilibration with normal CO_2 developed by Cohn and Urey.[2] To speed up the three-day equilibration process it has been carried out in the gas phase on a heated platinum wire[25] or using electric discharge.[26] A simple, convenient and accurate version of the equilibration method has been proposed for the assay of the ^{18}O abundance in natural waters.[27] Sometimes a serious disadvantage of the method is the large amount of water required for a single determination in order to keep isotopic dilution by the added CO_2 negligible. Using small amounts of CO_2 and H_2O whose molar quantities are accurately measured, one can accurately determine the ^{18}O content on samples of 0.1 g of H_2O.[28] In all cases, the K for isotopic distribution must be known at the equilibration temperature, $K = [C^{18}O_2]^{1/2}[H_2{}^{16}O]/[C^{16}O_2]^{1/2}[H_2{}^{18}O]$, where $\ln K = 16.6T^{-1} - 1.569 \times 10^{-2}$.[29] For mg amounts of H_2O two other techniques are in rather general use. The first is frequently referred to as the modified Anbar technique.[30] Water (2–3 mg) is distilled into an anhydrous mixture of $Hg(CN)_2$–$HgCl_2$ in an evacuated breakseal tube. Decomposition is achieved by heating the breakseal tube at 375–425 °C for 1–1.5 h. Alternatively oxygen from H_2O can be converted into carbon dioxide using anhydrous paracyanogen, $(CN)_n$,[30] $AgCN$,[31] $Hg(CN)_2$[32] or HgI_2.[33] In each case the non-condensible gases are removed at liquid N_2 temperatures and CO_2 is separated from $(CN)_2$ and HCN and other impurities preferably by preparative gas chromatography using a silicon oil on fire brick column and helium as carrier gas.[13,34] The purified CO_2 is collected and analysed mass spectrometrically.

The second technique is based on heating of mg amounts of water with guanidine hydrochloride at 300 °C.[35] The CO_2 formed is freed from NH_3 by a concentrated H_2SO_4 trap.

Occasionally other methods for ^{18}O analysis in solvent water are utilized, e.g. when H_2O is reacted with $S_2O_8^{2-}$ in alkaline medium the oxygen liberated originates only from water and not from the persulphate ion.[36,37]

In addition it has been shown that the dioxygen–dihydrogen mixture produced electrolytically can be accurately analysed for ^{18}O content which is representative of the water.[38,39]

Solvent water can be also analysed for ^{18}O by catalytic decomposition of hypobromite ion[40] which is formed by the addition of Br_2 to the solvent.

2. ^{18}O content of oxo-ions

In favourable cases the oxo-ion can be converted into a solid compound which can be pyrolysed to give oxygen directly for mass spectrometric analysis (e.g. reference [41]). This is the simplest and probably most accurate method. More frequently applicable is the modified Anbar technique consisting of sealing the oxygen containing solid with a $Hg(CN)_2$–$HgCl_2$ mixture,[30] $AgCN$[31] or other materials (as with H_2O), in an evacuated breakseal tube which is heated at 375–425 °C. As with solvent water, preparative gas chromatography is the method of choice for purifying the CO_2 before it is analysed on the mass spectrometer.[13,34]

The guanidine hydrochloride method is also applied very often to convert oxygen in compounds into CO_2.[35]

For substances which are difficult to decompose by either of these methods reaction with carbon at approximately 1400 °C yields CO which is suitable for mass spectrometric analysis.[38,42] Recently this method was successfully applied on $BaMoO_4$ and $BaWO_4$.[43] About 10 mg of these substances were mixed with an equal amount of ultra-pure graphite and placed in a graphite crucible fixed on a molybdenum or aluminium oxide rod. This was contained in a quartz tube attached to a cooling trap, a Toepler pump and connected to a vacuum line. Inductive heating was effected by a helical coil connected to a 1.5 kW-radio-frequency generator. First, H_2O was removed by degassing at 800 °C, then the $BaMo^{18}O_4$ or $BaW^{18}O_4$ was decomposed at 1400 °C to give mainly CO. The small amount of CO_2 was removed in the trap with liquid nitrogen. The CO gas was collected using the Toepler pump and isotopically analysed. The ^{18}O composition of nitrite ion is usually determined using the reaction with hydrazoic acid at a controlled pH of 3.5–4.5

$$HN_3 + HNO_2 \rightleftharpoons N_2O + N_2 + H_2O \tag{9}$$

and analysing the N_2O in the mass spectrometer.[44,45] Another special case is $S_2O_3^{2-}$, where the ^{18}O analysis has been performed on SO_2 gas liberated thermally from PbS_2O_3.[46]

For isotopic sampling of ClO^- and BrO^- a rather sophisticated method has been developed.[47] When ClO^- or BrO^- oxidize NO_2^- almost complete transfer of oxygen to the reducing agent takes place. The nitrate ion formed is precipitated as nitron nitrate, reacted with ammoniacal solutions and the nitron base extracted by ethylacetate. The remaining solution is evaporated to dryness and the NH_4NO_3 obtained thermally decomposed to give N_2O for mass spectrometric analysis. While the method is not accurate, it provides a good example how ^{18}O techniques can be adapted to difficult cases. Complete scrambling of oxygen isotopes during all of the thermal degradation procedures is usually assumed and has generally been found to be the case.

B. ^{18}O determination by densimetry

The determination of the ^{18}O content of solvent water can be carried out densimetrically.[48] Simple and accurate float methods have been described by Baertschi and Thürkauf[49] and by Staschewski.[50] In 1960 Tereshkevich *et al.*[51] started a series of papers dealing with the ^{18}O exchange between inert oxo-anions and water using a float method. This method demands relatively large amounts of solvent and high solute concentrations and is restricted to comparatively inert oxo-ions. To evaluate the reliability of this method it was attempted to compare the data of Fig. 1 in reference [52] on H_2SO_4 exchange with that of reference [38] but the agreement was poor.

The oxygen exchange rates of aqueous solutions of $LiBrO_3$ have been studied at 100–130 °C.[53] Association between cation and anion occurs as a rapid ion pair formation prior to the rate-determining step, which consists then in the reversible addition of water. Ionic association constants, K_{ass}, were calculated from the rate constant, k, using the formula (10)

$$1/k = 1/k_{true} + 1/(k_{true} \times K_{ass} \times c) \tag{10}$$

where c is molality. For $LiBrO_3$ recalculations of K_{ass} at 120 °C between $c/m^* = 2.0$–4.6 suggest that no detailed analysis of K_{ass} values seems to be justified due to the large uncertainties and the fact that a rigorous regression analysis of the selected data resulted in a meaningless negative intercept.

Although a large amount of information has been accumulated[54–67] it is felt that this method is of limited accuracy for kinetic ^{18}O exchange studies and

---

* Lower case m denotes the unit of molality, mol kg^{-1}.

may find its greatest usefulness in concentrated solutions studying the presently not understood medium effects.

C. Procedure for ^{18}O exchange studies

The basic tracer experiment consists of creating a different ^{18}O isotopic composition between solvent water and oxo-ion. After appropriate time intervals, the reaction is stopped. This can be achieved either by cooling, or separation by some sort of chemical quenching to be discussed subsequently.

1. Direct sampling

Sometimes a useful method of sampling for ^{18}O analysis consists of the evaporation of H_2O,[4,8] the exchange reaction usually being stopped by cooling. This method is intrinsically less precise because of fractionation effects and vapour–liquid non-equilibrium and requires comparatively high concentrations of oxo-ions in order to obtain sufficient differences for accuracy and precision. Its advantage lies in being very generally applicable and often useful when no other methods are available.[10] Also, no foreign substances are added, or solution concentrations varied which may induce exchange.

Another example of direct sampling is the equilibration of normal CO_2 with the solvent in the case of sulphate ion–water exchange, where it was shown that direct SO_4^{2-}–CO_2 exchange does not occur. Thus any enrichment detected in CO_2 reflects the isotopic composition of the solvent.[68] Finally carbonate ion exchange studies fall in this category since CO_2 can be sampled directly from acidic solutions.[70,71]

2. Sampling by precipitation

Probably the most generally applicable quenching method consists of precipitating the respective ion. Usually heterogeneous reactions are several orders of magnitude slower than homogeneous ones and thus the exchangeable oxygen sites are effectively rendered inactive once they are fixed in a precipitate. The procedure typically consists of removing the mother liquor by centrifugation, washing with an organic solvent, drying under vacuum and decomposing the precipitate to obtain a mass spectrometrically measurable gas, preferentially CO_2 or O_2. Clearly any individual procedure has to be checked for induced exchange. In favourable cases induced exchange is negligible (see e.g. reference [72]). It is, however, possible to draw reliable conclusions even from results showing considerable precipitation or separation induced exchange provided the effect is reproducible.[43,73,74] Very often different chemical changes are utilized for quenching and for separation. Acid or base catalysed reactions can be "stopped" by shifting the pH to a region where exchange is negigible (e.g. see references [75] and [76]) followed by a method of separation. As another example it was shown that the $Mo_2O_4^{2-}$–H_2O exchange can be stopped by complexing Mo(V) with EDTA. Then the $[Mo_2O_4\,EDTA]^{2-}$-ion is crystallized with $Pt(en)_2^{2+}$ and the ^{18}O measurements made on the dried solid.[14] Competition with redox reactions was exploited for the investigation of the VO_{2aq}^{+} exchange. The VO_2^{+} aqua ion is rapidly reduced and complexed by excess NCS^- to $VO(NCS)_5^{3-}$ which exchanges its yl-oxygen slowly.[77] For sampling, anhydrous $[(CH_3)_4N]_3[VO(SCN)_5]$ was crystallized and its ^{18}O ratio determined.

3. Rapid quenching

Whichever of the methods described are used, they are typical batch methods applicable only for slow reactions. A simple, inexpensive rapid-injection apparatus has been described[111] to follow ^{18}O exchange processes with half-lives as short as 10 s. For rapid chemical quenching within time intervals of 10^{-2} to 10 s the Durrum-multi-mixing-system is commercially available and has been employed for some faster exchange reactions.[43,78]

Although it is constructed as an accessory to the normal stopped-flow apparatus it can be used quite independently. Oxo-ion solutions are mixed with equal volumes of $H_2^{18}O$, both solutions having been adjusted to the desired pH and ionic strength. After variable time intervals, selected with a programmable electronic control system, the exchange reaction is quenched by rapid addition of a reagent which precipitates the oxo-ion.

Doubtless this technique would be useful for quenching reactions other than precipitation, but seems to have been applied so far only for the latter.

D. Other methods for the determination of the ^{18}O exchange behaviour

The use of infrared spectral differences has been applied to the determination of ^{18}O exchange behaviour. Solution or gaseous spectra are generally used in order to achieve small half-widths and suitable line separations and high concentrations of the enriched isotope are required. Quantitative measurements, with the precision and accuracy of the other methods, are probably not possible. However, for purposes of deciding if exchange is non-existent or is complete (under the experimental conditions), ir spectra are extremely valuable.[79]

A valuable tool, which has not been used with any regularity is the measurement, in aqueous solution, of the Laser-Raman spectra in the ir region for isotopically substituted species.[14] At the present stage of development it is not suitable for precision kinetic studies but can easily indicate whether or not ^{18}O exchange occurs in a finite time. It has the disadvantage of using large quantities of expensive isotopes and relatively long data collection times but does not require separation. Furthermore, with ions having several types of exchanging oxygens the exchanging sites can be unambiguously identified.

Recently the application of ^{13}C-nmr to ^{18}O transfer or exchange of carbon containing substances has been highly successful.[80] When ^{18}O is directly bound to a carbon in the molecule(ion) the ^{13}C resonance is shifted upfield about 0.025 ppm per ^{18}O (for acetic acid) and the integrated intensity is proportional to the concentration of that isotopic form. The rate of ^{18}O exchange of acetic acid[81] with water was followed by this method and the results agreed reasonably well with standard methods. One difficulty involves the fact that all three species $RC^{18}O^{18}OH$, $RC^{16}O^{18}OH$ and $RC^{16}O^{16}OH$ are present in comparable quantities resulting in composite rate equations. This increases the estimated error at each time but the estimated overall error consistently remained between 2–5% in this study. Problems with the method are the high concentrations of isotope which are needed (but only small volumes), and the difficulty in obtaining close temperature control. The question of accuracy and precision are not as yet clear. Similar results were obtained for the *t*-butyl alcohol–water exchange. Of especial interest is the fact that ^{18}O substitution also changes the nmr signal of ^{31}P, ^{55}Mn, ^{95}Mo and ^{195}Pt[82–86] and thus can be used to determine the ^{18}O environment of these ions in complexes or in aqua ions. Other methods of ^{18}O analysis which have not as yet been used in studying oxygen exchange reactions are gas chromatographic separation and analysis of O_2 on coated glass capillary columns,[87] isotope ratio monitoring gas chromatography[88] utilizing fragment ions of the parent molecule, emission spectroscopy of O_2 excited by a RF field (not yet proven), but in principle similar to that for ^{15}N in N_2,[89] and ^{18}O analysis by $^{18}O(n, \gamma)^{19}O$ activation analysis.[90] Each of these, in principle, could be as accurate and precise as the conventional mass spectrometric methods but so far, in practice, they have not been applied extensively.

V. REVIEW OF RESULTS

A. Kinetics of oxo-anion exchange with solvent

1. Oxo-anions of group VII.b elements

Perhalates. The tetrahedral perhalate ions are notoriously inert to water exchange. Aqueous perchloric acid (9 M $HClO_4$), at room temperature, shows an estimated half-life greater than one hundred years.[91] Similarly slow to exchange is perbromic acid.[92] A 1 M solution of ^{18}O enriched $HBrO_4$ shows no appreciable change of its isotopic composition after 14 d at 120 °C.[93] On the other hand oxygen exchange between periodate and water is fast and was therefore studied comparatively early by an ^{17}O nmr technique.[94]

The rate parameters for reaction (11)

$$H_5IO_6 + H_2{}^*O \rightleftharpoons H_5IO_5{}^*O + H_2O \tag{11}$$

at 25 °C are: $k_1 = 4.5 \times 10^3$ s^{-1}, $\Delta H_1^{\ddagger} = 54$ kJ mol^{-1}, $\Delta S_1^{\ddagger} = 6.2$ J mol^{-1} K^{-1}. Reaction (11) is not catalysed by hydrogen or chloride ions. A dissociative exchange mechanism according to reaction (12) is consistent with the experimental data

$$H_5IO_6 \underset{k_r \text{ (large)}}{\overset{k_f \text{ (small)}}{\rightleftharpoons}} H_3IO_5 + H_2O \tag{12}$$

Halates. The halic acids $HClO_3$, $HBrO_3$ and HIO_3 are strong acids. Thus even at low pH the deprotonated forms predominate. In aqueous media only the protonation constant* of HIO_3 has been determined directly[95] and is $\log K_1 = 0.31$ at 25 °C and I = 1.0 m $LiClO_4$.[96] Whereas only monomer chlorates and bromates are known, dimeric forms of iodate occur in more concentrated solutions.[97] Oxygen exchange reactions between pyramidal halates, XO_3^- and water have been studied extensively.[41,78,91,98,101] In the absence of catalysts other than H^+ and OH^- the four exchange paths which have been found are summarized in equation (13)

$$R/[XO_3^-] = k_0 + k_{1H}[H^+] + k_{2H}[H^+]^2 + k_{OH}[OH^-] \tag{13}$$

A summary of relevant kinetic data is compiled in Table 2.

Generally rate constants obtained by different authors agree reasonably well, whereas values for the solvent deuterium isotope effects, k^H/k^D, and activation parameters $\Delta H^{\ddagger}$ and $\Delta S^{\ddagger}$ vary considerably. In Table 2 a selection of the most reliable data are given.

Only the k_{2H} term on the right-hand side of equation (13) is common to all halates. The k_{2H} values for chlorate, bromate and iodate differ by ca 14 orders of magnitude when both of the former are extrapolated to 5 °C for comparison with the latter. All $[H^+]^2$ catalysed paths show a pronounced inverse deuterium solvent isotope effect, which is usually considered to be indicative of rapid acid-base equilibria prior to the rate-determining step. This implies a two-step mechanism:

$$X^*O_3^- + 2H^+ \overset{\text{fast}}{\rightleftharpoons} H_2X^*O_3^+ \tag{14}$$

---

* Throughout this paper equilibrium constants have been either defined specifically, by reference to an equation, or denoted according to the now widely-accepted conventions as indicated in reference [95] where $K_1 = [HL]/[H^+][L]$ and $K_2 = [H_2L]/[H^+][HL]$.

TABLE 2

Kinetic data for ^{18}O exchange between halate ions and water

$$R/[XO_3^-] = k_0 + k_{1H}[H^+] + k_{2H}[H^+]^2 + k_{OH}[OH^-]$$

Halate ion	I/M	T/K	Rate constant		k^H/k^D	$\Delta H^{\ddagger}/kJ\ mol^{-1}$	$\Delta S^{\ddagger}/JK^{-1}\ mol^{-1}$	Reference
ClO_3^-	1.34	373.15		8.90×10^{-4}	0.35	110.3	-9.6	[91]
BrO_3^-	1.00	298.15	$k_{2H}/M^{-2}\ s^{-1}$	4.02×10^{-3}	0.30	74.5	-41.0	[99]
IO_3^-	1.00	278.15		1.38×10^5	0.49	—	—	[78]
IO_3^-	1.00	278.15	$k_{1H}/M^{-1}\ s^{-1}$	3.20×10^3	2.1	61.5	43.1	[78]
BrO_3^-	1.00	333.15	k_0/s^{-1}	1.59×10^{-6}	3.40	90.8	-83.7	[99]
BrO_3^-	1.00	333.15	$k_{OH}/M^{-1}\ s^{-1}$	8.10×10^{-6}	2.0	94.1	-79.5	[99]
IO_3^-	1.00	278.15		2.49×10^2	1.7	47.1	-28.3	[78]

$$H_2{*}OXO_2^+ + H_2O \xrightarrow{\text{slow}} H_2OXO_2^+ + H_2{*}O \qquad (15)$$

or

$$H_2{*}OXO_2^+ \xrightarrow{\text{slow}} XO_2^+ + H_2{*}O \qquad (16)$$

For bromate ion the slow step is reaction (15). This is supported by the fact that the exchange reaction is catalysed by chloride ions[98] and carboxylate ions[76] leading to a rate term (17)

$$R/[BrO_3^-] = k[H^+]^2[A] \qquad (17)$$

where A is Cl^-, chloroacetate, α- and β-chloropropionate and acetate ions.

The determination of $\Delta V^{\ddagger}$ using high-pressure techniques would be of interest since it could distinguish between rate paths (15) or (16).

The iodate–water exchange differs from the others in that the rate equation contains a term first order in H^+. For this exchange the mechanism given by equations (18) and (19) is proposed.

$$IO_3^- + H^+ \xrightleftharpoons{\text{fast}} HIO_3 \qquad (18)$$

$$HIO_3 + H_2{*}O \longrightarrow
\begin{array}{c}
H-O \overset{*}{\diagdown} H \\
\vdots \\
H-O \diagup \underset{O}{\overset{I}{\diagdown}} O
\end{array}
\xrightarrow{\text{slow}} HI{*}OO_2 + H_2O \qquad (19)$$

The activated complex in reaction (19) is quite similar to that invoked for the complexing of iodate with inert aqua-metal ions via an associative mechanism.[102] Although iodic acid is weaker in D_2O than in H_2O[96] the overall isotope effect on k_{1H} is normal, indicating that the isotope effect in reaction (19) exceeds that in reaction (18). General acid and general base catalysis of the iodate–water exchange was observed.[101] It was shown that acetate ion catalysis leads to a rate term first order both in the hydrogen and the acetate ion concentrations.[103]

Only the bromate–water system has a comparatively broad range dominated by spontaneous exchange (k_0).[99] Also a normal solvent hydrogen deuterium isotope effect is observed indicating proton transfer in the rate-determining step. An OH^--catalysed path has been found with bromate and iodate ions. Normal deuterium solvent isotope effects on k_{OH}, numerically similar, suggest related mechanisms. Thus, the spontaneous and the OH^--dependent exchanges are tentatively described as associatively activated reactions between XO_3^- and H_2O or OH^-.

Oxo-anions of halogens with oxidation state lower than V. Exchange data on oxo-anions of halogens with oxidation state lower than V are scarce.

It has been established that in solutions buffered by borate or acetate ions or acidified with perchloric acid, decomposition of chlorous acid, $HClO_2$, is faster than the oxygen exchange with water.[91]

Hypoflurous acid, HOF, prepared by the reaction of F_2 on water at low temperatures appears to be slow to exchange with water at least in comparison with its reactions with water and with reducing agents. While no quantitative studies have been made on the exchange rate the success of transfer experiments implies slow exchange amenable to conventional studies.[104]

The fluoroxysulphate ion, SO_4F^-, which may be regarded as a derivative of HOF also appears to be quite slow to exchange with solvent water[105] based on oxygen transfer studies on its decomposition in water to O_2 and H_2O_2. Little or no exchange between the ion and water was found during decomposition which occurred with a rate constant of around $3 \times 10^{-4} \, s^{-1}$.

Based on the observation that complete oxygen transfer takes place when hypochlorite, ClO^-, or hypobromite, BrO^-, oxidize NO_2^- to NO_3^-, the oxygen exchange in the systems $ClO^- - H_2O$ and $BrO^- - H_2O$ has been studied.[47] Owing to the experimental difficulties the quality of the data obtained was rather poor. However, some features of general interest have been observed. In alkaline solutions, exchange proceeds by the paths

$$R = k_A [ClO^-][OH^-]^{-1} \tag{20}$$

and

$$R = k_B [ClO^-][Cl^-][OH^-]^{-1} \tag{21}$$

with $k_A = 5.8 \times 10^{-8} \, M \, s^{-1}$ and $k_B = 5 \times 10^{-5} \, s^{-1}$ at 25 °C. Similar rate equations have been found for BrO^- and H_2O, and both Cl^- and Br^- catalyse the exchange. The respective rate constants for OBr^- at 25 °C are $k_A = 9.3 \times 10^{-5} \, M \, s^{-1}$, $k_B(Cl^-) = 3.8 \times 10^{-2} \, s^{-1}$, $k_B(Br^-) = 3.3 \times 10^{-2} \, s^{-1}$. By comparison with exchange of chlorine between Cl^- and ClO^-, which is often slower than the oxygen exchange, it was suggested that whatever the nature of the attack of Cl^- on HOCl is, the atoms of chlorine do not become equivalent.

2. Oxo-anions of group VI.b elements

Sulphate ion. In neutral and alkaline solutions sulphate ion is immeasurably slow to exchange. This has been tested by dissolving over 90% ^{18}O enriched sodium sulphate in normal water and in 1 M NaOH.[68] The solutions were kept at 100 °C for 63 d. Solvent water samples of these solutions were definitely less than 0.1% enriched in ^{18}O. From this result a $t_{1/2} > 100$ years can be estimated.

In acidic solutions the following rate equation was found (22)[38]

$$R = k[H^+][HSO_4^-] \tag{22}$$

With increasing concentration of sulphuric acid the kinetic parameters R and $\Delta H^‡$ depend on the concentration of water. Therefore some selected results on the rates of exchange together with $\Delta H^‡$ values are compiled in Table 3.

When $\log R$ at a given temperature was plotted against a quantity

TABLE 3
The rate of exchange in sulphuric acid solutions

H_2SO_4/M	H_2O/M	T/K	$R/M\ s^{-1}$	$\Delta H^‡/kJ\ mol^{-1}$
1.04	51.2	373.15	5.28×10^{-5}	—
3.52	45.3	373.15	1.43×10^{-3}	128
3.00	49.1	298.15	2.16×10^{-8}	—
8.00	36.5	298.15	2.70×10^{-5}	100
13.00	22.5	298.15	6.53×10^{-3}	83
14.00	19.8	283.15	2.41×10^{-3}	—
16.00	13.1	283.15	2.06×10^{-2}	—

proportional to the concentration of undissociated sulphuric acid, obtained from activity coefficient considerations, the data fell on a straight line with slope 0.95. This seems to indicate that the sulphuric acid–water exchange occurs by the following mechanism

$$H^+ + HSO_4^- \overset{fast}{\rightleftharpoons} H_2SO_4 \tag{23}$$

$$H_2SO_4 \overset{slow}{\longrightarrow} H_2O + SO_3 \tag{24}$$

Thus a D or I_d rate-determining step is suggested and $\Delta V^‡$ measurements would help to clarify the situation.

Selenate ion. Selenate ion exchanges much faster than does sulphate ion and has been studied carefully at 80 °C in the pH range 1.0 to 2.3 ($[Se(VI)]_{tot}$ ca 0.07 M). For higher total selenate concentrations (0.56–5.46 M), the exchange had to be followed at 30 °C. The exchange rates have been found to be consistent with the rate law[106]

$$R = k_1[H^+][HSeO_4^-] + k_2[H^+]^2[HSeO_4^-]^2 \tag{25}$$

At constant $[Se(VI)] = [SeO_4^{2-}] + [HSeO_4^-]$ the first term on the right-hand side of equation (25) was shown to shift from $[H^+]$ dependence to a $[H^+]^2$ dependence with increasing pH as a consequence of the protonation equilibrium of selanate with $\log K_1 = 1.93–2.03$ at 80 °C and the pertinent ionic strengths. For the data at 0.56–5.46 M Se(VI) the concentration of the ionic species were calculated according to Raman spectroscopic evidence.[107] Up to $[Se(VI)]_{tot}$, ca 4 M, this led to the following estimates $[HSeO_4^-] \simeq 0.7[Se(VI)]_{tot}$ and $[H^+] \simeq 1.3Se[(VI)]_{tot}$. Thus equation (25) can be rearranged to

$$R/[Se(VI)]_{tot}^2 = 0.91k_1 + 0.828k_2[Se(VI)]_{tot}^2 \tag{26}$$

Plotting of $R/[Se(VI)]_{tot}^2$ against $[Se(VI)]_{tot}^2$ resulted in a straight line and k_1 and k_2 were calculated from its intercept and slope. The kinetic parameters of the selenate–water exchange are listed in Table 4.

TABLE 4
Kinetic parameters for the selenate–water exchange

$$R = k_1[H^+][HSeO_4^-] + k_2[H^+]^2[HSeO_4^-]^2$$

	T/K	$\Delta H^{\ddagger}/kJ\ mol^{-1}$	$\Delta S^{\ddagger}/J\ mol^{-1}\ K^{-1}$
$k_1 = 8.2 \times 10^{-3}\ M^{-1}\ s^{-1}$	353.15	93.7	−20.9
$k_2 = 3 \times 10^{-6}\ M^{-3}\ s^{-1}$	303.15	88.8	−41.4

In view of the negative entropy the rate step of path 1 of equation (25) seems to be a bimolecular one. The fourth-order rate term, $k_2[H^+]^2[HSeO_4^-]^2$, may be interpreted as a bimolecular path between two selenic acid molecules

$$H_2SeO_4 + H_2SeO_4 \rightleftharpoons H_2Se_2O_7 + H_2O \tag{27}$$

Tellurate ion. Recently a definitive kinetic investigation of the tellurate–water exchange using the ^{18}O tracer method has been carried out[76] under such conditions in which monomeric species predominate. The pH profile (Fig. 1) of the rate data reveals that no $[H^+]$-dependent pathway is operative between pH 0–2 and moreover in this range the rates of exchange are almost the same in H_2O and D_2O. With increasing pH the rates increased, with $TeO(OH)_5^-$ and probably $TeO(OH)_4^{2-}$ becoming the reactive species. At the prevailing conditions (25 °C, $I = 1.0$ m $NaClO_4$) the respective protonation constants are $\log K_1 = 10.13$, $\log K_{12} = 7.17$. All data are consistent with the rate equation (28)

$$R = k_1[Te(OH)_6] + k_2[TeO(OH)_5^-] + k_3[TeO_2(OH)_4^{2-}] \tag{28}$$

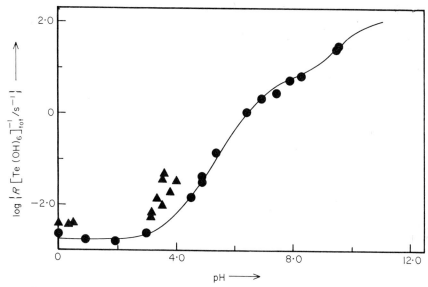

Fig. 1. pH rate profile of the oxygen exchange of tellurate and water at 25 °C. ●
^{18}O data, ▲ ^{17}O nmr data. The full curve has been calculated with the rate constants
given in Table 5.

The apparent deviation between the ^{18}O mass spectrometer and the ^{17}O nmr data largely disappears when the pH values in the latter work[108] are corrected. A positive activation volume has been found for the exchange reaction in the $[H^+]$-independent region. This together with the absence of a solvent deuterium isotope effect provides strong evidence for a dissociative mechanism. The situation so far is less clear-cut for the $TeO(OH)_5^- - H_2O$ exchange since solvent assisted oxygen dissociation seems to play an important role in the exchange reactions of negatively charged ions and water.[72] The relevant kinetic data which have been determined are summarized in Table 5.

TABLE 5

Kinetic parameters for the tellurate–water exchange (25 °C, $I = 1.0$ m $NaClO_4$)

$$R = k_1[Te(OH)_6] + k_2[TeO(OH)_5^-] + k_3[TeO_2(OH)_4^{2-}]$$

	$\Delta H^{\ddagger}$/kJ mol^{-1}	$\Delta S^{\ddagger}$/JK^{-1} mol^{-1}	$\Delta V^{\ddagger}$/cm^3 mol^{-1}
$k_1 = 1.7 \times 10^{-3}$ s^{-1}	104	51	6.1
$k_2 = 6.6$ s^{-1}	58.5	−73	—
$k_3 = 1.2 \times 10^2$ s^{-1}	—	—	—
		$k_1^H/k_1^D = 1.0$	

There is a striking difference in the exchange behaviour of octahedral tellurate as compared with tetrahedral sulphate and selenate ions. Whereas with the tellurate $[H^+]$ catalysis is totally absent up to pH ca 0 and the partially deprotonated species exchange much faster than neutral $Te(OH)_6$, protonation labilizes the oxygen in sulphate and selenate ion.

Sulphite ion. Although SO_2 is quite soluble in water solution, sulphurous acid, H_2SO_3, is either not present or only in minute quantities. The kinetics of oxygen exchange between pyramidal sulphite ion and water have been studied in the range $9 < pH < 10.5$ and $0.075 \leqslant [S(IV)]_{tot} \leqslant 0.6$ M at $I = 0.9$ M (KNO_3) and $24.7\,°C$.[69]

Under these conditions $[S(IV)]_{tot} \simeq [HSO_3^-] + [SO_3^{2-}]$ and $\log K_1 = 6.34$.[109] The observed rate dependency on $[H^+]$ and $[S(IV)]_{tot}$ was consistent with the expression (29)

$$R = k_1[H^+][HSO_3^-] + k_2[HSO_3^-]^2 \tag{29}$$

The latter can be interpreted by the steps (30–32).

$$H^+ + SO_3^{2-} \underset{}{\overset{K_1}{\rightleftharpoons}} HSO_3^- \quad \text{fast} \tag{30}$$

$$HSO_3^- + H^+ \underset{k_1}{\overset{k_{-1}}{\rightleftharpoons}} SO_2 + H_2O \tag{31}$$

$$2HSO_3^- \underset{k_{-2}}{\overset{k_2}{\rightleftharpoons}} S_2O_5^{2-} + H_2O \tag{32}$$

With experimentally determined values for $k_{-1} = 2.5 \times 10^9$ $M^{-1}\,s^{-1}$ and $k_2 = 7.0 \times 10^2$ $M^{-1}\,s^{-1}$ and the respective equilibrium constants $\log K_{12} = 1.37$[109] and $\log K = -1.06$ (32),[110] the rate constants of hydration of SO_2, k_1, and $S_2O_5^{2-}$, k_{-2} can be obtained. The rate R was measured at constant pH and different temperatures but no attempt was made to determine $\Delta H^{\ddagger}$ and $\Delta S^{\ddagger}$ for paths (31) and (32) separately.

Selenite ion. The oxygen exchange between pyramidal selenite ion and water shows remarkably different features compared with sulphite ion. It has been studied at $0\,°C$ over the range $8.7 \leqslant pH \leqslant 12.5$ and $0.02 \leqslant [Se(IV)]_{tot} \leqslant 0.16$ M, employing two different ionic strengths $I = 0.16$ and 0.54 M.[111] At the prevailing conditions the protonation constants are $\log K_1 = 8.10_1$ $(I = 0.56$ M$)$ and $\log K_1 = 8.38_2$ $(I = 0.14$ M$)$.[111] Four exchange paths with no $[OH^-]$ catalysis have been identified corresponding to rate equation (33)

$$R = k_0[SeO_3^{2-}] + k_1[HSeO_3^-] + k_2[HSeO_3^-]^2 + k_3[HSeO_3^-][SeO_3^{2-}] \tag{33}$$

and the following steps can be assigned to them

$$Se^*O_3^{2-} + H_2O \rightleftharpoons SeO_3^{2-} + H_2^*O \tag{34}$$

$$HSe^*O_3^- + H_2O \rightleftharpoons HSeO_3^- + H_2^*O \tag{35}$$

$$HSe^*O_3^- + HSeO_3^- \rightleftharpoons Se_2O_5^{2-} + H_2^*O \tag{36}$$

$$HSe^*O_3^- + SeO_3^{2-} \rightleftharpoons Se_2O_5^{2-} + {}^*OH^- \tag{37}$$

Evidence for the occurrence of $Se_2O_5^{2-}$ comes from Raman spectroscopic investigations.[112] The relevant kinetic data are compiled in Table 6.

TABLE 6
Rate constants of $SeO_3^{2-}-H_2O$ exchange at 0 °C

Exchange reaction	Rate constant	Ionic strength	
		0.16 M	0.54 M
$SeO_3^{2-} + H_2O \rightleftharpoons$	k_0/s^{-1}	1.5×10^{-4}	1.5×10^{-4}
$HSeO_3^- + H_2O \rightleftharpoons$	k_1/s^{-1}	2×10^{-4}	(2×10^{-4})
$2HSeO_3^- \rightleftharpoons Se_2O_5^{2-} + H_2O$	$k_2/M^{-1}s^{-1}$	1.3×10^{-1}	1.8×10^{-1}
$HSeO_3^- + SeO_3^{2-} \rightleftharpoons Se_2O_5^{2-} + OH^-$	$k_3/M^{-1}s^{-1}$	1×10^{-2}	2×10^{-2}

The activation energies have been determined for two pH values, but since at least two exchange paths were operative under each condition selected, it is not possible to assign $\Delta H^{\ddagger}$ and $\Delta S^{\ddagger}$ values to a single path (34–37). It should be noted that only the third term on the right-hand side of equation (33) has an equivalent in the $SO_3^{2-}-H_2O$ system and the exchange rate constant is larger in the latter.

Thiosulphate ion. The exchange of oxygen between water and thiosulphate has been measured in aqueous solutions at 60 to 100 °C and $5.3 \leqslant pH \leqslant 6.5$.[46] The rate equation (38) contains only one term

$$R = k[H^+][S_2O_3^{2-}] \tag{38}$$

Neither general acid nor chloride ion catalysis was observed. The exchange is faster in D_2O than in H_2O, with $k^H/k^D = 0.63$. The kinetic parameters have been determined and are $k = 25.7\ M^{-1}s^{-1}$, $\Delta H^{\ddagger} = 53.1\ kJ\ mol^{-1}$ and $\Delta S^{\ddagger} = -69\ JK^{-1}\ mol^{-1}$ at 80 °C. The mechanism proposed consists of rapid protonation of $S_2O_3^{2-}$ followed by an associative attack of H_2O at the inner sulphur of $HO-SO_2-S^-$ as depicted in scheme (39)

$$H_2O + \underset{\underset{-S}{\overset{O}{\|}}{\overset{}{|}}}{S}-OH \rightleftharpoons H_2O^+ - \underset{\underset{-S}{\overset{O^-}{|}}{\overset{}{|}}}{S}-OH \rightleftharpoons HO - \underset{\underset{-S}{\overset{OH}{|}}{\overset{}{|}}}{S}-OH \rightleftharpoons$$

$$\text{(39)}$$

$$HO - \underset{\underset{-S}{\overset{-O}{|}}{\overset{}{|}}}{S}-OH_2^+ \rightleftharpoons HO - \underset{\underset{-S}{\overset{O}{\|}}{\overset{}{|}}}{S} + H_2O$$

The main arguments for this mechanism are the negative entropy of activation and the magnitude of the inverse deuterium solvent isotope effect. The latter is similar to that observed for the A-2 type acid catalysed hydrolysis of organic sulphate and selenate esters. For the A-1 type, hydrolysis values of k^H/k^D lie in the range of 0.39–0.53, whereas for A-2 reactions a range of 0.59–0.77 is normally observed. It should be noted that the acid-base pre-equilibrium ($H^+ + S_2O_3^{2-} \rightleftharpoons HS_2O_3^-$) is expected to give rise to an inverse solvent isotope effect which is obviously partly offset by proton transfer in the rate step.

3. Oxo-anions of group V.b elements

Nitrate and nitrite ion. The oxygen exchange between planar nitric acid, HNO_3, and water has been investigated extensively in concentrated nitric acid solutions at 0 °C.[113,114] In the concentration range 8–28 mol% HNO_3, the catalytic effect of nitrous acid was studied.[115] At lower acidities and in the presence of chloride, a simple nucleophile which does not contain oxygen, the following rate equation (40) has been found at 100 °C[98]

$$R = k_1[H^+][HNO_3]_f + k_2[H^+][HNO_3]_f[Cl^-] \qquad (40)$$

where $[HNO_3]_f$ is the concentration of undissociated nitric acid as calculated or extrapolated from values given by Hood and Reilly.[116] The respective kinetic parameters together with data of two actual experiments are listed in Table 7.

The $H_2O–NO_2^-$ exchange has been studied extensively. Anbar and Taube[44] found the rate equation in phosphate buffered systems (pH 4–6, I = 1.0 M) to be

$$R = k_{2H}[H^+]^2[NO_2^-] \qquad (41)$$

Rate equation (41) was confirmed by Bunton and Stedman[45] by measuring the isotopic composition of N_2O evolved when HNO_2 and HN_3 react in $H_2^{18}O$ at 0 °C under conditions in which the kinetics and mechanism of the chemical reactions (42) were known, the rate being at least 10 times faster than

TABLE 7

Kinetic data for the nitrate–water exchange at $100\,°C$

$$R = k_1[H^+][HNO_3]_f + k_2[H^+][HNO_3]_f[Cl^-]$$

$[NO_3^-]_{tot}/M$	$[H^+]/M$	$[HNO_3]_f/M$	$R/M\,s^{-1}$	$R[H^+]^{-1}[HNO_3]_f^{-1}/$ $M^{-1}\,s^{-1}$
1.00	0.96	0.04	1.70×10^{-6}	4.5×10^{-5}
7.40	3.92	3.48	1.88×10^{-3}	1.4×10^{-4}

	$\Delta H^{\ddagger}/kJ\,mol^{-1}$	$\Delta S^{\ddagger}/JK^{-1}\,mol^{-1}$
$k_1 = 8.0 \times 10^{-5}\,M^{-1}\,s^{-1}$	89.4	-85.7
$k_2 = 5.3 \times 10^{-3}\,M^{-2}\,s^{-1}$	88.1	-54.2

the corresponding exchange rate

$$H_2NO_2^+ + N_3^- \xrightarrow{\text{slow}} H_2O + N_3NO \xrightarrow{\text{fast}} N_2O + N_2 \tag{42}$$

The variation of the enrichment of the evolved nitrous oxide after complete reaction, with the concentration of azide, and with the acidity, shows that there is no appreciable hydrolysis of the intermediate nitrosyl azide in aqueous solution; all of it breaks down to nitrogen and nitrous oxide. The results of this "competition" method agreed reasonably for quite different pH regions where HNO_2—N_3^-—H_2O $(4.1 < pH < 5.7)$ and HNO_2—HN_3—H_2O $(0.5 < pH < 1.7)$ respectively are the reacting species. In addition the exchange rate between HNO_2 and H_2O was measured directly and a mean value of $k_{2H} = 7.1 \times 10^5\,M^{-2}\,s^{-1}$ was obtained at $0\,°C$, where the protonation constant of HNO_2 was taken to be $\log K_1 = 3.49$.[117]

Another path for O exchange between HNO_2 and H_2O has been demonstrated to be operative in more concentrated solutions of NO_2^- $(0.5–2.0\,M)$. The rate equation was of the form

$$R = k_2[HNO_2]^2 \tag{43}$$

with $k_2 = 0.53\,M^{-1}\,s^{-1}$ at $0\,°C$.[118]

In the presence of other nucleophilic anions catalysed exchange paths of similar forms and reactivity become available.[119] This implies that hydrated nitrosonium ion, $H_2NO_2^+$, discriminates little between reagents of similar charge. With acetate ion the rate equation (44) was found between pH 4.6–6.0 and $[NO_2^-] = 0.025–0.165\,M$ to be

$$R = k_{ac}[H^+]^2[NO_2^-][OAc^-] \tag{44}$$

with $k_{ac} = 1.5 \times 10^7\,M^{-3}\,s^{-1}$ at $0\,°C$.

In dilute solutions of NO_2^- the exchange probably proceeds by a nucleophilic attack of water or other nucleophiles on the hydrated nitrosonium ion as in (45) and (46)

$$\begin{array}{c} H \\ \diagdown \\ \diagup \\ H \end{array} {}^*O{-}N^*O^+ \; + \; H_2O \; \rightleftharpoons \; \begin{array}{c} H \\ \diagdown \\ \diagup \\ H \end{array} O{-}N^*O^+ \; + \; H_2{}^*O \qquad (45)$$

$$\begin{array}{c} H \\ \diagdown \\ \diagup \\ H \end{array} {}^*O{-}N^*O^+ \; + \; OAc^- \; \rightleftharpoons \; AcO{-}N^*O \; + \; H_2{}^*O \qquad (46)$$

whereas in more concentrated solutions, where the rate of exchange was proportional to $[HNO_2]^2$ and independent of $[NO_2^-]_{tot}$, the most plausible mechanism seems to be the formation and rehydration of dinitrogen trioxide as in reaction (47)

$$\begin{array}{c} H \\ \diagdown \\ \diagup \\ H \end{array} {}^*O{-}N^*O^+ \; + \; N^*O_2^- \; \rightleftharpoons \; {}^*O_2N{-}N^*O \; + \; H_2{}^*O \qquad (47)$$

Free NO_2^- in base does not show any exchange with solvent water in 1 h at 60 °C.[120] Thus alkalification stops the NO_2^-–H_2O exchange effectively.[45]

Phosphate and phosphite ion. A very unique pH profile for the rate constants of exchange between orthophosphoric acid and water has been found.[121] The data, measured at 100.1 °C, are shown in Fig. 2. The range of maximum rates coincides with the predominance of $H_2PO_4^-$. A minimum is observed at pH ca 1 where exchange occurs mainly between H_3PO_4 and H_2O. However, at higher acidities rates increase rapidly. Rate equation (48) describes the exchange between pH 0–9 at 100.1 °C and $[PO_4^{3-}]_{tot} = 0.4–0.8$ M.

$$R = k_A[H_3PO_4][H^+]e^{\beta I} + k_N[H_3PO_4] + k_M[H_2PO_4^-] \qquad (48)$$

where $k_A = 5.45 \times 10^{-7}$ M^{-1} s^{-1}, $k_N = 1.28 \times 10^{-6}$ s^{-1}, $k_M = 4.03 \times 10^{-6}$ s^{-1}, $I = 1.37$ M, $\beta = 0.212$ M^{-1}. It should be noted that in the calculation of k_A, k_N and k_M, protonation constants of orthophosphoric acid were used which are valid only for 20 °C and $I = 0$[122] (log $K_{12} = 7.206$, log $K_{13} = 2.102$). Taking into account the change of these constants with T and I would result in numerically different rate constants, but the shape of the solid curve in Fig. 2 would remain the same. A hydrogen-bonded intermediate between an $H_2PO_4^-$ ion and H_2O has been postulated to be responsible for the special reactivity of this ion. Oxygen exchange is first order with respect to $[PO_4^{3-}]_{tot}$, and higher orders are observed only for high concentrations of orthophosphoric acid,[39] where the half-time of exchange at 100 °C decreases from 250 h at 5.9 M H_3PO_4 to 0.20 h at 18.3 M H_3PO_4. Support for exchange

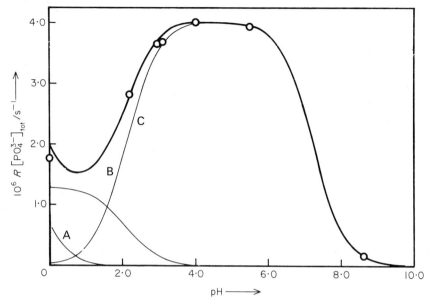

Fig. 2. pH rate profile of the oxygen exchange between orthophosphate and water at 100.1 °C. ○ Experimental data. Contribution of the k_A (A), k_N (B) and k_M (C) term of equation (48) to total exchange.

via reversible formation and hydrolysis of $H_4P_2O_7$ is given by the equivalence of the exchange rate and the rate of $H_4P_2O_7$ hydrolysis in the concentrated solutions.

The rate of isotopic exchange of oxygen between H_3PO_3 and H_2O was measured over the range from pH 10 to 9.4 M in $HClO_4$.[123] Between 2.12 M $HClO_4$ and pH 10 rate equation (49) was obeyed

$$R = k_3[H_3PO_3][H^+] + k_2[H_3PO_3^-] + k_1[H_2PO_3^{2-}] + k_0[HPO_3^{2-}] \quad (49)$$

The respective rate constants at 100 °C were calculated using protonation constants (log $K_{12} = 1.29$, log $K_1 = 6.74$) valid at 18 °C[124] and are $k_3 = 1.7 \times 10^{-4}$ M^{-1} s^{-1}, $k_2 = 3.0 \times 10^{-5}$ s^{-1}, $k_1 = 1.0 \times 10^{-7}$ s^{-1}, $k_0 = 6.3 \times 10^{-8}$ s^{-1}. While it is difficult to speculate about mechanistic details of the four reaction paths (since no activation parameters are available), it is clear that the monoanion $H_2PO_3^-$ has little special reactivity as it is the case with $H_2PO_4^2$. This can be easily rationalized on the basis of the P—H and O—H bonds occurring in the former and the two O—H bonds or O—H$_2$ occurring in the latter. Also the pH profiles shown in Fig. 2 and Fig. 3 demonstrate that the often cited rule that exchange rates increase with the decrease in the oxidation state of a given central atom is not universally valid.

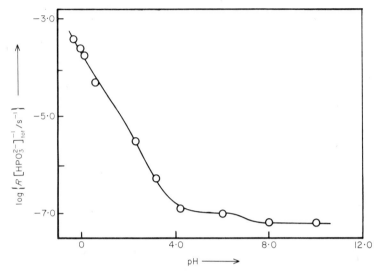

Fig. 3. pH rate profile of the oxygen exchange between phosphite and water at 100 °C. ○ Experimental data. The full curve has been calculated using equation (49).

In the present example H_3PO_3 exchanges faster and slower than H_3PO_4 depending on the pH range, i.e. the reaction paths operative.

The rates of reaction in strong acid (1–9.42 M $HClO_4$, 80 °C) were also investigated,[123] but the interpretation is not entirely clear although evidence for the formation of the protonated species $H_4PO_3^+$ comes from nmr studies.[125] It may be that the deviations from linear relationships between the rate of exchange and acidity observed in very concentrated acid are due to multiple protonation.

Arsenate and arsenite ion. The complex rate equation (50) has been derived from an extensive ^{18}O tracer investigation of isotopic exchange between arsenate ion and water over the range $6.5 \leqslant pH \leqslant 12.5$.[74]

$$R = k_0[AsO_4^{3-}] + k_1[HAsO_4^{2-}] + k_2[H_2AsO_4^-] + k_3[HAsO_4^{2-}]^2$$
$$+ k_4[H_2AsO_4^-][HAsO_4^{2-}] + k_5[H_2AsO_4^-]^2 \qquad (50)$$

In addition catalysis of exchange by arsenious acid[126] and periodate ions[127] has been observed. The oxygen exchange between arsenite ion and solvent water proved too fast for ^{18}O techniques and was therefore studied by ^{17}O nmr.[128] For the detailed interpretation of multi-path exchange reactions it is obviously very important to know the equilibrium constants valid at the conditions of the kinetic experiments. These have been determined for the

TABLE 8

Protolysis constants of arsenic, arsenious and periodic acid at 30 °C

Reaction	I/M	log K	Reference
$H^+ + HAsO_4^{2-} \rightleftharpoons H_2AsO_4^-$	0.55	6.53	[74]
	0.20	6.56	[126]
$H^+ + AsO_4^{3-} \rightleftharpoons HAsO_4^{2-}$	0.55	11.01	[74]
	0.20	11.33	[127]
$H^+ + H_2AsO_3^- \rightleftharpoons H_3AsO_3$	0.20	9.11	[126]
$H^+ + H_4IO_6^- \rightleftharpoons H_5IO_6$	0.20	1.34[a]	[127, 129]
$H^+ + H_3IO_6^{2-} \rightleftharpoons H_4IO_6^-$	0.20	7.87[a]	[127, 129]
$H^+ + H_2IO_6^{3-} \rightleftharpoons H_3IO_6^{2-}$	0.20	11.35[a]	[127, 130]

[a] Apparent constants where the kinetically indistinguishable species $H_4IO_6^-$ and IO_4^- have been lumped together.

protolysis reactions of arsenic[74] and arsenious acid[126] and extrapolated from data valid at I = 0 for periodic acid,[127] and are compiled in Table 8.

The rate constants and activation parameters pertinent to equation (50) are given in Table 9. Also included are the kinetic data for the paths catalysed by arsenite and periodate as well as the arsenite oxygen exchange.[128]

Both first- and second-order processes for arsenate ion exchange are very much slower than for arsenite ion. The difference is attributable mostly to larger enthalpies of activation in the latter case, reflecting the stronger As(V)—O bonds. The observation that the arsenate exchange process is catalysed by As(III) and I(VII) is of considerable interest. General acid catalysis is inconsistent with the fact that exchange rates on $H_2AsO_4^-$ increase with reactants in the following order $H_2AsO_4^- < H_3AsO_3 < H_4IO_6^-$, differing from the relative acid strengths $H_3AsO_3 < H_4IO_6^- < H_2AsO_4^-$. Although it has been demonstrated that less than 5% exchange of radioactive arsenic occurs between arsenite and arsenate in 3 h at 100 °C,[131] it is not certain that the conditions (0.1 M HCl; ca 1 M NaOH) selected allow predictions for the pH range (7–11), where arsenite and periodate ions catalyse oxygen exchange between As(V) and water. Reversible condensation processes seem to be responsible for the second-order paths in Table 9. Periodate ion does not effect the oxygen exchange of phosphate ions and selenic acid respectively.[127] Thus in the latter two cases no condensation mechanism is involved.

Oxo-anions of nitrogen with oxidation state lower than III. Only qualitative information is available for anions of nitrogen with an oxidation state lower than III. For $Na_2N_2O_3$, no exchange was found before or during decomposition. Also during its life-time in water solutions sodium hyponitrite, $Na_2N_2O_2$, showed no appreciable exchange on $N_2O_2^{2-}$ or of the N_2O formed occurs. The maximum time of contact was 16 h in the most basic region.[132]

TABLE 9

Kinetic data for oxygen exchange between arsenate, arsenite ion and water at 30 °C

Reactants	k	I/M	$\Delta H^{\ddagger}$/kJ mol^{-1}	$\Delta S^{\ddagger}$/JK^{-1} mol^{-1}	Reference
$AsO_4^{3-} + H_2O$	1.5×10^{-6} s^{-1}	0.55	—	—	[74]
$HAsO_4^{2-} + H_2O$	1.2×10^{-5} s^{-1}	0.55	92	−46	[74]
$H_2AsO_4^- + H_2O$	1.0×10^{-4} s^{-1}	0.55	—	—	[74]
$H_2AsO_3^- + H_2O$	1.67×10^2 s^{-1}	variable	25	−120	[128]
$HAsO_4^{2-} + HAsO_4^{2-}$	8.5×10^{-6} M^{-1} s^{-1}	0.55	—	—	[74]
$HAsO_4^{2-} + H_2AsO_4^-$	6.4×10^{-3} M^{-1} s^{-1}	0.55	—	—	[74]
$H_2AsO_4^- + H_2AsO_4^-$	7.4×10^{-2} M^{-1} s^{-1}	0.55	—	—	[74]
$H_2AsO_4^- + H_3AsO_3$	6.8 M^{-1} s^{-1}	0.20	52	−65[a]	[126]
$H_2AsO_4^- + H_2AsO_3^-$	<7 M^{-1} s^{-1}	0.20	—	—	[126]
$HAsO_4^- + H_3AsO_3$	<2 M^{-1} s^{-1}	0.20	—	—	[126]
$H_2AsO_4^- + H_4IO_6^-$	3.38×10^2 M^{-1} s^{-1}	0.20	—	—	[127]
$H_2AsO_4^- + H_3IO_6^{2-}$	$<7.5 \times 10^2$ M^{-1} s^{-1}	0.20	—	—	[127]
$HAsO_4^{2-} + H_4IO_6^-$	$<3.6 \times 10^1$ M^{-1} s^{-1}	0.20	—	—	[127]
$H_2AsO_3^- + H_2AsO_3^-$	6.9×10^1 m^{-1} s^{-1}	variable	33	−102	[128]

[a] Recalculated value. In the original paper $\Delta S^{\ddagger} = -38$ JK^{-1} mol^{-1} was given for that path.

4. Oxo-anions of group IV.b elements

Carbonate ion. The rate constant for hydration of CO_2 in acidic media was first studied using ^{18}O labels in the pioneering work of Mills and Urey.[133] Several reaction paths contributing to the exchange of carbon dioxide with water and hydroxide ions have been identified by measuring the rate of oxygen exchange between sodium carbonate and bicarbonate, and ^{18}O-enriched water as a function of pH (7.6–13.0), ionic strength (0.5–2.5 m) and carbonate–bicarbonate concentration (2×10^{-3}–2×10^{-2} m).[134] It has been shown that exchange occurs by hydration and is also catalysed by carbonate and bicarbonate ions according to the overall rate equation (51)

$$R = k_1[CO_2][OH^-] + k_2[CO_2] + k_3[CO_2][OH^-][CO_3^{2-}]$$
$$+ k_4[CO_2][CO_3^{2-}] + k_5[CO_2][HCO_3^-]\tag{51}$$

Selecting the best values available for the protonation constants at 25 °C, $\log K_{12} = 6.352$[135] and $\log K_1 = 10.329$,[136] and allowing for activity coefficient variations the data listed in Table 10 were obtained. The kinetics of

TABLE 10
Kinetic data for the oxygen exchange between carbonate and water at 25 °C

$$R = k_1[CO_2][OH^-] + k_2[CO_2] + k_3[CO_2][OH^-][CO_3^{2-}]$$
$$+ k_4[CO_2][CO_3^{2-}] + k_5[CO_2][HCO_3^-]$$

	I = 0.5 M (NaCl)	I = 1.5[a] m (NaCl)	I = 2.5 m (NaCl)	$\Delta H^{\ddagger}$/kJ mol^{-1}	$\Delta S^{\ddagger}$/ JK^{-1} mol^{-1}
$k_1/m^{-1} s^{-1}$	8.4×10^3	8.0×10^3	4.8×10^3	47.7	−10.12
k_2/s^{-1}	3.64×10^{-2}	2.70×10^{-2}	2.47×10^{-2}	71.2	−36.3
$k_3/m^{-2} s^{-1}$	1.6×10^5	1.4×10^5	1.1×10^5	47.7	13.7
$k_4/m^{-1} s^{-1}$	1.3	1.7	0.7	—	—
$k_5/m^{-1} s^{-1}$	4.8×10^{-2}	5.0×10^{-2}	4.3×10^{-2}	85.4	16.6

[a] The activation parameters are calculated from measurements at I = 1.5 m (NaCl).

^{18}O exchange between H_2O and the carbonate species obtained by dissolving either $NaHCO_3$ or $(NH_3)_5CoCO_3^+$ in H_2O have been measured.[70] Both systems were studied in the pH range 7.2–8.6 at 20, 26, 30 °C and I = 1.0 M ($NaClO_4$). The results are consistent with previous studies[134] and confirm that the rate of exchange of carbonate complexed to $(NH_3)_5Co^{3+}$ and of free carbonate species is controlled by the hydration of carbon dioxide.[137]

Recently a value for $k_2 = 4.04 \times 10^{-2} s^{-1}$, 25 °C (I = 0.5 M NaCl), in excellent agreement with that given in Table 10, has been found by a completely different method,[138] thereby underscoring the accuracy of the older ^{18}O study.

In this context it should be mentioned that the reaction of gaseous CO_2 and $H_2^{18}O$ has been carefully measured over a wide range of temperatures (5–90 °C at $I = 0$, $k_2 = 5.0 \times 10^{-2}$ s^{-1}, 25 °C)[139] using an elaborate version of the float method.[50] Plots of $\ln(k_2/T)$ versus $1/T$ were curved leading to the following activation parameters in H_2O and D_2O respectively, $\Delta H_2^{\ddagger}/\text{kJ mol}^{-1} = 64.2$, 72.2; $\Delta S_2^{\ddagger}/\text{JK}^{-1}$ mol$^{-1} = -55.2$, -36.2; $\Delta C_2^{\ddagger}/\text{JK}^{-1}$ mol$^{-1} = -537$, -595. A normal solvent isotope effect for reaction (52)

$$CO_2 + H_2O \overset{k_2}{\rightleftharpoons} H_2CO_3 \tag{52}$$

has been observed, $k_2^H/k_2^D = 2.69$ at 25 °C. Kinetic data for the reverse reaction (53) have also been determined[139] in H_2O at 25 °C; $k_{-1} = 1.25 \times 10^{-3}$ s^{-1}, $\Delta H_{-1}^{\ddagger} = 51.5$ kJ mol^{-1}, $\Delta S_{-1}^{\ddagger} = -128$ JK^{-1} mol^{-1}, and in D_2O, $k_{-1} = 7.78 \times 10^{-4}$ s^{-1}, $\Delta H_{-1}^{\ddagger} = 51.5$ kJ mol^{-1}, $\Delta S_{-1}^{\ddagger} = -132$ JK^{-1} mol^{-1}

$$CO_2 + OH^- \overset{k_1}{\underset{k_{-1}}{\rightleftharpoons}} HCO_3^- \tag{53}$$

In addition it has been confirmed that this exchange reaction is catalysed by carbonate ions and some less accurate values for k_{-3} as in equation (54) are given between 60 and 90 °C.[139]

$$CO_2 + OH^- + CO_3^{2-} \overset{k_3}{\underset{k_{-3}}{\rightleftharpoons}} HCO_3^- + CO_3^{2-} \tag{54}$$

The rate of oxygen exchange between gaseous $C^{18}O_2$ and H_2O has been studied mass spectrometrically giving $k_2 = 2.95 \times 10^{-2}$ s^{-1} and $\Delta H_2^{\ddagger}/\text{kJ}$ mol$^{-1} = 69.5$.[140] Intermolecular oxygen exchange in the pH region 8–10 between CO_2 and CO_3^{2-} [141] was observed by placing ^{18}O labelled carbonate, not enriched in ^{13}C, into solution with ^{13}C enriched carbonate, not enriched in ^{18}O. The rate of depletion of ^{18}O from the ^{12}C containing species and the rate of appearance of ^{18}O in the ^{13}C containing species was measured by mass spectrometry. It was established that equation (55) is responsible for the exchange.

$$^{13}C^{16}O_2 + {}^{12}C^{18}O_3^{2-} \rightleftharpoons {}^{12}C^{18}O^{18}O + {}^{13}C^{16}O^{16}O^{18}O^{2-} \tag{55}$$

The rate constant for exchange of oxygen between CO_2 and CO_3^{2-} at 25 °C is 114 M^{-1} s^{-1}. This effect is important in studies using ^{18}O labels to determine the fate of CO_2 in biochemical and physiological processes.

Carboxylate ions. The exchange of the oxygen atoms of carboxylic acids and carboxylate ions with solvent water is assumed to go through formation of tetrahedral intermediates I–III, which decompose rapidly to give exchange products.[142–146]

$$
\begin{array}{ccc}
\text{OH} & \text{OH} & \text{O}^- \\
| & | & | \\
\text{R--C--OH}_2^+ & \text{R--C--OH} & \text{R--C--OH} \\
| & | & | \\
\text{OH} & \text{OH} & \text{OH} \\
\text{I} & \text{II} & \text{III}
\end{array}
$$

For pathways leading to I, direct H_3O^+ attack on the neutral acid molecule or attack of molecular H_2O on the $RCO_2H_2^+$ cation formed in a protonation pre-equilibrium, are kinetically indistinguishable. Raman data[147] and matrix isolation spectroscopy[148] seem to favour direct H_3O^+ attack on the acid molecule. It is, however, difficult to understand how H_3O^+ can act as a nucleophile. Solvent H_2O attack on the protonated acid seems a more likely process. Similar ambiguities exist in exchange pathways leading to II and III. Recently it was attempted to decide the question by studying the oxygen transfer between dodecylammonium propionate and $H_2^{18}O$ under neutral and acidic conditions with benzene as the solvent, using water pools of varying size. Even the results obtained by this study cannot be interpreted unequivocally.[149]

In the acetic acid–water system rate equation (56) described the exchange kinetics:[142]

$$R = k_2[CH_3COOH][H^+] + k_0[CH_3COO^-] \tag{56}$$

In the kinetic data evaluation allowance was made for the variation of the protonation constant of acetic acid with temperature using the empirical equation (57)[150,151]

$$\log K_1 = 4.754 + 5.10^{-5}(T - 295.75)^2 \tag{57}$$

Other paths become available with CF_3COOH and CCl_3COOH, and rate equation (58) has been reported,[143] where X is F or Cl.

$$R = k_2[CX_3COOH][H^+] + k_1[CX_3COOH] + k_{OH}[CX_3COO^-][OH^-] \tag{58}$$

In the whole temperature range investigated the following protonation constants were used: $\log K_1(CF_3COOH) = 0.231$[152] and $\log K_1(CCl_3COOH) = 0.60$.[153] Some reservations with respect to the numerical values of these acetic acid and halogeno-acetic acid exchange rate constants, listed in Table 11, seem to be in order since no allowance has been made for pH variation with temperature. Reaction paths corresponding to equations (56) and (58) can clearly be distinguished, with the pH profile of the

TABLE 11

Kinetic data for the oxygen exchange between carboxylic acids and water

Carboxylic acid	Exchange path	I/M	T/K	k	$\Delta H^\ddagger/\text{kJ mol}^{-1}$	$\Delta S^\ddagger/\text{JK}^{-1}\,\text{mol}^{-1}$
CH_3COOH	$-CO_2H + H^+ + H_2O$	1.0	374.15	$1.19 \times 10^{-1}\ M^{-1}\,s^{-1}$	62.2	-99
	$-CO_2^- + H_2O$	1.0	374.15	$3.98 \times 10^{-7}\ s^{-1}$	118.9	-52
CF_3COOH	$-CO_2H + H^+ + H_2O$	4.0	298.15	$1.40 \times 10^{-3}\ M^{-1}\,s^{-1}$	58.5	-101
	$-CO_2H + H_2O$	4.0	298.15	$7.77 \times 10^{-4}\ s^{-1}$	55.8	-119
	$-CO_2^- + OH^-$	4.0	298.15	$7.39 \times 10^{-2}\ M^{-1}\,s^{-1}$	46.4	-111
CCl_3COOH	$-CO_2H^+ + H_2O$	4.0	298.65	$1.07 \times 10^{-4}\ M^{-1}\,s^{-1}$	62.5	-112
	$-CO_2H + H_2O$	4.0	298.65	$7.88 \times 10^{-5}\ s^{-1}$	53.9	-143
	$-CO_2^- + OH^-$	4.0	298.65	$3.11 \times 10^{-4}\ M^{-1}\,s^{-1}$	57.9	-130
$(COOH)_2$	$C_2O_4H_2 + H^+ + H_2O$	1.0–4.0	298.15	$5.13 \times 10^{-4}\ M^{-1}\,s^{-1}$ [a]	63.3	-95
	$C_2O_4H^- + H^+ + H_2O$	1.0–4.0	298.15	$6.33 \times 10^{-4}\ M^{-1}\,s^{-1}$ [a]	48.6	-142
	$C_2O_4^{2-} + H_2O$	1.0	374.15	$2.62 \times 10^{-6}\ s^{-1}$	112.7	-54

[a] Data from measurements at $I = 4.0$ M.

exchange rate being displaced.[142,143] For $CH_2ClCOOH$ and $CHCl_2COOH$ only k_2 values were measured and are, at 25 °C: 6.7×10^{-4} M^{-1} s^{-1} and 4×10^{-4} M^{-1} s^{-1} respectively.[144] It is interesting to note that for k_2 of CH_3COOH ($k_H/k_D = 0.70$ at 74 °C) and CCl_3COOH ($k_H/k_D = 0.60$ at 25 °C) inverse solvent isotope effects have been observed.[142,144] Based on this information proton transfer in the rate-determining step was ruled out.[144]

Three different paths (equation (59)) can be identified in the oxygen exchange of oxalic acid with water.[145,154] The solvent H_2O concentration is included in the rate constants for comparison with similar rate equations

$$R = k_2[C_2O_4H_2][H^+] + k_2'[C_2O_4H^-][H^+] + k_0[C_2O_4^{2-}] \tag{59}$$

Allowance was made for the variation of the protonation constants of oxalic acid with temperature, by using the empirical relation (60).[155]

$$\log K = A/T - B + CT \tag{60}$$

The following values were used: $A_1 = 1424$, $B_1 = 6.50$, $C_1 = 0.0201$ and $A_2 = 9100, B_2 = 61.1, C_2 = 0.1066$. Obviously proton ambiguities exist in the k_2' and k_0 path. It is, however, more likely that H_2O attacks the protonated acid group $CO_2H_2^+$ than the carboxylic group $—CO_2H$, and consequently the second term on the right-hand side of equation (59) has been considered to be more realistic. The third term could have been also given as $k_{01}[C_2O_4H^-][OH^-]$. The other alternative was selected only because it is simpler. Again the relevant kinetic data are listed in Table 11.

Unless there are strong inductive effects as in the case of CF_3COOH and CCl_3COOH the protonated acid group exchanges much more effectively than any other.

Some studies of exchange on carboxylic acids of biochemical interest have been made[156] with emphasis on enzyme catalysis.[157] Interpretation of the kinetic results is difficult and somewhat ambiguous but it appears that direct transfer of oxygen from the substrate to the enzyme is involved in the rate controlling step and that the mechanism is not closely related to that which occurs without an enzyme.

5. Oxo-anions of group V.a elements

Vanadate ion. The exchange between ^{18}O labelled solvent water and V(V) (0.02–0.05 M) in basic media (0.5 M > $[OH^-]$ > 0.05 M) was studied at 0, 5 and 10 °C.[11] Under these conditions it was shown that 4.0 ± 0.1 oxygens per vanadium exchange equivalently. This supports the orthovanadate (VO_4^{3-}) structure as the predominant species in H_2O at high pH. The exchange rate follows equation (61)

$$R = k[VO_4^{3-}] \tag{61}$$

and is essentially independent of $[OH^-]$. The rate is an inverse function of ionic strength and has kinetic parameters of $k = 2.4 \times 10^{-2} s^{-1}$ (0 °C), $\Delta H^\ddagger = 92.05$ kJ mol^{-1} and $\Delta S^\ddagger = 71.8$ JK^{-1} mol^{-1} at $I = 1.0$ M. The mechanism of exchange is suggested to follow solvent assisted oxygen dissociation. The comparatively high value for $\Delta H^\ddagger$ can be viewed as required to bring a water molecule into the inner coordination sphere with concurrent V—O bond stretching. The large positive $\Delta S^\ddagger$ on the other hand may arise from the easily deformed tetrahedral VO_4^{3-}, which is due to the lower formal charge on the metal ion, a well-known tendency of V(V) which leads to solvent assisted I_d oxygen exchange. It is also noteworthy that the rate of ^{18}O exchange of $V_2O_7^{4-}$ and the rate of reversible "dimerization" are approximately of the same order of magnitude as the exchange rate of VO_4^{3-}, meaning that V—O bond breakage by the same mechanism as that in exchange with solvent may be required for dimer formation.

6. Oxo-anions of group VI.a elements

Chromate ion. Several studies of the oxygen exchange between chromate ion and water have been carried out.[75,158,159] Under the following conditions: 25 °C, pH = 7–12, $[CrO_4^{2-}]_{tot} = 0.075$ M, $I = 0.2$ and 1.0 M; the rate equation (62) has been established.[75]

$$R = k_0[CrO_4^{2-}] + k_1[HCrO_4^-] + k_2[H^+][HCrO_4^-]$$
$$+ k_3[HCrO_4^-][CrO_4^{2-}] + k_4[HCrO_4^-]^2 \tag{62}$$

The protonation constant, K_1, and the condensation constant, $K_d = [Cr_2O_7^{2-}]/[HCrO_4^-]^2$, for $I = 0.2$ M and at 25 °C, can be interpolated from literature values[95] and are log $K_1 = 6.03$ and log $K_d = 1.75$. For $I = 1.0$ M (NaCl) and at 25 °C they were determined to be log $K_1 = 5.73$ and log $K_d = 2.14$.[75] Only the activation parameters for the spontaneous exchange of the k_0 path have been measured separately (25 °C, $\Delta H_0^\ddagger = 96.4$ kJ mol^{-1}, $\Delta S_0^\ddagger = -45.9$ JK^{-1} mol^{-1}). The rate constants of the most comprehensive study[75] are summarized in Table 12.

Usually k values obtained from ^{18}O studies refer to the transfer of all oxygens in the ion under consideration. However, the data given in Table 12 refer to the transfer of one oxygen only. Consequently there is a discrepancy of roughly one order of magnitude between the k_0 value given in Table 12 and reference [158]. It should be pointed out that rate constants of reaction (63)

$$2HCrO_4^- \overset{k_s}{\rightleftharpoons} Cr_2O_7^{2-} + H_2O \tag{63}$$

measured by other than ^{18}O tracer methods agree within one order of magnitude, with those of Table 12.[75] Table 12 shows the effects of

TABLE 12

Rate constants for the oxygen exchange reaction of chromate ions with water at 25 °C

$$R^{(a)} = k_0[CrO_4^{2-}] + k_1[HCrO_4^-] + k_2[H^+][HCrO_4^-]$$
$$+ k_3[HCrO_4^-][CrO_4^{2-}] + k_4[HCrO_4^-]^2$$

I/M	k_0/s^{-1}	k_1/s^{-1}	$k_2/M^{-1}s^{-1}$	$k_3/M^{-1}s^{-1}$	$k_4/M^{-1}s^{-1}$
0.2		2.4×10^{-3}	1.9×10^6	$\approx 10^{-3}$	5.0
	3.2×10^{-7}				
1.0		2.3×10^{-3}	0.73×10^6	$\approx 10^{-3}$	9.0

[a] R refers to the rate of transfer of one oxygen only.

protonation on the reactivity of chromate ion towards water. The enhanced reactivity of hydrogen chromate ion as compared with that of chromate is noteworthy. Since the effect of a proton in facilitating oxygen exchange of oxo-anions consists of polarization of the bond between the oxygen and the central atom, the bond seems to be more polarizable in chromate than in arsenate (Table 9) and selenite ions (Table 6). In addition it was found that periodate ion catalyses the chromate water exchange.[127] Preliminary results on the rate constant of reaction (64)

$$HCrO_4^- + H_4IO_6^- \overset{k}{\rightleftharpoons} H_3CrIO_9^{2-} + H_2O \tag{64}$$

gave an estimate of $k = 10^4 \ M^{-1} \ s^{-1}$ at 0 °C. Thus for oxo-anions which undergo condensation processes with themselves such as arsenate[126,127] and chromate ions, a condensation mechanism with other oxo-anions leading to oxygen exchange seems to operate.

Molybdate and tungstate ion. A kinetic investigation of the oxygen exchange between water and molybdate and tungstate in basic media under conditions given in parenthesis (MoO_4^{2-}: $3 \times 10^{-3} \leqslant [OH^-] \leqslant 1.5 \times 10^{-1}$ M, and WO_4^{2-}: $2 \times 10^{-3} \leqslant [OH^-] \leqslant 7.5 \times 10^{-3}$ M, I = 1.0 M $NaClO_4$) has been carried out.[43] The exchange occurs by spontaneous and hydroxide catalysed paths (X = Mo or W) according to rate equation (65)

$$R = k_0[XO_4^{2-}] + k_1[XO_4^{2-}][OH^-] \tag{65}$$

The kinetic parameters determined are summarized in Table 13.

Comparison with the rate constants of Table 12 shows that the spontaneous exchange processes (k_0) are much faster both in the $MoO_4^{2-}-H_2O$ and $WO_4^{2-}-H_2O$ systems than in $CrO_4^{2-}-H_2O$. The difference is attributable to

TABLE 13

Kinetic data for the ^{18}O exchange between MoO_4^{2-}–WO_4^{2-} and water respectively

$$R = k_0[XO_4^{2-}] + k_1[XO_4^{2-}][OH^-]$$

		T/K	$\Delta H^{\ddagger}/kJ\,mol^{-1}$	$\Delta S^{\ddagger}/JK^{-1}\,mol^{-1}$
MoO_4^{2-}	$k_0/s^{-1} = 0.33$	298.15	62.8	−43.5
	$k_1/M^{-1}s^{-1} = 2.22$	298.15	70.3	− 2.5
	$k_0^H/k_0^D = 3.6$	278.15		
	$k_1^H/k_1^D = 2.3$	278.15		
WO_4^{2-}	$k_0/s^{-1} = 0.44$	298.15	29.3	−153.6
	$k_1/M^{-1}s^{-1} = 2.73$	298.15	71.1	40.2
	$k_0^H/k_0^D = 3.0$	274.15		
	$k_1^H/k_1^D = 1.7$	274.15		

the larger enthalpies of activation in the case of chromate reflecting "tighter" Cr(VI)—O bonds than the corresponding Mo(VI)—O and W(VI)—O bonds. Despite the remarkable differences in $\Delta H_0^{\ddagger}$ and $\Delta S_0^{\ddagger}$ the rates are very similar for MoO_4^{2-} and WO_4^{2-}. This is a consequence of the unusually large negative activation entropy in the latter case suggesting that more than one water molecule is involved in the spontaneous tungstate exchange. Indeed, nucleophilic displacements known to be termolecular have entropies of activation in the range -90 to $-140\,JK^{-1}\,mol^{-1}$.[160] A second water molecule in the transition state is held responsible for the large negative entropy ($-120\,JK^{-1}\,mol^{-1}$) of the $AsO(OH)_2^-$–H_2O exchange also.[128] Normal solvent-isotope effects have been observed for the spontaneous and the OH^--catalysed exchange reaction and are assigned to proton transfer in the rate-determining step. The values of k_1^H/k_1^D are remarkably smaller than k_0^H/k_0^D. This seems to be a common feature of similar oxo-anion exchange reactions (see Table 2); probably it simply reflects that one and two O—H bonds are involved in the OH^- catalysed and the spontaneous paths respectively.

7. Oxo-anions of group VII.a elements

Permanganate and manganate ion. Data for the MnO_4^- exchange are rather controversial.[161−163] According to Hoering and McDonald[161] in the pH region of 1 to 8 at $I = 0.28$ M the exchange reaction follows the rate equation (66)

$$R = k_0[MnO_4^-] + k_{2H}[MnO_4^-][H^+]^2 \tag{66}$$

The respective kinetic data recalculated from a preprint are listed in Table 14.

TABLE 14

Kinetic data of the ^{18}O exchange in the $MnO_4^- - H_2O$ system

$$R = k_0[MnO_4^-] + k_{2H}[MnO_4^-][H^+]^2$$

25 °C	$\Delta H^{\ddagger}/kJ\ mol^{-1}$	$\Delta S^{\ddagger}/JK^{-1}\ mol^{-1}$	k^H/k^D
$k_0/s^{-1} = 1.9 \times 10^{-5}$	42.6	−192	1.62
$k_{2H}/M^{-2}\ s^{-1} = 1.1 \times 10^{-1}$	53.6	−83	0.56

A different rate equation (67) has been found by Heckner and Landsberg[162]

$$R = k_0[MnO_4^-] + k_{1H}[MnO_4^-][H^+] + k_{OH}[MnO_4^-][OH^-] \qquad (67)$$

The k_0 value recalculated for 60 °C from the experimental data (7.32×10^{-5} s^{-1}), taking into account a factor of 4 which appears to have been erroneously dropped upon derivation of equation (3) from (1) and (2) in reference [162], agrees within a factor of two with that extrapolated from the data of Table 14 ($1.36 \times 10^{-4}\ s^{-1}$). However, the agreement of the activation parameters is rather poor ($\Delta H_0^{\ddagger} = 59.2\ kJ\ mol^{-1}$, $\Delta S_0^{\ddagger} = -147\ JK^{-1}\ mol^{-1}$, $k_0^H/k_0^D = 2.0$ at 60 °C). For two reasons it is difficult to evaluate the other rate terms in equation (67) without additional experiments. First, very weakly basic oxo-anions usually exchange in the acid region by a $[H^+]^2$ path and not by a $[H^+]$ one. Second, the rate constant of the $[OH^-]$ path recalculated from the activation parameters given[162] does not agree with the value measured directly (60 °C). An additional discrepancy exists with respect to the $MnO_4^{2-} - H_2O$ exchange, according to reference [161] MnO_4^{2-} does not measurably exchange its oxygen with water at 30 °C during long periods of time in the pH region where manganate is stable. When MnO_4^{2-} was precipitated as $BaMnO_4$, an exchange process was induced. Therefore sampling was carried out by distilling off water from the reaction mixture. However, in reference [163] fast exchange is reported to occur by reaction (68)

$$2HMnO_4^- \rightleftharpoons Mn_2O_7^{2-} + H_2O \qquad (68)$$

It is probably safe to say that so far neither the permanganate nor the manganate exchange has been studied exhaustively with ^{18}O techniques.

Perrhenate ion. The rate equation (69) for the exchange of oxygen between ReO_4^- and H_2O is

$$R = k_0[ReO_4^-] + k_{2H}[ReO_4^-][H^+]^2 + k_{OH}[ReO_4^-][OH^-] \qquad (69)$$

TABLE 15
Kinetic parameters for the perrhenate–water exchange at $I = 0.10$ M (LiCl)

$$R = k_0[\text{ReO}_4^-] + k_{2\text{H}}[\text{ReO}_4^-][\text{H}^+]^2 + k_{\text{OH}}[\text{ReO}_4^-][\text{OH}^-]$$

25 °C	$\Delta H^{\ddagger}/\text{kJ mol}^{-1}$	$\Delta S^{\ddagger}/\text{JK}^{-1}\text{ mol}^{-1}$
$k_0 = 7.7 \times 10^{-7}\text{ s}^{-1}$	72.8	− 118.5
$k_{2\text{H}} = 1.9 \times 10^3\text{ M}^{-2}\text{ s}^{-1}$	19.8	− 21.1
$k_{\text{OH}} = 8.6 \times 10^3\text{ M}^{-1}\text{ s}^{-1}$	49.1	− 24.2

The respective kinetic parameters[72] are listed in Table 15.

In addition the ^{18}O exchange between ReO_4^- and H_2O has been studied in methanol solution.[164] The order with respect to H_2O has been established as zero for both the spontaneous and the $[\text{H}^+]^2$ catalysed reaction paths. This suggests that in these cases the mechanism of oxygen exchange is closer to a dissociation facilitated by solvent hydrogen bonding than by displacement. It can be concluded from this first and probably only study of the water dependence of an $\text{H}_2{}^{18}\text{O}$ exchange with a tetrahedral oxo-anion that exchange is facilitated by hydrogen bonding to proton "showing" solvents, or by association with two solvated H^+ as in the reaction path leading to the $k_{2\text{H}}$ term of equation (69).

8. Oxo-anions of group VIII elements

Ferrate ion. In aqueous basic media Fe(VI) forms the ion FeO_4^{2-} and all oxygens are kinetically equivalent.[13] The ^{18}O exchange in the pH region 9.6–14 with $[\text{FeO}_4^{2-}] \sim 5 \times 10^{-3}$ M follows the rate equation (70)

$$R = k[\text{FeO}_4^{2-}] \tag{70}$$

where $k = 1.6 \times 10^{-2}\text{ s}^{-1}$ at 25 °C, $\Delta H^{\ddagger} = 62.0$ kJ mol^{-1} and $\Delta S^{\ddagger} = -71.2$ JK^{-1} mol^{-1}. No appreciable $[\text{OH}^-]$ dependence was found. Addition of OCl^-, which is assumed to oxidize Fe(IV) and Fe(V) rapidly, did in fact slightly increase the rate. Thus, lower oxidation states of iron can only play a minor role in the exchange mechanism. Both water exchange and water oxidation are accelerated by dilute acid. The spontaneous exchange occurs either via a non-specific solvent assisted dissociation or the formation of symmetrical $\text{HO}-\text{FeO}_3-\text{OH}$ from HFeO_4^- and OH^-.

B. Kinetics of aqua-cation exchange with solvent

1. Aqua-cations of group VI.a elements

Hexaaquachromium(III) ion. The rate equation (71) of the $Cr(OH_2)_6^{3+}$–H_2O exchange is simply

$$R = k[Cr(OH_2)_6^{3+}] \tag{71}$$

In the acid region no conjugate-base path has been established.[6,7] Probably the best data for the activation parameters can be obtained by a combination of the results of Hunt and Plane[165] and the pressure dependence study of Stranks and Swaddle.[166] They are given in Table 17. Since the effect of pressure on the rate of solvent isotopic exchange of aqua-cations of transition metals is reviewed by Swaddle in this volume, and has been reviewed, elsewhere[167] the results need not be considered in detail here. The comparatively large negative value of $\Delta V^{\ddagger}$ and the near zero value of $\Delta S^{\ddagger}$ provide strong evidence for the exchange reaction (71) to proceed via an I_a mechanism. It should, however, be mentioned that only recently[168] the idea has been advanced that the molar volumes of the transition states for many water exchange reactions M_{aq}^{2+}, M_{aq}^{3+}, $M(NH_3)_5OH_2^{3+}$ are insensitive to the nature of M and the kinetic characteristics are governed mainly by initial not transition state properties.

Aquapentaamminechromium(III) ion. The $[Cr(NH_3)_5OH_2]^{3+}$–H_2O exchange rate equation (72)

$$R = k_0[Cr(NH_3)_5OH_2^{3+}] + k_1[Cr(NH_3)_5OH^{2+}] \tag{72}$$

has been established.[169,170]

The activation parameters of the k_0 path have been determined carefully[171] and are listed in Table 17.

The carbon dioxide catalysis of the exchange between $Cr(NH_3)_5OH^{2+}$ and H_2O[170] is a most interesting observation. The rate equation (73) has been obtained in the range pH 1–5

$$R = k_0[Cr(NH_3)_5OH_2^{3+}] + (k_1 + k_c[CO_2])[Cr(NH_3)_5OH^{2+}] \tag{73}$$

with $k_0 = 6.3 \times 10^{-5}\,s^{-1}$, $k_1 = 17 \times 10^{-5}\,s^{-1}$ and $k_c = 7\,M^{-1}\,s^{-1}$ at 25 °C and I = 0.1 M $NaClO_4$. When labelled $HC^*O_3^-$ is introduced, ^{18}O appears rapidly in $Cr(NH_3)_5OH^{2+}$. These results require a mechanism involving formation of a carbonato–Cr(III) complex and quite rapid scrambling of the oxygen atoms of this complex. Water exchange of $Co(NH_3)_5OH^{2+}$ is slower than that of $Co(NH_3)_5OH_2^{3+}$ and no CO_2 catalysis has been observed[172] although carbonate complexes of Co(III) are well known. In addition, with Co(III) it was unambiguously demonstrated using ^{18}O labelled

$(NH_3)_4CoOCO_2^+$ that the oxygen coordinated to cobalt does not undergo intramolecular exchange with the other two oxygens of the coordinated carbonate.[70] Obviously the scrambling process occurs with Cr(III) but not with Co(III). This is attributable to the greater tendency of Cr(III), relative to Co(III), to adopt seven-coordinate structures, as indicated by the pressure dependence studies.[166,171]

Pentaaquachromium(III) complex ion. In 1965[173] it was shown that I^- and NO in the coordination sphere of aquated Cr(III) labilized one of the waters (presumably the *trans* water). *Trans* labilization in $[Cr(OH_2)_5I]^{2+}$ was also suggested by the fact that acid hydrolysis of that ion in 1 M HCl leads to about 10% of the chloro complex. In a later study[174] the rates of water exchange of $[CrCl(OH_2)_5]^{2+}$, $[CrBr(OH_2)_5]^{2+}$ and $[CrNCS(OH_2)_5]^{2+}$ were measured over about 80% of the total exchange. The McKay graphs were curved and could be resolved into one fast and four slow exchanging oxygens in each complex ion and the rate constants for each type, k_{cis}, k_{trans}, were evaluated and are listed together with activation parameters in Table 16. The values for k_{cis} were found to be the same within experimental error, while k_{trans} was significantly larger. Thus, the k_{cis} values are essentially constant but, as can be seen from the values in Table 16, the ratios k_{trans}/k_{cis} are qualitatively directly related to the k_{aq} (for aquation) values.

2. Aqua-cations of group VIII elements

Hexaaquacobalt(III) ion. Water exchange of $Co(OH_2)_6^{3+}$ has been reported to be too fast to be measured using ^{18}O techniques. The explanation given is that $Co(OH_2)_6^{3+}$ is oxidizing water and the $Co(OH_2)_6^{2+}$ formed is very

TABLE 16

Kinetic parameters for the exchange of pentaaquachromium(III) complex ions with water at 25 °C

	$10^6 k_{cis}/$ s^{-1}	$k_{trans}/$ k_{cis}	$k_{aq}/$s^{-1}	$\Delta H^{\ddagger}/$ kJ mol^{-1}		$\Delta S^{\ddagger}/$ JK^{-1} mol^{-1}		Refer-ence
				trans	cis	trans	cis	
CrCl^{2+}	3.0	13	3.1×10^{-7}	109	105	38	+1	[174]
CrBr^{2+}	3.0	25$^{(a)}$	5.0×10^{-6}					[174]
CrI^{2+}	3.0	84						[173]
CrNCS^{2+}	3.0	5.5	9.0×10^{-9}	121	104	63	−1	[174]

$^{(a)}$ The value of CrBr^{2+} was estimated.

labile, thus catalysing the exchange reaction via electron transfer.[5] However, with care the reductions of $Co(OH_2)_6^{3+}$ with $Cr(OH_2)_6^{2+}$ and $V(OH_2)_6^{2+}$ can be studied and the tendency of $Co(OH_2)_6^{3+}$ to oxidize water is probably less than was previously believed.[175] Studies on the oxidation using 0.6 M Co(III) in 6 M $HClO_4$[176] suggest that hydroxy-bridged dimers exist which exchange the bridged oxygen slowly. The spontaneous reduction of Co(III) gives oxygen of a composition closely related to that of the coordinated bridged hydroxy groups. Another study[177] did not observe hold-back by the Co(III) species. Further studies in this area are needed.

Aquapentaamminecobalt(III) ion. This ion was the first aqua-cation where the effect of temperature, pressure, acidity and solvent on exchange was studied.[172] A summary of the kinetic data are listed in Table 17. The reaction

TABLE 17

Kinetic data for the reaction

$$ML_5^*OH_2^{3+} + H_2O \rightleftharpoons ML_5OH_2^{3+} + H_2^*O$$

Reactant	$k/s^{-1(a)}$	$\Delta H^{\ddagger}/$ kJ mol^{-1}	$\Delta S^{\ddagger}/$ JK^{-1} mol^{-1}	$\Delta V^{\ddagger}/$ cm^3 mol^{-1}	Reference
$Cr(OH_2)_6^{3+(b)}$	4.5×10^{-7}	109.6	1.3	-9.3	[165] [166]
$Cr(NH_3)_5(OH_2)^{3+}$	6.1×10^{-5}	97.1	0.0	-5.8	[169] [171]
$Co(NH_3)_5(OH_2)^{3+}$	5.7×10^{-6}	111.3	28.0	$+1.3$	[172]
$Rh(OH_2)_6^{3+(b)}$	$5.6 \times 10^{-9(c)}$	134.1	46.8		[16]
$Rh(NH_3)_5(OH_2)^{3+}$	8.6×10^{-6}	102.9	3.3	-4.1	[171] [184] [185]
$Ir(NH_3)_5(OH_2)^{3+}$	$6.1 \times 10^{-8(d)}$	117.6	11.3	-3.2	[186] [187]

(a) 25 °C.
(b) Referring to the exchange of one aqua ligand.
(c) Extrapolated from data between 64.4–80 °C.
(d) Extrapolated from data obtained between 65.1–95 °C.

rate is strictly first order in $Co(NH_3)_5OH_2^{3+}$, independent of acidity over a considerable range (0.008–0.07 M), and almost independent of the concentration of water when CH_3OH is the principal component of the solvent mixture. This together with the positive activation entropy and volume indicates that the replacement of the aqua group in $Co(NH_3)_5OH_2^{3+}$ proceeds by an I_d mechanism.

The oxygen exchange rates of $Co(NH_3)_5OH^{2+}$ have been studied in aqueous ammonia solutions (pH 8–9), where the conversion to the hydroxo form of the complex is virtually complete.[178] The protonation constant of $Co(NH_3)_5OH^{2+}$ as a function of ionic strength and temperature is given in the classical work of Bjerrum.[179]

Since the limited data measured indicated an independence of pH and ammonia concentration, an apparent rate constant as well as activation parameters were calculated from the relation $R = k[Co(III)]$. The following values were obtained $k = 2.3 \times 10^{-7}$ s^{-1} (25 °C), $\Delta H^{\ddagger} = 111$ kJ mol^{-1}, $\Delta S^{\ddagger} = 1$ JK^{-1} mol^{-1}. This value of $\Delta S^{\ddagger}$ differs from that given in reference [178] ($\Delta S^{\ddagger} = 17$ JK^{-1} mol^{-1}). Since no obvious curvature of the log (k/T) versus $1/T$ plot was observed, $\Delta H^{\ddagger}$ and $\Delta S^{\ddagger}$ were recalculated by linear regression. As also concluded from nitrogen tracer experiments, the general mechanism of both nitrogen and oxygen exchange involve the equilibria (74) and (75)

$$Co(NH_3)_5OH^{2+} \underset{k_{-1}}{\overset{k_1}{\rightleftharpoons}} Co(NH_3)_4OH^{2+} + NH_3 \tag{74}$$

$$Co(NH_3)_4OH^{2+} + OH^- \underset{k_{-2}}{\overset{k_2}{\rightleftharpoons}} Co(NH_3)_4(OH)_2^+ \tag{75}$$

It has been shown that the oxygen exchange between $Co(NH_3)_5OH^{2+}$ and H_2O is not catalysed by the faster electron transfer reaction with Co(II) or $[Co(NH_3)_5OH]^+$.[180] This is evidence of a hydroxo-bridged mechanism for electron transfer where the hydroxo ligand is always transferred from and to an inert Co(III)—OH bond, without hydroxide exchange with the solvent. For the simple bridged mechanism it would be expected that five ammonia ligands would exchange simultaneously with one electron. However, the rate constants for catalysed nitrogen exchange were a maximum of four times the rate constants for electron transfer. This strongly suggests that some of the ammonia on the initial $Co(NH_3)_5OH^{2+}$ is somehow transferred to the Co(III) complex resulting from electron exchange. A possible explanation of this phenomena is multiple bridging in the activated complex.

Trans-diaquabis(ethylenediamine)cobalt(III) ion. The kinetics of aqua exchange of *trans*-diaquabis(ethylenediamine)cobalt(III) ion in acidic aqueous solution has been studied[181,182] in detail. The first-order rate constant for the exchange of both aqua ligands is 6.3×10^{-5} s^{-1} at 34.8 °C, and the respective activation parameters are $\Delta H^{\ddagger} = 126.2$ kJ mol^{-1}, $\Delta S^{\ddagger} = 84.2$ JK^{-1} mol^{-1}, $\Delta V^{\ddagger} = 5.9$ cm^3 mol^{-1}, $(\partial \Delta V^{\ddagger}/\partial P)_T = 0$. It follows from these data that there is predominantly Co—OH$_2$ bond breaking with little or no change in solvation on going to the transition state of this reaction. Significant changes in solvation usually manifest themselves in a pressure dependence of the volume of activation. Thus the mechanism is I$_d$ or D; similar to the general behaviour

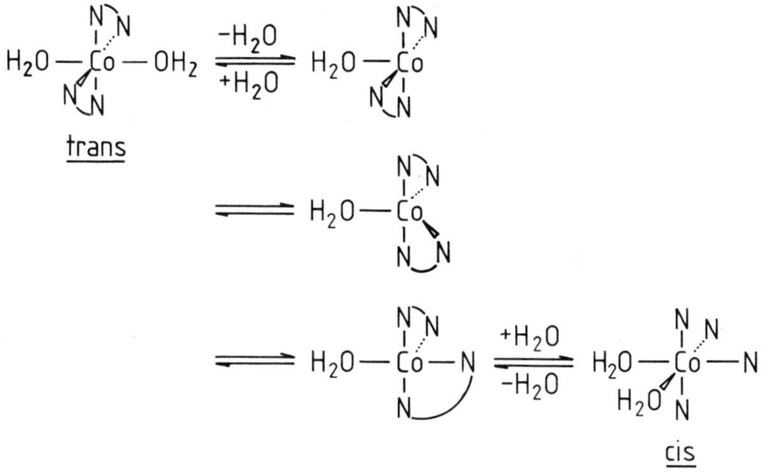

Fig. 4. Aqua exchange of cis- and trans-$Co(en)_2(OH_2)_2^{3+}$.

in substitution of Co(III) complexes and differing from other octahedral trivalent transition metals which generally yield negative values for $\Delta V^{\ddagger}$ and imply a I_a mechanism. Since the isomerization equilibrium lies in favour of the cis-isomer in acidic solution,[181] the reaquation of the trigonal-bipyramidal intermediate (shown in Fig. 4) to the trans configuration is not favoured.

Thus, aqua exchange with trans-$Co(en)_2(OH_2)_2^{3+}$ proceeds almost exclusively via a tetragonal-pyramidal five-coordinate intermediate without significant solvational change. This mechanism is best described as I_d rather than D, since lack of significant pressure dependence of $\Delta V^{\ddagger}$ shows that the second coordination sphere does not relax before six-coordination is regained.

Hexaaquarhodium(III) ion. Plumb and Harris[16] showed that the $Rh(OH_2)_6^{3+}$–H_2O exchange follows the rate equation

$$R = k_0[Rh(OH_2)_6^{3+}] + k_1[Rh(OH_2)_5OH^{2+}] \tag{76}$$

The two-term rate equation (76), when compared with (71), indicates a fundamental difference between $Cr(OH_2)_6^{3+}$ and $Rh(OH_2)_6^{3+}$. Whereas the former exchange follows an I_a mechanism, the latter seems to proceed via an I_d. The estimation of the ratio k_1/k_0 involves a rather long extrapolation of the first protolysis constant, $*K_1$, of $Rh(OH_2)_6^{3+}$ to 64.4 °C and I = 12 M. Originally it was assumed that $*K_1$ changes with temperature in much the same way as does that for $Co(OH_2)_6^{3+}$ and a value of $k_1/k_0 = 160$ was obtained.[16] When the more recently determined $*K_1$ values (5–25 °C) of $Rh(OH_2)_6^{3+}$ are utilized[183] the ratio calculated is $k_1/k_0 = 690$. In any case it is of the expected order of magnitude for the labilizing effect of OH^- on adjacent ligands. From the kinetic data summarized in Table 17 it can be seen that $\Delta S_0^{\ddagger}$ for the $Rh(OH_2)_6^{3+}-H_2O$ exchange has a conspicuously high positive value suggesting also dissociative activation. Measuring $\Delta V_0^{\ddagger}$ would greatly contribute to clarifying the situation. At this stage it cannot be readily rationalized why the larger $Rh(OH_2)_6^{3+}$ should prefer the I_d path whereas the smaller $Cr(OH_2)_6^{3+}$ prefers the I_a path. It should, however, be noted that the $Rh(OH_2)_6^{3+}$ study[16] was carried out at $I = 12$ M as compared with $I \sim 0.6-0.7$ M for the $Cr(OH_2)_6^{3+}$ studies.[165,166] It is possible that high ionic strengths favour the I_d path.

Aquapentamminerhodium(III) ion. Activation parameters for the H_2O exchange of this ion have been measured[171,184,185] and are listed in Table 17. In contrast to $Rh(OH_2)_6^{3+}$ the mechanistic information on $Rh(NH_3)_5OH_2^{3+}$ supports an I_a mechanism (see also the review of Swaddle in this Volume).

Aquapentammineiridium(III) ion. From ^{18}O tracer studies on the temperature[186] and pressure effects[187] of the H_2O exchange with $Ir(NH_3)_5OH_2^{3+}$, activation parameters have been determined and are listed in Table 17. Again evidence for I_a character of the reaction has been found. Thus, of the trivalent transition metal ion studies by this method only cobalt(III) seems to form cationic complexes which react by I_d mechanisms in water substitution reactions. There still remains, however, the problem of the $Rh(OH_2)_6^{3+}-H_2O$ exchange where at the present stage the kinetic evidence favours an I_d mechanism. By analogy to the other aqua-ions in this series I_a would be more plausible.

C. Kinetics of oxo-cation and oligomer exchange with water

1. Monooxo-cations

The only monooxo-cation which has been studied thoroughly with ^{18}O techniques is the oxovanadium(IV) ion, VO^{2+}_{aq}. It contains three coordinated oxygen types which are structurally and kinetically distinct (Fig. 5). The exchange rates are widely separated and related to the bond distances (in the solid state). ^{17}O nmr has provided rate measurements[188] of the rate constants for the basal and apical waters while the slower exchange rates for the yl-oxygen, (oxo), are best determined by ^{18}O studies. The basal oxygens exchange with a rate constant of 5×10^2 s^{-1} while the water *trans* to the yl-oxygen has a residence time of about 10^{-11} s. The first measurements[189] of the oxo-oxygen–water exchange showed no exchange but were apparently in error. More recent studies[10,33] involved three different methods each of which gave a $t_{1/2}$ of about 400 min at 0 °C. The exchange followed the rate equation

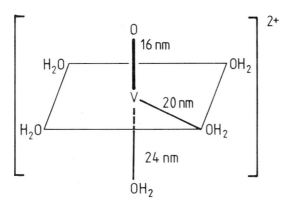

Fig. 5. Oxygen bond distances at three distinct coordination sites of the oxovanadium(IV) ion.

$$R = k_0[VO^{2+}] + k_{OH}*K_1[VO^{2+}]/[H^+] \tag{77}$$

The parameters kinetically relevant for equation (77) are $k_0 = 2.4 \times 10^{-5}$ s^{-1}, $k_{OH} = 1.32$ s^{-1} and $*K_1 = 3.98 \times 10^{-7}$ M at 0 °C,[190] I = 2.5 M. At $[VO^{2+}] = 0.18$ M, I = 0.64 M, $[H^+] = 0.10$ M, $\Delta H_0^{\ddagger} = 85.8$ kJ mol^{-1} and $\Delta S_0^{\ddagger} = -18.4$ JK^{-1} mol^{-1}.

The inverse hydrogen ion dependence was interpreted in terms of the hydrolysed species having an OH group in a basal position. Catalysis by VO_2^+ was observed in all solutions not protected with a small excess of hydrazine or Fe(II) which rapidly and effectively converted VO_2^+ to VO^{2+}. The V(V) catalysed term was $R = k[VO^{2+}][VO_2^+]$ suggesting rapid, though incomplete dimerization followed by electron transfer being responsible for the exchange. Recently[191] such a species has been observed and identified. Complexation at the basal positions and perhaps at the apical sites of VO^{2+} by ligands stronger than water generally results in a slower rate. Some information is available on complexing of VO_{aq}^{2+} with NCS^-, $C_2O_4^{2-}$ or ethylenediaminetetraacetate, $EDTA^{4-}$, which caused a diminution of the k_0 terms and increased the rates in the acid region. For example, the rate constant ratio H_2O to NCS^- is about 40 at 0 °C. With the $C_2O_4^{2-}$ or $EDTA^{4-}$ complexes the exchange rate essentially stopped in the neutral region and was faster than the parent ion, VO_{aq}^{2+} at a pH of 1.5. With $N(CH_2CO_2)_3^{3-}$, NTA^{3-}, where a basal water is probably present, the rate is faster and inversely related to acidity. These observations and others were used to develop the IER (internal electronic rearrangement) mechanism which is thought to play a dominant role in isotopic exchange of many types of oxo-ions. Basically it consists of an electron migration which effectively converts an yl-oxygen to a *cis*-water with concurrent proton transfer. The water rapidly exchanges with the solvent compared with the yl-oxygen and reverts back to its original yl-state completing the exchange.[33]

2. Dioxo-cations

Dioxovanadium(V) ion. Of the dioxo-metal ions available for study only VO_2^+ is believed, with considerable confidence, to be in the *cis*-configuration. Oxygen exchange studies have been hampered by the scarcity of precipitating ions and the low concentrations of stable solutions. Recently[77] two methods were attempted to measure the oxygen exchange rate. The first (rapid conversion to *cis*-$VO_2(C_2O_4)_2^{3-}$ followed by precipitation with $Co(en)_3^{3+}$), provided a separation in less than 0.6 s. However, it did not show any ^{18}O holdback due to a slow exchange. In the second method, isotopic exchange was in competition with the very rapid V(V)–SCN^- oxidation–reduction reaction which produces $VO(NCS)_5^{3-}$. This complex is slower to exchange and can be easily precipitated by $Co(en)_3^{3+}$. A value of $t_{1/2} = 0.15$ s at 0 °C with $[VO_2^+] = 0.126$ M and $CH_3SO_3H = 1.0$ M was estimated. No $[VO_2^+]$ dependence was found and, due to the magnitude of the inherent errors, the hydrogen ion dependence could not be determined. The extreme rapidity is surprising when this ion is compared with all of the *trans*-dioxo species and may result in some fashion from the *cis*-structure.[77]

Complexation of VO_2^+ with $C_2O_4^{2-}$ gives the well-defined species, $[VO_2(C_2O_4)_2]^{3-}$. This ion is much slower to exchange than VO_{2aq}^+ and follows the rate equation (78)

$$R = k_0[\text{complex}] + k_H[\text{complex}][H^+] \tag{78}$$

where $k_0 = 0.31$ s^{-1} and $k_H = 4.7 \times 10^3$ M^{-1} s^{-1} at 0 °C and pH = 6.0. An impurity, probably VO_{aq}^{2+} catalysed the reaction rate but it was easily removed by a slight excess of $H_4IO_6^-$. *Trans*-$[VO(C_2O_4)_2OH_2]^{2-}$ does not act as a catalyst presumably because electron transfer is no doubt slow between the *cis*-(V) and the *trans*-(IV) states.

Uranyl(VI) ion. The rate of oxygen exchange between the axial oxygen of UO_2^{2+} and water has been reported to be very slow.[8]

More exact studies[192] on the non-reproducibility and the non-linear McKay graphs explained the deviations on the basis of UO_2^+ catalysis. The UO_2^+ disproportionates according to the rate equation $-d[UO_2^+]/dt = k[H^+][UO_2^+]^2$, where $k = 4.35 \times 10^2$ M^{-2} s^{-1} at $I = 1.58$ M and 25 °C. Catalysis occurs through UO_2^{2+}–UO_2^+ electron exchange and relatively rapid UO_2^{2+}–H_2O exchange. In the presence of excess Cl_2, which rapidly oxidizes UO_2^+, the intrinsic UO_2^{2+}–H_2O exchange was shown to give reproducible, linear McKay plots.[192,193] The UO_2^{2+}–H_2O

exchange, in the absence of UO_2^+ catalysis followed the equation

$$R = k[UO_2^{2+}][H^+]^{-1} \qquad (79)$$

at 25 °C and I = 3.79 M, $k = 9.9 \times 10^{-9}\,s^{-1}$; in 0.8 M HCl the half-life of oxygen exchange was found to be 2.3×10^3 h.[194] It was suggested that the dominant path for exchange is through the $UO_2(OH)^+$ ion when UO_2^+ is absent. The estimated lower limit to the specific rate of UO_2^+ exchange is $1.8 \times 10^2\,s^{-1}$ in 1.0 M $HClO_4$, dramatically larger than for UO_2^{2+}. Complete exchange between UO_2^{2+} and H_2O within 24 h in concentrated HCl has been reported.[37] Since no additional oxidant like Cl_2 was used, catalytically-active lower oxidation states of uranium may be responsible for this relatively fast exchange.

Neptunyl(VI) ion. In a careful study of the water exchange with NpO_2^+ and NpO_2^{2+}, Rabideau[195] also found catalysis of NpO_2^{2+} exchange by NpO_2^+. The value $0.31\,s^{-1}$ was deduced for the specific rate constant for exchange between NpO_2^+ and water in 1.0 M $HClO_4$ at 23 °C. In the presence of Cl_2, linear McKay graphs were obtained but the rate was variable, probably due to the slow Cl_2–NpO_2^+ reaction, but with MnO_4^- present, constant values were obtained for the NpO_2^{2+}–water exchange and k was $6 \times 10^{-7}\,s^{-1}$ (23 °C). Remarkably, stronger oxidizing agents such as O_3 and Ce(IV) caused rapid NpO_2^{2+}–H_2O exchange ($t_{1/2}$ was about 30 min compared with several hundred hours uncatalysed). It was suggested that this was due to radical-induced exchange through water decomposition.

In a study of the NpO_2^+–$Rh(OH_2)_6^{3+}$ reaction[18] which leads to a Np(V)–Rh(III) complex the NpO_2^+–H_2O exchange was directly measured. The number of yl-oxygens was counted and found to be 2.1 and the specific rate increased with acid concentration and with either NpO_2^+ concentration or with ionic strength. The $t_{1/2}$ is highly variable depending on solution conditions. For instance the $t_{1/2}$ was 3900 min when $[NpO_2^+] = 2.3 \times 10^{-3}$ M and $[H^+] = 3.4 \times 10^{-2}$ M while it was 18 min with 0.86 M and 0.20 M respectively (25 °C).

Plutonyl(VI) ion. The PuO_2^{2+}–H_2O exchange is also catalysed by trace amounts of PuO_2^+. The traces normally present were removed with excess Cl_2.[196] Low concentrations were used to lower the radiation-induced exchange and solvent decomposition. Even at 83 °C a lower $t_{1/2}$ limit of only 4×10^7 s can be assigned. This is about the same magnitude as with UO_2^{2+} and, as was pointed out, such a small rate could be provided by roughly 10^{-9}–10^{-10} M of the PuO_2^+ ion. The PuO_2^{2+}–H_2O exchange is considerably accelerated by F^- ($t_{1/2} = 6.1 \times 10^4$ s).[197] This is interesting from a structural viewpoint. In solution a $UO_2(OH_2)_6^{2+}$ ion has been suggested where the linear

O—U—O^{2+} group is surrounded equatorially by a puckered ring of six oxygen atoms.[198] If a similar structure prevails in the PuO$_2^{2+}$ ion in which H$_2$O is successively substituted by F$^-$, these equatorial ligands would be expected to undergo electrostatic interaction with axial oxygen atoms, and, as a consequence, the ionic contribution to the axial bonding would be considerably weakened. No exchange of PuO$_2^{2+}$ and H$_2$O was observed in an acid–base–acid cyclic sequence indicating that in the basic plutonates the axial oxygens retain their identity. This result is in contrast with that obtained for the UO$_2^{2+}$–H$_2$O system. However, the latter may have been influenced by the presence of trace amounts of UO$_2^+$. In the formation of the PuO$_2^{2+}$ ion by the ozonization of Pu(III), it has been noted that one of the oxygens is derived from the water and one from the ozone.

In general, exchange rates of actinyl(VI) ions are slow whereas those of the actinyl(V) ions are fast. Exchange similarities of isoelectronic members are not evident.[195]

3. *Trans*-dioxo metal ion complexes

Detailed studies have been made on the ions $[\text{Re(en)}_2\text{O}_2]^+$, $[\text{Re(CN)}_4\text{O}_2]^{3-}$ and $[\text{Os(en)}_2\text{O}_2]^{2+}$ while some information is available on $[\text{Mo(CN)}_4\text{O}_2]^{4-}$ and $[\text{Re(py)}_4\text{O}_2]^+$. Each of these is a d^2 ion and except for $[\text{Mo(CN)}_4\text{O}_2]^{4-}$, the non-oxo ligand is non-labile.[199] Although coordination numbers of eight are well established for Mo(IV), Re(V) and Os(VI), there appears to be little tendency for this to occur by water association with these substances as shown by the fact that there are two non-labile oxygens per complex ion. The fast exchange on Mo(IV) prevents a count of the number of coordinated oxygens on it. For all except Os(VI), protonation of the oxo groups occur in two steps giving $[\text{O}{=}\text{M}{-}\text{OH}]^{(n+1)+}$ and $[\text{O}{=}\text{M}{-}\text{OH}_2]^{(n+2)+}$ and the acidity constants depend on the π-bonding characteristics of the equatorial ligands.

Trans-dioxo molybdenum(IV) ion. In neutral and basic media exchange between $[\text{Mo(CN)}_4\text{O(OH)}]^{3-}$ and water was found[200] to have a $t_{1/2}$ of less than 10 s at 0 °C in the 0.1–2.0 M concentration range. Excess NaCN added to the exchanging solutions did not decrease the apparent exchange rate. Three sampling methods were used which gave the same results suggesting that separation-induced exchange was not important.

Trans-dioxo rhenium(V) ion. The $[\text{Re(en)}_2\text{O}_2]^+$ exchange has been studied[201] over the pH range 6–12 within which the complex ion is stable. There is a minimum in the k_{obs}–pH curve at a pH of about 7.8 and the rate is sensitive to $[\text{enH}_2^{2+}]$ as well as ionic atmosphere. The best fit to the observed data was obtained with equation (80)

$$R/[\text{complex}] = k_0 + k_{enH_2}[enH_2^{2+}] + k_{en}[en] + k_{OH}[OH^-] \qquad (80)$$

with $k_0 = 7.86 \times 10^{-5}$ s^{-1}, $k_{enH_2} = 6.47 \times 10^{-3}$ M^{-1} s^{-1}, $k_{en} = 1.42 \times 10^{-3}$ M^{-1} s^{-1} and $k_{OH} = 3.26 \times 10^{-1}$ M^{-1} s^{-1} at 50 °C, I = 1.5 M. The activation parameters are composites because of overlapping paths but values of $\Delta H^{\ddagger}/$kJ mol$^{-1} = 125.6$, 125.0, 73.2, 98.7 and $\Delta S^{\ddagger}/$JK mol$^{-1} = 62.2$, 98.6, -73.6, 49.0 were obtained for the respective paths. Small rate changes were found when the supporting electrolyte was changed or if organic amines were added. A SN1CB mechanism was suggested based upon the pH dependence and the parallel kinetics of oxo and en exchange.

$Re(CN)_4O_2^{3-}$ is very stable in neutral and slightly basic solutions but in dilute acid is very rapidly converted to $[Re(CN)_4(O)(OH)]^{2-}$ which slowly (at room temperature) converts to $[ORe(CN)_4—O—Re(CN)_4O]^{4-}$.[202] The rate of oxygen exchange has been studied in an acidic and basic range.[203] At unit ionic strength the rate law is

$$R = k_1[Re(CN)_4O(OH)^{2-}] + k_b[Re(CN)_4O_2^{3-}] \qquad (81)$$

In the presence of free CN$^-$, $k_b = k_2[CN^-]^{-0.9}$, while in its absence $k_b = k_3[OH^-]^{0.22}$ where $k_1(35\ °C) = 3.42 \times 10^{-2}$ s^{-1}, $k_2(89.7\ °C) = 4.16 \times 10^{-7}$ M s^{-1}, $k_3(70.3\ °C) = 4.23 \times 10^{-3}$ s^{-1} and the activation enthalpies for k_1 and k_3 are 94.8 and 81.8 kJ mol^{-1} respectively. In the presence of free CN$^-$, the exchange rate was very slow (none observed at 25 °C for 75 h), while in acidic media the hydroxo and dimeric species were formed. Thus, different temperatures were necessary for each rate term. McKay plots were not linear with time due to the CN$^-$ hydrolysis at about 90 °C as shown by product detection. This was corrected for by a separate evaluation of the CN$^-$ hydrolysis rate equation and incorporation into the overall rate equation.

The kinetics in the acidic region were interpreted in terms of rapid formation of $[Re(O)(OH)(CN)_4]^{2-}$ followed by reversible replacement in the rate-determining step of the OH$^-$ group by solvent. No evidence was found for the reversible formation of $[Re_2O_3(CN)_8]^{4-}$ and the exchange it would involve. In basic media a CN$^-$ is removed to reach the activated state (trace amounts) which, it was thought, decreases the Re=O bond strength. However, it is more likely in view of more recent work that the IER (internal electronic rearrangement) mechanism is operable here (see mechanism section).

A comparison of the O=Re=O exchange rate with that of the O=Re—O—Re=O cyano complex shows the latter to be about a factor of 100 slower as one would anticipate. Also, the bridging oxygen exchange rate is approximately 2% of that of the yl-oxygens. With $[Re(py)_4O_2]^+$ only a preliminary observation appears to be available.[199] In the neutral region, pH = 6–8, the $t_{1/2}$ was found to be 8×10^3 min at 25 °C. This is about a factor of two less than for $[Re(CN)_4O_2]^{3-}$ under similar conditions, but is much slower than $[Re(en)_2O_2]^+$ at a pH of 6.0. Thus it would appear that of primary importance for these complexes is the ability of the equatorial ligands to accept electron density from the yl-oxygens, through the metal ion and reduce the basicity of the oxo-group. The K_a's of the complexes are inversely related to the magnitude of the oxygen exchange rate. When amine hydrogens are available on the equatorial ligands and can be ionized in basic media a SN1CB mechanism becomes dominant.

Trans-dioxo osmium(VI) ion. In conjunction with an X-ray structural study of the *trans*-$[Os(en)_2O_2]^{2+}$ ion, the water exchange was examined.[204] This ion has little or no basic properties and shows no evidence of protonation even in 6 M HCl although in the solid state one yl-oxygen is H-bonded to HSO_4^-. However, it occurs without M—O bond distance modification. The rate law observed in acidic media was $R = k_0[Os(en)_2O_2]^{2+}$ with $k_0 = 2.4 \times 10^{-7}$ s^{-1} at 25°C. In neutral and basic media the rate was faster but decomposition of the complex ion also occurred so that a conclusive decision as to the rate law could not be made. It was noted, as has been previously done in the actinide series, that isoelectronic dioxo-ions show little resemblance in their kinetic behaviour for oxygen exchange.

4. Oligomeric oxo-ions

Decavanadate(V) ion. In the pH range of 4 to 10, above 10^{-3} M, the main V(V) species in non-complexing media is $V_{10}O_{28}^{6-}$ (Fig. 6) and two protonated

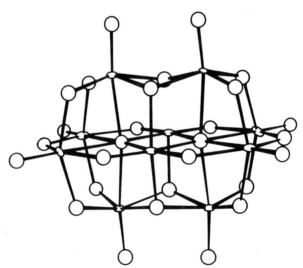

Fig. 6. Structure of decavanadate ion, $V_{10}O_{28}^{6-}$.

species. Isotopic oxygen exchange studies have been conducted on this ion over a wide pH and concentration range.[205,206] Linear McKay graphs were obtained and all 28 oxygens were equivalent in exchange properties or were so similar that no deviation from the linear plot could be ascertained up to 93% of the total exchange (Fig. 7). The rate of exchange is nearly constant in the pH range 4.0–6.3, increases at higher acidities and drops to nearly zero at a pH of

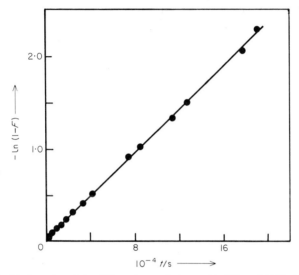

Fig. 7. McKay-plot of the ^{18}O exchange between $V_{10}O_{28}^{6-}$ and H_2O at 25 °C.

10. Comparison of the kinetics of depolymerization and exchange of the ion in slightly basic solutions suggests a "common intermediate" mechanism involving the one-ended dissociation of a V_4 group leading to dissociation and/or exchange. The mechanism provides for the exchange equivalency of all oxygens and is consistent with the activation parameters: $\Delta V^{\ddagger} = -5.0 \text{ cm}^3 \text{ mol}^{-1}$, $\Delta H^{\ddagger} = 85.3 \text{ kJ mol}^{-1}$, $\Delta S^{\ddagger} = -27 \text{ JK}^{-1} \text{ mol}^{-1}$.

Dimeric molybdenum(V) ion. Molybdenum(V), at millimolar concentrations is $Mo_2O_4^{2+}$. In solid complex structures the

$$O{=}Mo\!\!\!\overset{\displaystyle O}{\underset{\displaystyle O}{\diagup\!\!\!\diagdown}}\!\!\!Mo{=}O^{2+}$$

structure dominates and in aqueous solution the ion

$$\begin{bmatrix} H_2O \\ H_2O \end{bmatrix}\overset{\displaystyle O}{\underset{\displaystyle OH_2}{\diagup\!\!\!\diagdown}}Mo\overset{O}{\diagup}\overset{O}{\underset{O}{\diagup\!\!\!\diagdown}}Mo\overset{\displaystyle O}{\underset{\displaystyle OH_2}{\diagup\!\!\!\diagdown}}\begin{bmatrix} OH_2 \\ OH_2 \end{bmatrix}^{2+}$$

is also highly stable. Oxygen exchange with the solvent occurs rapidly with the bound waters but is much slower with the bridging and oxo-type oxygens.[14] It has been observed that $Mo_2O_4^{2+}$ reacts quantitatively with $EDTA^{4-}$ to give $Mo_2O_4(EDTA)^{2-}$, transferring its oxygen ligands quantitatively, and that after complexation oxygen exchange is effectively stopped. Since no insoluble salts of $Mo_2O_{4aq}^{2+}$ have been found, oxygen exchange on it was followed by looking at the ^{18}O content of the EDTA complex prepared from it. McKay graphs of the $Mo_2O_{4aq}^{2+}$ exchange showed two well-separated linear regions corresponding to the two types of oxygen. The faster exchanging oxygens have a half-life of about 4 min at 0 °C, while the others require 100 h at 40 °C for the same degree of completion. It was shown by Laser-Raman spectra of solutions and by ir spectra of solids, heavily enriched in, but only half exchanged with $H_2{}^{18}O$, that the yl-(oxo)-oxygens were the first to exchange. The oxo-exchange was not dependent on $[H^+]$ within the 0.001–3.1 M range. The bridged oxygens showed curved McKay plots unless $Hg_{(1)}$ was present, due to traces of oxidation over the extended periods of study ($Hg_{(1)}$ reduces MoO_4^{2-} to $Mo_2O_4^{2+}$). In 0.30 M HCl values for the activation parameters were $\Delta H^{\ddagger} = 108.4$ kJ mol^{-1} and $\Delta S^{\ddagger} = 1.7$ JK^{-1} mol^{-1}. The presence of MoO_4^{2-} increased the rate of $Mo_2O_4^{2+}$ (bridged oxygen) exchange according to the rate equation (88)

$$k_{obs} = k_0 + k_1[MoO_4^{2-}] \tag{88}$$

with $k_0 = 4 \times 10^{-6}$ s^{-1} and $k_1 = 4.6 \times 10^{-2}$ M^{-1} s^{-1} at 40 °C. When $Mo_2O_4^{2+}$ is complexed with cysteine, a tridentate ligand which does not bridge the two metals, the ^{18}O exchange rate of the yl-oxygens is considerably slower than that of the aqua ion. With the EDTA complex, where the ligand bridges the metal ions, only two oxygens exchange and at a very reduced rate.[207] Both exchanges are much faster in basic media.

Trimeric molybdenum(IV) ion. The thermodynamically stable form of Mo(IV) in acidic media at millimolar or above concentrations is $Mo_3O_{4aq}^{4+}$. Based on ^{18}O transfer experiments and an X-ray structure of a crystal containing the ion $[Mo_3O_4(NCS)_8OH_2]^{4-}$,[208] it was deduced that the structure of the ion in solution can be depicted as in Fig. 8.[15] This ion contains a capping oxo-oxygen, three bridging oxygens, three waters *trans* to the capping oxygens, and six waters *trans* to the bridging oxygens side. At the present time, the magnitude of the exchange rate has been determined for the first three of these types while the last type appears to be too fast for static ^{18}O studies. At 25 °C the $t_{1/2}$ in 0.1 M CH_3SO_3H for the bridging oxygens is estimated to be 2.5 yr, $k = 9 \times 10^{-9}$ s^{-1}; for the capping oxygen it is 5 d, $k = 2 \times 10^{-6}$ s^{-1} and for the three waters *trans* to capping oxygens it is 1.1 h; $k = 2 \times 10^{-4}$ s^{-1}. Again it was necessary to convert aqua ion into a complex

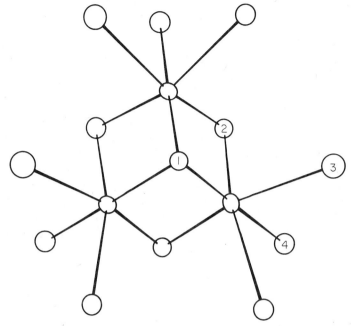

Fig. 8. Trimeric molybdenum(IV) ion. Each molybdenum is surrounded by a distorted octahedral configuration of one capping oxygen (1), two bridging oxygens (2) and probably two water molecules on the capping-O side (3) and one on the bridging-O side (4).

(with oxo and aqua transfer), in order to obtain a solid for ^{18}O analysis. When the waters coordinated to $Mo_3O_{4aq}^{4+}$ are replaced by other ligands such as NCS^- or $C_2O_4^{2-}$ the rate of water exchange of the waters on the bridging oxygen side are hardly, if at all, affected.

D. Kinetics of oxygen exchange between neutral substances and water

1. Chlorine dioxide

The exchange of oxygen between ClO_2 and H_2O in acidic media has been studied.[209] In the range of $HClO_4$ of 10^{-4} to 2.0 M at 0 to 25 °C no exchange was found over a period up to 168 h. Exposure to sunlight for a period of 2 h or the presence of 0.10 M Cl^- ($HClO_4 = 2.0$ M) also showed no exchange. Thus oxygen transfer experiments with ClO_2 as a reactant may be performed in acid solution without the complication of intrinsic exchange between ClO_2 and water. In basic media, ClO_2 disproportionates to ClO_3^- and ClO_2^- and it has been shown[210] that very little ClO_2–H_2O exchange occurs during the disproportionation.

2. Hydrogen peroxide

The exchange between H_2O_2 and water is very slow.[211,212] In highly acidic media, fluorosulfonic acid, some experiments suggest a measurable exchange[213] with the rate being highly dependent on the acidity. However, note that even in 11 M H_2SO_4 the $t_{1/2}$ at 60 °C is over 10 yr[214] and in strong nitric acid solutions the H_2O_2–H_2O exchange occurs at the same time as the NO_3^-–H_2O_2 exchange and interpretation is very difficult. The inertness to exchange of H_2O_2 is also suggested by the lack of O—O bond cleavage upon oxidation to O_2 by various one and two-electron oxidizing agents. A recent study[215] suggests that H_2O_2–H_2O exchange can be accomplished through peroxovanadium(V) and peroxomolybdenum(VI) catalysis. However, neither method seems to be suitable for the preparation of ^{18}O enriched H_2O_2.

3. Oxides of nitrogen

It has been shown[132,216] that N_2O has a lower limit to the $t_{1/2}$ for exchange of 10 yr at 22 °C in strongly alkaline or acidic (1.75 M H_2SO_4) solution.

Oxygen exchange between H_2O and NO is unexpectedly slow[217] in aqueous solution and in the gaseous state provided the NO is free of NO_2 and/or O_2. In 150 h at 25 °C no exchange ($\pm 1\%$ the experimental error), was found in pure water. Acid had no effect since a 24 h contact with 4.4 M HCl solution also showed no ($\pm 1\%$) exchange.

Likewise after 18 d at 25 °C a gaseous mixture (24 torr H_2O, 300 torr NO) had an unchanged NO ^{18}O content. Since no oxygen exchange occurred, it was concluded that molecular NO exists in water solution and acidic media with no contribution from the anhydride $H_2N_2O_3$. An NO_2 catalysis in both the gas and liquid phase exchange was observed. The NO_2 came from a partial oxidation of NO by atmospheric oxygen or by direct addition. Dilute HNO_3 did not cause exchange to occur at elevated rates but HNO_2–NO_2^- mixtures did. It was concluded that the H_2O–NO_2^- oxygen exchange is slower than the NO–NO_2^- oxygen exchange rate. Since the studies were conducted with the NO in both the liquid and gaseous states, catalysed rate constants were not obtained. Both N and O exchange between NO and aqueous solutions of HNO_3 have been explored by isotopic analyses of ^{15}NO brought into contact with aqueous solutions of HNO_3 in $H_2^{18}O$.[218] Nitrogen exchange has been shown to be limited by NO_3^-–HNO_2 exchange, at an overall rate that appears to correspond to the reversible NO–HNO_3 reaction under equilibrium conditions. This same process will produce O exchange, but NO–H_2O oxygen exchange has been found to occur at a much greater rate via HNO_2 by a mechanism similar to that pertaining in the $H_2O-NO_2^-$ system.

Kinetic experiments have been carried out in exploration of the simultaneous exchange reactions $^{15}NO-NO_2^-$ (nitrogen) and $NO-H_2{}^{18}O$ (oxygen).[219] The rate equation for oxygen exchange appears to be

$$R = k[NO][H^+][HNO_2] \tag{89}$$

If $H_2O-NO_2^-$ is rate limiting a direct catalytic attack of NO upon the hydrated nitrosonium ion is implied

$$NO + H_2NO_2^+ \overset{slow}{\rightleftharpoons} (N_2O_2)^+ + H_2O \tag{90}$$

$$(N_2O_2)^+ + H_2O \overset{rapid}{\rightleftharpoons} NO + HNO_2 + H^+ \tag{91}$$

The rate data of reference [219] compared with that of $H_2O-NO_2^-$ exchange[44] indicate a striking catalytic activity on the part of NO, and it is difficult to rationalize this effect other than by an $H_2O-NO_2^-$ process that is catalysed by NO.

4. Oxo-compounds of phosphorus

The exchange of oxygen between $(Ph)_3PO$ and water has been shown to be slow even in boiling water.[79] During a study on the oxidation and oxygen transfer to $(Ph)_3P$, observations on the exchange of $(bipy)_2pyRuO^{2+}$ were made.[220] While no quantitative results are available this oxo-Ru(IV) complex does not exchange $\pm 20\%$ in 30 min at room temperature.

VI. GENERAL DISCUSSION OF MECHANISMS

A. Correlation of activation parameters

Throughout this review we have emphasized the definitive nature of knowing the value of $\Delta V^{\ddagger}$, especially with respect to the mechanism of a reaction. The interpretation of volumes of activation in terms of reaction mechanism is probably more straightforward than entropies of activation, but not necessarily so. The $\Delta V^{\ddagger}$s observed are composite parameters consisting of the volume change of the reactants in forming the activated complex and the change in the solvent molecules. Qualitatively it would appear that the factors leading to $\Delta V^{\ddagger}$ should be directly related to the change in order and thus $\Delta S^{\ddagger}$ and thus an interdependence is likely to exist. Such an approximate relationship was shown to exist in 1959[221] and a more complete study for aquation and water exchange reactions of complexes was recently reported.[222] For this series of reactions the correlation (92) is reasonably good, where $\Delta V^{\ominus} = 1\,cm^3\,mol^{-1}$ and $\Delta S^{\ominus} = 1\,JK^{-1}\,mol^{-1}$. Both $\Delta V^{\ddagger}$ and $\Delta S^{\ddagger}$ are difficult

$$\Delta V^{\ddagger}/\Delta V^{\ominus} = (0.249 \pm 0.024)\Delta S^{\ddagger}/\Delta S^{\ominus} - (4.4 \pm 0.3) \tag{92}$$

to measure accurately and therefore considerable scatter of data must be expected. Certainly the close parallel between $\Delta V^{\ddagger}$ and $\Delta S^{\ddagger}$ will be helpful when either cannot be accurately measured.

A linear correlation between $\Delta S^{\ddagger}$ and $\Delta H^{\ddagger}$ for some spontaneous exchange paths of oxo-anions seemed to exist.[43] In Fig. 9 $\Delta H^{\ddagger}$ is plotted against $\Delta S^{\ddagger}$ for all simple oxo-anions where data of the k_0 path are available. The compara-

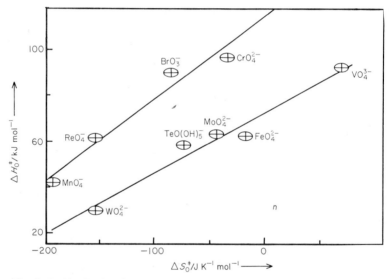

Fig. 9. Isokinetic plots for spontaneous O-exchange reactions. The upper curve corresponds to an isokinetic temperature of ca 87 °C, the lower curve corresponds to an isokinetic temperature of ca −3 °C.

tively inert oxo-anions MnO_4^-, ReO_4^-, BrO_3^-, CrO_4^{2-} seem to fall on one isokinetic plot, whereas the more labile oxo-anions WO_4^{2-}, $TeO(OH)_5^-$, MoO_4^{2-}, FeO_4^{2-}, VO_4^{3-} fall on another. No really convincing rationale for these compensatory effects can be given, but for simultaneous comparison of different ions a graphical analysis of $\Delta H^{\ddagger}$ versus $\Delta S^{\ddagger}$ values is certainly informative.

B. Mechanistic generalizations

While each exchange reaction is unique and is carried by its own mechanisms, it may be helpful, for predictive purposes, at least, to give an overview of the available results and arrive at tentative mechanistic generalizations. Usually, ligand exchange reactions are classified and discussed in terms of a hypothetical intermediate of increased or decreased coordination number and the corresponding processes are called associative A, or dissociative D. In most cases an actual intermediate has not been detected and the A–D classification is supplemented by two interchange processes I_a and I_d, associative and dissociative respectively, depending on whether the incoming and outgoing ligands are tightly or weakly bound in the transition state. For isotopic exchanges involving solvent and its ions, few kinetic tests can be applied and for the most part one has to rely on the interpretation of the acid-base effects, activation parameters and isotope effects.

For tetrahedral and pyramidal oxo-anions one usually finds rate terms containing $[Anion][H^+]^2$, $[Anion]$ and $[Anion][OH^-]$. It is difficult to distinguish between a dehydration reaction (93) and a bimolecular substitution (94) as the rate-determining step for the first term. The H/D isotopic effects, k_H/k_D, are in the 0.4 region indicating an acid-base pre-equilibrium.[78,91,99]

$$XO_n^z + 2H^+ \rightleftharpoons XO_{n-1}^{z+2} + H_2O \tag{93}$$

$$H_2XO_n^{z+2} + H_2O \rightleftharpoons H_2XO_n^{z+2} + H_2O \tag{94}$$

The rate constant is then a composite of the protonation constant and the dissociation or substitution rate constant and generally decreases as the central atom's oxidation state increases and as its size decreases. Nucleophilic anions such as Cl^-, NO_2^-, OAc^- etc. often accelerate this rate suggesting either ion-pair formation or an I_a process.[76,98,118,119] It is usually assumed that the pH-independent term is predominantly associative facilitated by solvent and the $[OH^-]$ term is an associative process involving OH^-. The water dependence cannot be determined in either term but a normal hydrogen isotope effect $k_H/k_D \sim 2$ is generally observed. With octahedral complexes having formally predominantly OH^- ligands, i.e. $IO(OH)_5$, (H_5IO_6) or $Te(OH)_6$, (H_6TeO_6), no acid dependence is found in the acid region and the mechanism is thought to be of the D or I_d class suggesting (95) and (96) for the equations leading to exchange.[76,94,108]

$$IO(OH)_5 \rightleftharpoons IO_2(OH)_3 + H_2O \tag{95}$$

$$Te(OH)_6 \rightleftharpoons TeO(OH)_4 + H_2O \tag{96}$$

The much larger k_1 for periodic acid, by a factor of 10^6, is probably due to the *trans* effect of the yl-oxygen. Thus the term for $TeO(OH)_5^-$, which also has an yl-oxygen is approximately 10^4 times that of Te(OH)$_6$. The activation parameters and hydrogen isotope effect agree with this interpretation. For octahedral aqua metal ions only a few examples are available from ^{18}O measurements and the large number of nmr results are most valuable. In acidic media the most important rate term is first order in the metal ion and no [H$^+$] term is found.[165,166,171] The most useful diagnostic parameter for mechanism appears to be $\Delta V^{\ddagger}$. The first row transition metal $+2$ and $+3$ aqua ions (high spin) show a gradual change over with increasing atomic number from I$_a$ to I$_d$ (from negative to positive in $\Delta V^{\ddagger}$),[167] see also the review of Swaddle, this Volume. Also greater I$_a$ character seems to occur in the second and third transition series within a group. Many octahedral aqua ions show an important inverse [H$^+$] or first order in [OH$^-$] term.[16,33] While this has not been studied in detail it can be related to the expected labilizing effect of a coordinated OH$^-$ group on the remaining coordinated water molecules, and is probably closely related to the SN1CB mechanism often applied to ammine complexes of cobalt(III).

Little is known concerning the reactions leading to exchange of single or double bridging oxo or hydroxo ligands. It is usual to find a [H$^+$] dependence either first or second order which suggests that opening of a bridge leads to exchange (97).

$$\text{(97)}$$

However, even if this is the main overall reaction giving exchange, the slow step is not identified. The question of the associative or dissociative nature of the rate-controlling step has hardly been considered.

From studies on yl-type ions in which one or more multiply-bound oxygens are coordinated it is clear that water molecules *trans* to the yl-oxygen are very labile. This is probably attributable to very weak bonds to those waters as evidenced by the long distances in X-ray solid state crystal structures. In the case of VO^{2+} for instance the *trans*-water is too fast to exchange even for nmr studies. The effect on *cis*-waters is considerably smaller.

Exchange of yl-oxygen can be on three types of ions: MO$_{aq}^{n+}$, *cis*-MO$_{2aq}^{n+}$, *trans*-MO$_{2aq}^{n+}$. For aqua-oxo ions the basicity of the yl-oxygen seems to be very small and protonation does not play an important role.

Dissociation or direct replacement do not seem to be reasonable as low-energy pathways. The reaction mechanism which seems to be emerging from studies of these ions and their complexes is one in which a rate-controlling electronic rearrangement (coupled with proton–transfer reactions) causes the yl-oxygen to be changed into a water with a fast exchange rate. Thus the primary step is an intramolecular electron rearrangement (IER). This requires a

$$
\begin{array}{ccc}
O & OH & OH \\
\diagdown \vdots \big| & \diagdown \big| & \diagdown \big| \\
-M-OH_2 & \longrightarrow \quad -M-OH & \longrightarrow \quad -M\cdots O \\
\diagup \big| & \diagup \big| & \diagup \big|
\end{array}
\qquad (98)
$$

water or OH group in one of the inner sphere positions. In complexes having no water ligands, one may be formed by partial dissociation of the ligand. In the acid region, no acid dependence is observed, *cis*-oxygens are much faster than *trans*, and often there is an OH^- dependence probably related to proton ionization on a coordinated water. In many cases the main rate term is caused by fast electron exchange with traces of another oxidation state of the element which is often present as an impurity. For large poly-oxo-ions such as $V_{10}O_{28}^{6-}$, the yl-oxygens on the surface of the ion seem highly resistent to exchange as do the internal bridging oxygens. Based on a limited number of examples, exchange seems to occur by a reversible partially opening of the structure into partially connected fragments which requires additional coordination of solvent to complete the coordination sphere of the metal ions. Other studies are needed to discern if this mechanism is widely applicable.

In conclusion it seems appropriate to point out the sensitivity of exchange kinetics to electronic factors by a comparison of the tetrahedral ions CrO_4^{2-}, MnO_4^{2-} and FeO_4^{2-} which are isomorphous as the potassium salts.[223] The average, thermally-corrected M—O distances are 1.659(4), 1.660(8) and 1.666(2) Å respectively. For these ions, d^0, d^1 and d^2 the rates of exchange and the rate laws are very different. Thus it is clear that even substances which are extremely similar structurally the paths for exchange with solvent may be almost unrelated; or at least seem so.

VII. PROBLEM AREAS AND REGIONS FOR FUTURE STUDY

It seems clear that ^{18}O studies on oxo-ions are capable of filling a significant gap in our knowledge of the structural and kinetic features which other techniques cannot satisfy. The main drawback to progress in this field appears to be the expense in equipment and time in obtaining precision ^{18}O determinations. For some studies it is sufficient to use high enrichments and measure, by mass spectrometry, the isotope ratio in the parent ion or in a fragment ion using a non-dedicated instrument on a slightly volatile liquid or even solid. Such measurements, while suitable for tracing the pathway of an atom, are seldom of high enough precision to be applied to basic kinetic studies or to solution structural studies. Thus there is a need for development of techniques, either specific or general, for determining the ^{18}O content of inorganic molecules, salts and complexes in or out of solution quickly and precisely. In certain specific cases the ^{18}O isotope effect on nmr spectra[80] appears to be capable of refinement to a point where it is a significant improvement over the methods used in the past. Chromatographic separation and analysis[87,88] of simple isotopic molecules may also prove to be highly valuable. The potential of Laser-Raman isotopic analysis[14] of ions and complexes in aqueous solution is very great and only the future will show if its inherent precision and accuracy can be sufficiently improved to be of significant value in this area of research.

From previous sections of this review, one notes that our understanding of both the mechanisms of exchange and of solution structures are highly tentative in many cases and are subject to extensive modification with each new definitive study. Significant and unambiguous experiments seem to be slow in coming, however, perhaps due to the relatively small number of investigators actively engaged in pursuing this type of information. Suffice it to point out that this area of investigation probably deserves more emphasis than it presently enjoys in order to produce optimum results. Numerous areas need attention. Investigation of the features of the borates and silicates has hardly been touched and is likely to contribute to our structural knowledge of solutions of these materials and to the pathways for reaction.

An area which needs considerable attention is that of the poly-molybdates, tungstates and the entire heteropoly-acid group of compounds. In most cases the exchange rate will be quite slow and highly suited for static ^{18}O studies. With the knowledge that coordinated OH groups, even if not bridging, are often slow to exchange with solvent, the question of the structural and kinetic nature of the species formed when metal ions are dissolved in basic solution becomes interesting from the standpoint of ^{18}O studies. Our present state of knowledge suggests that the composition of, for instance, Cr(III), Rh(III) and Ir(III) ions in basic media could be determined by ^{18}O studies and there is even the chance that the first coordination number of Zn(II) and Al(III) may be slow enough to exchange to be determined by this method. Of course the kinetic properties of water and its ions in the first coordination sphere of most ions of charge greater than three are not well known and should provide considerable knowledge about their aqueous structures. There is the potential for the characterization of species analogous to VO_2^{2+} such as MoO_3^{3+} (both d^1) or TiO^{2+} for which evidence is not satisfying. Also the very difficult aqueous chemistry of Zr, Nb, Hf and Ta in their high oxidation states could be better understood if kinetic ^{18}O studies were available.

It appears to the authors that this area is ripe for study and on the basis of what is presently known shows the promise of providing significant advances in our knowledge of the solution structure and kinetic properties of aqueous oxo-ions.

Acknowledgements

This review was planned and started when H.G. was European Science Exchange visitor to Leeds during 1979, and R.K.M. was Fulbright Professor in Leoben during 1980. One of us (H.G.) is grateful to the Austrian Foundation for the Promotion of Scientific Research for support. We thank Professor J. Swinehart for helpful suggestions.

REFERENCES

[1] Saito, K.; Sasaki, Y. In "Advances in Inorganic and Bioinorganic Mechanisms";
Vol. 1. Sykes, A. G., Ed.; Academic Press: London, 1982, pp. 179–216.

[2] Cohn, M.; Urey, H. C. J. Amer. Chem. Soc. 1938, 60, 679.

[3] Hall, N. F.; Alexander, O. R. J. Amer. Chem. Soc. 1940, 62, 3455.

[4] Hunt, J. P.; Taube, H. J. Chem. Phys. 1950, 18, 757.

[5] Friedman, H. L.; Taube, H.; Hunt, J. P. J. Chem. Phys. 1950, 18, 759.

[6] Hunt, J. P.; Taube, H. J. Chem. Phys. 1951, 19, 602.

[7] Plane, R. A.; Taube, H. J. Phys. Chem. 1952, 56, 33.

[8] Crandall, H. W. J. Chem. Phys. 1949, 17, 602.

[9] Baldwin, H. W.; Taube, H. J. Chem. Phys. 1960, 33, 206.

[10] Murmann, R. K. Inorg. Chim. Acta 1977, 25, L43.

[11] Murmann, R. K. Inorg. Chem. 1977, 16, 46.

[12] Kolaczkowski, R. W.; Plane, R. A. Inorg. Chem. 1964, 3, 322.

[13] Goff, H.; Murmann, R. K. J. Amer. Chem. Soc. 1971, 93, 6058.

[14] Murmann, R. K. Inorg. Chem. 1980, 19, 1765.

[15] Murmann, R. K.; Shelton, M. E. J. Amer. Chem. Soc. 1980, 102, 3984.

[16] Plumb, W.; Harris, G. M. Inorg. Chem. 1964, 3, 542.

[17] Beutler, P.; Gamsjäger, H.; Baertschi, P. Chimia (Switz.) 1978, 32, 163.

[18] Murmann, R. K.; Sullivan, J. C. Inorg. Chem. 1967, 6, 892.

[19] McKay, H. A. C. Nature 1938, 142, 997; McKay, H. A. C. J. Amer. Chem. Soc.
1943, 65, 702.

[20] Duffield, R. B.; Calvin, M. J. Amer. Chem. Soc. 1946, 68, 557; McKay, H. A. C.
"Principles of Radiochemistry"; Butterworths: London, 1971.

[21] Fleck, G. M. J. Theor. Biol. 1972, 34, 509.

[22] Harris, G. M. Trans. Faraday Soc. 1951, 47, 716.

[23] Bunton, C. A.; Craig, D. P.; Halevi, E. A. Trans. Faraday Soc. 1955, 51, 196.

[24] Melander, L.; Saunders, W. H., Jr. "Reaction Rates of Isotopic Molecules";
John Wiley and Sons: New York, 1980, p. 115.

[25] Dostrovsky, I.; Klein, F. S. Anal. Chem. 1952, 24, 414.

[26] Falcone, A. B. Anal. Biochem. 1961, 2, 147.

[27] Baertschi, P. Helv. Chim. Acta 1953, 36, 1352.

[28] Samuel, D. "Oxygenases"; Hayaishi, O., Ed.; Academic Press: New York, 1962,
p. 67.

[29] Webster, L. A.; Wahl, M. H.; Urey, H. C. J. Chem. Phys. 1935, 3, 129; O'Neil,
J. R.; Adami, L. H. J. Phys. Chem. 1969, 73, 1553.

[30] Anbar, M.; Guttmann, S. Int. J. Appl. Radiation Isotopes 1959, 4, 233.

[31] Shakhashiri, B. Z.; Gordon, G. Talanta 1966, 13, 142.

[32] Murmann, R. K. Unpublished results.

[33] Johnson, M. D.; Murmann, R. K. *Inorg. Chem.* **1983**, *22*, 1068.
[34] Boyd, R. H.; Taft, R. W., Jr; Wolf, A. P.; Christman, D. R. *J. Amer. Chem. Soc.* **1960**, *82*, 4729.
[35] Boyer, P. D.; Graves, D. J.; Suelter, C. H.; Dempsey, M. E. *Anal. Chem.* **1961**, *33*, 1906.
[36] Brodskii, A. I.; Gol'denfel'd, I. V.; Gragerov, I. P. *Zhur. Analit. Chim.* **1962**, *17*, 893.
[37] Nemodruk, A. A. *Radiokhimiya* **1972**, *14*, 843.
[38] Hoering, T. C.; Kennedy, J. W. *J. Amer. Chem. Soc.* **1957**, *79*, 56.
[39] Keisch, B.; Kennedy, J. W.; Wahl, A. C. *J. Amer. Chem. Soc.* **1958**, *80*, 4778.
[40] Anbar, M. *Int. J. Appl. Radiation Isotopes* **1958**, *3*, 134.
[41] Hoering, T. C.; Butler, R. C.; McDonald, H. O. *J. Amer. Chem. Soc.* **1956**, *78*, 4829.
[42] Cohn, M.; Drysdale, G. R. *J. Biol. Chem.* **1955**, *216*, 831.
[43] Von Felten, H.; Wernli, B.; Gamsjäger, H.; Baertschi, P. *J. Chem. Soc. Dalton Trans.* **1978**, 496.
[44] Anbar, M.; Taube, H. *J. Amer. Chem. Soc.* **1954**, *76*, 6243.
[45] Bunton, C. A.; Stedman, G. *J. Chem. Soc.* **1959**, 3466.
[46] Pryor, W. A.; Tonellato, U. *J. Amer. Chem. Soc.* **1967**, *89*, 3379.
[47] Anbar, M.; Taube, H. *J. Amer. Chem. Soc.* **1958**, *80*, 1073.
[48] Dole, M. *J. J. Chem. Phys.* **1936**, *4*, 778; Dole, M. *J. Chem. Rev.* **1952**, *51*, 263.
[49] Baertschi, P.; Thürkauf, M. *Helv. Chim. Acta* **1959**, *42*, 282.
[50] Staschewski, D. *Ber. Bunsenges. Phys. Chemie* **1969**, *73*, 59.
[51] Skarre, O. K.; Tereshkevich, M. O.; Shelekhova, T. S. *Zhur. Fiz. Khim.* **1960**, *34*, 1599.
[52] Garus, L. I.; Tereshkevich, M. O.; Skarre, O. K. *Teor. i Eksp. Khim.* **1967**, *3*, 412.
[53] Tereshkevich, M. O.; Volkova, S. A.; Kuratova, T. S.; Dlugach, R. E. *Zhur. Fiz. Khim.* **1971**, *45*, 413.
[54] Pozhidaeva, E. Yu.; Tereshkevich, M. O. *Zhur. Fiz. Khim.* **1969**, *43*, 339.
[55] Skarre, O. K.; Tereshkevich, M. O.; Kuratova, T. S.; Larchenko, L. N. *Russ. J. Phys. Chem.* **1963**, *37*, 457.
[56] Skarre, O. K.; Tereshkevich, M. O.; Kuratova, T. S. *Russ. J. Phys. Chem.* **1963**, *37*, 598.
[57] Tereshkevich, M. O.; Garus, L. I.; Kulish, A. F.; Varenko, E. S.; Galushko, V. P. *Teor. i Eksp. Khim.* **1966**, *2*, 213.
[58] Garus, L. I.; Tereshkevich, M. O.; Skarre, O. K. *Zhur. Fiz. Khim.* **1966**, *40*, 2222.
[59] Tereshkevich, M. O.; Pozhidaeva, E. Yu.; Dlugach, R. E. *Zhur. Obshchei. Khim.* **1967**, *37*, 17.
[60] Tereshkevich, M. O.; Pozhidaeva, E. Yu.; Gol'teuzen, E. E.; Baturin, A. N.; Sokolov, V. G. *Teor. i Eksp. Khim.* **1967**, *3*, 349.
[61] Tereshkevich, M. O.; Valenchuk, M. I.; Kuprik, A. V.; Volkova, S. A.; Skidan, N. A. *Zhur. Strukt. Khim.* **1972**, *13*, 785.
[62] Kuratova, T. S.; Ivashina, G. A.; Tereshkevich, M. O. *Zhur. Fiz. Khim.* **1972**, *46*, 932.
[63] Tereshkevich, M. O.; Valenchuk, M. I.; Shkaranova, A. A. *Zhur. Obshchei. Khim.* **1973**, *43*, 456.
[64] Valenchuk, M. I.; Tereshkevich, M. O. *Zhur. Fiz. Khim.* **1972**, *46*, 2904.
[65] Ivashina, G. A.; Tereshkevich, M. O.; Kuratova, T. S. *Zhur. Obshchei. Khim.* **1972**, *42*, 2602.
[66] Tereshkevich, M. O.; Volkova, S. A.; Kuprik, A. V.; Dlugash, R. E.; Kuratova,

T. S. *Teor. Rastvorov.* **1971**, 178.
[67] Tereshkevich, M. O.; Pozhidaeva, E. Yu.; Lebed, S. B.; Nikolaeva, T. I. *Zhur. Obshchei. Khim.* **1977**, *47*, 2643.
[68] Radmer, R. *Inorg. Chem.* **1972**, *11*, 1162.
[69] Betts, R. H.; Voss, R. H. *Can. J. Chem.* **1970**, *48*, 2035.
[70] Francis, D. J.; Jordan, R. B. *Inorg. Chem.* **1972**, *11*, 1170.
[71] Francis, D. J.; Jordan, R. B. *Inorg. Chem.* **1972**, *11*, 461.
[72] Murmann, R. K. *J. Phys. Chem.* **1967**, *71*, 974.
[73] Prestwood, R. J.; Wahl, A. C. *J. Amer. Chem. Soc.* **1949**, *71*, 3137.
[74] Okumura, A.; Okazaki, N. *Bull. Chem. Soc. Jap.* **1973**, *46*, 2937.
[75] Okumura, A.; Kitani, M.; Toyomi, Y.; Okazaki, N. *Bull. Chem. Soc. Jap.* **1980**, *53*, 3143.
[76] Wernli, B. PhD Thesis, Montanuniversität Leoben, Austria, 1980.
[77] Rahmoeller, K. M.; Murmann, R. K. *Inorg. Chem.* **1983**, *22*, 1072.
[78] Von Felten, H.; Gamsjäger, H.; Baertschi, P. *J. Chem. Soc. Dalton Trans.* **1976**, 1683.
[79] Halmann, M.; Pinchas, S. *J. Chem. Soc.* **1958**, 3264.
[80] Risley, J. M.; Van Etten, R. L. *J. Amer. Chem. Soc.* **1979**, *101*, 252; Risley, J. M.; Van Etten, R. L. *J. Amer. Chem. Soc.* **1980**, *102*, 4609; Risley, J. M.; Van Etten, R. L. *J. Amer. Chem. Soc.* **1980**, *102*, 6699.
[81] Risley, J. M.; Van Etten, R. L. *J. Amer. Chem. Soc.* **1981**, *103*, 4389.
[82] Lutz, O.; Nolle, A.; Staschewski, D. *Z. Naturforsch. A* **1978**, *33A*, 380.
[83] Cohn, M.; Hu, A. *Proc. Natn. Acad. Sci. USA* **1978**, *75*, 200; Cohn, M.; Hu, A. *J. Amer. Chem. Soc.* **1980**, *102*, 913.
[84] Webb, M. R.; Trentham, D. R. *J. Biol. Chem.* **1980**, *255*, 1775.
[85] Haase, A. R.; Lutz, O.; Müller, M.; Nolle, A. *Z. Naturforsch. A* **1976**, *31A*, 1427; Buckler, K. V.; Haase, A. R.; Lutz, O.; Müller, M.; Nolle, A. *Z. Naturforsch. A* **1977**, *32A*, 126.
[86] Gröning, Ö.; Drakenberg, T.; Elding, L. I. *Inorg. Chem.* **1982**, *21*, 1820.
[87] Bruner, F.; Cartoni, G. P.; Liberti, A. *Anal. Chem.* **1966**, *38*, 2989; Shepard, A. T.; Danielson, N. D.; Pauls, R. E.; Mahle, N. H.; Taylor, P. J.; Rodgers, L. B. *Separation Sci.* **1976**, *11*, 279.
[88] Matthews, D. E.; Hayes, J. M. *Anal. Chem.* **1978**, *50*, 1465.
[89] Keeney, D. R.; Tedesco, M. J. *Anal. Chim. Acta* **1973**, *65*, 19; Goleb, J. A.; Middelboc, V. *Anal. Chim. Acta* **1968**, *43*, 229.
[90] Kamemoto, T. *Nature* **1964**, *203*, 513.
[91] Hoering, T. C.; Ishimori, F. T.; McDonald, H. O. *J. Amer. Chem. Soc.* **1958**, *80*, 3876.
[92] Appelman, E. H. *Inorg. Chem.* **1969**, *8*, 223.
[93] Antonsen, O. EIR, Würenlingen, Switzerland, personal communication.
[94] Pecht, I.; Luz, Z. *J. Amer. Chem. Soc.* **1965**, *87*, 4068.
[95] Sillén, L. G.; Martell, A. E. "Stability Constants of Metal–Ion Complexes"; Chemical Society: London, 1964, Supplement, No. 1, 1970.
[96] Gamsjäger, H.; Gerber, F.; Antonsen, O. *Chimia (Switz.)* **1973**, *27*, 94.
[97] Pethybridge, A. D.; Prue, J. E. *Trans. Faraday Soc.* **1967**, *63*, 2019.
[98] Anbar, M.; Guttmann, S. *J. Amer. Chem. Soc.* **1961**, *83*, 4741.
[99] Gamsjäger, H.; Grütter, A.; Baertschi, P. *Helv. Chim. Acta* **1972**, *55*, 781.
[100] Gamsjäger, H.; Baertschi, P. *Helv. Chim. Acta* **1972**, *55*, 2154.
[101] Anbar, M.; Guttmann, S. *J. Amer. Chem. Soc.* **1961**, *83*, 781.
[102] Wharton, R. K.; Taylor, R. S.; Sykes, A. G. *Inorg. Chem.* **1975**, *14*, 33.

[103] Von Felten, H. PhD Thesis, Bern, 1976.
[104] Appelman, E. H.; Thompson, R. C.; Engelkemeir, A. G. *Inorg. Chem.* **1979**, *18*, 909.
[105] Thompson, R. C.; Appelman, E. H. *Inorg. Chem.* **1980**, *19*, 3248.
[106] Okumura, A.; Okazaki, N. *Bull. Chem. Soc. Jap.* **1973**, *46*, 1080.
[107] Walrafen, G. E. *J. Chem. Phys.* **1963**, *39*, 1479.
[108] Luz, Z.; Pecht, I. *J. Amer. Chem. Soc.* **1966**, *88*, 1152.
[109] Frydman, M.; Nilsson, G.; Torsten, R.; Sillén, L. G. *Acta Chem. Scand.* **1958**, *12*, 878.
[110] Connick, R. E.; Tam, T. M.; von Deuster, E. *Inorg. Chem.* **1982**, *21*, 103.
[111] Okumura, A.; Okazaki, N. *Bull. Chem. Soc. Jap.* **1973**, *46*, 1084.
[112] Simon, A.; Paetzold, R. *Z. Anorg. Allg. Chem.* **1960**, *303*, 46.
[113] Bunton, C. A.; Halevi, E. A.; Llewellyn, D. R. *J. Chem. Soc.* **1952**, 4913.
[114] Bunton, C. A.; Halevi, E. A. *J. Chem. Soc.* **1952**, 4917.
[115] Bunton, C. A.; Halevi, E. A.; Llewellyn, D. R. *J. Chem. Soc.* **1953**, 2653.
[116] Hood, G. C.; Reilly, C. A. *J. Chem. Phys.* **1960**, *32*, 127.
[117] Klemenc, A.; Hayek, E. *Monatsh.* **1929**, *54*, 407.
[118] Bunton, C. A.; Llewellyn, D. R.; Stedman, G. *J. Chem. Soc.* **1959**, 568.
[119] Bunton, C. A.; Masui, M. *J. Chem. Soc.* **1960**, 304; Seel, F.; Wölfle, R.; Zwarg, G. *Z. Naturforsch.* **1958**, *13b*, 136.
[120] Goff, H.; Kidwell, S.; Laugher, J.; Murmann, R. K. *Inorg. Chem.* **1973**, *12*, 2631.
[121] Bunton, C. A.; Llewellyn, D. R.; Vernon, C. A.; Welch, V. A. *J. Chem. Soc.* **1961**, 1636.
[122] Nims, L. F. *J. Amer. Chem. Soc.* **1933**, *55*, 1946; Nims, L. F. *J. Amer. Chem. Soc.* **1934**, *56*, 1110.
[123] Samuel, D.; Silver, B. L. *J. Chem. Soc.* **1964**, 1049.
[124] Takahasi, K.; Yui, N. *Bull. Inst. Phys. Chem. Research (Tokyo)* **1941**, *20*, 521.
[125] Haas, T. E.; Gillman, H. D. *Inorg. Chem.* **1968**, *7*, 2051.
[126] Okumura, A.; Yamamoto, N.; Okazaki, N. *Bull. Chem. Soc. Jap.* **1973**, *46*, 3633.
[127] Okumura, A.; Watanabe, S.; Sakaue, M.; Okazaki, N. *Bull. Chem. Soc. Jap.* **1979**, *52*, 2783.
[128] Copenhafer, W. C.; Rieger, P. H. *J. Amer. Chem. Soc.* **1978**, *100*, 3776.
[129] Crouthamel, C. E.; Hayes, A. M.; Martin, D. S. *J. Amer. Chem. Soc.* **1951**, *73*, 82.
[130] Buist, G. J.; Hipperson, W. C. P.; Lewis, J. D. *J. Chem. Soc. A* **1969**, 307.
[131] Wilson, J. N.; Dickinson, R. G. *J. Amer. Chem. Soc.* **1937**, *59*, 1358.
[132] Bonner, F.; Bigeleisen, J. *J. Amer. Chem. Soc.* **1952**, *74*, 4944.
[133] Mills, G. A.; Urey, H. C. *J. Amer. Chem. Soc.* **1940**, *62*, 1019.
[134] Poulton, D. J.; Baldwin, H. W. *Can. J. Chem.* **1967**, *45*, 1045.
[135] Harned, H. S.; Davies, R. *J. Amer. Chem. Soc.* **1943**, *65*, 2030.
[136] Harned, H. S.; Scholes, S. R., Jr. *J. Amer. Chem. Soc.* **1941**, *63*, 1706.
[137] Dasgupta, T. P.; Harris, G. M. *J. Amer. Chem. Soc.* **1968**, *90*, 6360.
[138] Van Eldik, R.; Palmer, D. A. "Abstract 3rd International Conference on the Mechanisms of Reactions in Solution"; 1982, p. 50.
[139] Staschewski, D. *Chem.-Ing.-Techn.* **1969**, *41*, 1111.
[140] Gerster, R. *Int. J. Appl. Radiation Isotopes* **1971**, *22*, 339.
[141] Tu, C. K.; Silverman, D. N. *J. Phys. Chem.* **1975**, *79*, 1647.
[142] Llewellyn, D. R.; O'Connor, C. *J. Chem. Soc.* **1964**, 545.
[143] Llewellyn, D. R.; O'Connor, C. *J. Chem. Soc.* **1964**, 4400.
[144] McTigue, P. T.; Renowden, P. V.; Watkins, A. R. *Aust. J. Chem.* **1970**, *23*, 381.
[145] O'Connor, C.; Llewellyn, D. R. *J. Chem. Soc.* **1965**, 2197.

[146] O'Connor, C. J. *J. Inorg. Nucl. Chem.* **1968**, *30*, 2697.
[147] O'Connor, C. J.; Turney, T. A.; Bridson, M. E.; Hardie, A. B. *Nature Phys. Sci.* **1972**, *237*, 128.
[148] Redington, R. L. *J. Phys. Chem.* **1976**, *80*, 229.
[149] Lomax, T. D.; O'Connor, C. J. *Amer. Chem. Soc.* **1978**, *100*, 5910.
[150] Harned, H. S.; Embree, N. D. *J. Amer. Chem. Soc.* **1934**, *56*, 1042.
[151] Harned, H. S.; Embree, N. D. *J. Amer. Chem. Soc.* **1934**, *56*, 1050.
[152] Henne, A. L.; Fox, C. J. *J. Amer. Chem. Soc.* **1951**, *73*, 2323.
[153] Drucker, K. *Z. Phys. Chem.* **1904**, *49*, 563; Drucker, C. *Z. Phys. Chem.* **1920**, *96*, 381.
[154] Milburn, R. M.; Taube, H. *J. Amer. Chem. Soc.* **1959**, *81*, 3515.
[155] Robinson, R. A.; Stokes, R. H. "Electrolyte Solutions"; Butterworths: London, 1959, p. 357; p. 520.
[156] Bender, M. L. *J. Amer. Chem. Soc.* **1962**, *84*, 2582.
[157] Silver, M. S.; Stoddard, M.; Stein, T. P. *J. Amer. Chem. Soc.* **1970**, *92*, 2883.
[158] Baloga, M. R.; Earley, J. E. *J. Phys. Chem.* **1963**, *67*, 964.
[159] Holyer, R. H.; Baldwin, H. W. *Can. J. Chem.* **1967**, *45*, 413.
[160] Dankleff, M. A. P.; Curci, R.; Edwards, J. O.; Pyun, H-Y. *J. Amer. Chem. Soc.* **1968**, *90*, 3209.
[161] Hoering, T. C.; McDonald, H. O. Preprint.
[162] Heckner, K-H.; Landsberg, R. *J. Inorg. Nucl. Chem.* **1967**, *29*, 413.
[163] Heckner, K-H.; Landsberg, R. *J. Inorg. Nucl. Chem.* **1967**, *29*, 423.
[164] Murmann, R. K. *J. Amer. Chem. Soc.* **1971**, *93*, 4184.
[165] Hunt, J. P.; Plane, R. A. *J. Amer. Chem. Soc.* **1954**, *76*, 5960.
[166] Stranks, D. R.; Swaddle, T. W. *J. Amer. Chem. Soc.* **1971**, *93*, 2783.
[167] Palmer, D. A.; Kelm, H. *Coord. Chem. Rev.* **1981**, *36*, 89; Van Eldik, R.; Kelm, H. *Rev. Phys. Chem. Jap.* **1980**, *50*, 185.
[168] Swaddle, T. W. ACS Symposium Series, preprint.
[169] Duffy, N. V.; Earley, J. E. *J. Amer. Chem. Soc.* **1967**, *89*, 272.
[170] Earley, J. E.; Alexander, W. *J. Amer. Chem. Soc.* **1970**, *92*, 2294.
[171] Swaddle, T. W.; Stranks, D. R. *J. Amer. Chem. Soc.* **1972**, *94*, 8357.
[172] Hunt, H. R.; Taube, H. *J. Amer. Chem. Soc.* **1958**, *80*, 2642.
[173] Moore, P.; Basolo, F.; Pearson, R. G. *Inorg. Chem.* **1966**, *5*, 223.
[174] Bracken, D. E.; Baldwin, H. W. *Inorg. Chem.* **1974**, *13*, 1325.
[175] Hyde, M. R.; Davies, R.; Sykes, A. G. *J. Chem. Soc. A* **1972**, *18*, 32.
[176] Anbar, M.; Pecht, I. *J. Amer. Chem. Soc.* **1967**, *89*, 2553.
[177] Murmann, R. K. *Inorg. Chem.* **1971**, *10*, 2070.
[178] Williams, T. J.; Hunt, J. P. *J. Amer. Chem. Soc.* **1968**, *90*, 7210.
[179] Bjerrum, J. "Metal Ammine Formation in Aqueous Solution"; P. Haase and Son: Copenhagen, Denmark, 1941, p. 278.
[180] Williams, T. J.; Hunt, J. P. *J. Amer. Chem. Soc.* **1968**, *90*, 7213.
[181] Kruse, W.; Taube, H. *J. Amer. Chem. Soc.* **1961**, *83*, 1280.
[182] Tong, S. B.; Krouse, H. R.; Swaddle, T. W. *Inorg. Chem.* **1976**, *15*, 2643.
[183] Beutler, P. PhD Thesis, Bern, 1976.
[184] Monacelli, F.; Viel, E. *Inorg. Chim. Acta* **1967**, *1*, 467.
[185] Bott, H. L.; Poë, A. J.; Shaw, K. *J. Chem. Soc. A* **1970**, 1745.
[186] Borghi, E.; Monacelli, F. *Inorg. Chim. Acta* **1971**, *5*, 211.
[187] Tong, S. B.; Swaddle, T. W. *Inorg. Chem.* **1974**, *13*, 1538.
[188] Wüthrich, K.; Connick, R. E. *Inorg. Chem.* **1967**, *6*, 583; Wüthrich, K.; Connick, R. E. *Inorg. Chem.* **1968**, *7*, 1377; Reuben, J.; Fiat, D. *Inorg. Chem.* **1967**, *6*, 579.

[189] Kim, M. Z.; Choi, B. S. J. Korean Chem. Soc. 1974, 4, 259.
[190] Baes, B.; Mesmer, P. "Hydrolysis of Cations"; Wiley: New York, 1976, p. 199.
[191] Blanc, P.; Madic, C.; Launay, J. P. Inorg. Chem. 1981, 21, 2923.
[192] Gordon, G.; Taube, H. J. Inorg. Nucl. Chem. 1961, 16, 272.
[193] Gordon, G.; Taube, H. J. Inorg. Nucl. Chem. 1961, 16, 189.
[194] Kato, Y.; Suzuki, F.; Fukutomi, H.; Tomiyasu, H.; Gordon, G. Bull. Tokyo Inst. Tech. 1970, 96, 133.
[195] Rabideau, S. W. J. Phys. Chem. 1963, 67, 2655.
[196] Masters, B. J.; Rabideau, S. W. Inorg. Chem. 1963, 2, 1.
[197] Rabideau, S. W.; Masters, B. J. J. Phys. Chem. 1963, 67, 318.
[198] Connick, R. E.; Hugus, Z. Z., Jr. J. Amer. Chem. Soc. 1952, 74, 6012.
[199] Beard, J. H.; Calhoun, C.; Casey, J.; Murmann, R. K. J. Amer. Chem. Soc. 1968, 90, 3389.
[200] Murmann, R. K.; Robinson, P. R. Inorg. Chem. 1975, 14, 203.
[201] Kriege, L. B.; Murmann, R. K. J. Amer. Chem. Soc. 1972, 94, 4557.
[202] Toppen, D. L.; Murmann, R. K. J. Inorg. Nucl. Chem. Lett. 1970, 6, 139.
[203] Toppen, D. L.; Murmann, R. K. Inorg. Chem. 1973, 12, 1611.
[204] Malin, J. M.; Schlemper, E. O.; Murmann, R. K. Inorg. Chem. 1977, 16, 615.
[205] Murmann, R. K. J. Amer. Chem. Soc. 1974, 96, 7836.
[206] Murmann, R. K.; Giese, K. C. Inorg. Chem. 1978, 17, 1160.
[207] Landis, C. R.; Robinson, P. R.; Murmann, R. K.; Haight, G. P., Jr. "Proceedings of the Third International Conference on the Chemistry and Uses of Molybdenum"; Mitchel, P. C. H., Ed.; Climax Molybdenum Co. Ltd: London, 1979, p. 245.
[208] Schlemper, E. O.; Hussein, M. S.; Murmann, R. K. Cryst. Struct. Commun. 1982, 11, 89.
[209] Murmann, R. K.; Thompson, R. C. J. Inorg. Nucl. Chem. 1970, 32, 1404.
[210] Halperin, J.; Taube, H. J. Amer. Chem. Soc. 1952, 74, 375.
[211] Bassey, M.; Bunton, C. A.; Davies, A. G.; Lewis, T. A.; Llewellyn, D. R. J. Chem. Soc. 1955, 2471.
[212] Cahill, A. E.; Taube, H. J. Amer. Chem. Soc. 1952, 74, 2312.
[213] Chung, S-K.; Decapite, P. J. Org. Chem. 1978, 14, 2935.
[214] Anbar, M.; Guttmann, S. J. Amer. Chem. Soc. 1961, 83, 2035.
[215] Bortolini, O.; Di Furia, F.; Modena, G. J. Amer. Chem. Soc. 1981, 103, 3924.
[216] Friedman, L.; Bigeleisen, J. J. Chem. Phys. 1950, 18, 1325.
[217] Bonner, F. T. Inorg. Chem. 1970, 9, 190.
[218] Jordan, S.; Bonner, F. T. Inorg. Chem. 1973, 12, 1369.
[219] Bonner, F. T.; Jordan, S. Inorg. Chem. 1973, 12, 1363.
[220] Moyer, B. A.; Sipe, B. K.; Mayer, T. J. Inorg. Chem. 1981, 20, 1475.
[221] Chen, D. T. Y.; Laidler, K. J. Can. J. Chem. 1959, 37, 599.
[222] Twigg, M. V. Inorg. Chim. Acta 1977, 24, L84.
[223] Hoppe, M. L.; Schlemper, E. O.; Murmann, R. K. Acta Cryst. 1982, B38, 2237.

Index